Physics by Experiment

An Advanced-Level Course

Also from Stanley Thornes (Publishers) Ltd:

Muncaster   A-LEVEL PHYSICS (2nd Edition)
Lowe & Rounce CALCULATIONS FOR A-LEVEL PHYSICS

PHYSICS BY EXPERIMENT
AN ADVANCED-LEVEL COURSE

J. R. L. Hartley B.Sc. (Hons)

D. L. Misell B.Sc., Ph.D., F.Inst.P., C.Phys., Dip.R.M.S.

Epsom College, Surrey

Stanley Thornes (Publishers) Ltd

First published in 1987 by:
Stanley Thornes (Publishers) Ltd
Old Station Drive
Leckhampton
CHELTENHAM GL53 0DN
England

British Library Cataloguing in Publication Data
Hartley, J.
    Physics by experiment–an advanced-level course.
    1.   Physics—Experiments
    I.   Title   II.   Misell, D.
    530'.0724   QC33

    ISBN 0-85950-191-4

Typeset by Tech-Set, Gateshead, Tyne & Wear.
Printed and bound in Great Britain at The Bath Press, Avon.

CONTENTS

PREFACE

We believe that many aspects of an A-level physics course can be learnt through experimental investigations. While we do include many of the standard experiments, we hope that a challenge exists either in the form of the analysis of the experimental results or in the form of further work. The major addition is the introduction of analogue and digital electronics into the A-level physics core. These topics are intended to be taught entirely through practical work. In this book the requirements of all A-level physics Examining Boards are covered. The electronics sections are intended to be self-sufficient, without the requirement for any further course books.

In addition to the standard sections comprising an A-level physics practical course, we have included sections on the uncertainties of experimental measurements, graphical and data analysis, and a set of introductory experiments designed to introduce a sixth form set to A-level practical work. Each major new section includes an introduction to the techniques, instrumentation and theoretical basis of the experiments in that section. Each experiment includes an introduction to the principles involved, intended for those students who may not yet have covered that particular A-level topic. From the information given in each experiment, the student is expected to develop the ability to choose the best way of analysing data.

In the early stages of a course we think that some guidance is required, and so we have provided a section at the back of the book, 'Hints and further guidance'. This should not be used as a set of model answers (in which respect it would fail dismally), but just to provide some assistance if the student suspects that a result is incorrect or if the student is uncertain as to how to analyse the data.

It is expected that students with experience will find it unnecessary to use this section, except as a check on their own conclusions.

Occasionally we felt that an experiment merited further work outside of the A-level syllabus.

A section of problem experiments taken from A-level practical examinations has been provided. These experiments, arranged by topic, may be used either as part of a continuous assessment scheme or as a preparation for a practical examination.

Three appendices have been included. The first appendix describes the use of the CRO. The second appendix provides a listing of a BBC BASIC computer program and its use for fitting experimental data to a straight line. While we do not advocate the omission of the student's initial analysis of data, we do believe that it is useful for a student to obtain the parameters of a straight line by a regression analysis. The third appendix includes tables of selected physical constants, which we hope will encourage students to make comparisons between their results and accepted values. These tables are arranged in the order of the topics within the book. This appendix is not intended as a replacement for comprehensive tables that are available, but it does provide information in a more accessible form. Where relevant the variation of a physical quantity with external conditions, such as temperature, is given.

J.R.L.H.
D.L.M.
Epsom College, Surrey
1987

ACKNOWLEDGEMENTS

While writing this book we have received advice and encouragement from Geoff Camplin, Patricia Hayes, Ian Host, Mark Purdon and David Wright. We have valued the help and support from our wives and families. We are grateful to Janet Misell for writing the BBC BASIC computer program for the least squares fitting of experimental data.

We are grateful to the following Examining Boards for permission to reproduce A-level practical problems from their examination papers:

The Associated Examining Board
Joint Matriculation Board
Oxford and Cambridge Schools Examination Board
University of Cambridge Local Examinations Syndicate
University of London School Examinations Board
University of Oxford Delegacy of Local Examinations.

1 AN INTRODUCTION TO PRACTICAL PHYSICS

... when you can measure what you are speaking about, and express it in numbers, you know something about it; but when you cannot measure it, when you cannot express it in numbers, your knowledge is of a meagre and unsatisfactory kind; it may be the beginning of knowledge, but you have scarcely, in your thoughts, advanced to the stage of science.

Lord Kelvin in *Popular Lectures and Addresses*

"This is indeed a mystery," remarked Watson "what do you imagine that it means?"
"I have no data yet. It is a capital mistake to theorize before one has data. Insensibly one begins to twist facts to suit theories, instead of theories to suit facts."

from *The Memoirs of Sherlock Holmes* by A. Conan Doyle

Many scientists and philosophers have written about the importance of experience and observation. It is very easy from an A-level physics syllabus to deduce that the theoretical explanations preceded the observations of the various physical phenomena. But until recently the significant steps in physics were all made as a result of careful observations followed by a model designed to explain these observations. One of the finest examples of this is the development of the quantum theory following the breakdown of classical mechanics at the atomic level.

There were three aspects of atomic behaviour for which classical theory proved inadequate:

a) the failure to explain the distribution of radiation emitted by a hot body. This led Planck to postulate that radiation could only be emitted or absorbed in discrete packets of energy (quanta).

b) the failure to explain why an atom did not collapse. According to classical theory an accelerating electron would emit electromagnetic radiation and the electron would eventually fall into the nucleus. In fact such continuous radiation was not observed and any radiation emitted by atoms as a result of excitation consisted of very well defined wavelengths. The Bohr model of the atom was the first to suggest that electrons can only adopt specific orbits around the nucleus and that electro-magnetic radiation is emitted or absorbed only as a result of electrons making transitions between these orbits. This model explained the appearance of the hydrogen spectrum.

c) the failure to explain the photoelectric effect, where electrons are emitted from the surface of a metal when illuminated by light of a sufficiently high frequency. The wave model was inadequate to explain all the observations and led to Einstein proposing that light could be considered to be made up of quanta of energy depending on the frequency of the light.

While you will be unlikely to make observations that lack a theoretical explanation, you should develop your skills of observation during a practical course. Remember that a theoretical model has no value until it has been tested to its limits by experiment.

There are other reasons why practical physics is included in the course. These are not nearly so exciting: learning to use instruments; learning to measure and to assess the value of your measurements; analysing your data so as to obtain a physical quantity or to confirm a theoretical model; and, finally, to prepare you for a practical examination.

Many of the techniques and instruments will only be met in a school laboratory. Our justification for including these is that they still appear in most A-level syllabuses and they are often required either in the theory paper or in the practical examination. Where such experiments occur, we have attempted to include a challenging measurement, some advanced analysis, or extension work. However, we hope that most of the experiments introduce new and useful techniques beyond those required for an A-level physics course.

1.1 THE PURPOSE OF EXPERIMENTAL PHYSICS

The experiments in this book fall into four categories:

a) confirming a theoretical model and thus providing support for the theoretical sections of the course.

b) measuring a physical quantity.

c) observing a physical phenomenon.

d) designing an experiment to produce a particular effect.

In all these four categories you will develop the following skills:

a) setting up the apparatus according to a specification or, particularly in electronics, to produce the required output.

b) measuring and assessing the value of those measurements.

c) analysing and interpreting your results. Where relevant you should make an objective comparison with an accepted value of a physical quantity or with the theoretical predictions.

d) presenting your experimental results, so that it is clear to a fellow student what you were trying to achieve, how you analysed your results and what conclusions you came to.

The last point is often neglected. However, irrespective of your skills as an experimental physicist, unless you can write a coherent report of your work, it will be of little value subsequently. Throughout your career you will be required to write reports, often for a non-specialist in your subject. It is essential that it is clear what you set out to achieve and an objective assessment of how far you achieved your aims should be included. Do not hesitate to be critical of an experimental procedure and suggest improvements.

A complete account should include:

a) an informative title and the date on which you did the experiment.

b) a general introduction to set the scene. It should be aimed at a fellow student. Do not include theoretical derivations.

c) a well-labelled diagram.

d) a brief description of the experimental procedure. Include all the precautions and checks that you make.

e) neat tabulation of your results. Every result should have a unit, the correct number of significant figures and an estimate of its uncertainty.

f) results presented in a graphical form, whenever possible.

g) a conclusion, which should include a summary of your results. Add also a discussion of assumptions, approximations, consistency of readings, random and systematic errors, limitations of the apparatus, suggestions for improvements, abnormal behaviour and comparison with the expected result.

1.2 HOW TO USE THIS BOOK

Most of the sections (6–16) consist of a series of experiments on the main subject categories in the A-level physics syllabus. However, each new section is preceded by an introduction, which includes a summary of the basic instrumentation, measurement techniques and theoretical basis of the measurements appropriate to that section. These are not intended to be read through as you might in a text book, but to be referred to when required in an experiment. We chose this option so as not to pad out individual experiments with repetitive paragraphs in similar experiments. Also, you may already be quite familiar with a particular instrument or technique. Examples of this include a summary of rotational dynamics (section 6), the use of special vernier scales (section 8), the use of ammeters and voltmeters (section 10), the principle of the potentiometer (section 10) and radiation detectors and counters (section 14).

Two other sections are intended for reference only: section 2 on experimental errors and minimising their effects; and section 3 on plotting graphs and graphical analysis. Section 4 is intended to provide you with some practice in analysing data using graphs.

As a preliminary exercise in experimental physics we have included three introductory experiments in section 5.

Each main experiment will consist of the following sections:

a) a list of apparatus required, although exceptionally, where a series of experiments is included, there may be several lists of apparatus.

b) the principles involved in the experiment as it is possible that you may not have covered the theory in class.

c) the experimental procedures, subtitled as appropriate. Paragraphs requiring action on your part have a grey rule alongside them as here. Other paragraphs include explanations, advice and analysis that in principle can be completed outside the laboratory.

d) notes. These include advice on writing up your experiment, ways in which the experiment could be used to measure other physical quantities, and applications outside the laboratory.

e) further work. Some experiments will include further experimental work or a more advanced analysis of your experimental results. Often the further experimental work will include additional measurements on the original apparatus; this will be referred to in the main experimental procedure and you should therefore leave your apparatus set up if you intend to complete the further work. Occasionally further work will include a new experimental arrangement. Further analysis most frequently involves a re-examination of your original data and a different way of analysing it.

Appendix 1 at the end of the experimental section gives a practical guide to setting up a cathode ray oscilloscope (CRO), which is used in experiments in several sections of the book.

In every experiment you will be expected either to compare your results with an accepted value or to analyse your data in the form of a straight line graph. Two other appendices are provided to assist you in this:

a) appendix 2 gives a listing in BBC BASIC of a straight line fitting program, with examples of its use.

b) appendix 3 gives tables of the physical quantities that you are most likely to measure while using this book. Occasionally the variation of a physical quantity with the conditions of observation will be given, as, for example, the variation of viscosity and thermal conductivity with temperature. Such variations may affect your conclusions. Also included is a list of physical constants.

In addition to these appendices, we have also provided at the end of the book guidance on choosing which graphs to plot, approximate values for quantities and suggested answers to questions in each experiment. These are not to be used in the same way as answers in a text or question book, but merely for you to refer to should you wish to check a step or if you really cannot work out an answer. You will not be getting very much from a practical if you use the back of the book before you make a valiant attempt yourself. Also, for numerical results you are most likely to obtain different values as a result of variations in the apparatus and materials used. The numerical values given are only intended as a guide should you obtain a value that you suspect is totally wrong.

Finally, section 17 includes a series of problem experiments taken from past A-level practical examinations. You may use these throughout your course as you complete a particular section or as a final preparation for your practical examination.

2 MEASUREMENT, INSTRUMENTATION AND EXPERIMENTAL ERROR

Through practical work you will learn how to handle data, and how to convert your observations into an estimate of some physical quantity. You will learn how to assess the accuracy and precision of your results, how to choose the best instruments and how to assess the experimental procedure used. In this section some of the factors affecting your experimental results are examined. The items included apply to all the practicals in this book; the number of factors may seem daunting but as you complete your sixth-form course you will find that these become second nature:

a) planning an experiment – have you considered all the factors affecting the final results?

b) limitations on the accuracy of experimental data – have you minimised the errors from all sources?

c) minimising the effect of experimental uncertainty – have you made the best readings?

d) significant figures – how precise are your results?

e) statistical calculation of errors – how can you assign an uncertainty to your final result?

f) comparison of results and verifying principles – how do your results compare with the accepted value?

2.1 PLANNING AN EXPERIMENT

There is always a temptation to get started on your experiment as quickly as possible, collect your apparatus, assemble it, take the readings and dismantle the apparatus. This is bad practice and can be disastrous if you have made a mistake in your readings. Always leave your apparatus intact at least until you have plotted your graphs and calculated a final result.

You should first read the practical instructions to ensure that you are clear what measurements are required. When possible run through the experiment once to check that meters and other instruments are suitable for the extreme ranges of the readings you are likely to obtain. This helps in plotting graphs as you go along: knowing the range of your experimental quantities enables you to work out the scales of the axes. A graph will often show up deviations from the expected behaviour that a single set of readings will not show. The two major tasks before an experiment are to consider the external factors affecting your readings (section 2.1.1) and the factors affecting the physical quantity you are measuring (section 2.1.2). These are best illustrated by considering some typical experimental investigations.

2.1.1 External factors

These are a) laboratory conditions such as temperature variations, air resistance and draughts and b) disturbances of a system as a result of measurements made on the system, such as measuring the thickness of rubber using a micrometer screw gauge or the electrical heating of a wire whose resistance is being measured.

a) LABORATORY CONDITIONS

Temperature effects

Example 1 The speed of sound in air c depends on the temperature. So the value of c should always be corrected to a standard temperature (0 °C or 273 K) using the fact that c is proportional to the square root of the temperature in kelvin. c also depends on the humidity of the air, but this is rather more difficult to correct for. Note that using a resonance tube with water in the column is likely to give a different result for c from that measured in dry air.

Example 2 The speed of fall of a ball-bearing in a viscous liquid such as glycerol varies with the viscosity (friction in a liquid, or its resistance to shear forces). The viscosity depends critically on the temperature, varying by as much as 10% for a 1 K change in temperature. This can be corrected for but the experimenter must ensure that there are no temperature variations down the column of liquid through which the ball-bearing is falling.

Air resistance and draughts

Example 1 The oscillations of a simple pendulum or spring decrease in amplitude because of air damping. If you wished to find out how the period of the oscillation varied with amplitude you would have to perform the experiment in a vacuum. However, for small damping, the period is independent of the damping. So for most oscillation experiments you can ignore this factor or certainly check in a subsidiary experiment that damping had little or no effect.

Example 2 The rate of energy loss from a hot solid depends on the air conditions. The rate is proportional to the excess temperature θ above the surroundings for forced convection (a steady draught), but the rate is proportional to $\theta^{5/4}$ in still air. The difference is considerable even for excess temperatures of only 20–40 K (Fig. 2.1). So if you are making an energy loss (cooling) correction in a heat experiment you must decide the conditions in which to perform the experiment: either use a draught shield or use a hair dryer (running cold) to produce forced convection.

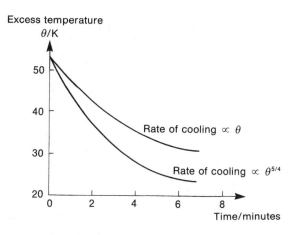

Fig. 2.1 The different rates of energy loss for forced convection (proportional to θ) and in still air (proportional to $\theta^{5/4}$).

b) DISTURBANCES OF A SYSTEM

Example 1 Measuring the thickness of an object using a micrometer screw gauge (see appendix, page 16) can cause problems. You should always use the ratchet mechanism to avoid squashing the object but a soft material such as rubber is still difficult to measure accurately. Other methods of measuring the thickness have to be considered, such as using the other linear dimensions of the object and its mass and density to calculate the thickness, or using a travelling microscope.

Example 2 The measurement of the resistivity of a metal may be made using a large current to measure the resistance of the wire from V/I, but this will cause heating of the wire. Since resistance increases with temperature for metals you will obtain a high value for the resistivity. So either you could measure the temperature of the wire (not very easy) and correct the resistance value for the rise in temperature or you could use very low currents through the wire and more sensitive meters.

2.1.2 Factors affecting a physical quantity

You should decide which quantities you need to consider when measuring the physical properties of a system. This will usually be evident from the theory together with common sense. Again this is best illustrated by specific examples.

Example 1 You may wish to investigate the fusing current of a wire. A fuse breaks when its temperature reaches the melting point of the fuse wire θ_{mp}. Just before the fuse melts the rate of electrical heating I^2R is equal to the rate of energy loss from the surface of the wire. This will depend on the dimensions of the wire (Fig. 2.2), the excess temperature of the wire above the surroundings and the nature of the surface of the wire (e.g. blackened or shiny). The resistance R depends on the resistivity of the wire, its length l and its diameter d. Clearly there are a large number of factors involved, but many may be eliminated by working with one material, thus keeping the melting point, resistivity and surface characteristics fixed. Theory then shows that the fusing current is proportional to $d^{3/2}$ and is independent of the length of the wire. So, you can now plan an experiment based on a selection of wire diameters and varying lengths for one selected diameter.

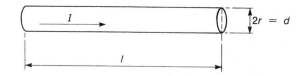

Fig. 2.2 Measurement of the fusing current I for a wire of length l and diameter d.

Example 2 The measurement of the absorption of γ-radiation by materials would be complicated by the fact that most radioactive sources emit α- or β-radiation as well. The α-radiation can be eliminated by interposing a thin sheet of aluminium. The effect of the β-radiation can be eliminated by measuring the absorption of the radiations as the thickness of the absorbing material is increased. At large thicknesses of a material such as lead there will be virtually no contribution from the β-radiation (Fig. 2.3); the line from large thicknesses can then be extended back (extrapolated) to small thicknesses. The absorption of the two radiations can then be separated by subtraction.

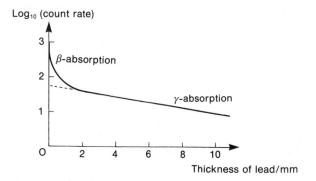

Fig. 2.3 Investigation of the absorption of γ-radiation by thin sheets of lead. The dashed line is obtained by extrapolating the γ-absorption curve, which is assumed to be linear.

2.2 LIMITS ON THE ACCURACY OF EXPERIMENTAL DATA

The everyday meaning of the word 'error' is 'mistake'. However, the term error is used in experimental physics to describe 'the quantity by which a result obtained by observation differs from an accurate determination'. Error used in this sense expresses the uncertainty in a result. Errors can be assessed by common sense or by a more rigorous statistical analysis.

2.2.1 Human error

This can arise from carelessness, perhaps where a scale is misread. Repeated readings of a quantity often reveal this. It is more difficult to detect an error in a technique where readings are biased. A common example is the parallax error, which occurs when reading the position of a pointer on a scale (for example, on an ammeter or a stopwatch). Fig. 2.4a shows such a pointer as seen from above and Fig. 2.4b shows the end-on view. Clearly R_c is the correct reading and in order to make it, the eye should be placed directly above the pointer at E_c. Either side of this position, such as E_w, will give an incorrect reading R_w.

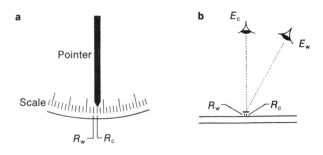

Fig. 2.4 How to avoid a parallax error in reading a scale.

Some instruments also help to avoid the parallax error by including a mirror behind the scale. The reading is correct when the pointer and its reflection are superimposed. Digital meters avoid this problem but their use leads to other difficulties, such as fluctuating readings which are genuine but difficult to read.

2.2.2 Instrumental limitations

Instruments have their own limitations; some may have inaccurate scales and others are not precise enough for the measurement you wish to make (for example, using vernier callipers instead of a micrometer screw gauge). Screw mechanisms of micrometer gauges, travelling microscopes, and micrometer eyepieces may have non-uniform threads. Sometimes when the screw has been rotated in one direction, it does not immediately respond

when the direction of screw is reversed. This is called backlash. It can cause readings to differ according to the direction from which the measurement or alignment is made. This can be avoided by always moving the screw thread in the same direction.

Always use an instrument with the appropriate sensitivity: insensitivity and oversensitivity can be equally misleading. For example, if you needed to measure the diameter of a wire of about 0.4 mm, vernier callipers would give you a result correct only to the nearest 0.1 mm. The error could be as large as 0.05 mm or 12.5%. With a micrometer screw gauge you could measure the diameter to the nearest 0.01 mm with an error of less than 2%. Do not choose a 0–1 A current scale (sensitivity 0.01 A) when the maximum current is only 100 mA. If readings do go up to 200 mA, then use a 0–100 mA scale for the initial readings and a 0–1 A scale for readings of 100 mA and above.

Oversensitivity may not seem to be undesirable but there is always the risk that you will give undue weight to what seems to be a precise result. For example, if you measured the acceleration of free fall g by hand timing a ball-bearing falling through 5 m, you could not measure the time to better than 0.1 s. However, a digital stopwatch would display a reading to the nearest 0.01 s; a time of 1.01 s should be corrected to 1.0 s, since the last figure is meaningless when your reaction time could have been as large as 0.1 s.

2.2.3 Systematic and random errors

In assessing errors, whether human or instrumental, there are two types of error: a) *systematic* errors and b) *random* errors.

a) SYSTEMATIC ERRORS

A reading consistently shifted in one direction is called a systematic error. Examples include: a zero error on any scale, a calibration error, a background count in a radioactivity experiment, an end correction in a resonance tube, a stray magnetic field, backlash on screw threads. Some systematic errors can be corrected either by adjustment of the instrument or by noting the error and correcting all readings appropriately. Systematic errors are the more serious form of error since they cannot be reduced by taking repeated readings or by any other form of averaging.

b) RANDOM ERRORS

Random errors occur as deviations from the true value; the readings are just as likely to be either too small or too large. Their effect can be reduced by taking a large number of readings, or by a similar averaging technique.

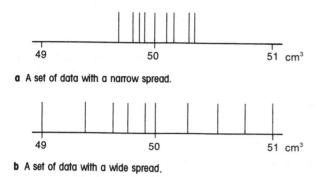

a A set of data with a narrow spread.

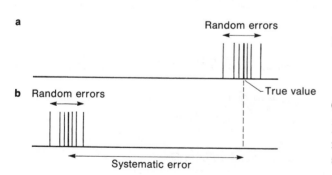

b A set of data with a wide spread.

Fig. 2.5 A series of measurements on the volume of a container, presented in the form of a histogram.

This does not mean that you should not be concerned with taking the most accurate readings possible. For example, in measuring the volume of a container the two sets of readings shown in Fig. 2.5 were obtained. The sets may give the same result for the average value of the volume, but you would place more reliability on the measurements shown in Fig. 2.5a, with a small spread of measurements, than on those shown in Fig. 2.5b.

2.2.4 Treatment of systematic errors

Fig. 2.6a shows a spread of readings caused by random errors; these are approximately centred about the true value. If a systematic error is also present these readings will be shifted so they are no longer centred about the true value but about some other value (Fig. 2.6b). Under these experimental conditions, no matter how many readings are taken, the final result will not approach the true value.

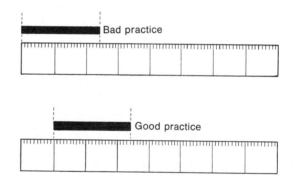

Fig. 2.6 **a** Random errors distributed about the true value. **b** Random errors superimposed on a systematic error.

An *accurate* measurement is one in which the systematic errors are small. A *precise* measurement is one in which the random errors are small. If both types of error are small the measurement is accurate and precise.

The treatment of systematic errors largely depends on the skill of the experimenter and good planning of an experiment. The aim is to keep systematic errors as small as possible. The most common systematic errors and their treatments are given below.

a) PARALLAX ERROR

The parallax error can be avoided by always viewing the pointer or scale at the correct angle or by using instruments fitted with mirrors (see section 2.2.1 and Fig. 2.4).

b) ZERO ERROR

Always check the reading of a scale and if possible (as in an ammeter) adjust the reading to zero before use. Otherwise record the zero error and add or subtract it as appropriate from all your readings. A common zero error arises from using a ruler from one end, which may be worn. It is easier to make measurements from one end but it is better practice to use the centre of the ruler, as shown in Fig. 2.7.

Bad practice

Good practice

Fig. 2.7 How to avoid a zero error on a ruler.

c) BACKGROUND COUNT

In radioactivity experiments always measure the count rate in the absence of the source and subtract this from subsequent readings.

d) BACKGROUND FIELD

In measuring the magnetic field inside a solenoid or between the poles of a magnet with a probe, make a measurement of the field when the current through the solenoid is zero or in the absence of the magnet. Subtract this reading from all subsequent readings.

e) END CORRECTION

In the resonance tube two successive measurements can be used to eliminate the end correction e: $l_2 - l_1 = \lambda/2$ (Fig. 2.8). End corrections also occur in electrical experiments using the metre bridge to compare resistance values; these can be reduced by interchanging the two resistors.

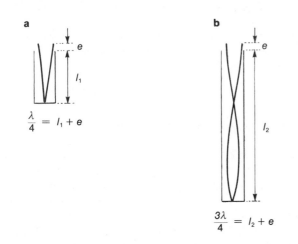

Fig. 2.8 **a** First resonance and **b** Second resonance for a vibrating air column. The end correction e for the vibration of the air column beyond the end of the tube is the same for a and b.

f) HEATING LOSS

Heating losses occur in all calorimetry experiments. Either apply a cooling correction or repeat the experiment with a different rate of heating.

g) BACKLASH IN SCREW MECHANISMS (see section 2.2.2)

To avoid backlash always approach a measurement by rotating the screw thread in one direction.

h) MISREADING A MULTIPLE SCALE

Many meters, particularly ammeters, voltmeters and multimetres, include more than one scale. Misreading such scales can be avoided by noting the range of values you are measuring and choosing the appropriate scale. For example, if you were using a shunt for a full-scale deflection of 1 A you would read the 0–10 scale in Fig. 2.9 and divide all readings by 10.

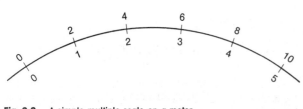
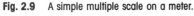

Fig. 2.9 A simple multiple scale on a meter.

i) CALIBRATION ERROR

Calibration errors are usually a result of a faulty instrument, a repair (as in a shunt on an ammeter) or old age. In all these examples there is little that you can do. These errors are often percentage errors, whose magnitude increases with the value of the reading.

j) AIR RESISTANCE

Air resistance is unavoidable and it is often unimportant, as in measuring the period of oscillation of some vibrating systems. Where it does have an effect, the solution is to perform an experiment where the magnitude of the air resistance varies. This is not always easy, but one example where it may be possible is in the measurement of g by free fall. Using ball-bearings of varying diameters will indicate whether air resistance has a significant effect on the value obtained for g (Fig. 2.10).

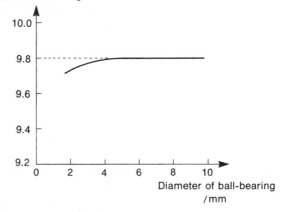

Fig. 2.10 Investigating the effect of ball-bearing diameter on the value of g determined by free fall. The solid line represents the experimental results obtained. The horizontal dashed line represents the expected results in the absence of air resistance.

2.3 MINIMISING THE EFFECT OF EXPERIMENTAL ERROR

The following list provides some advice on minimising random errors when measuring quantities.

2.3.1 Timing experiments

The random error in a timing experiment is usually 0.1 s for hand timing. So you should always record measurements for a sufficiently long time for this to represent a negligible percentage error. For example, for a simple pendulum of period $T = 2$ s, timing a single oscillation could represent an error of 1 part in 20 or 5%. However, timing twenty oscillations taking 40 s would represent an error of only 0.25%. Of course, if you miscounted the number of oscillations by one, you would revert to an error of 5%. Miscounting should be evident by repeating the timing for 20 oscillations as a time difference of 2 s should be obvious.

Sometimes you may not be able to time as many as 20 oscillations because the system is heavily damped. Then you must rely on reducing the effect of random errors by making a large number of individual measurements (see section 2.5).

2.3.2 Counting experiments (radioactivity)

The average rate of decay over a long time period may be 100 counts in each second. In any one-second interval the count rate could vary between 90 and 110 because radioactive decay of nuclei is a random process. In fact there is a statistical uncertainty of $\sqrt{N}$ in a count of N. To reduce the effect of this uncertainty increase the time over which the counts are recorded:
(100 ±10) counts in 1 s represents an uncertainty of 10%.
(10 000 ±100) counts in 100 s represents an uncertainty of only 1%.

2.3.3 Measuring dimensions

Whenever possible measure multiples of a dimension. The measurement of the thickness of a single sheet of aluminium foil could be in error by as much as 50%, but measuring 16 or more thicknesses using a micrometer screw gauge on a folded sheet or cut sheets would reduce the error to less than 3%. Measuring the fringe separation in a two-slit interference experiment could lead to a large error in the calculation of the slit separation or of the wavelength of the light used. A measurement must be made across at least 11 fringes.

2.3.4 Measuring angles

In measuring angles it is possible to avoid centering errors by measuring twice the angle required. For example, in measuring the angle of diffraction for a first-order diffraction grating spectrum, measuring the angle 2θ between corresponding lines either side of the zero

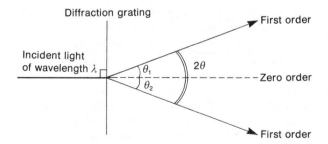

Fig. 2.11 Measuring the wavelength λ of light using the first order diffraction.

order avoids the problem of finding the exact position of the zero order and aligning the diffraction grating exactly normal to the incident light (Fig. 2.11).

2.3.5 Repeated single readings

As an alternative the average of repeated single readings can be used to reduce the uncertainty in a quantity. If the errors are randomly distributed about the true value, the average or mean value $\bar{x}$ of N measurements:

$$\bar{x} = \frac{x_1 + x_2 + x_3 + \ldots + x_N}{N} = \frac{1}{N} \sum_{i=1}^{i=N} x_i \qquad [2.1]$$

is more likely to be nearer to the true value than any single reading x_i. (The summation symbol $\sum$ merely denotes that all x values are to be added.) If, for example, you measured the wavelength of sodium light using a diffraction grating, a single measurement may give you a value of 587 nm. Without any further measurements you cannot assign any reliability to your result. Making nine further measurements could give the results shown below.

λ/nm 587 588 589 589 591 590 591 590 588 590

The mean value of the wavelength $\bar{\lambda} = 589.3$ nm. Because you only determined the wavelength to the nearest nm you cannot justify the figure after the decimal point, but you can assign a value of 589 nm to the wavelength with a maximum uncertainty of 2 nm.

Taking a series of measurements can also eliminate a result; for example a tenth reading of 580 nm instead of 590 nm can be rejected as inconsistent with the rest. A more objective assessment of the error or uncertainty in the mean value can be obtained by using the standard deviation as shown in section 2.5; this can also be used as a criterion for rejecting a result.

The next question to be answered is how many readings you should take: a simple rule would be to stop when a further reading or result does not alter the mean value at the level of significance justified by your experimental results. An eleventh reading of 587 nm would alter the mean value of the wavelength to 589.1 nm – still consistent with a value of 589 nm. Again the standard deviation would be a more objective way of assessing the value of your final result.

The important point is that *you should never rely on a single reading or result for any quantity.*

2.4 SIGNIFICANT FIGURES

It is very tempting to enter your raw data onto a calculator and accept the figures displayed as your final result. For example, in calculating the volume of a regular solid of dimensions $a = 10.1$ cm, $b = 5.1$ cm, $c = 2.0$ cm, the result displayed for the volume $V = a \times b \times c$ would be 103.02 cm³. But if you think about your original measurements, made on a scale with millimetre divisions, the uncertainty in each of your measurements is 0.5 mm. The actual volume could have a value as large as $V_{max} = 10.15 \times 5.15 \times 2.05 = 107.16$ cm³ or a value as small as $V_{min} = 10.05 \times 5.05 \times 1.95 = 98.97$ cm³. The actual value is therefore between 99 and 107 cm³ and the two figures after the decimal point cannot be justified. The final result should therefore be given as 103 cm³, although if you were a pessimist, you may argue that even the third figure is uncertain and the result is 100 cm³. It would be reasonable to quote the final result as (103 ± 4) cm³, clearly indicating your doubt about the value of the third figure. The conclusion of this type of calculation is that while you always use raw (non-truncated) data to calculate a final result, the number of significant figures in this final result is governed by the least accurate measurement. The number of significant figures in the final result should be taken as the number of significant figures in the least accurate measurement. The remainder of the result will just be meaningless digits.

You should also be careful in quoting an answer in decimal form with all its zeros: for example, 3800 cm³ could imply (3800 ± 1) cm³, when you actually mean (3800 ± 100) cm³. A result must always be quoted with its uncertainty so that it is clear that the zeros mean very little; or, if you do write the result as an isolated figure, it should be quoted as 3.8×10^3 cm³. Never quote the result as (3800 ± 112) cm³, because this implies that the third and fourth figures are significant, even though the error could be in excess of 100 cm³.

A further example illustrates the importance of not over-valuing a result. If you measured the time of free fall of a ball-bearing through a height of 5 m using hand timing to be:

$$t/\text{s} \quad 1.0 \quad 1.1 \quad 0.9 \quad 0.9 \quad 1.1$$

the mean value of t would be 1.0 s leading to a value of $g = 10.0$ m s⁻² (using $s = \frac{1}{2}gt^2$). However, based on your measurements, g could be between 8.3 m s⁻² and 12.3 m s⁻², values that arise from the two extreme values of t.

2.5 STATISTICAL CALCULATION OF ERRORS

In this section a more detailed evaluation of random errors based on statistical analysis is given. Also examined is the way in which errors are combined when several independent quantities are used in an equation. This means that you will be able to assess objectively the value of your final result; for example, a result of $g = (9.9 \pm 0.1)$ m s⁻² is clearly more reliable than $g = (10 \pm 1)$ m s⁻²; (10.2 ± 0.1) m s⁻² indicates that your

result is different from the accepted value of 9.8 m s⁻² by more than your estimate of the experimental error. Stating the uncertainty gives your result much more value than a simple numerical answer of 9.9 m s⁻². It is a comment on the precision of the experimental work, and, in research, indicates to other scientists the reliability and reproducibility of your result. Any worthy scientific publication will include an assessment of the experimental error and quote a final value with an associated uncertainty.

The first step in the calculation is to collect a large number (at least 10) of measurements of any quantity that is subject to uncertainty or random variations.

The calculation of the mean value $\bar{x}$ of a whole set of measurements x_i is not quite sufficient unless you also make an assessment of the spread of your measurements about the mean value. In Fig. 2.12 you would place more reliance on the mean value obtained in Fig. 2.12a, with a small spread of values, than the results shown in Fig. 2.12b. To obtain an objective assessment of this spread the statistical analysis of random errors is used.

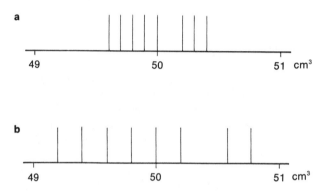

Fig. 2.12 Two sets of data with the same mean value. The standard deviation of set **a** is considerably smaller than that of set **b**.

Statistical analysis can strictly only be applied to large samples, but most scientists agree that the sample sizes of 10–20 used in most experiments are large enough.

2.5.1 The standard deviation

If a large number of measurements is taken of a quantity x subject to random error, then a graph can be plotted of the number of readings with a particular value against that value: it will be a bell-shaped curve (a gaussian) as shown in Fig. 2.13. The maximum corresponds to the mean value $\bar{x}$ of the quantity. The width of the curve reflects the spread of the values of x; this spread should be as small as possible for you to have confidence in the final value of $\bar{x}$.

The spread of values of x is measured using a statistic called the standard deviation σ. In fact a mathematical

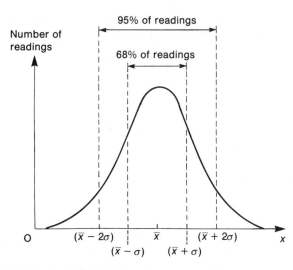

Number of readings

95% of readings

68% of readings

O $(\bar{x} - 2\sigma)$ $\bar{x}$ $(\bar{x} + 2\sigma)$ x

$(\bar{x} - \sigma)$ $(\bar{x} + \sigma)$

Fig. 2.13 The distribution of a large number of readings subject to random error.

analysis shows that 68% of the readings should be between $(\bar{x} - \sigma)$ and $(\bar{x} + \sigma)$ and 95% of the values between $(\bar{x} - 2\sigma)$ and $(\bar{x} + 2\sigma)$. Thus if a result is quoted as $(\bar{x} \pm \sigma)$ using a value of σ derived from your results, it informs other scientists that there is a 68% probability that the true value of x lies between $(\bar{x} - \sigma)$ and $(\bar{x} + \sigma)$. Conventionally σ is used rather than 2σ. 2σ is used for a different purpose, namely, to reject results. If any reading in your set of results of x differs by more than 2σ from the mean value $\bar{x}$ then it can be discarded. This would, of course, mean that you would have to recalculate $\bar{x}$ and σ omitting the rejected value of x.

For N data points (values of x) the equation for σ is:

$$\sigma = \sqrt{\frac{1}{N} \sum_{i=1}^{i=N} (x_i - \bar{x})^2} \qquad [2.2]$$

The summation symbol $\sum$ indicates that all the values of $(x_i - \bar{x})^2$ (the square of the difference between the ith reading and the mean value $\bar{x}$) are to be added for N experimental measurements.

σ is called the *standard deviation* of the set of N results.

The calculation of σ is quite simple, but many calculators have a standard deviation option (SD): you just enter your data values x_i into the memory and then press the $\bar{x}$ and σ_N keys. Perhaps it should be mentioned that statisticians use σ_{N-1} with $(N-1)$ in equation [2.2] instead of N because there are strictly only $(N-1)$ independent measurements of x. In practice the difference is negligible in the calculation of errors.

Remember that you are calculating errors so precision is not important. Never quote an uncertainty to more precision than your mean value, and also do not include too many significant figures in the final result:

(103 ± 1.6) cm^3 should be written as (103 ± 2) cm^3
(103.2 ± 1.6) cm^3 should be written as (103 ± 2) cm^3.

2.5.2 An example of the calculation of a standard deviation

The following wavelengths λ were measured using a diffraction grating spectrometer on a sodium source:

λ/nm   587   588   589   589   591   590   591   590   588   589

Using equation [2.1] the mean value $\bar{\lambda}$ is 589 nm ($N = 10$), since each measurement includes only three significant figures.

Now calculate the values of $(\lambda - \bar{\lambda})$ and $(\lambda - \bar{\lambda})^2$ to the nearest nm and nm^2 only:

$(\lambda - \bar{\lambda})$/nm -2 -1 0   0 $+2$ $+1$ $+2$ $+1$ -1 0
$(\lambda - \bar{\lambda})^2$/nm^2 4   1   0   0   4   1   4   1   1   0

The sum of the squares of the differences is 16 nm^2, so $\sigma = \sqrt{16/10} = 1.3$ nm. Therefore the value of λ is $(\bar{\lambda} \pm \sigma) = (589 \pm 1)$ nm. 68% of the values of λ should be between 588 nm and 590 nm (actually 7/10 or 70%) and 95% of the values should be between 587 nm and 591 nm (actually 10/10 or 100%). So by quoting the value of the wavelength as (589 ± 1) nm a statistically valid interpretation can be given to the final result.

2.5.3 Rejecting a result

If the tenth reading of the results above gave a value of 580 nm instead of 589 nm, you would suspect an error in that measurement. The mean value of λ to three significant figures is now 588 nm. Recalculating $(\lambda - \bar{\lambda})$ and $(\lambda - \bar{\lambda})^2$ gives a value for σ of $\sqrt{93/10} = 3$ nm. Clearly (588 ± 3) nm indicates a less reliable result than that obtained above but it could be left as a valid result. But that one reading, 580 nm, is more than two standard deviations below the mean value of 588 nm. Using the criterion that 95% of the results should be between 582 nm and 594 nm, the 580 nm result can be discarded as statistically outside the accepted limits. This reduces the data to nine results with a mean value of 589 nm and a standard deviation of 1 nm.

2.5.4 Combining errors

At this stage you should have an assessment of the uncertainties in all the quantities that you have measured, based on either the accuracy of the scales of the instruments used, fluctuations in readings or a standard deviation for a quantity measured a number of times. Here you will be shown how to combine these errors to give the uncertainty in the final result. Initially only simple arithmetical operations will be considered: a) addition and subtraction, b) multiplication and division and c) powers. The mathematical derivations of the results are not required.

a) ADDITION AND SUBTRACTION

$Z = A + B$ or $Z = A - B$.

The uncertainty in Z, ΔZ, can simply be taken as the sum of absolute errors in A, ΔA and in B, ΔB:

$$\Delta Z = \Delta A + \Delta B \qquad [2.3a]$$

This represents the maximum error in Z, because the errors are always added. A less pessimistic (and statistically valid) calculation of the error is obtained by adding the squares of the individual errors, then taking the square root; the *standard error* is then:

$$\Delta Z_s = \sqrt{(\Delta A)^2 + (\Delta B)^2} \qquad [2.3b]$$

For example, if $A = (10.1 \pm 0.1)$ cm and $B = (6.2 \pm 0.2)$ cm are added:

$\Delta Z = 0.1 + 0.2 = 0.3$ cm and $Z = (16.3 \pm 0.3)$ cm

$\Delta Z_s = \sqrt{0.1^2 + 0.2^2} = 0.2$ cm and $Z = (16.3 \pm 0.2)$ cm

Clearly the second result is more realistic: the minimum error in Z could be 0.1 cm (if the errors in A and B are subtracted) and the maximum error could be 0.3 cm. The most likely error is between these two extremes.

Be careful when subtracting two nearly equal quantities. The error in their difference can sometimes be larger than the difference. Subtraction of masses, lengths and temperatures are common occasions of very high percentage errors.

The general result for any number of additions or subtractions is:

$$\Delta Z = \Delta A + \Delta B + \Delta C + \ldots \qquad [2.4a]$$

or: $$\Delta Z_s = \sqrt{\Delta A^2 + \Delta B^2 + \Delta C^2 + \ldots} \qquad [2.4b]$$

b) MULTIPLICATION AND DIVISION

$Z = A \times B$ or $Z = A/B$.

In this calculation of the uncertainty in Z, fractional or percentage errors are used. Some students find it easier to work with percentage errors since these are usually integers (seldom is the decimal place required). The maximum fractional error in Z, $\Delta Z/Z$, is:

$$\frac{\Delta Z}{Z} = \frac{\Delta A}{A} + \frac{\Delta B}{B} \qquad [2.5a]$$

The standard error is calculated from:

$$\frac{\Delta Z_s}{Z} = \sqrt{\left(\frac{\Delta A}{A}\right)^2 + \left(\frac{\Delta B}{B}\right)^2} \qquad [2.5b]$$

For example, in the measurement of a force F from the acceleration of a trolley and its mass using $F = ma$:

$$m = (1.00 \pm 0.01) \text{ kg}, \quad \Delta m/m = 1/100 \quad \text{or} \quad 1\%$$

$$a = (2.1 \pm 0.1) \text{ m s}^{-2}, \quad \Delta a/a = 1/21 \quad \text{or} \quad 4.8\%$$

The maximum fractional error in F is
$$\Delta F/F = 0.01 + 0.048 = 0.058 \quad (\text{or } 5.8\%)$$

The value of F calculated from the data above is 2.10 N.

The uncertainty $\Delta F = F \times$ fractional error $= 2.1 \times 0.058$ (or 5.8% of 2.1) $= 0.12$ N. The value of F is then given as (2.10 ± 0.12) N or more realistically as (2.1 ± 0.1) N.

Generally the contribution of an error can be neglected if the error is less than about 1/10 of the dominant error. This can save some unnecessary calculations, since often only one error is important in determining the reliability of the final result.

The general result for all arithmetic operations involving multiplication and division:

$$Z = \frac{A \times B}{C \times D}$$

is:

$$\frac{\Delta Z}{Z} = \frac{\Delta A}{A} + \frac{\Delta B}{B} + \frac{\Delta C}{C} + \frac{\Delta D}{D} \qquad [2.6a]$$

or:

$$\frac{\Delta Z_s}{Z} = \sqrt{\left(\frac{\Delta A}{A}\right)^2 + \left(\frac{\Delta B}{B}\right)^2 + \left(\frac{\Delta C}{C}\right)^2 + \left(\frac{\Delta D}{D}\right)^2}$$

$$[2.6b]$$

Note that a constant factor K such as π or a physical quantity not subject to experimental error does not contribute to the error in Z.

c) POWERS

$Z = KA^n$, where K is a constant assumed to be error free.

The fractional error in Z is n times the fractional error in A:

$$\Delta Z/Z = n \, \Delta A/A \qquad [2.7]$$

For example, the uncertainty in the cross-sectional area $A = \pi d^2/4$ is calculated as follows for a wire of diameter $d = (0.46 \pm 0.01)$ mm. The fractional error in d is 1/46 (or 2.2%), so that the fractional error in A is 2/46 (or 4.4%) since $n = 2$.
Since the value of A is $\pi \times (0.46)^2/4 = 0.166$ mm^2,
$\Delta A = 0.044 \times 0.166 = 0.007$ mm^2 (or 4.4% of 0.166)
$A = (0.166 \pm 0.007)$ mm^2 or $(0.166 \pm 0.007) \times 10^{-6}$ m^2.
The third decimal place is probably justified.

If the same dimension is used to calculate the volume of a sphere $V = \pi d^3/6$, the fractional error in V is now $3/46$ (or 6.6%). $V = 0.0510$ mm^3 and so $\Delta V = 0.066 \times 0.051 = 0.0034$ mm.

Now the third significant figure cannot be justified and the value of V should be given as (0.051 ± 0.003) mm^3.

Quantities raised to a power of more than one in an equation must be measured more carefully because their effect on the final uncertainty is multiplied by a factor of n. The reverse is true for fractional powers of less than unity.

d) OTHER COMBINATIONS

Sometimes functions, such as sines, cosines, exponentials and logarithms, occur in an equation. The equations for the fractional errors can still be derived but they are more complicated than those combinations dealt with previously. The simplest way to treat such errors is to calculate the extreme values of the function using the error in the quantity concerned. For example, in the diffraction grating experiment, the wavelength λ is calculated from $d \sin \theta$ for the first-order spectrum.

If the number of lines per mm of the grating is (300 ± 1), then the grating spacing d is $(3.33 \pm 0.01) \times 10^{-6}$ m. If the value of θ is (10.0 ± 0.5) °, the value of λ is 579.4 nm.

Now the maximum fractional error in λ is:

$$\frac{\Delta \lambda}{\lambda} = \frac{\Delta d}{d} + \frac{\Delta (\sin \theta)}{\sin \theta}$$

$\Delta d/d = 0.003$ (or 0.3%); $\Delta (\sin \theta)$, the error in $\sin \theta$, can be calculated from the change in $\sin \theta$ when θ is altered from 10 ° to 9.5 ° or from 10 ° to 10.5 °. $\sin (9.5°) = 0.165$, $\sin (10°) = 0.174$, $\sin (10.5°) = 0.182$; so for a change of angle of 0.5 ° the average change in the value of $\sin \theta$ is $(0.009 + 0.008)/2 = 0.008$. The fractional error in $\sin \theta$ is then $8/174$ (or 4.6%). Hence the maximum fractional error in λ is 0.049 (or 4.9%). The uncertainty in $\lambda = 0.049 \times 579.4 = 28.4$ nm. The value of λ is (579 ± 28) nm or even (580 ± 30) nm.

The standard error is almost identical because of the dominant effect of the error in $\sin \theta$. An exact calculation of the percentage error using mathematical analysis gives 5%, so the calculation above is quite satisfactory.

Questions on errors (answers given on page 316)

a) The following measurements were obtained for the diameter of a wire along its length.

d/mm 1.26 1.26 1.29 1.31 1.28 1.27 1.26 1.25
1.28 1.32 1.21 1.27 1.22 1.29 1.28

Calculate the mean value of the diameter and the standard deviation.

b) Three objects have masses of (100.0 ± 0.4) g, (50.0 ± 0.3) g and (200.0 ± 0.5) g. Calculate the uncertainty in the sum of their masses.

c) Two objects have masses (100.0 ± 0.4) g and (94.0 ± 0.3) g. Calculate the percentage uncertainty in the sum and the differences in their masses.

d) Calculate the density of a rectangular block of dimensions 10 cm by 5 cm by 2 cm and mass 270 g. If the uncertainty in all dimensions is 0.1 cm and the uncertainty in the mass is 1 g, calculate the uncertainty in the density.

e) The pressure of a gas can be estimated from the force exerted on a given area. If the force is (20.0 ± 0.5) N, and the area is rectangular with sides (5.0 ± 0.2) mm and (10.0 ± 0.5) mm, calculate the fractional or percentage error on the value of the pressure.

f) A motorist drives at a constant speed such that the reading on the speedometer is 60 km h^{-1}. The speedometer is assumed to be accurate to ± 3 km h^{-1}. At the end of a journey he would like to know how far he has travelled but he forgot to look at the distance meter at the beginning of the journey. He reckoned that he had been travelling for 4 hours, give or take a quarter of an hour. Estimate how far he had travelled and assign an uncertainty to your result.

g) Calculate the uncertainty in the value of the area of a circle whose radius is determined to be (0.146 ± 0.005) m.

h) The time period T of a simple pendulum is given by $T = 2\pi \sqrt{l/g}$, where l is the length of the pendulum and g is the acceleration of free fall due to gravity. A pendulum of length (0.600 ± 0.002) m is used to determine the value of g. The value of T was found to be (1.55 ± 0.01) s. Find the percentage error in g and the uncertainty in g.

i) Calculate the refractive index of a glass block from the following measurements: angle of incidence $i = (47 \pm 1)$ °, angle of refraction $r = (29 \pm 1)$ °.

2.6 COMPARISON OF RESULTS AND VERIFYING PRINCIPLES

2.6.1 Comparison of results

Often, the physical constant obtained in an experiment can be compared with an accepted value. This is a good opportunity to assess the quality of your experimental work and the procedure that you used. It is most unlikely that you will obtain an exact agreement but your value should agree with an accepted value within experimental error. In statistical terms your result should be within two standard deviations of the accepted value. If this is not so, then you can be fairly certain that you have overlooked a systematic error; you should think carefully about the source of an error that would result in too low or too high a value.

The following results for g from the free fall of a ball-bearing could have been obtained:

a) 9.6 m s^{-2}

b) (9.6 ± 0.2) m s^{-2}

c) (9.6 ± 0.1) m s^{-2}

d) (9.60 ± 0.02) m s^{-2}

e) (10 ± 1) m s^{-2}

f) (10.1 ± 1.3) m s^{-2}.

Think about which result you would take as the most reliable, or the one that you could compare with the accepted value of 9.81 m s^{-2} (varying slightly with latitude).

a) This result is unacceptable. Not only does it differ from the accepted value but no uncertainty is quoted.

b) This result is acceptable. The value of g is within one standard deviation of the accepted value and there is a fairly small experimental error.

c) This result is barely acceptable. The value is just within two standard deviations of the accepted value.

d) The result is more than two standard deviations from the accepted value. It seems that the experimenter has been optimistic in calculating the errors, or a serious systematic error has been overlooked.

e) This result could be accepted because it is within a standard deviation of the accepted value. However, the uncertainty quoted indicates a large spread in the readings taken to find g. It is certainly not as good as the result in b).

f) The comments in e) apply. In addition, since the uncertainty exceeds 1 m s^{-2}, the first figure after the decimal point cannot be significant. The result is therefore the same as in e), $g = (10 \pm 1)$ m s^{-2}.

Finally, when comparing your result either with an accepted value or with other experimental results, list any external conditions that may have affected your result. The most likely quantity is temperature. Many physical quantities depend on the temperature at which they are measured. Some quantities are relatively insensitive to temperature variations, for example, the resistivity of metals and the specific heat capacities of metals. Other quantities are sensitive to temperature variations, for example, the speed of sound in air and the viscosity of a liquid. It is good practice to give the value of the physical quantity together with the value of the temperature and the range of temperatures at which it was measured: the specific heat capacity of aluminium measured between 20 °C and 60 °C should be given as $c = (880 \pm 10)$ J kg^{-1} K^{-1} at a mean temperature of 40 °C.

2.6.2 Verifying principles

If a single result or a series of results is obtained, it should always be possible to state that within experimental error the results agree with the principle or law investigated.

Ideally, for sets of readings, a suitable graph should be plotted showing whether a relationship is valid (see section 3: Graphical analysis). But even then you should calculate the errors in the quantities plotted; it is most unlikely that the best straight line drawn will pass through all experimental points. In some experiments a graph cannot be plotted because you are attempting to show that two quantities are identical. An example of this is the verification of the principle of conservation of momentum. A series of results for an inelastic collision of two trolleys of masses m_1 and m_2 is shown in Table 2.1; u is the initial velocity of the trolley of mass m_1 and v is the velocity of the two trolleys, mass $(m_1 + m_2)$, after the collision.

Table 2.1

m_1/kg	u/m s^{-1}	m_2/kg	$(m_1 + m_2)$/kg	v/m s^{-1}
1.00	1.85	1.00	2.00	0.87
2.00	1.52	1.00	3.00	0.95
2.00	1.46	2.00	4.00	0.68
1.00	1.94	2.00	3.00	0.62

The initial momentum $m_1 u$, the final momentum $(m_1 + m_2)v$, and the difference can now be calculated as in Table 2.2; ideally this difference should be zero.

Table 2.2

Initial momentum/ kg m s^{-1}	Final momentum/ kg m s^{-1}	Initial − final momentum/ kg m s^{-1}	Estimated uncertainty in the difference/ kg m s^{-1}
1.85	1.74	0.11	0.15
3.04	2.85	0.19	0.25
2.92	2.72	0.20	0.30
1.94	1.86	0.08	0.20

As the differences are quite significant, it is necessary to find out whether these differences are within the limits of experimental error. It will be assumed that the error in measuring mass is negligible compared with the error in measuring velocity using a ticker-tape timer. If the error in measuring the separation between two dots on a ticker-tape is 1 mm for a time interval of 1/50 s, the error in u and v is 0.05 m s^{-1}.

The maximum error in the difference $m_1 u - (m_1 + m_2)v$ is simply $m_1 \Delta u + (m_1 + m_2) \Delta v$, the sum of the individual errors in the momenta. The numbers in the fourth column of the table above have been obtained in this way with $\Delta u = 0.05$ m s^{-1} and $\Delta v = 0.05$ m s^{-1}. Within these errors the principle of conservation of momentum has been verified for inelastic collisions.

2.7 SUMMARY OF THE ANALYSIS OF DATA AND ITS ERRORS

Averaging

a) Measurements should be repeated where possible.

b) The mean value $\bar{x}$ of readings $x_1, x_2, x_3 \ldots x_N$ is:

$$\bar{x} = \frac{x_1 + x_2 + x_3 + \ldots x_N}{N}$$

Errors

c) For random errors, the mean value is characterised by a standard deviation σ of the sample:

$$\sigma = \sqrt{\frac{d_1^2 + d_2^2 + d_3^2 + \ldots d_N^2}{N}}$$

where $d_N = (x_N - \bar{x})$.

68% of the readings should be within $\pm \sigma$ of $\bar{x}$.

d) Keep systematic errors as small as possible. Note parallax errors, zero errors, meter calibration errors.

Combining errors

e) To find the maximum resultant error of individual errors you add either the absolute errors (for addition or subtraction) or the fractional errors (for multiplication, division and powers). The standard error is calculated by adding either the squares of the absolute errors or the squares of the fractional errors, and then taking the square root.

f) Any error contributing less than a tenth of the dominant error can be neglected.

g) Special care is needed when two almost equal quantities have to be subtracted.

h) Measure quantities appearing as powers greater than one with care as the fractional error is multiplied by the power n.

Recording your results

i) Do not use scraps of paper for your readings and comments. Use a notebook kept for this purpose.

j) Record *direct* observations.

k) Record readings in tables with columns headed with the name of the quantity and its unit.

l) Underline important quantities such as mean values.

m) Do not dismantle your apparatus until you have checked that you have all the readings you need.

Calculation of results

n) Check all calculations in reverse order of multiplication/division.

o) Ask yourself whether the result of a calculation or measurement looks reasonable.

p) Use powers of 10 to avoid giving the impression that noughts used for placing the decimal point are significant figures.

q) Suppress meaningless digits arising from calculations. The final result of a multiplication or division can have no more significant figures than the number of significant figures in the factor with the fewest.

r) Always include a conclusion. In it discuss assumptions, approximations, limitations of apparatus, abnormal behaviour, comparison of the result with that expected.

s) Every physical quantity calculated should have a unit, the correct number of significant figures and an estimated uncertainty.

APPENDIX – USING VERNIER CALLIPERS AND A MICROMETER SCREW GAUGE

A metre rule can normally be used to measure dimensions to the nearest millimetre, although with a bit of imagination you could, for example, distinguish between a reading of 45.2 mm and 45.4 mm. However, for measurements requiring the dimensions of an object to the nearest 0.1 mm vernier callipers are used. For even greater precision (± 0.01 mm) a micrometer screw gauge is used.

Vernier callipers

Vernier callipers consist of a pair of jaws, one of which moves over a main scale divided into mm divisions (Fig. 2.14). A vernier scale is marked on the movable jaw. The position of the 0 of the vernier on the main scale gives the object's size to the nearest mm. Thus in Fig. 2.14, the object's size is between 2.1 cm (21 mm) and 2.2 cm (22 mm). An intelligent guess would give a size of 2.15 cm (21.5 mm). Now the vernier is used to give the next significant figure: look along the vernier until one of the vernier divisions coincides with a main scale division; which one it coincides with is irrelevant to the final reading. You should be able to see that the 5th vernier division coincides with the main scale division 2.6. The reading of the vernier is then 2.15 cm (21.5 mm). A frequent mistake is to forget all about the original reading between 2.1 and 2.2 cm and to put the reading down as 2.6 or 2.65 cm.

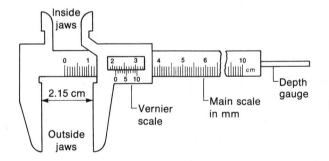

Fig. 2.14 Vernier callipers reading to ± 0.1 mm (0.01 cm). The main scale indicates a reading between 2.1 and 2.2 cm. The 5th division on the vernier coincides with the main scale division (2.6). The reading is therefore 2.15 cm.

If you had difficulty in seeing where the marks on the two scales coincided, perhaps the enlargement shown in Fig. 2.15 will help. The reading on the main scale is between 1.3 and 1.4 cm. As you move from 0 on the vernier towards the right, you will see that the divisions 1, 2, 3, etc. are getting closer to coincidence with a main scale division. For division 7 the coincidence is almost perfect. After this the misalignment between the two scales increases. The reading is therefore 1.37 cm.

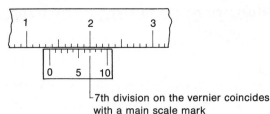

7th division on the vernier coincides with a main scale mark

Fig. 2.15 An enlargement of the vernier scale. This shows that the 7th division on the vernier coincides with a main scale division (2.0). The reading is therefore 1.37 cm.

Note that the vernier callipers shown in Fig. 2.14 are quite versatile: the outside jaws can be used to measure the external diameter of an object, such as a sphere or cylinder; the inside jaws can be used to measure the internal diameter of an object, such as a hollow cylinder; the rod which extends beyond the end of the main scale can be used as a depth gauge, and can therefore be used to measure the depth of a hole in a block of material.

Most vernier callipers will read zero when the jaws are closed, without an object in place. However, as a result of misuse or wear the instrument may not read zero. Should this be so, a zero error must be added or subtracted. In Fig. 2.16 the vernier callipers read $+1.0$ mm with the jaws closed. With an object in place the reading is 18.7 mm, so the corrected reading for the object diameter is $(18.7 - 1.0) = 17.7$ mm.

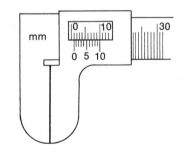

a The vernier jaws, when closed, give a scale reading of 1.0 mm.

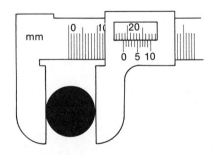

b With an object in place the reading is 18.7 mm. The object's diameter is therefore $(18.7 - 1.0) = 17.7$ mm.

Fig. 2.16 Taking account of the zero error.

Now try the two vernier settings in Fig. 2.17. (The answers are given on page 316.)

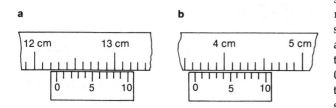

Fig. 2.17 Two vernier readings for you to try.

Micrometer screw gauge

The object is placed between the anvil and spindle (Fig. 2.18). The spindle is moved using the thimble, except for the final adjustment for holding the object between the anvil and spindle. The ratchet mechanism must always be used at this stage, otherwise the object can easily be squashed or the screw mechanism can be damaged. The main scale on the sleeve is marked in mm, with intermediate half mm divisions marked below. The screw thread usually has a pitch of 0.5 mm; thus when the thimble is rotated one revolution, the spindle moves

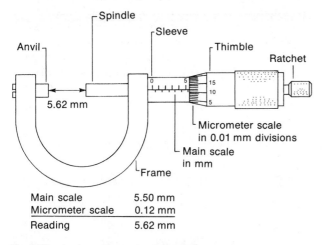

Main scale	5.50 mm
Micrometer scale	0.12 mm
Reading	5.62 mm

Fig. 2.18 A micrometer screw gauge reading to ±0.01 mm. The main scale is marked in mm and half mm divisions. The pitch of the micrometer screw is 0.5 mm, so each division on the micrometer (thimble) scale is 0.01 mm.

0.5 mm. The micrometer scale on the thimble is divided into 50 divisions; each division therefore corresponds to a spindle movement of 0.01 mm. The procedure for reading a micrometer screw gauge is first to read the main scale to the nearest half mm visible, 5.50 mm in Fig. 2.18, and then to read the thimble division corresponding to the horizontal line on the main scale, 12 divisions or 0.12 mm in Fig. 2.18. The final reading is the sum of these two, 5.62 mm in Fig. 2.18. Of course, the micrometer screw gauge reading with the anvil and spindle in contact should be checked for any zero error.

Now try the two micrometer screw gauge settings in Fig. 2.19. (The answers are given on page 316.)

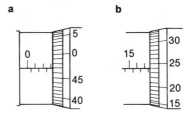

Fig. 2.19 Two micrometer readings for you to try.

Correct use of vernier callipers and micrometer screw gauges

a) Never force the jaws together or squash the object to be measured. This can be avoided by always using the ratchet mechanism of the micrometer screw gauge.

b) Check for any zero error.

c) Always make several measurements along the length of an object so as to check for uniformity. If there are random variations in a dimension, an average should be taken. Systematic changes in a dimension usually indicate that the object is unsuitable for the experiment.

d) In measuring the diameter of a cylinder or sphere, always measure the diameter in several orientations. The object may be elliptical, or deviate in some other way from a perfect circle.

3 INVESTIGATING RELATIONSHIPS: GRAPHICAL ANALYSIS

3.1 GRAPHS: WHY USE THEM?

One of the most important reasons for experimental work is to investigate the relationships between two or more physical quantities. Taking a single set of readings of a physical quantity often gives very little information on the form of the relationship between the readings and the limitations of their validity. A single set of readings could be used to calculate the physical constant involved; for example, measuring the potential difference V across and the current I through a device will give a value of the resistance R of the device for those particular values of V and I, but it would not tell you anything about the device or whether R depends on I. A single pair of values of V and I (marked as +) could be interpreted in many ways (Fig. 3.1).

Clearly several sets of readings of V and I would enable a distinction between Figs. 3.1a, b and c to be made. (A graph is easier to interpret than a table of values of V and I.) There is another important reason for using several sets of readings of V and I, namely, experimental error. There are random errors which relate to the precision with which an instrument can be read, concerning the inability of the experimenter to record an exact value. Repeated measurements of the same quantity will give different values. This type of error can be reduced by taking many readings and averaging them; but a graph can also be used to achieve the same end (Fig. 3.2). There will always be a deviation of experimental points from the straight line. The straight line should pass symmetrically between the points. The slope or gradient of the line $\Delta V/\Delta I = $ AC/BC gives an average value of R.

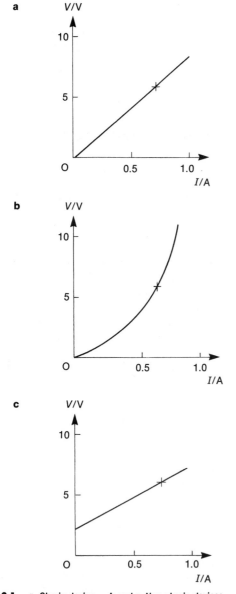

Fig. 3.1   **a** Ohmic device.   **b** and **c** Non-ohmic devices.

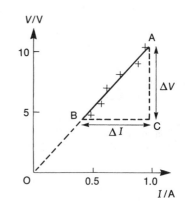

Fig. 3.2   Averaging random errors graphically.

Systematic errors are much more serious and usually arise from zero or calibration errors, for example an ammeter which reads 0.1 A with no current flowing in the circuit, or a meter which reads 10 V when the potential difference is actually 9 V. Of course, zero errors should always be eliminated by zeroing the meter, or by recording the zero error and then correcting all readings by that amount. However, systematic errors can still occur. Graphically the simple zero error on our ammeter will have no effect on the slope (Fig. 3.3a); but a percentage systematic error would change the slope (Fig. 3.3b).

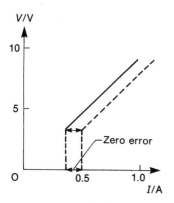

a A single systematic error does not affect the slope of the line.

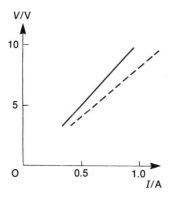

b A percentage systematic error affects the slope of the line.

Fig. 3.3

Finally, despite careful experimental work the anomalous point will always occur. This is often difficult to detect in a table of results but it will be evident on a graph (Fig. 3.4). Occasionally such a point is accurate and draws attention to an important phenomenon, e.g. resonance.

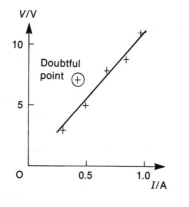

Fig. 3.4   Detecting a doubtful experimental point ⊕.

The graph will also show the limitations of a relationship. For example, consider the extension e of a loaded wire with a mass of M hung on one end (Fig. 3.5). The extension e is proportional to M up to the elastic limit. Detecting the elastic limit from a table of e and M is not easy unless successive differences in e are calculated for equal increments in M. From the graph (Fig. 3.5) the departure from linear behaviour is evident.

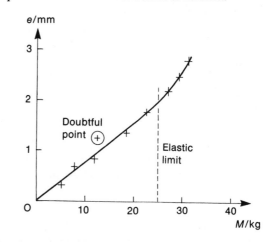

Fig. 3.5   The extension of a loaded wire.

3.2 ADVICE ON PLOTTING A GRAPH

a) Always plot a graph as the experiment proceeds. This will help to detect errors and deviations.

b) Decide on the range of values of each variable which will occur in the experiment. This may sometimes involve doing a quick preliminary experiment to find maximum and minimum values.

c) If an intercept (point where the graph cuts an axis) is not required, the origin need not be included. This is often useful if the values of one quantity cover only a small range.

d) It is usually a good thing to spread the points to fill the graph. For example, in Fig. 3.6a it would be difficult to decide whether R were linearly related to T but it should be evident from Fig. 3.6b.

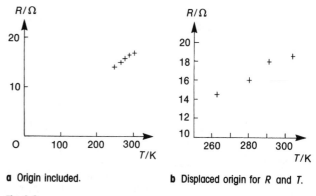

a Origin included.

b Displaced origin for R and T.

Fig. 3.6

e) Title the graph and label the axes with the name of the quantity and its units (use a stroke (solidus) '/' or 'in'). It is conventional to choose the horizontal x-axis (abscissa) for the independent variable, that is the quantity which is varied (e.g. M in Fig. 3.5). The y-axis (ordinate) is used for the dependent variable (the one you measure, e.g. e in Fig. 3.5). Sometimes these are interchanged to make the slope more meaningful.

f) For very small or very large numbers use the sub-multiples or multiples of units, e.g. for 0.001 A use either mA or 10^{-3} A on the axis, for $P = 10^6\,\text{N m}^{-2}$ use either MN m^{-2} or $10^6\,\text{N m}^{-2}$. Both are correct, but when calculating a slope, the second format is less likely to lead to the omission of a factor of 10^{-3} or 10^6.

g) Choose simple scale divisions to make points easier to plot e.g. 1 cm ≡ 0.1 A but not 3 cm ≡ 0.1 A. This can cause difficulties if the maximum values do not conveniently fit on your graph paper.

h) Plot points as crosses (+) as in coordinate geometry; error bars (⊢⊣) can be added to a graph to indicate the uncertainty in each point. A circled dot will do (⊙) but not a dot alone (difficult to see) or an x (difficult to place accurately).

i) When drawing the curve always draw a smooth curve. In reality one quantity will usually vary smoothly with the other, though there are some exceptions like calibration errors in a meter. Place your upper wrist firmly on the paper and use it as a pivot to help you draw a smooth curve.

j) When taking readings it is best to space the points evenly, except   (i) if an intercept is required, when it is best to take points closer together near to the axis (Fig. 3.7); and   (ii) when non-linear behaviour occurs or one variable starts to change rapidly with the other (Fig. 3.8).

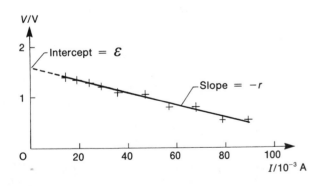

Fig. 3.7 Variation of the potential difference V across the terminals of a cell when it provides a current I to an external circuit. ε is the e.m.f. of the cell and its internal resistance is r.

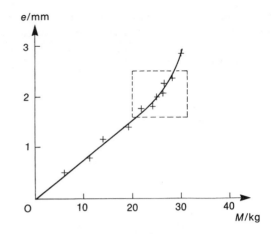

Fig. 3.8   Non-linear behaviour of a loaded wire.

Now list the defects in this graph (Fig. 3.9) for the variation of the volume V of a gas with its pressure P (at constant temperature).

The defects on Fig. 3.9 are given on page 316.

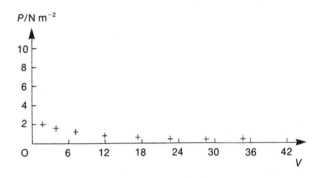

Fig. 3.9   A poorly-presented graph showing the variation of the volume V of a gas with its pressure P.

3.3 OBTAINING STRAIGHT LINE GRAPHS

Many experimental relationships are not linear, that is a graph of y against x will be a curve, for example the period T of a simple pendulum against its length l (Fig. 3.10a), or the volume V of a gas versus its pressure P (Fig. 3.10b), or the decrease in activity of a radioactive source with time t (Fig. 3.10c), or the variation of the e.m.f. ε of a thermocouple with temperature θ (Fig. 3.10d). Clearly the exact relationship could be worked out from the experimental curve, but it is difficult to distinguish between different types of curve over a small range of values and it is not easy to determine the constants from a curve. To find the slope you would have to draw a tangent.

We shall come back to curves later (section 3.4) but a word of warning here. When plotting a graph during an experiment always plot the variables as measured and

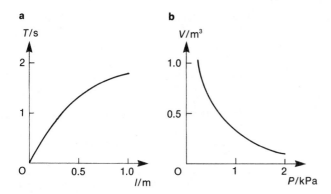

a Variation of the period T of a simple pendulum with its length l.
b Variation of the volume V of a gas with its pressure P at constant temperature.

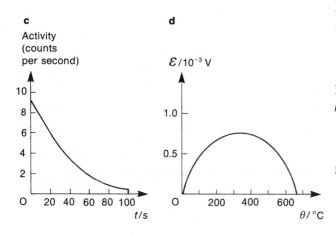

c The radioactive decay of a nucleus (activity) with time t.
d The variation of the e.m.f., ε of a thermocouple with the temperature difference θ between its junctions.

Fig. 3.10   Non-linear relationships.

then decide whether the graph should be a curve or a straight line (Fig. 3.11).

Fig. 3.11a probably represents a linear relationship – the points are spaced either side of the line drawn. In Fig. 3.11b this is not so – remember the main reason for the

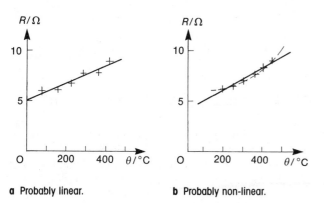

a Probably linear.   **b** Probably non-linear.

Fig. 3.11   Variation of the resistance of a device with temperature.

spread of points is random errors. Fig. 3.11b shows systematic deviations from the straight line drawn and a curve is probably a more accurate way of relating R and θ for the device.

The purpose of this section is to look at particular relationships and decide what form the final graph should take if it is to be a straight line. This will enable us to see whether the relationship is valid for our experiment and, more importantly, find the constants of the equation from the slope and the intercept.

3.3.1 Linear relationships: proportionality

A proportional relationship takes the form $y = mx$. If we plot y against x the graph will be a straight line through the origin (Fig. 3.12).

$$\text{slope} = m = \frac{\text{change in } y}{\text{change in } x} = \frac{\Delta y}{\Delta x} = \frac{(y_2 - y_1)}{(x_2 - x_1)}$$

In the example shown in Fig. 3.12b $R = \rho l/A$ where ρ = resistivity and A = cross-sectional area.

$$\text{slope} = \frac{\Delta R}{\Delta l} = \frac{(R_2 - R_1)}{(l_2 - l_1)} = \frac{\rho}{A}$$

gives the resistivity of the material of the wire.

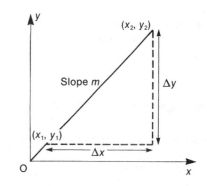

a Proportional relationship.

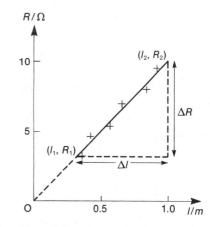

b Variation of the resistance R of a wire with its length l.

Fig. 3.12

N.B. Do not force the graph through the origin unless it is a *genuine* experimental point. The deviation from the origin may mean that the relationship is no longer proportional near the origin, or be evidence of a systematic error and a measure of the error in your experiment.

Showing the proportionality of two variables may make you decide not to plot the graph with a displaced origin for quantities which vary by only very small amounts (Fig. 3.13).

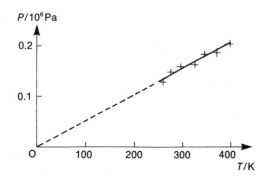

Fig. 3.13 Variation of the pressure P of a gas with its temperature T.

In principle this graph could be plotted with a displaced origin at $P = 1 \times 10^5 \, \text{N m}^{-2}$ (or Pa) and $T = 250 \, \text{K}$ and the slope and a point *on the line* can be used to calculate the value of T when $P = 0$ (see section 3.3.2). But this is beyond A level. Remember that a straight line does not show proportionality unless it goes through the origin; it shows only linearity, $y = mx + c$ (see section 3.3.2).

3.3.2 Linear relationships

These take the form $y = mx + c$ (Fig. 3.14a).

$$\text{slope} = m = \frac{\text{change in } y}{\text{change in } x} = \frac{\Delta y}{\Delta x} = \frac{(y_2 - y_1)}{(x_2 - x_1)}$$

The intercept c on the y-axis corresponds to $x = 0$ when $y = c$.

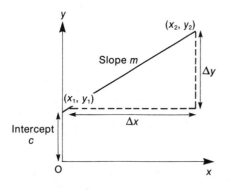

Fig. 3.14 **a** A linear relationship between x and y.

(*cont.*)

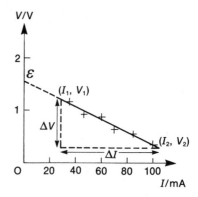

Fig. 3.14 **b** Variation of the potential difference V across the terminals of a cell when a current I is drawn by an external circuit.

In the example in Fig. 3.14b:

$$\text{slope} = \frac{\Delta V}{\Delta I} = \frac{(V_2 - V_1)}{(I_2 - I_1)} = -r$$

r is the internal resistance of the cell and the intercept on the V-axis is $\mathcal{E}$, the e.m.f. of the cell.

If for some reason the x variable covers only a small range and you want to know the intercept on the y-axis, you can use a displaced origin and measure the intercept on the x-axis ($y = 0$) instead, then calculate the y intercept c from that (Fig. 3.15).

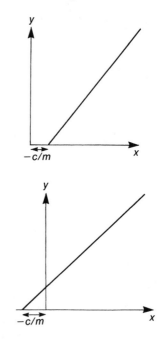

Fig. 3.15 Calculating the constant c for a displaced x origin.

Take care with intercepts: the physics of the experiment will usually tell you to expect a positive y intercept, but occasionally you will get a negative one. If you have not allowed room below the x-axis of your graph for this all is not lost, as for example in the graph of l against $1/f$ for a vibrating air column (Fig. 3.16).

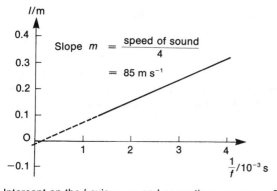

Intercept on the l-axis $=$ $-$ end correction $= c = -0.01$ m

Intercept on the $\frac{1}{f}$-axis $= -\frac{c}{m} = 1.5 \times 10^{-4}$ s

$c = -1.5 \times 10^{-4} \times 85 = -0.013$ m

Fig. 3.16 Vibrating air column, length l, and the calculation of the end correction ($= -c$).

Alternatively, you can calculate c using the measured value of m and a point (x, y) *on the line* in the equation $y = mx + c$.

In a directly proportional relationship, c should be zero, or negligible in comparison with values of y.

3.3.3 Power law relationships

These have the form $y = kx^n$.

a) n IS KNOWN FROM THEORY OR FROM DIMENSIONAL ANALYSIS

In order to obtain a linear relationship plot y against x^n. Comparing this with $y = mx$, you can see that x is now replaced by x^n and m is replaced by k. So the graph should be a straight line through the origin with slope k (Fig. 3.17a).

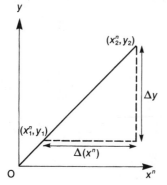

Fig. 3.17 a A linear relationship between y and x^n.

(cont.)

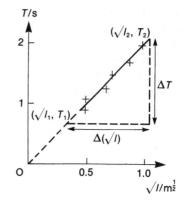

Fig. 3.17 b The period T of a simple pendulum plotted against the square root of its length $\sqrt{l}$.

$$\text{slope} = k = \frac{(y_2 - y_1)}{(x_2^n - x_1^n)}$$

One example of this relationship is the way the period T of a simple pendulum varies with its length l:

$$T = 2\pi \sqrt{\frac{l}{g}}$$

where the graph of T against $\sqrt{l}$ should be a straight line of slope $(T_2 - T_1)/(\sqrt{l_2} - \sqrt{l_1}) = 2\pi/\sqrt{g}$ (Fig. 3.17b).

Sometimes when n is less than 1 it is convenient to raise the y value to the appropriate power, instead of the x value. So for the simple pendulum the variables would be T^2 and l ($T^2 = 4\pi^2 l/g$) giving a straight line of slope $4\pi^2/g$. This is also formally more correct, since l is the independent variable and T^2 is the dependent variable.

b) n IS TO BE DETERMINED OR ITS VALUE CONFIRMED BY THE EXPERIMENT

To obtain a linear relationship of the form $y = mx + c$ we take logarithms of both sides of the equation $y = kx^n$ to give:

$$\log_{10} y = n \log_{10} x + \log_{10} k \quad *$$

or: $\qquad\qquad \lg y = n \lg x + \lg k \quad *$

*The statement that $y = \log_{10} x$ means that $x = 10^y$, that is, it represents the power of 10 that corresponds to the number x. Thus if $x = 100$, $x = 10^2$; so the logarithm of x to base 10 is 2. Similarly $y = \log_e x$ represents the power of the number e ($= 2.718$). Thus $100 = e^{4.605}$ and so $\log_e 100 = 4.605$.

The two types of logarithms are distinguished on calculators and computer keyboards as log (or lg) for $\log_{10}$ and ln for $\log_e$. Their inverses are 10^x and e^x respectively.

Now the independent variable is $\log_{10} x$ and the dependent variable is $\log_{10} y$. Comparison with $y = mx + c$ shows that the y-axis is equivalent to the $(\log_{10} y)$-axis and the x-axis is equivalent to the $(\log_{10} x)$-axis. The slope $m = n$ and the intercept on the $(\log_{10} y)$-axis is equal to $\log_{10} k$. The intercept on the $(\log_{10} x)$-axis $= -c/m = -\log_{10} k/n$ (Fig. 3.18a).

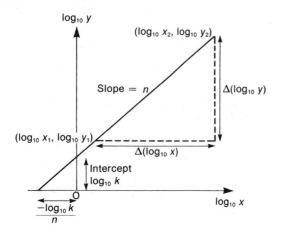

a Obtaining a linear relationship for $y = kx^n$.

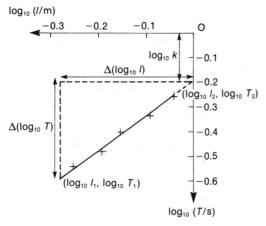

b The vibration of a loaded metre rule, period T and length l.

Fig. 3.18

$$\text{slope } n = \frac{(\log_{10} y_2 - \log_{10} y_1)}{(\log_{10} x_2 - \log_{10} x_1)}$$

and the intercept on the $(\log_{10} y)$-axis $= \log_{10} k$.

Note that for quantities of less than one the logarithms will be negative but the relationship is still valid. An example of this type of power law is the period of vibration of a loaded metre rule as it varies with the free length of the rule: $T = kl^{3/2}$.

Then
$n = (\log_{10} T_2 - \log_{10} T_1)/(\log_{10} l_2 - \log_{10} l_1)$. The slope of the line should be 1.5 and the antilog of the intercept will give k, which is related to the elastic properties of the metre rule, its cross-sectional dimensions, and the mass used for loading it.

3.3.4 Exponential relationships

These have the form $y = a \exp(kx)$ or $y = ae^{kx}$. Usually in physics this type of relationship is met in decay, when k is negative (Fig. 3.19a) rather than in growth (Fig. 3.19b) which is common in biological systems, as for example in the growth of bacteria.

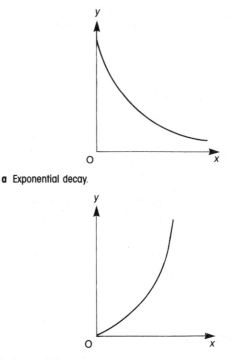

a Exponential decay.

b Exponential growth.

Fig. 3.19

To produce a linear relationship for plotting we have to take logarithms to base e, (see footnote on page 23) which gives:

$$\log_e y = \log_e a + kx$$

or:

$$\ln y = \ln a + kx$$

Comparison with $y = mx + c$ shows that a graph of $\log_e y$ against x should give a straight line of slope k and with intercept on the $(\log_e y)$-axis of $\log_e a$.

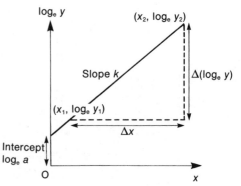

Fig. 3.20 **a** Obtaining a linear relationship for $y = a \exp(kx)$.

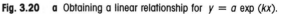

(cont.)

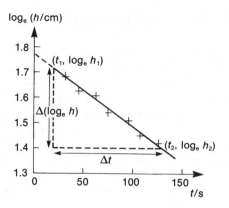

Fig. 3.20 b The variation in the height h of a liquid column with time t.

In Fig. 3.20a the slope $k = (\log_e y_2 - \log_e y_1)/(x_2 - x_1)$ and the intercept c on the $(\log_e y)$-axis $= \log_e a$.

For those who prefer to work in logarithms to base 10, the linear relationship can be expressed as:

$$\log_{10} y = \frac{kx}{2.303} + \log_{10} a$$

(since $\log_e y = \log_e 10 \cdot \log_{10} y$).

In this case the slope of the line on your graph will be $k/2.303$.

An example of this kind of relationship is the variation of the height of water flowing down a burette with time: $h = h_0 \exp(-\lambda t)$. This can be written as:

$$\log_e h = -\lambda t + \log_e h_0$$

hence the slope of the graph in Fig. 3.20b is $-\lambda$:

$$-\lambda = \frac{(\log_e h_2 - \log_e h_1)}{(t_2 - t_1)}$$

The intercept is $\log_e h_0$, which is of no interest in this example.

The time taken for the water to reach half of its original height is:

$$t_{\frac{1}{2}} = \frac{\log_e 2}{\lambda} = \frac{0.693}{\lambda}$$

If logarithms to base 10 are taken then:

$$\lambda = -\text{slope} \times 2.303$$

3.3.5 Inverse relationships

These have the form $y = k/x^n$.

a) n IS KNOWN FROM THEORY OR FROM DIMENSIONAL ANALYSIS

Plot a graph of y against $1/x^n$; this will be a straight line of slope k passing through the origin (Fig. 3.21a).

The slope of the line in Fig. 3.21a is:

$$k = \frac{(y_2 - y_1)}{\left(\dfrac{1}{x_2^n} - \dfrac{1}{x_1^n}\right)}$$

The inverse square law is an example of this type of relationship, for instance, the variation in intensity of a light source with its distance r from the observer: $I = k/r^2$.

From the graph in Fig. 3.21b the constant k is measured from the slope of the line:

$$k = \frac{(I_2 - I_1)}{\left(\dfrac{1}{r_2^2} - \dfrac{1}{r_1^2}\right)}$$

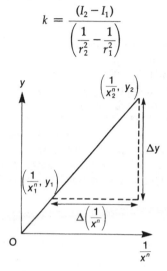

a Obtaining a linear relationship for $y = 1/x^n$.

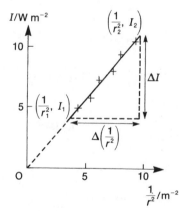

b The variation of the intensity I of a light source with the distance r from the source.

Fig. 3.21

b) n IS TO BE DETERMINED OR ITS VALUE TO BE CONFIRMED BY EXPERIMENT

Take logarithms of both sides of the equation to give:

$$\log_{10} y = -n \log_{10} x + \log_{10} k$$

then follow the same method as in section 3.3.3(b). In this case the line will have a negative slope $-n$.

$$\frac{1}{x} + \frac{1}{k}$$

... in A-level physics is the
... g the image and object
... f the mirror or lens:

... ositive convention)

...ve measure u and v and we want to find f, so we re-arrange the equation:

$$\frac{1}{v} = \frac{-1}{u} + \frac{1}{f}$$

Comparing this with $y = mx + c$, we can see that $1/v$ is equivalent to y, $1/u$ is equivalent to x and $1/f$ is equivalent to c. So if we plot $1/v$ against $1/u$ the graph should be a straight line with slope -1 and with intercepts on both axes of $1/f$ (Fig. 3.22a). It is particularly important with this relationship to choose a big enough range of values for x and y so that you can measure both intercepts accurately (see section 3.2b). A restricted range for x and y can lead to inaccurate values for intercepts (Fig. 3.22b).

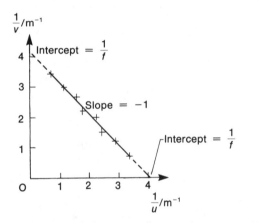

a Obtaining a linear relation between the object distance u and image distance v for a lens or mirror.

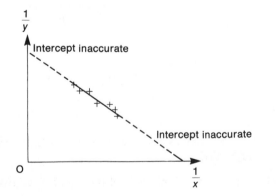

b A poor choice of the range of values for x and y, leading to uncertain intercepts.

Fig. 3.22

3.4 ANALYSIS OF NON-LINEAR GRAPHS

It is possible that the form of the relationship between two quantities is not known – it can only be said to be non-linear, that is, plotting a graph of y against x produces a curve. However, the slope may be a useful physical quantity. For example, on a velocity–time curve it may be helpful to find the acceleration. So first in this section we will consider how to measure the slope by drawing the tangent to the curve. We think that drawing a tangent is most easily done by first drawing the normal to the curve with the aid of a mirror placed across on the smooth curve (Fig. 3.23).

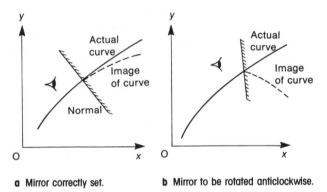

a Mirror correctly set.   **b** Mirror to be rotated anticlockwise.

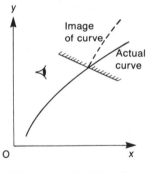

c Mirror to be rotated clockwise.

Fig. 3.23   Using a plane mirror to draw the normal to a curve.

As the mirror is rotated the image of the curve will vary in orientation and looking into the mirror you will see a sharp bend in the curve. When the mirror is normal to the curve the graph and its reflection will form a smooth curve. Draw the normal in pencil along the front face of the mirror and remove the mirror. Now use a protractor to draw a line at 90° to the normal; this is the tangent (Fig. 3.24). The slope can then be measured in the usual way:

$$\text{slope} = \frac{\Delta y}{\Delta x} = \frac{(y_2 - y_1)}{(x_2 - x_1)}$$

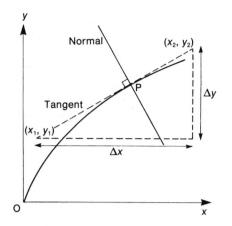

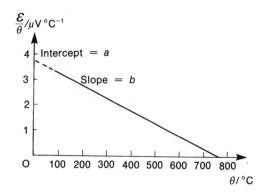

Fig. 3.24 Drawing the tangent to the curve at P and measuring its slope.

Fig. 3.26 Obtaining a relationship between the e.m.f. $\mathcal{E}$ of a thermocouple and its temperature θ.

It must be emphasised that this is usually a last resort because drawing smooth curves and producing a tangent for normal experimental data is often an inaccurate procedure, particularly if one quantity is varying rapidly with respect to the other. Whenever possible see if there is a theoretical model which will enable you to produce a linear relationship between two variables. For example, the e.m.f. of a thermocouple and its temperature are related by the equation $\mathcal{E} = a\theta + b\theta^2$ (Fig. 3.25), so measuring the slope s at two points on the curve will give two equations:

$$s_1 = \left(\frac{d\mathcal{E}}{d\theta}\right)_1 = a + 2b\theta_1$$

$$s_2 = \left(\frac{d\mathcal{E}}{d\theta}\right)_2 = a + 2b\theta_2$$

from which the constants a and b can be found. However, examination of the equation for $\mathcal{E}$ shows that if we divide by θ we get:

$$\frac{\mathcal{E}}{\theta} = a + b\theta$$

so if we plot $\mathcal{E}/\theta$ against θ we get a straight line of slope b and with intercept on the $(\mathcal{E}/\theta)$-axis of a (Fig. 3.26).

3.5 CALCULATING ERRORS FROM GRAPHS

Graphical analysis is an excellent means of obtaining an average value for a physical quantity from the slope of the graph. The graph is slightly less reliable for measuring intercepts. A small change in slope can give a large variation in the intercept. Whenever possible you should try to assess this. In section 3.1 the advice is given that the line drawn should pass symmetrically through the experimental points. You can now obtain an estimate of the error in the slope and intercept by drawing two straight lines passing approximately through the centre of your best straight line and enclosing all the data points (Fig. 3.27). Measure the slopes (m_1, m_2) and the intercepts (c_1, c_2) for the two lines (i) and (ii). Calculate the difference between these values and those for the best straight line. This will give you an average error, Δm, for the slope: $\Delta m = (\Delta m_1 + \Delta m_2)/2$ and an average error, Δc, for the intercept on the y-axis: $\Delta c = (\Delta c_1 + \Delta c_2)/2$. Thus you will be able to calculate the error in any physical quantity derived from the slope $(m \pm \Delta m)$ and the intercept $(c \pm \Delta c)$.

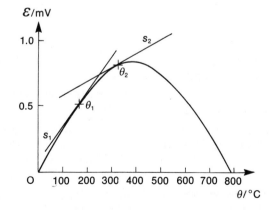

Fig. 3.25 Variation of the e.m.f. $\mathcal{E}$ of a thermocouple with its temperature θ.

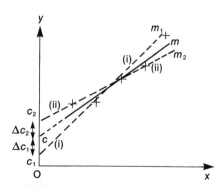

Fig. 3.27 Determining the errors Δm and Δc in the slope m and intercept c for a straight line.

3.6 AREAS UNDER GRAPHS

Sometimes the area enclosed between an axis and the graph line represents a physical quantity. For example, the area under the force–extension graph for a wire represents the stored elastic energy W and the area under a force–time curve for a moving trolley represents its total momentum p. Clearly, if the graph is linear the area can be calculated by trigonometry (Fig. 3.28): area $= \frac{1}{2} \times (AD + BC) \times DC$ in the appropriate units (for example, y in newtons, x in metres for the extension of a wire). If the graph is non-linear then the area should be determined by counting graph squares; a convenient unit for this is 1 cm^2. This may seem tedious but remember that a precise answer is not required. An error of 1 cm^2 in 100 cm^2 is usually acceptable. First count the whole cm^2 squares marking each with a pencil as it is counted. This will take you quite near to the curve. Now count squares to the nearest $\frac{1}{2}$ cm^2; this procedure will usually compensate for overestimates and underestimates of the remaining area. You have now measured the area A in cm^2, which must next be converted to the appropriate units by using the scales on the axes. In Fig. 3.29, suppose that the area measured is A cm^2; a force F of 50 N on the vertical scale corresponds to 1 cm on the axis, and an extension of 0.5 mm on the horizontal scale corresponds to 1 cm on the axis. Then the area in joules is $A \times 50 \times 0.5 \times 10^{-3}$ J. The factor of 10^{-3} is for the conversion of e to metres. Thus $W = 0.81$ J in this example.

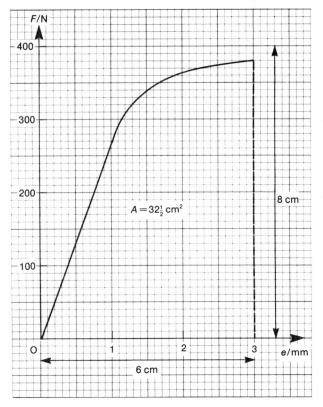

Fig. 3.29 Calculating the area under a curve for the force F–extension e curve of a wire.

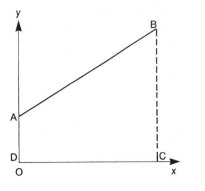

Fig. 3.28 Calculating the area under a graph for a linear variation.

3.7 SUMMARY OF GRAPHICAL ANALYSIS

Plotting graphs
a) Plot the dependent variable (that is, the one that changes as a result of changes you make to the other) along the vertical axis (ordinate) and the independent variable along the horizontal axis (abscissa).

b) Choose the scales on the axes so that points are widely spread over the page.

c) Use simple scale divisions.

d) Plot points as crosses ($+$) or circles ($\odot$).

e) Label axes with the name of the quantity and its unit.

f) Draw a smooth curve through the points and not a zig-zag, unless you are producing a calibration curve for a meter.

g) Spread readings evenly over the range of your scales, unless an intercept is required. Then readings should be taken as close to the appropriate axis as possible.

h) Plot a graph as the experiment proceeds.

Straight line graphs
i) Whenever possible choose your variables so as to obtain a straight line. This applies to variables related by an equation of the form $y = mx + c$.

j) Draw the best straight line passing symmetrically through your experimental points.

k) Measure the gradient m using a large triangle. If an intercept is required the origin of the x or y coordinate should normally be included. The intercept on the y-axis ($x = 0$) is c and the intercept on the x-axis ($y = 0$) is $-c/m$. Alternatively, c can be calculated using a point (x, y) on the line and the measured value of m in $y = mx + c$.

DATA ANALYSIS

Six sets of experimental data are included in this section. These sets will provide practice in analysing data to produce straight line graphs, in measuring slopes and intercepts and finally in testing whether experimental data conform to a theoretical model. Since you will be using genuine experimental results, you must not expect to obtain perfect straight lines or smooth curves. However, you should always draw the best straight line or the smoothest curve, as physical data is not usually discontinuous. The data can also be analysed using the least squares fitting program given in appendix 2 (page 292); this method gives a quantitative assessment of the way in which the data conforms to linear behaviour, and also of the uncertainties in the slope and intercept.

4A The Inverse Square Law for γ-Radiation

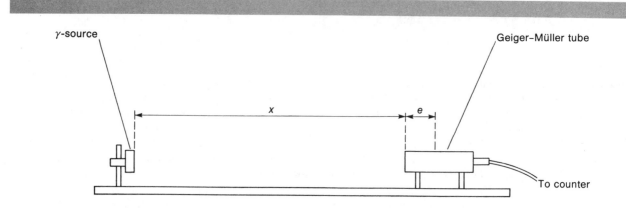

Fig. 4.1   The inverse square law for γ-radiation. $(x + e)$ is the effective distance of the γ-source from the Geiger-Müller tube. e allows for the fact that all ionisation does not occur at the window of the tube.

a   The results in Table 4.1 were obtained for the counts in two-minute intervals from a γ-source as the distance x between the source and detector was varied (Fig. 4.1). The background count in the absence of the γ-source was 57 in a two-minute interval.

Table 4.1

x/m	0.04	0.05	0.06	0.07	0.08	0.09
Counts	211	203	182	152	136	129

x/m	0.10	0.12	0.14	0.16	0.18	0.20
Counts	117	113	111	101	89	82

b   Theoretically it is expected that the count rate varies inversely as x^2, that is, count rate $N = c/x^2$. c is a constant which depends on the activity of the source and the characteristics of the detector.

c   Produce a table of the count rate (counts per second) corrected for background radiation, and x. Plot a suitable graph to find out if the relationship in (b) is valid. You should include the origin in your graph.

d   You may find that the graph drawn in (c) deviates significantly from a straight line for smaller values of x. The main reason for this is the assumption that the effective distance between the γ-source and the detector is x. Since ionisation occurs beyond the window of the Geiger–Müller tube, this effective distance is larger than x by an average distance e.

e   In order to investigate whether this correction leads to an improvement in the linearity of your graph, the inverse square law equation is rewritten as $N = c/(x + e)^2$. Clearly you can no longer use the data as it stands because you do not know the value of e. You could estimate a value between 0.0 and 0.1 m but there is a much neater way of verifying the inverse square law and determining a value for e.

f   The equation in (e) is rewritten as $(x + e)^2 = c/N$ or $(x + e) = c^{\frac{1}{2}}/N^{\frac{1}{2}}$. Produce a table of x and $1/N^{\frac{1}{2}}$ and plot a suitable graph in order to confirm the inverse square law.

g   From your graph determine a value for the constant c and a value for e. Comment on whether the results confirm the inverse square law relationship and whether the value you obtained for e is reasonable.

4B Vibrations of a Loaded Metre Rule

a   The results in Table 4.2 were obtained for the vibrations of a metre rule loaded with a mass $M (= 0.2$ kg) as the projecting length l was varied (Fig. 4.2).

Table 4.2

l/m	Time for twenty complete vibrations/s				
0.9	11.5	11.0	11.1	11.0	11.2
0.8	9.0	9.7	9.7	9.2	9.4
0.7	7.6	7.5	7.1	8.0	7.3
0.6	6.8	6.0	6.7	6.0	6.8
0.5	5.0	5.6	5.6	5.1	4.7

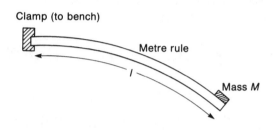

Clamp (to bench)

Metre rule

l

Mass M

Fig. 4.2   Vibrations of a loaded metre rule.

b   Draw up a table of l and the average time vibration (the period) T.

c   Theoretically $T = kl^{3/2}$, where k is a constant depending on M, the dimensions of the cross-section of the metre rule and the elastic properties of the material of the rule.

d   In order to determine the constant k and confirm the form of the relationship in (c), the equation is rewritten as $T = kl^n$. Hence taking logarithms to the base 10 of both sides of the equation $\log_{10} T = n \log_{10} l + \log_{10} k$.

e   Draw up a table of $\log_{10} (T/s)$ and $\log_{10} (l/m)$ and plot a suitable graph in order to confirm the relationship in (d).

f   From your graph determine a value for n and $\log_{10} k$, and hence k.

g   Comment on whether these results confirm the theoretical relationship with a value of $n = 1.5$. Can you suggest any reasons for deviations from the linear relationship expected in (e)?

4C Flow of Water Through a Burette

a   In this experiment the variation in the height h of the water column was measured with time t when the tap was opened by a small amount (Fig. 4.3). The results are shown in Table 4.3.

Table 4.3

h/cm	59	53	48	42	37	31	25	20
t/s	0	14	27	42	58	75	97	123

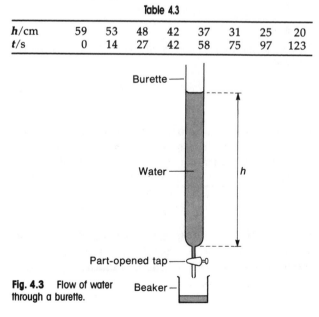

Burette

Water — h

Part-opened tap

Fig. 4.3   Flow of water through a burette.

Beaker

b   Theoretically it is expected that the rate of flow of water depends on the fluid pressure $h\rho g$. Since the burette is of uniform cross-section (except near to the tap), h is proportional to the volume of water Q. Thus $dh/dt = -\lambda h$, where λ is a constant depending on the cross-sectional area of the burette, the density of water and g. This equation may be solved to give $h = h_0 \exp(-\lambda t)$, where h_0 is the height of the water column at $t = 0$.

c   Plot a graph of h against t and find the time for the water to decrease to one-half of its initial height.

d   In order to confirm the exponential relationship in (b) take logarithms to the base e: $\log_e h = -\lambda t + \log_e h_0$. Draw up a table of $\log_e h$ and t and plot a suitable graph so as to determine a value for λ.

e   It can be shown that the time for h to decrease to $h_0/2$, the half-life $t_{\frac{1}{2}} = \log_e 2/\lambda = 0.693/\lambda$. Hence calculate a second value for $t_{\frac{1}{2}}$. Compare this value with the one determined in (c). Which value do you consider to be more reliable?

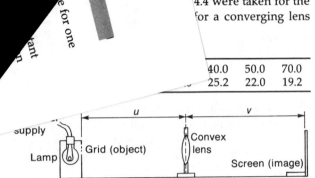

4.4 were taken for the ... for a converging lens

	40.0	50.0	70.0
	25.2	22.0	19.2

Fig. 4.4 Measurement of the focal length of a converging lens.

b The focal length f can be determined from the equation for a thin lens $1/f = 1/v + 1/u$, or $1/v = -1/u + 1/f$.

c Draw up a table of $1/v$ and $1/u$. Plot a suitable graph to verify the relationship in (b). Determine values for $1/f$ from your graph.

d Theoretically the slope of the correctly plotted graph is -1. See if your graph gives this value within experimental error. Calculate the average value for f and estimate the uncertainty in f.

4E Measurement of the Energy Loss from an Aluminium Calorimeter

a In order to examine the validity of Newton's law of cooling, an aluminium calorimeter was heated electrically to about 80 °C and its cooling curve determined under conditions of forced convection (Fig. 4.5). The results are given in Table 4.5.

Table 4.5

t/min	0	2	4	6	8	10	12	14
θ/°C	80	77	72	68	65	61	58	55

t/min	16	18	20	22	24	26	28	30
θ/°C	52	49	47	45	43	41	39	38

b Theoretically, the rate of fall of temperature $d\theta/dt$ is proportional to the excess temperature $(\theta - \theta_R)$, where θ_R is room temperature ($= 22$ °C). The constant of proportionality k depends on the mass of the calorimeter, the exposed surface area of the surface, the nature of the surface and the specific heat capacity of the aluminium.

c Plot a graph of θ against t. Determine the rate of cooling $d\theta/dt$ at five temperatures 75, 65, 55, 45 and 40 °C by drawing tangents to the cooling curve. Remember that t is in minutes.

d If Newton's law of cooling is valid a graph of $d\theta/dt$ against $(\theta - \theta_R)$ should be a straight line of slope $-k$ ($d\theta/dt$ is negative). Plot this graph and assess whether it

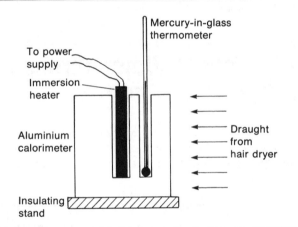

Fig. 4.5 Measurement of the energy losses from an aluminium calorimeter.

verifies Newton's law of cooling. Determine a value for k in units of s^{-1}.

e Drawing tangents to a curve is quite tedious and often not very accurate. In this experiment a further examination of the theoretical equation gives an alternative way of verifying Newton's law of cooling: $d\theta/dt = -k(\theta - \theta_R)$ can be integrated to give $(\theta - \theta_R) = (\theta_I - \theta_R) \exp(-kt)$, where θ_I is the initial temperature (at $t = 0$).

f Taking logarithms to the base e of both sides of the equation in (e) gives $\log_e (\theta - \theta_R) = -kt + \log_e (\theta_I - \theta_R)$. Tabulate $\log_e [(\theta - \theta_R)/K]$ and t/s. Plot a suitable graph to verify this relationship. Determine a second value for k and compare it with the value of k determined in (d).

4F Investigation of the Power Dissipated by a Tungsten Filament Lamp

a In this experiment an attempt is made to assess the major ways in which energy is lost from a filament lamp as the temperature of the filament is increased. Using a 12 V, 24 W lamp the measurements in Table 4.6 were obtained for the potential difference V across the lamp and the current I through the lamp (Fig. 4.6).

Table 4.6

V/V	10.0	8.8	8.0	7.0	6.0	5.0
I/A	1.80	1.70	1.60	1.50	1.35	1.20

V/V	4.0	3.0	2.0	1.0	0.5	0.2
I/A	1.10	0.99	0.83	0.63	0.45	0.22

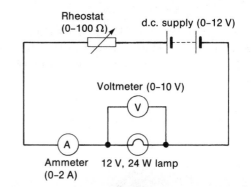

Fig. 4.6 Measurement of the power dissipated by a filament lamp.

b The main ways in which energy is lost are convection and radiation from the outer surface of the lamp. The rate of energy loss by convection is expected to be proportional to the excess temperature $(T - T_R)$, where T_R is room temperature in kelvin. The rate of energy loss by radiation is expected to obey Stefan's law: $dQ/dt = -k(T^4 - T_R^4)$. Radiation is the major source of energy loss at high temperatures (above 1000 K). Thus if you plot a graph of the power dissipated by the lamp $P = IV$ against T you would expect to obtain an initial linear section, where P is proportional to the excess temperature, followed by a rapidly rising curve as P becomes more nearly proportional to T^4.

c In order to obtain an estimate of the lamp filament temperature, the variation of resistance R of the filament with temperature will be used: $R_\theta = R_0(1 + \alpha\theta)$, where R_θ is the resistance of the filament at θ °C, R_0 is the filament resistance at 0 °C and α is the average value of the temperature coefficient of resistance. Take $R_0 = 0.5\ \Omega$ and $\alpha = 0.005\ \text{K}^{-1}$.

Thus $\theta = (R_\theta/R_0 - 1)/\alpha$ and $T/\text{K} = \theta/\text{°C} + 273$.

Using the results in (a) calculate $R_\theta = V/I$, θ and T. Produce a table of P and T. Leave four more columns in the table for further analysis. Plot a graph of P against T and see if your graph confirms the behaviour predicted in (b). Start the T-axis at about 500 K.

d You now investigate whether the power dissipated by the lamp conforms to Stefan's radiation law at high temperatures (above 1000 K). Assuming that the energy loss by convection is negligible and that T^4 is much greater than T_R^4, $P = kT^4$. Thus a graph of $\log_{10} P$ against $\log_{10} T$ should be a straight line of slope 4; the intercept on the $\log_{10} P$ axis is of no interest here.

e Add to the table produced in (c) columns for $\log_{10} (P/\text{W})$ and $\log_{10} (T/\text{K})$. Plot the graph of $\log_{10} P$ against $\log_{10} T$. The points plotted are unlikely to fall on a single straight line, but remember you are particularly interested in the behaviour at high temperatures. Therefore draw the best straight line for these points. Measure the slope of this line and compare it with the theoretical value of 4.

f In (e) you have neglected the effects of convection and probably obtained a low value for the slope. You can now complete a further analysis of the radiation losses by subtracting the convection power losses using the P, T graph produced in (c). If you assume that at low temperatures the graph is linear as a result of convection losses only, you can extrapolate this linear section to higher temperatures. The differences between the curve and the straight line should then be predominantly the power losses by radiation.

g For each temperature T calculate P_R, the value of the radiation power loss. Add these values of P_R to the table in (d). Hence plot a further graph of $\log_{10} P$ against $\log_{10} T$. If the correction has been successful the graph should be linear over a larger range than in (e). Measure the slope of the graph and compare it with the theoretical value of 4.

5 INTRODUCTORY EXPERIMENTS

These three experiments are based on elementary topics that you may have met during your earlier, pre-A-level work in physics. They may be used to introduce you to some of the techniques you will have to use for practical physics at A level. They also provide practice in graphical analysis and the calculation of uncertainties.

5A Measurement of the e.m.f. and Internal Resistance of a Cell

APPARATUS REQUIRED

- 1.5 V dry cell mounted on a block with 4 mm terminals (an artificially high internal resistance is incorporated)

- 0–5 V d.c. voltmeter

- 0–100 mA d.c. ammeter

- 0–25 Ω rheostat or 0–100 Ω resistance box with 1 Ω steps

- switch (optional since the circuit can be broken by removing the appropriate 4 mm connection)

- connecting wire with 4 mm terminals

PRINCIPLES INVOLVED

a The e.m.f. of a cell (or generator more generally) is defined as the energy produced for every coulomb of electric charge which circulates. In practice some of the energy produced in the cell is dissipated internally and this can be considered to be due to an internal resistance r. The potential difference V across the terminals of the cell will then be the e.m.f. of the cell ε less the potential difference across the internal resistance Ir, where I is the current delivered by the cell to an external circuit (Fig. 5.1).

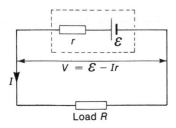

Fig. 5.1 A cell of e.m.f. ε and internal resistance r delivering a current I to an external load R.

b The practical definition of e.m.f. can be taken as the potential difference across the terminals of the cell on open circuit, that is, when $I = 0$. A high resistance voltmeter should be used so that little current passes through the voltmeter. In this experiment you will investigate how the terminal potential difference across a dry cell varies with current drawn from the cell. You will then be able to determine the e.m.f. and internal resistance of the cell by plotting a suitable graph.

PROCEDURE

c Connect up the circuit as shown in Fig. 5.2 with the rheostat or resistance box set to its maximum value. Varying the current in the circuit is achieved by adjusting this resistance value. You are advised to connect the series circuit first and then to connect the voltmeter across the terminals of the cell.

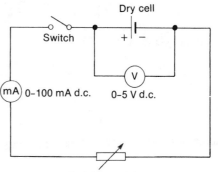

Fig. 5.2 Circuit diagram for measuring the e.m.f. ε and internal resistance r of a dry cell.

d With the switch open record the voltmeter reading V_0.

e Close the switch and record ten pairs of readings of the current I through the external resistance and the potential difference V across the cell. Obtain these readings by varying R so that the increments in I are approximately constant (about 10 mA, up to 100 mA).

You should open the switch (or break the circuit) after you have taken each pair of readings.

Tabulate your results for V and I.

f You should plot a graph of V as ordinate (y-axis) against I as abscissa (x-axis) as the experiment proceeds so as to identify any doubtful points. In this experiment you cannot repeat your readings after completion because it is very likely that the cell e.m.f. will be lower than at the start. Because of the range of values for I you may find it convenient to plot your graph with the long axis of the graph paper horizontal.

35

g Open the switch and record a second value for V_0.

h From your graph and the equation $V = \mathcal{E} - Ir$ determine a value of r from the slope and a value of $\mathcal{E}$ from an appropriate intercept. Remember that I is in mA. Estimate the uncertainties in r and $\mathcal{E}$ from your graph.

i Compare the value of $\mathcal{E}$ determined graphically with the two values of V_0 determined in (d) and (g).

Should they be the same? If not, which measurement do you consider to be more reliable?

NOTES

j Your account should include a circuit diagram, a table of results, a graph and its analysis, the values of $\mathcal{E}$ and r together with their uncertainties. You should also explain why you opened the switch (or broke the circuit) between readings. Explain why this is a bad method for measuring the e.m.f. of a dry cell.

5B Measurement of the Acceleration of Free Fall Using a Simple Pendulum

APPARATUS REQUIRED

- brass weight on a thread about 2 m in length
- wooden block with a slit or two pieces of thin wood for clamping the pendulum thread
- retort stand, boss and clamp
- optical pin and Plasticine
- metre rule
- stopwatch reading to 0.1 s
- protractor

PRINCIPLES INVOLVED

a The period of an oscillation T is the time taken for the pendulum to make one complete swing past a fixed point O in one direction and back and then through O again in the first direction (O → A → B → O in Fig. 5.3).

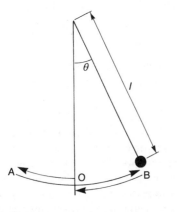

Fig. 5.3 The simple pendulum.

T depends on the length l of the pendulum and the strength of the gravitational field g. T is independent of the angle of the swing θ provided that θ is small and the approximation $\sin \theta = \theta$ in radians is valid; this approximation is valid to within 1 part in 1000 for θ less than 5° (0.0873 radians).

b The theoretical relationship is $T = 2\pi\sqrt{l/g}$ or $T^2 = 4\pi^2 l/g$. l should be measured from the top of the pendulum thread to the centre of gravity of the pendulum bob, but this is often difficult to measure for a large irregular bob such as a brass weight. It is then preferable to measure the distance from the top of the pendulum (at the support) to a *small* knot tied about 2 cm above the bob.

PROCEDURE

c Assemble the apparatus as shown in Fig. 5.4, setting the pendulum length so that the period of oscillation is about 2 s (take g to be approximately 10 N kg^{-1}). Ensure that the pendulum thread is clamped firmly in the wooden block or between the two pieces of wood and that the pendulum is well clear of the edge of the bench. A G-cramp may be needed to keep the stand rigid. Tie a knot in the thread about 2 cm above the bob. Make a reference mark using an optical pin either mounted horizontally on the stand or fixed vertically on the bench with Plasticine, and in line with the undisplaced position of the pendulum.

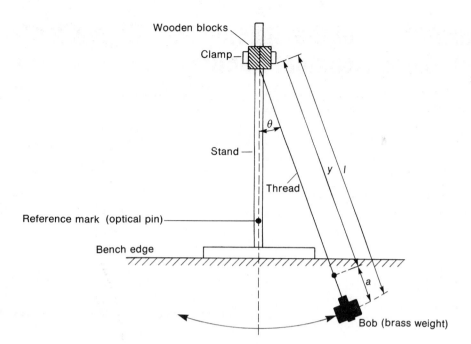

Fig. 5.4 Apparatus for simple pendulum experiment.

d Displace the pendulum a few centimetres to one side and release it. The pendulum should oscillate in one plane and not in a cone or ellipse. As the pendulum passes the reference mark start the stopwatch, count zero and determine the time for twenty oscillations. Measure the length y from the bottom of the wooden block to the knot.

e Repeat this procedure for five further values of y to give a reasonably large range of T values (about 1.4 to 2.8 s). You may have to move your reference mark further up the stand for small values of y.

f Plot a graph of the time for twenty oscillations against y as the experiment proceeds so as to identify any doubtful points. The graph should be a smooth curve.

g Tabulate your values for the times for 20 oscillations, the period T, T^2 and y (in metres).

h The equation for the period of oscillation of the pendulum is $T = 2\pi\sqrt{(y + a)/g}$, where a is the distance of the knot from the centre of gravity of the bob. Hence $T^2 = 4\pi^2 y/g + 4\pi^2 a/g$.

i From your results plot a suitable graph in order to obtain a straight line. From the slope determine a value for g and from an appropriate intercept determine a value for a. Estimate from your graph uncertainties in these two quantities.

j Compare your value of g with the accepted value and the value of a with that measured using a metre rule.

NOTES

k Your record should include a diagram of the apparatus, a table of results, graphs and analysis leading to values for g and a, together with their uncertainties.

FURTHER WORK

l The equation for the simple pendulum period $T = 2\pi\sqrt{l/g}$ is derived assuming that the angle of oscillation is small. Investigate how the period of the pendulum varies for a fixed length l of about 1 m for a range of values of θ from about 10° to 50°. You will need to determine the period of oscillation to an accuracy of ± 0.01 s to see any effects. Damping will also occur, decreasing θ as you make your timings; you will therefore need to take an average value for θ. Comment on whether you would have expected the change in T observed.

m In (d) you were instructed to ensure that the pendulum oscillates in one plane. Compare T for a conical oscillation and for a vertical plane oscillation. Is there a significant difference?

37

5C Measurement of the Specific Heat Capacity of a Metal Block Using Electrical Heating

APPARATUS REQUIRED

- aluminium block (calorimeter)
- insulating board (to protect bench)
- 50 W, 12 V immersion heater to *fit* the block
- mercury-in-glass thermometer for 0–100 °C (preferably reading to 0.5 °C)
- glycerol
- power supply 12 V d.c.
- voltmeter 0–10 V d.c.
- ammeter 0–5 A d.c.
- rheostat 0–12 Ω (up to 5 A maximum current)
- switch
- connecting wires
- stopwatch or stopclock

PRINCIPLES INVOLVED

a A standard method for determining the specific heat capacity c of a solid is to measure the temperature rise θ of the solid when electrical energy is supplied at a constant rate $P = IV$. Assuming that no energy is lost, the electrical energy supplied in a time t is equal to the gain in internal energy of the solid $mc\theta$ for a solid of mass m.

b Using $IVt = mc\theta$ usually leads to an overestimate of the value of the specific heat capacity, mainly as a result of energy losses to the surroundings from the surface of the solid. If information were available on the rate of energy loss then a correction could be applied to the equation above. In this experiment the correction to θ for the effect of energy losses is determined by monitoring the cooling of the solid after the electrical heating has been switched off.

c The heating–cooling curve in the absence of energy losses is shown by the dashed line in Fig. 5.5; the actual heating–cooling curve is shown by the continuous line. θ is the excess temperature of the solid above the temperature of the surroundings θ_R; t_1 is the heating time and t_2 is the cooling time. From this curve and the temperature fall $\delta\theta_2$ after cooling for a time t_2, it is possible to obtain an estimate of the cooling correction $\delta\theta_1$ to be added to the measured temperature rise θ_1 of the solid.

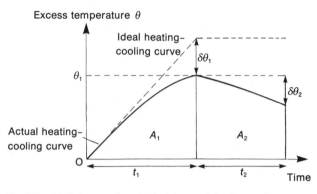

Fig. 5.5 Ideal (— — —) and actual (———) heating–cooling curves for a solid.

d Assuming that the rate of energy loss is proportional to the excess temperature of the solid θ (Newton's law of cooling), it can be shown that $\delta\theta_1 = \delta\theta_2 A_1/A_2$. A_1 and A_2 are the areas (in cm^2) under the solid curve as shown in Fig. 5.5

PROCEDURE

e Measure the mass m of the aluminium block using a balance.

f Connect up the electrical circuit as shown in Fig. 5.6. Before inserting the immersion heater into the block, close the switch and adjust the rheostat to give a potential difference V of about 10 V. Open the switch.

g Place the immersion heater and thermometer in the block. A *few* drops of glycerol should be placed in the thermometer hole to improve thermal contact with the block.

h Record the initial temperature θ_R of the block. This should be subtracted from all subsequent temperature readings to give the excess temperature θ of the block. Close the switch and record the current I and potential difference V; if necessary adjust the rheostat during the experiment to main this value of V.

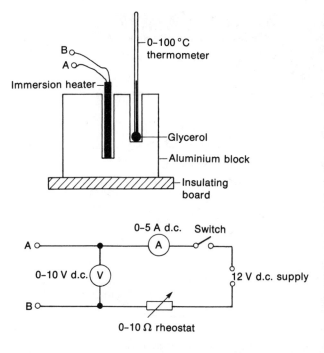

Fig. 5.6 Electrical connections for the measurement of the specific heat capacity of an aluminium block.

i Record the temperature of the block at one-minute intervals for about 20 minutes or until the temperature of the block is about 40 °C above its initial temperature θ_R. Note the time t_1.

j Open the switch and continue to record the temperature of the block every minute until the temperature has fallen to about 10 °C below the maximum temperature recorded. Note that the temperature of the block will initially rise when the switch is opened (Fig. 5.7) because of the time lag of the energy reaching the thermometer from the immersion heater. Record the cooling time t_2.

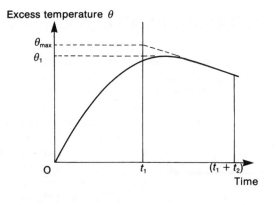

Fig. 5.7 Obtaining the maximum excess temperature θ_{max} of the block.

k Plot a graph of the temperature *excess* θ as ordinate (*y*-axis) against time *t* as abscissa (*x*-axis).

l An approximate value of the specific heat capacity of aluminium may be calculated from $IVt_1 = mc\theta_1$. Now the temperature rise θ_1 cannot simply be taken as the maximum recorded temperature of the block as this temperature is reached *after* the electrical heating has been switched off and the block is actually starting to cool. An estimate of the actual maximum temperature θ_{max} correcting for the time lag referred to in (j) can be obtained by extrapolating back the cooling curve to the time t_1 when the electrical supply was switched off as shown by the dashed line in Fig. 5.7. Use this value for θ_{max} to calculate a value of c for aluminium.

m Calculate the temperature correction $\delta\theta_1$ using the method of areas in (d). The areas A_1 and A_2 can be estimated by counting 1 cm squares; remember that this is only a correction and the areas need not be calculated with a precision greater than 1 cm². Add this correction to θ_{max} determined in (l) and calculate a value for c.

NOTES

n Your record should include a circuit diagram, a brief account of the measurements taken, the heating–cooling curve, the application of the cooling correction and the comparison of the two values of c.

o An alternative method for reducing the effects of energy losses is to perform the experiment again using a different rate of electrical heating but heating the block to the same maximum temperature θ. In the first experiment the current is I_1, the potential difference is V_1 and the heating time is t_1. In the second experiment the values are I_2, V_2 and t_2. If the average rate of energy loss is h then:

$$I_1V_1t_1 = mc\theta + ht_1$$

and

$$I_2V_2t_2 = mc\theta + ht_2$$

These two equations can be subtracted to give a value for $h = (I_1V_1t_1 - I_2V_2t_2)/(t_1 - t_2)$. This value for h can then be substituted in either of the above equations to give a value for c.

FURTHER WORK

p Try to derive the equation for the cooling correction $\delta\theta_1 = \delta\theta_2 A_1/A_2$. The rate of energy loss $mc(\mathrm{d}\theta/\mathrm{d}t) = k\theta$, where k is the constant of proportionality in Newton's law of cooling. You will need to integrate this equation so as to derive the cooling correction.

6 MECHANICS AND MECHANICAL PROPERTIES OF MATTER

For convenience, a summary will be given of the main equations of linear and rotational dynamics. These equations will be used in experiments 6B, 6C, 6D, 6E and 6F.

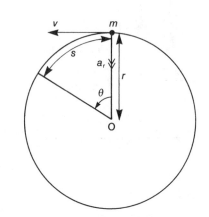

Fig. 6.1 Circular motion of a particle of mass m.

6.1 MOTION OF A PARTICLE IN A CIRCLE

Consider a point mass (a particle) m moving in a circle of radius r with a speed v. Even if the speed of the particle is constant its velocity v varies since the direction of the particle is changing with time.

6.1.1 Centripetal acceleration of a particle moving in a circle

From Newton's first law a particle travelling in a circle must be subject to a resultant force. Thus from $F = ma$ the particle must be accelerating. This acceleration must be in the same direction as F (towards the centre of the circle O). This radial component of the acceleration a_r can be shown to have a value of v^2/r, where r is the radius of the circle. The resultant force acting on m must be towards O; its magnitude is calculated from $F = ma_r$:

$$F = ma_r = mv^2/r \qquad [6.1]$$

6.1.2 Relationship between linear and rotational dynamics

For circular motion, and particularly for rotational dynamics of solids, it is more convenient to use angular measurements. In Fig. 6.1 particle m rotates through an angle θ (measured in radians) in a time t. The relationship between the distance s (travelled by m along the arc of the circle) and θ is:

$$s = r\theta \quad \text{or} \quad \theta = s/r \qquad [6.2]$$

The angular velocity ω is defined as the rate of change of θ:

$$\omega = \theta/t \quad \text{or more formally} \quad \omega = d\theta/dt \qquad [6.3]$$

From equation [6.2] the relationship between ω and the speed of the particle v is:

$$v = r\omega \quad \text{since} \quad v = ds/dt \qquad [6.4]$$

The angular acceleration α of m is defined as the rate of change of ω:

$$\alpha = d\omega/dt = d^2\theta/dt^2 \qquad [6.5]$$

The relationship between the angular acceleration α and the tangential acceleration a_t (the rate at which the speed changes) is:

$$a_t = r\alpha \qquad [6.6]$$

6.2 ROTATIONAL DYNAMICS OF A SOLID BODY

In Fig. 6.2 a solid body of total mass M is rotating with a constant angular velocity ω about an axis O. Now the problem in applying linear dynamics to this body is that each elemental mass m_i which makes up the body moves with a different speed v_i depending on its distance r_i from O ($v_i = r_i\omega$). It is therefore necessary to define a rotational quantity I, the moment of inertia of the body about its axis of rotation; I in rotational dynamics plays the same role as inertia or mass M in linear dynamics. As an example consider the calculation of the rotational kinetic energy of the body. The rotational kinetic energy

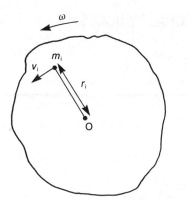

Fig. 6.2 Rotational dynamics of a solid body.

of each elemental mass is $\frac{1}{2}m_i v_i^2$. The total rotational kinetic energy of the body is the sum of the elemental contributions:

$$\text{rotational kinetic energy} = \sum_i \frac{1}{2}m_i v_i^2$$

Using equation [6.4]:

$$\text{rotational kinetic energy} = \sum_i \frac{1}{2}m_i r_i^2 \omega^2 = \frac{1}{2}\omega^2 \sum_i m_i r_i^2 \quad [6.7]$$

since ω is the same for all elemental masses m_i.

The quantity $\displaystyle\sum_i m_i r_i^2$ is defined as the moment of inertia

I of the body about the axis of rotation through O.

Thus the rotational kinetic energy of a body is $\frac{1}{2}I\omega^2$. I depends on the distribution of mass within the body: for example two cylinders, one hollow and the other solid, of identical mass and external dimensions (see Fig. 6.3) will have different values of I, with $I_h > I_s$. A larger proportion of the mass of the hollow cylinder is distributed at a larger radius from the axis.

6.3 SIMULTANEOUS LINEAR AND ROTATIONAL MOTION

If the body is not only rotating but also rolling, then a combination of linear and rotational dynamics must be used to describe its motion. If, for example, a cylinder or sphere of radius R is rolling down an inclined plane, the total kinetic energy of the body would be the sum of its rotational and linear kinetic energies:

$$\text{total kinetic energy} = \frac{1}{2}I\omega^2 + \frac{1}{2}Mv^2 \quad [6.8]$$

where $v =$ linear velocity of the body down the plane.

Clearly for a given change in the gravitational potential energy Mgh for a fall through a height h, the value of v or $\omega\,(=v/R)$ will depend on the distribution of mass in the object. You should be able to show that the linear velocity of the hollow cylinder in Fig. 6.3b will be less than that of the solid cylinder in Fig. 6.3a for the same value of h.

If the body slides without rotation then the body possesses only linear kinetic energy. In this situation the linear velocity after falling through a height h on the inclined plane would depend only on the total mass M of the body and not on its moment of inertia I. The hollow and solid cylinders would therefore arrive at the same time at the bottom of an inclined plane.

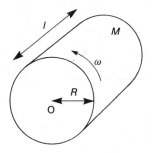

a Solid cylinder.

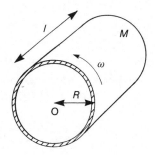

b Hollow cylinder.

Fig. 6.3 The rotation of two cylinders of identical mass and external dimensions.

6.4 COMPARISON OF THE EQUATIONS OF LINEAR AND ROTATIONAL DYNAMICS

A summary of the main equations of motion is shown in Table 6.1 below:

Table 6.1

Linear motion		Rotational motion	
Displacement	s	Angle (in radians)	θ
Velocity	$v = \dfrac{ds}{dt}$	Angular velocity	$\omega = \dfrac{d\theta}{dt}$
Acceleration	$a = \dfrac{dv}{dt}$	Angular acceleration	$\alpha = \dfrac{d\omega}{dt}$
For constant acceleration	$v = u + at$ $s = ut + \frac{1}{2}at^2$ $v^2 = u^2 + 2as$	For constant angular acceleration	$\omega = \omega_0 + \alpha t$ $\theta = \omega_0 t + \frac{1}{2}\alpha t^2$ $\omega^2 = \omega_0^2 + 2\alpha\theta$
Mass (measures linear inertia)	m	Moment of inertia (measures rotational inertia)	$I = \displaystyle\sum_i m_i r_i^2$
Force	F	Couple or torque	Γ
Momentum	mv	Angular momentum	$I\omega$
Work	Fs	Work	$\Gamma\theta$
Impulse	Ft	Angular impulse	Γt
Kinetic energy	$\frac{1}{2}mv^2$	Energy	$\frac{1}{2}I\omega^2$
Equation of motion	$F = ma$ $F = \dfrac{d(mv)}{dt}$	Equation of motion	$\Gamma = I\alpha$ $\Gamma = \dfrac{d(I\omega)}{dt}$
For a constant force F:		For a constant torque Γ:	
Work done	$Fs = \frac{1}{2}mv_2^2 - \frac{1}{2}mv_1^2$	Work done	$\Gamma\theta = \frac{1}{2}I\omega_2^2 - \frac{1}{2}I\omega_1^2$
Impulse	$Ft = mv_2 - mv_1$	Angular impulse	$\Gamma t = I\omega_2 - I\omega_1$

6A Coplanar Forces
Investigation of the equilibrium of a body under the action of three coplanar forces

APPARATUS REQUIRED

- metre rule with median holes (about 2 mm diameter) drilled at the 5 cm and 95 cm marks
- a stout needle about 10 cm in length to fit the holes loosely
- protractor with hole drilled at the origin so as to fit needle tightly
- slotted masses (50 g holder and 4 50 g masses)
- pulley mounted on a short bar
- G-cramp
- plumb line
- thread of about 20 cm in length
- 2 retort stands, one of which should be at least 80 cm high
- 2 bosses
- large mass (about 5 kg)

PRINCIPLES INVOLVED

a For any body in equilibrium under the action of just three coplanar forces, the forces must satisfy the following conditions:

(i) *translational equilibrium* – the resultant of any two of the forces must be equal and opposite to the third force, that is, a triangle whose sides represent the magnitude and direction of the forces can be drawn as in Fig. 6.4a.

(ii) *rotational equilibrium* – the total moment of the forces about any point in the body must be zero, that is, the lines of action of the three forces must pass through a single point, as in Fig. 6.4b.

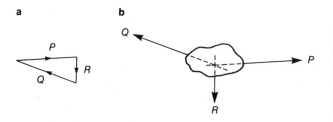

Fig. 6.4 Conditions for three force equilibrium: **a** The three forces *P, Q* and *R* can be represented by the sides of a triangle, and **b** Their lines of action are concurrent.

b These principles will be used to analyse the forces acting on a metre rule. The uniformity of the rule allows one of the forces, the rule's weight, to be specified. The magnitude and direction of one of the supporting forces of the metre rule can be measured. By taking moments about the point of application of the other supporting force, the weight of the metre rule can be determined. Finally the magnitude and direction of the unknown supporting force can be found by calculation or by measurement using a triangle of forces.

MEASUREMENTS ON A METRE RULE

c Assemble the apparatus as shown in Fig. 6.5. The top of the metre rule is pivoted on the needle, which is clamped horizontally at right angles to the plane of the diagram. The lower end of the metre rule is pulled by a horizontal thread, loosely tied to the hole in the rule. The thread passes over a pulley and supports a weight mg; it will be assumed that the tension in the thread is equal to mg.

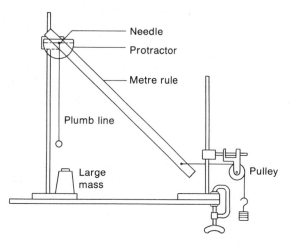

Fig. 6.5 General arrangement of apparatus for investigating the equilibrium of a metre rule.

d To prevent the stands from toppling, rest a large mass on the base of the taller stand and clamp the stand supporting the pulley to the bench using a G-cramp.

e Initially, the mass holder only should be attached to the thread ($m = 50$ g $= 0.05$ kg) to give a small horizontal force of about 0.5 N at the lower end of the rule. Adjust the relative heights of the needle and pulley until the thread is judged to be horizontal. You

43

can check this using measurements of the height of the thread above the bench top at several points along its length. Moving the needle's stand sideways cannot be used to achieve this.

f Check that the thread remains horizontal after the rule has been displaced from equilibrium. This will confirm that the frictional force at the pulley is relatively small.

g Place the protractor over the needle and close to the metre rule. Attach the plumb line (see Fig. 6.6).

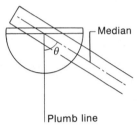

Fig. 6.6 Measurement of angle of inclination θ of the rule.

h Measure the angle θ between the median of the rule and the vertical. If a normal protractor is used θ will be the complement of the angle registered, that is, $\theta = (90° - \text{reading of protractor})$. If the hole in the protractor is too large you will need to hold the protractor in its correct position, with the median and vertical intersecting at the origin of the protractor.

i Increase m by 50 g. Alter the height of the pulley or needle, and the position of the larger stand until the thread is again horizontal. Measure θ as in (h). Repeat for three further values of m up to a maximum of 250 g, ensuring that the thread is horizontal for each measurement of θ. Tabulate m and θ. Leave a further column for graphical analysis.

CALCULATIONS OF THE FORCES ACTING ON THE METRE RULE

j Fig. 6.7 shows a free-body diagram of the rule with three forces acting. The weight of the rule Mg acts vertically downwards through the centre of gravity of the rule at C. As the rule is uniform C lies on the median at the 50 cm mark. The force mg acts horizontally through the point B. The force acting on the needle, R, passes through A.

44

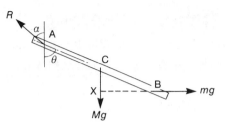

Fig. 6.7 Free-body diagram for the metre rule.

k Of the six quantities involved (three magnitudes and three directions) three are known: the magnitude and direction of the force mg and the direction of the force Mg. In order to find the magnitude Mg eliminate R by taking moments about the point A:

$$Mg \times (AC) \times \sin\theta - mg \times (AB) \times \cos\theta = 0$$

since: $\qquad AB = 2 \times (AC), \quad \tan\theta = 2m/M$

l Plot a suitable graph in order to obtain a linear relationship between θ and m. From the graph determine a value for M.

m Measure the mass M of the metre rule on a balance. Compare this value with the value determined in (l).

n Now that the magnitude of two forces Mg and mg are known, the magnitude and direction of the third force R may be determined from a triangle of forces (Fig. 6.8). The angle α between the line of action of R and the vertical can be found by geometrical construction as in (o) or by trigonometry as in (p) below. R varies with m and so there are five different constructions or calculations that could be made. You are only asked to find values of R and α for the extreme values of m (50 g and 250 g).

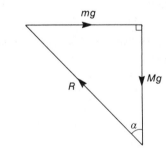

Fig. 6.8 Triangle of forces for the metre rule.

o Draw the two triangles of forces taking the value of M from (l). Take $g = 9.8$ N kg^{-1} and do not forget to convert m and M to kg so that the forces mg and Mg are in newtons. Determine R and α using the triangle shown in Fig. 6.8.

p   In (o) only one of the original variables θ and m was required to solve the triangle of forces for R and α. However, there is a relationship between θ and α. Referring to Fig. 6.7, the line of action of R must pass through the point of intersection of the lines of action of the other two forces mg and Mg if the rule is to be in rotational equilibrium. This point X is vertically below C and horizontally level with B.

In Fig. 6.9 $\tan \alpha = DX/AD$ and $\tan \theta = DB/AD$. Since $DB = 2 \times (DX)$, $\tan \theta = 2 \tan \alpha$.

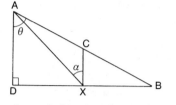

Fig. 6.9   The geometry required to relate θ and α.

q   Use the result derived in (p) to calculate α for the two extreme values of m in your table of results. Compare these values of α with those determined from the triangle of forces (o).

NOTES

r   Your account should include a labelled diagram of the apparatus, a free-body diagram of the rule with a description of the three forces, and a derivation of the equation on which your graph relating θ and m is based. Comment on whether there is any systematic deviation of the graph from linear behaviour and explain any intercept on the axes.

6B Acceleration due to Gravity
Direct measurement of *g*, the acceleration of free fall

APPARATUS REQUIRED

- electromagnet with a Mumetal or soft iron core
- shutter (soft iron) fitted with a small permanent magnet and mounted for clamping and with two 4 mm electrical connections
- tall stand (at least 2 m in height) with bosses and clamps for supporting electromagnet and shutter
- steel ball-bearings, diameter range 3–8 mm
- connecting wires at least 2 m long with 4 mm terminals
- metre rule
- box with foam rubber lining to collect ball bearings

  and

- a centisecond timer and single-pole, single-throw switch

  or

- electrical timer or scaler and double-pole, single-throw switch; power supply for electromagnet consisting of a 6 V d.c. supply, 0–100 Ω rheostat and connecting wire

PRINCIPLES INVOLVED

a   In this experiment you will determine a value for g by measuring the time of fall t of steel ball–bearings through a vertical distance s. The timing system consists of an electrical clock linked to an electromagnet and mechanical shutter system.

b   The equation of motion used to determine g (see Table 6.1, page 42) is:

$$s = ut + \tfrac{1}{2}at^2$$

with the acceleration $a = g$ in the absence of air resistance and buoyancy. If the ball-bearing is released from rest $s = \tfrac{1}{2}gt^2$. t must be determined with a precision of 0.01 s.

MEASUREMENTS ON THE FREE FALL OF BALL-BEARINGS

c   Set up the apparatus as shown in Fig. 6.10 (overleaf). Set the distance betwen the electromagnet and shutter to about 2 m.

d   If you are using the centisecond timer, connect the electromagnet and the single-pole, single-throw switch to the stop terminals (Fig. 6.11a, page 47). The centisecond timer provides an electric current for the coil of the electromagnet. Connect the shutter to the start terminals. When the stop circuit is broken by opening the switch, the timer starts and the electromagnet releases the ball-bearing. On striking the shutter the ball-bearing breaks the start circuit and stops the timer.

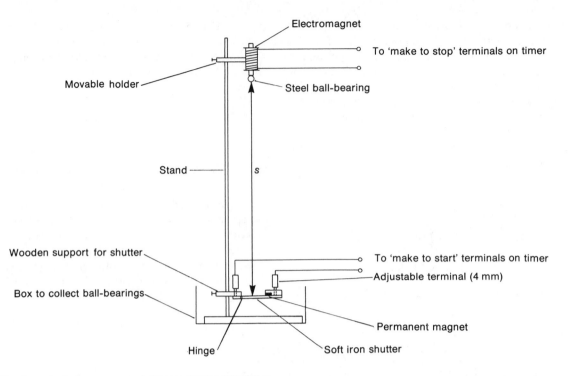

Electromagnet

To 'make to stop' terminals on timer

Movable holder

Steel ball-bearing

Stand s

Wooden support for shutter

To 'make to start' terminals on timer

Adjustable terminal (4 mm)

Box to collect ball-bearings

Permanent magnet

Hinge

Soft iron shutter

Fig. 6.10 Apparatus for the measurement of the acceleration of free fall g.

e If you are using an electrical timer or a scaler it will be necessary to provide a separate electrical supply for the electromagnet. The circuit used must simultaneously switch off the electromagnet and start the timer or scaler (switched to time or the internal oscillator). In order to achieve this a double pole-single throw switch is used in the circuit shown in Fig. 6.11b. Opening the switch starts the timer and releases the ball-bearing. Opening the shutter as a result of the impact of the ball-bearing opens the start circuit and stops the timer. Although this arrangement is more complicated than using the centisecond timer, it does have one clear advantage: the current in the electromagnet can be reduced to the minimum value (using the rheostat) required to hold a ball-bearing in position.

f You will now need to adjust the angular position of the electromagnet and level the stand so that a released ball-bearing strikes the shutter near to its centre. Ensure that the terminal makes good electrical contact with the free end of the shutter; otherwise the timer will not start when the electromagnet is switched off. Close the switch and reset the timer to zero.

g Attach the largest ball-bearing to the core of the electromagnet. Measure the distance s from the ball-bearing to the shutter with a metre rule. Measure the time of the fall of the ball-bearing at least ten times. Calculate the average time $\bar{t}$ and estimate its error (or standard deviation).

h Repeat the measurements in (g) for at least five further values of s down to about 0.8 m. Tabulate s and t. Leave a further column for data analysis. You should plot a graph of s against t as the experiment proceeds in order to identify any doubtful experimental points.

i Using $s = \frac{1}{2}gt^2$ plot a suitable graph so as to obtain a straight line. From its slope determine a value for g. Measure the intercept on the time (or other appropriate) axis and comment on whether its value is significant, when compared with the error in t calculated in (g).

j There are four sources of error in determining g: (i) the delay on releasing the ball-bearing as a result of residual magnetism in the steel; (ii) air resistance; (iii) buoyancy effects on the ball-bearing (density of steel = 7860 kg m^{-3}, density of air = 1.3 kg m^{-3}); (iv) the delay on opening the shutter after the impact of the ball-bearing. Decide which factors are most likely to cause a significant error in g and the direction of the error.

NOTES

k Your account should include a labelled diagram of the apparatus, details of the procedure and the graphical analysis leading to a value of g. Discuss the factors affecting the uncertainty in your value of g. (The circuit diagrams for the timer are not required.)

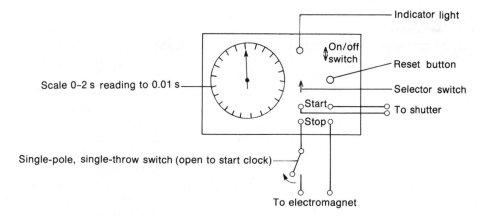

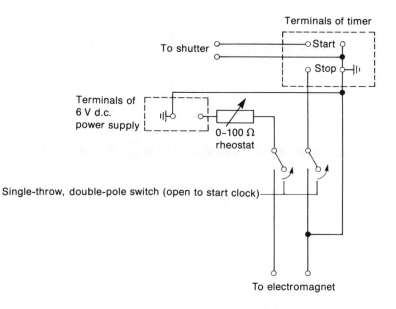

a Electrical connections to a centisecond timer.

b Electrical connections to a timer without its own power supply for the electromagnet.

Fig. 6.11

FURTHER WORK

l Investigate whether the timing errors (i) and (iv) in (j) are significant. Initially this does not involve making any further measurements, just an alternative way of analysing your results. If the total time delay as a result of these two errors is t_0 and the measured time of fall is t_m, then the corrected time of fall is $(t_m - t_0)$. The amended equation of motion is $s = \frac{1}{2}g(t_m - t_0)^2$. Rearrange this equation so that you obtain a straight line graph, whose slope gives a value for g and whose intercept on the t_m-axis gives a value for t_0. Comment on whether the value of t_0 is significant when compared with the error in t_m estimated in (g).

m The effect of air resistance (and buoyancy) on the time of fall can be investigated by using a range of ball-bearing sizes. Although the magnitude of the air resistance (and buoyancy) does increase as the size of the ball-bearing increases, its effect in comparison with the gravitational force mg acting on the ball-bearing actually decreases with increasing ball-bearing diameter. Choose a fixed value of s of about 2 m and time the fall of ball-bearings in the diameter range 3–8 mm. Unfortunately, below a certain size the ball-bearing may not have sufficient momentum to open the shutter, and so no time can be recorded.

n In view of the problems of timing using an electromagnetic/mechanical system suggest an alternative method of timing the free fall of an object between two points. If the initial velocity u in your system is not zero, explain how you would eliminate the effect of a fixed value of u in the equation $s = ut + \frac{1}{2}gt^2$.

6C Collisions
Investigation of momentum and kinetic energy conservation

APPARATUS REQUIRED

- 2 trolleys (nominal mass 1 kg), one with a spring-loaded rod
- 2 0.5 kg masses and 2 1 kg masses
- adhesive tape to fix the masses to the trolleys
- 2 ticker-tape timers with long leads (at least 1 m)
- 12 V a.c. supply for the ticker-tape timers
- ticker-tape with adhesive backing (or drawing pins will be required)
- 2 m of track
- wooden sheets to a thickness of about 5 cm for tilting track
- Plasticine and an optical pin

PRINCIPLES INVOLVED

a   The principle of conservation of momentum states that if no external forces act on a system the total momentum of the system is constant. External forces such as friction can be reduced: in this experiment on the collision of trolleys, the effect of friction between the trolley wheels and the track can be reduced by tilting the track.

b   Although momentum may be conserved in all types of collision, the kinetic energy of the system may decrease, remain unchanged or increase depending on the type of collision:

(i) if the colliding bodies stick together the collision is inelastic. The total kinetic energy of the system decreases, partly converted to deformation energy of the colliding bodies, sound energy and heat energy.

(ii) in an elastic collision the colliding bodies separate without any loss of kinetic energy. The colliding objects must not deform permanently on impact. Steel balls will collide elastically but the collision of rubber balls will be partially inelastic.

(iii) in an explosion (sometimes referred to as a superelastic collision) the kinetic energy of the system increases as a result of additional energy being provided. This can be provided by a spring between two trolleys at rest.

INELASTIC COLLISIONS (Fig. 6.12)

c   Tilt the track until a trolley runs down the track at constant velocity when gently pushed. Strictly, friction compensation applies only to this one trolley mass (the frictional force depends on the normal reaction between the trolley wheels and the track). See how serious this effect is by loading one trolley up to a total mass of 3 kg.

d   Fit an optical pin in the centre tube of one of the trolleys (mass m_1) using Plasticine. Put a large piece of Plasticine on the corresponding position on the second trolley (mass m_2). Before carrying out a collision with the ticker-tape and timer, check that when m_1 is given a sharp push it collides with and sticks to the second trolley m_2. You will need to carefully align the two trolleys about 0.5 m apart.

e   Stick a 1 m length of tape to m_1 and thread it carefully through the timer so that there is no significant drag on the trolley. Switch the ticker-tape timer on and carry out an inelastic collision. Mark the first part of the tape with the value of m_1 and the second part (after the collision) with the value of $(m_1 + m_2)$. Mark the tape 'inelastic collision'.

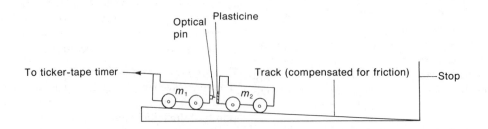

Fig. 6.12   An inelastic collision of two trolleys, masses m_1 and m_2.

f   Measure the initial velocity u of m_1 and the final velocity v of the combined system $(m_1 + m_2)$. There should be a short section of the tape where the first trolley decelerates rapidly on impact, before the two trolleys move together with a constant velocity. Calculate the initial momentum of the system $m_1 u$ and the final momentum of the system $(m_1 + m_2)v$. Tabulate these results and add to a final column the difference in the momenta before and after the inelastic collision.

g   Repeat (e) for different values of m_1 and m_2 using the 0.5 kg and 1 kg masses secured to the trolleys by adhesive tape. Increase each mass of the trolley to a maximum value of 2 kg. Do not forget to mark each tape with the relevant information, particularly if you are going to take the tapes away for analysis. Add the results to your table in (f).

h   Comment on whether your results confirm that momentum is conserved. You will have to estimate the experimental uncertainty in the values of the momenta. This is calculated by estimating the uncertainties in u and v from the variation in spacing of the dots on each tape. If these uncertainties are Δu and Δv, the uncertainties in the momenta are $m_1 \Delta u$ and $(m_1 + m_2)\Delta v$.

i   Investigate how much kinetic energy is lost in the collision by calculating the initial kinetic energy $\frac{1}{2}m_1 u^2$ and the final kinetic energy $\frac{1}{2}(m_1 + m_2)v^2$. Produce a table of m_1, m_2, initial kinetic energy and final kinetic energy.

j   For $m_1 = m_2$ it can be shown theoretically that 50% of the kinetic energy is lost in the collision. See if your results confirm this prediction. See if you can derive the theoretical result.

k   In principle you can determine the force exerted by the first trolley on the second trolley at collision. The short section of the tape where m_1 decelerates can be used to calculate an approximate value of the deceleration a. The force F is then approximately $m_1 a$. See if you can identify a sufficient number of dots on the tape to make a measurement of a and hence F.

ELASTIC COLLISIONS (Fig. 6.13)

l   For this experiment you will have to determine the velocities of both trolleys after the collision. You will therefore need two ticker-tape timers and two strips of tape. Remove the Plasticine and the optical pin from the trolleys and release one spring-loaded rod. The ticker-tape timers and tapes will have to be slightly displaced so they do not overlap. The trolleys should be in the same line about 0.5 m apart. Check that the friction compensation is still satisfactory.

m   Using the two trolleys, without added masses, carry out an elastic collision by giving m_1 a sharp push towards the stationary trolley m_2. Record the values of m_1 and m_2 on the appropriate tapes and the fact that the collision is elastic.

n   Calculate from the tapes the initial velocity u_1 of m_1, the final velocity v_1 of m_1 and the final velocity v_2 of m_2. The initial velocity u_2 of m_2 is zero. Tabulate m_1, m_2, the initial momentum of the system $(m_1 u_1 + m_2 u_2)$ and the final momentum of the system $(m_1 v_1 + m_2 v_2)$. Leave a further column for analysis.

o   Increase m_1 in steps of 0.5 kg up to 2 kg and repeat the measurements in (m) and (n). Mark all your tapes with the values of m_1 and m_2.

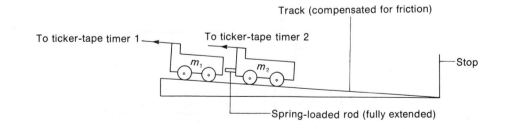

Fig. 6.13   An elastic collision of two trolleys, masses m_1 and m_2.

p   Returning to the value of $m_1 = 1$ kg, increase the mass of trolley m_2 to 2 kg. Observe what happens on collision without using any tape. Would you expect this result from theory?

q   From your table calculate the differences between the initial and final momenta. Comment on whether these results confirm the principle of conservation of momentum for an elastic collision (see (h)). Also see from your table for $m_1 = m_2$ whether the theoretical prediction that $v_2 = u_1$ and $v_1 = 0$ is true. Derive this result theoretically using the principles of conservation of momentum and kinetic energy for an elastic collision.

r   Calculate the initial and final kinetic energies of the system $(\frac{1}{2}m_1u_1^2 + \frac{1}{2}m_2u_2^2)$ and $(\frac{1}{2}m_1v_1^2 + \frac{1}{2}m_2v_2^2)$, for your tabulated values of m_1 and m_2. Do the results confirm the conservation of kinetic energy?

EXPLOSIONS (Fig. 6.14)

s   An explosion is achieved by placing the two trolleys in contact and releasing one of the spring-loaded rods. You will require two ticker-tape timers and tapes at opposite ends of the track. Note that the ticker-tape from m_1 is connected to the timer on the right-hand side and that from m_2 to the left-hand timer. The timers should be offset slightly to avoid overlap of the two tapes. Friction compensation is no longer possible and so the track should be horizontal.

t   Place the trolleys together at the centre of the track and trail about 2 m of tape from each trolley to its timer. The first metre of the tape will unfortunately be wasted. Release the spring by gently tapping the spring retainer with a mallet. Mark the tapes with the values of m_1 and m_2 and the fact that it is an explosion.

u   Calculate the velocities of the trolleys m_1 and m_2, v_1 and v_2, after the explosion. Note that one of these velocities should be designated as negative, since the trolleys move in opposite directions. Tabulate m_1, m_2, v_1, v_2, the initial momentum and the final momentum $(m_1v_1 + m_2v_2)$.

v   Repeat the measurements in (t) and (u) for the other values of m_1. Add these results to your table.

w   Examine your results to see if they confirm that the momentum of the system is zero before and after the explosion.

x   Since no compensation for friction is possible you might expect the momentum of the system to change. Explain why this does not matter when the trolleys are of equal mass.

y   From your results calculate the change in kinetic energy of the system. Would you expect this increase in kinetic energy to be constant?

NOTES

z   Your account should include a description of the experiment to verify the principle of conservation of momentum for one type of collision only. Include only the results and conclusions for the other two types of collision.

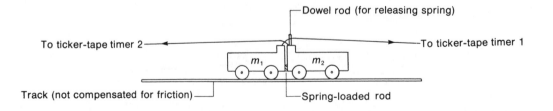

Fig. 6.14   An explosion caused by releasing a spring on one trolley.

6D Motion in a Circle
Investigation of the centripetal force acting on a body moving in a circle

APPARATUS REQUIRED

- nylon line or monofilament (breaking strength 30 N) about 1.5 m long
- glass or Perspex tube, internal diameter about 5 mm and length about 10 cm, with bevelled edges
- rubber tubing to fit tightly on the tube (assists the grip)
- petroleum jelly for lubricating one end of the tube
- rubber bungs with holes (masses 10–50 g)
- paper clip or crocodile clip to act as an indicator
- slotted masses and holder – the masses (4 50 g, 2 10 g, 1 5 g) should fit securely on the holder (see Fig. 6.15)
- metre rule
- stopwatch reading to 0.2 s

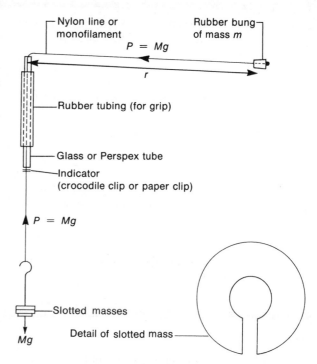

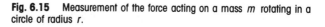

Fig. 6.15 Measurement of the force acting on a mass m rotating in a circle of radius r.

PRINCIPLES INVOLVED

a In this experiment you will investigate how the tension P in a nylon line or monofilament varies with the speed of rotation v of a rubber bung or mass m.

b Since the rubber bung can be considered to approximate to a point mass, it is expected that the centripetal force $F(=P)$ will be equal to mv^2/r for a circular orbit of radius r (equation [6.1]). A more convenient form of this equation includes the period of rotation of the mass, T since:

$$T = 2\pi r/v$$

$$F = 4\pi^2 mr/T^2$$

You should carry out this experiment on open ground.

THE RELATIONSHIP BETWEEN F AND T (m and r fixed)

c Tie one end of the nylon line to the hook on the mass holder, thread it through the tube and tie the other end firmly to a rubber bung of mass about 20 g (Fig. 6.15). Place the paper clip or crocodile clip on the mass holder side of the nylon line. Adjust the clip position so that it just touches the lower end of the tube when the length of the nylon line r is about 0.6–0.8 m. Measure r with a metre rule.

d The mass holder and added masses will be used to provide the tension in the line. It will be assumed that the friction between the tube and the line is sufficiently small that the tension in the line P can be taken to be equal to the weight Mg of the slotted masses M. This tension then provides the centripetal force that will hold the rubber bung of mass m in a circular orbit of fixed radius r. Petroleum jelly can be smeared on the top of the tube to reduce friction between the line and the tube.

e With the mass holder alone providing the tension in the line, hold the tube above your head and rotate the tube so as to obtain as near a horizontal circle as possible. Adjust the speed of rotation until the paper clip or crocodile clip is just touching or is just below the end of the tube. This is very difficult to achieve with consistency and the indicator is likely to move up and down. Once you think that you have achieved a constant speed of rotation, start the stopwatch and time 20 complete revolutions.

f Tabulate the tension in the line $P = Mg$, the time for 20 revolutions, and the period T of revolution. Leave a further column for analysis of your data. Remember to convert M to kg; take $g = 9.8$ N kg^{-1}.

g Repeat the measurements in (e) for values of M up to 150 g in steps of 25 g. Add these results to your table in (f).

h See if your results confirm the theoretical prediction that the centripetal force (P) is proportional to $1/T^2$.

i The graph drawn in (h) can also be used to determine a value for the mass m of the rubber bung. You will also need to use the value of the radius r of the circular orbit.

j Measure the mass of the bung on a balance and compare it with the value determined in (i).

THE RELATIONSHIP BETWEEN T AND r (F and m fixed)

k Set M to a fixed value of 100 g so that the tension P is kept constant. Use the same rubber bung for m as in the previous experiment.

l Adjust the indicator until the length r of the nylon line is 0.5 m. Determine the period of rotation by timing at least 20 revolutions. Tabulate the time for 20 (or more) revolutions, the period T, and r. Leave a further column for data analysis.

m Repeat the measurements of T for r values up to 1 m in steps of 0.1 m. Add these values to your table.

n Plot a suitable graph to confirm the theoretical prediction that T^2 is proportional to r. From this graph determine another value of m using the known value of P.

o It has been assumed that the tension P in the nylon line is equal to the weight Mg supported by the lower end of the thread. Explain why this assumption is not valid. Use the graph drawn in (h) to see if there is a systematic deviation from linear behaviour or a significant intercept on the P axis.

p In (e) it was impossible to obtain a circle in which the monofilament was horizontal. Explain why. The fact that the monofilament is not horizontal means that the actual radius r of the circle is not the same as the length l of the nylon line that you measured (see Fig. 6.16). A simple analysis indicates that this has no effect: resolving forces horizontally, the centripetal force F is given by:

$$F = P \cos \theta$$

since:

$$r = l \cos \theta$$

the relationship given in (b) becomes:

$$P \cos \theta = 4\pi^2 ml \cos \theta / T^2$$

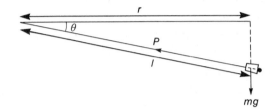

Fig. 6.16 The geometry of the rubber bung rotating in a circle.

The $\cos \theta$ terms cancel and so the relationship between P and l, which can both be measured, is the same as that between F and r. Note that the effect of friction at the top of the tube would become more significant as θ increases.

NOTES

q Your account should include a labelled diagram of the apparatus and the results leading to an experimental confirmation of the relationship $F = mv^2/r$ (or its equivalent $4\pi^2 mr/T^2$). Include your reasoning as to why your results are affected by the line sweeping out a cone rather than a horizontal circle.

r Only two sets of investigations were included in the main experiment above. In principle it should be possible to investigate how F varies with m (r and T or v fixed) and how F varies with r (m and T or v fixed). This would complete the investigation of the parameters affecting the centripetal force acting on a particle. However, it is almost impossible to obtain constant values for the period or speed of rotation by systematically changing F or r.

6E Moment of Inertia
Investigation of the rolling of cylinders down an inclined plane

APPARATUS REQUIRED

- hollow cylinder of steel
- solid cylinder of the same mass and external dimensions as the hollow cylinder
- track about 2 m long
- wooden blocks for tilting the track up to 0.5 m at one end
- metre rule
- stopwatch reading to 0.2 s
- pair of vernier callipers

PRINCIPLES INVOLVED

a   In this experiment you will investigate how the distribution of mass affects the rotational dynamics of a body. In linear dynamics two sliding bodies of identical mass M will behave in exactly the same way irrespective of the way in which the mass is distributed within the body. However, in rotational dynamics two rolling bodies of identical mass will behave quite differently according to the distribution of mass. The quantity which determines the dynamics of a rotating body is its moment of inertia I (see section 6.2).

b   Consider the rotation of a cylinder down an inclined plane (Fig. 6.17). If it is assumed that there is no sliding of the cylinder, the total kinetic energy of the cylinder is the sum of the rotational kinetic energy $\frac{1}{2}I\omega^2$ and the linear kinetic energy $\frac{1}{2}Mv^2$; ω is the angular velocity of the cylinder and v is its linear velocity $= R\omega$ for a cylinder of external radius R. Thus in falling through a height h, the loss in gravitational potential energy Mgh is equal to the gain in kinetic energy (see equation [6.8]):

$$Mgh = \tfrac{1}{2}I\omega^2 + \tfrac{1}{2}Mv^2 \qquad [6.9]$$

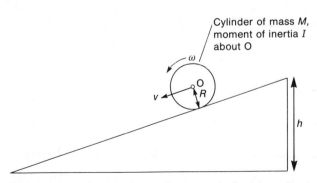

Fig. 6.17   Dynamics of a cylinder rolling down an inclined plane without slipping.

For a solid cylinder:

$$Mgh = \tfrac{1}{2}I_s\omega_s^2 + \tfrac{1}{2}M_s v_s^2$$

For a solid cylinder rotating about an axis through O $I_s = \frac{1}{2}MR^2$. Hence using $\omega_s = v_s/R$, the equation of motion of the solid cylinder becomes:

$$Mgh = \tfrac{1}{2}v_s^2(\tfrac{1}{2}M + M) = \tfrac{3}{4}Mv_s^2 \qquad [6.10]$$

For the hollow cylinder:

$$Mgh = \tfrac{1}{2}I_h\omega_h^2 + \tfrac{1}{2}Mv_h^2$$

Now for the hollow cylinder it will be assumed that the mass is effectively at the outer radius R of the cylinder; this is a reasonable approximation for a thin-walled cylinder. You can investigate the validity of this approximation in the Further work section. The moment of inertia of the hollow cylinder is then simply MR^2 and its equation of motion is:

$$Mgh = \tfrac{1}{2}v_h^2(M + M) = Mv_h^2 \qquad [6.11]$$

An examination of these equations should convince you that two cylinders, one hollow and one solid, will arrive at different times when rolling down an inclined plane through the same vertical height h.

MEASUREMENTS ON THE ROLLING CYLINDERS

c   Set up the track as shown in Fig. 6.18 (overleaf) with a value of h of about 0.1 m. Draw two chalk lines across the track about 2 m apart. Place a stop at the lower end of the track to stop the cylinders; this should preferably be soft. On no account must the steel cylinder hit the floor or it will be deformed and it will no longer roll smoothly down the plane. Check that the cylinders roll down the centre of the track; if not use small spacers to level the track from side to side.

d   Check that the masses of the two cylinders are the same within ± 5 g. Measure the external diameters of each cylinder using vernier callipers; these should agree within ± 0.5 mm.

e   Determine the times taken, t_s and t_h, for the solid and hollow cylinders to roll between the two lines on the track. Take at least five readings for each cylinder and calculate average values of t_s and t_h.

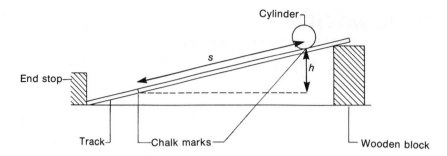

Fig. 6.18 Measurements on a rolling cylinder travelling a distance s and falling through a height h on an inclined plane.

f Tabulate h, t_s and t_h. Calculate the linear velocities v_s and v_h of the cylinders at the bottom mark. The distance travelled s is equal to the average velocity × time taken; since the initial velocity is zero, $v = 2s/t$. Leave two further columns for analysis.

g Repeat the measurements of t_s and t_h for at least five further values of h. Increase h in steps of about 0.05 m up to the height where it is evident that the cylinders are sliding. Add these values to your table in (f).

h Looking at equations [6.10] and [6.11] it should be evident that a graph of v_h^2 against v_s^2 should be a straight line with a slope of 3/4 up to the point where the cylinders start to slide.

i Plot the graph suggested in (h) for all your tabulated values of v_h and v_s. Draw the best straight line through the origin, ignoring for the present the points corresponding to the larger values of h. Measure the slope of the line and compare its value with the theoretical value of 0.75.

j Now see if you can identify a second straight line at large values of h. Measure its slope. Compare its value with that expected for sliding cylinders.

NOTES

k Your account should include an explanation of the role of moment of inertia in determining the rotational dynamics of the cylinders, a labelled diagram of the apparatus and the results leading to a graphical analysis of the dynamics of the cylinders.

l This experiment can also be used to measure the moment of inertia of a cylinder or sphere of external radius R. From equation [6.9]:

$$h = \frac{v^2}{2g}\left(\frac{I}{MR^2} + 1\right)$$

since $\omega = v/R$.

A graph of h against v^2 should be a straight line of slope:

$$\frac{1}{2g}\left(\frac{I}{MR^2} + 1\right)$$

M and R can be measured, and hence a value for I can be calculated.

FURTHER WORK

m Examine the validity of the approximation that the moment of inertia of the hollow cylinder is MR^2. The theoretical value of I for a cylinder of external radius R and internal radius r is $M(R^2 + r^2)/2$ (see Fig. 6.19). When $r = 0$ for a solid cylinder this result reduces to $MR^2/2$. Measure r and R using vernier callipers. Calculate the theoretical values for I_h and I_s and hence a revised value for the ratio v_h^2/v_s^2. Does your experimental value for the ratio determined in (i) give better agreement with the new theoretical value?

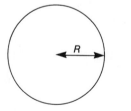 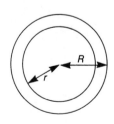

a Cross-section of solid cylinder.   **b** Cross-section of hollow cylinder.

Fig. 6.19

54

6F Rotational Kinetic Energy
Measurement of the moment of inertia of a flywheel

APPARATUS REQUIRED

- flywheel mounted on low friction bearings, either fixed to the edge of the bench or wall mounted
- G-cramps for a bench-mounted flywheel
- slotted masses and holder up to a total of 250 g in 50 g steps
- thread cut to the correct length so that it detaches from the flywheel when the mass strikes the floor
- stopwatch reading to 0.2 s (another stopwatch is useful)
- metre rule
- vernier callipers
- mat to protect floor

PRINCIPLES INVOLVED

a   The moment of inertia of a flywheel (or any other solid body) about its axis of rotation (see Fig. 6.20) can be determined by equating the loss in the gravitational potential energy of a falling mass, mgh, to the gain in rotational kinetic energy of the flywheel $\frac{1}{2}I\omega^2$ (see section 6.2). The linear kinetic energy of the falling mass, $\frac{1}{2}mv^2$, can usually be taken to be negligible in comparison with the rotational kinetic energy. You will be able to justify this approximation from your experimental results.

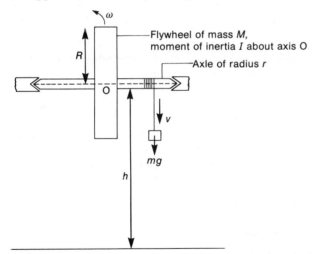

Fig. 6.20   Dynamics of a flywheel of mass M, moment of inertia I about its axis of rotation O.

b   Account must be taken of the friction between the bearings and axle of the flywheel. If W is the loss in kinetic energy as a result of friction:

$$mgh = \tfrac{1}{2}I\omega^2 + W \qquad [6.12]$$

W can be determined by counting the number of revolutions N the flywheel makes before coming to a stop after

the mass m has become detached from the axle. The total rotational kinetic energy lost in N revolutions is then $\frac{1}{2}I\omega^2$. If the flywheel makes n revolutions whilst the mass m is falling, the loss of kinetic energy $W \approx \frac{1}{2}(n/N)I\omega^2$ by simple proportions. Equation [6.12] becomes:

$$mgh = \tfrac{1}{2}I\omega^2\left(1 + \frac{n}{N}\right) \qquad [6.13]$$

Thus the value of I can be determined from measurements of m, h, ω, n and N.

MEASUREMENTS ON A ROTATING FLYWHEEL (Fig. 6.21)

c   Clamp the flywheel firmly to the bench using G-cramps. Ensure the slotted masses on the end of the thread fall clear of the bench edge. Cut the thread length so that the thread detaches from the axle when the masses strike the floor. For a bench mounted flywheel h will be about 0.7 m.

d   Make a chalk mark on the edge of the flywheel to assist you in counting the number of revolutions N.

e   Measure the radii of the axle r and the flywheel R using vernier callipers and a metre rule. Measure the distance h from the bottom of the mass holder using a metre rule. h should be maintained constant throughout the experiment.

f   Using $m = 50$ g (the mass holder alone) wind the thread around the axle until you reach your chosen value of h. Check that this mass will start the flywheel. If the friction in the bearings is too large you may find that the flywheel does not rotate. You should then start with a mass of 100 g.

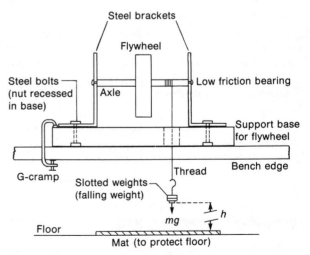

Fig. 6.21   Measurement of the moment of inertia of a flywheel.

g   As you release the flywheel start the stopwatch. As soon as the mass strikes the floor record the time t and start counting the revolutions of the flywheel. If you have a second stopwatch you should start this now. Record the number of revolutions N completed before the flywheel stops and the time taken for this to occur, t_s [(total time $- t$) if only one stopwatch is used].

h   You may find the procedure in (g) impossible on your own. It does help if you listen for the mass striking the floor rather than watching it fall. Also you do not need to determine N and t_s very accurately, since they are only used to calculate a correction for friction. However, if you have any difficulties, omit the measurement of the second time t_s and the subsequent calculations using t_s.

i   Tabulate m, t, N and t_s. Calculate the number of revolutions n made by the flywheel during the fall of the mass using $n = h/2\pi r$. Add this value to your table. Leave six further columns for the analysis of your data.

j   Repeat the measurements in (g) using four other values for m up to $m = 250$ g. Add these results to your table in (i).

CALCULATION OF THE MOMENT OF INERTIA OF THE FLYWHEEL

k   You will first calculate the moment of inertia of the flywheel using equation [6.13]. Calculate the loss in gravitational potential energy of m, mgh; do not forget to convert m to kg and take $g = 9.8$ N kg^{-1}. In order to work out the final angular velocity ω of the flywheel, you first need to work out the linear velocity v of the mass m as it strikes the floor. Since the initial velocity of the mass is zero, $v = 2h/t$. ω is then found from v/r, where r is the radius of the axle. Add these values of v and ω to your table. You can now evaluate the expression $\frac{1}{2}\omega^2(1 + n/N)$ in equation [6.13]. Hence calculate values for I. Obtain the average value of I and an estimate of its error (standard deviation). Graphical analysis is not considered to be useful in view of the large number of variables to be calculated.

l   In the final column of your table enter the final kinetic energy of the falling mass, $\frac{1}{2}mv^2$. Satisfy yourself that this is less than 1% of the total energy mgh and justifies the approximation in (a).

CALCULATION OF THE FRICTIONAL TORQUE

m   Using the average value of I calculated in (k) you can now calculate the frictional torque on the

flywheel in one of two ways using N or t_s. If you did not measure t_s omit (o).

n   In order to calculate the frictional torque Γ using N, the work done by the torque $\Gamma\theta = 2\pi N\Gamma$ is equated to the kinetic energy of the flywheel $\frac{1}{2}I\omega^2$ (see Table 6.1, page 42). Draw up a second table to facilitate this calculation: tabulate $2\pi N$ and $\frac{1}{2}I\omega^2$ and the result for Γ; in the fourth column calculate the work done by the frictional torque $2\pi n\Gamma$ as a fraction (or percentage) of the total energy mgh. Comment on whether the value of Γ is constant and on the variation in the fractional loss in energy as a result of friction.

o   In order to calculate the frictional torque Γ using t_s, it is necessary to calculate the angular deceleration α of the flywheel after the release of the mass m. The equation $\Gamma = I\alpha$ can then be used to calculate Γ (see Table 6.1). Since the final angular velocity of the flywheel is zero, $\alpha = \omega/t_s$. Draw up a third table with values of α and Γ.

NOTES

p   Your account should include a labelled diagram of the apparatus, the measurements you made to determine the moment of inertia of the flywheel, the calculation of an average value of I and an estimate of the error in I. Tabulate your results leading to values for the frictional torque Γ.

q   The main use of a flywheel is to provide a continuous (and smooth) movement from an intermittent source of power. The larger the moment of inertia of the flywheel, the smoother the motion will be, and the effect of interruptions in the original power supply on the final transmission system will be considerably reduced. In a car engine a flywheel is used to provide constant power to the transmission system of the car; the normal piston system alone would produce a jerky motion. With some common crankshaft shapes the engine would not even continue to turn without a flywheel.

FURTHER WORK

r   If the flywheel is detachable from its mountings you can determine the theoretical value of its moment of inertia. For a cylinder of radius R and mass M, $I = MR^2/2$. Since the mass of the axle and its radius r are much less than the values for the flywheel, you may neglect its effect on I. You will usually require a balance reading up to at least 10 kg to determine M. Compare your experimental value determined in (k) with the theoretical value.

6G Strength of Materials
Investigation of the force–extension curves for various materials

APPARATUS REQUIRED

- 2 stands, bosses and clamps
- 5–10 kg mass or G-cramps to hold one stand rigid
- 2 Hoffmann clips to secure material
- slotted masses (10 5 g, 10 10 g, 10 50 g, 1 0.5 kg, 1 1 kg) and holder (50 g)
- optical pin and Plasticine
- foam rubber to protect floor from falling masses
- 2 metre rules
- vernier callipers
- micrometer screw gauge
- materials: 1 m copper wire (38 SWG or about 0.15 mm diameter)

  0.2 m cut rubber band (cross-section about 1 mm by 2 mm)

  0.2 m natural rubber strip (cross-section about 0.4 mm by 5 mm)

  1 m nylon line or monofilament (diameter about 0.15–0.25 mm)

  1 m polythene film (cross-section about 0.05 mm by 10 mm)

PRINCIPLES INVOLVED

a In these experiments you will investigate how different categories of materials behave under tension. It is not intended that you should obtain accurate values for the mechanical properties of the materials, but basic quantities such as the breaking strength, the elongation at fracture and the Young modulus can be determined from the force–extension curves.

b A basic property of a material is the Young modulus E, which describes how easily a solid can be compressed or stretched. E is independent of the dimensions of the solid, unlike the force F required to produce a given extension. For a material under tension E is defined as the tensile stress/the tensile strain. The tensile stress is defined as $\sigma = F/A$ for a sample of cross-sectional area A. The tensile strain ε is defined as the fractional change in the length l when the material is subject to a stress σ, that is, $\varepsilon = e/l$ for an extension e.

Thus:
$$E = \frac{\sigma}{\varepsilon} = \frac{F/A}{e/l} \qquad [6.14]$$

c Up to the elastic limit the material returns to its original dimensions when the stress is removed. This region corresponds in many materials to the region where the extension is proportional to the applied force. Beyond the elastic limit, materials behave differently until fracture or breaking occurs. The stress required to produce fracture or breaking is called the tensile strength of the material σ_T.

For safety reasons you should not put your face close to materials under stress, particularly near to fracture or breaking. Where relevant you will be given approximate values for the tensile strength. You will then be able to calculate the applied force that will produce fracture or breaking. Safety glasses should be worn.

COPPER WIRE

The tensile strength of copper wire is 200 MN m^{-2} (or MPa).

d Wrap several turns of each end of the wire around each of the Hoffmann clips, and tighten the screws. Check that the clips are secure and the wire does not slip.

e Set up the arrangement shown in Fig. 6.22 (overleaf) for measuring the extension of the wire. Suspend the wire from one Hoffmann clip using a stand, boss and clamp placed near to the edge of the bench. The base of the stand should be secured using either the 5–10 kg mass or G-cramps. Attach the mass holder to the other Hoffmann clip; this should straighten the wire. Place a metre rule as close as possible to the mass holder. You can read the extension of the wire using an optical pin attached to the base of the mass holder by Plasticine.

f Measure the unextended length l of the wire using the second metre rule (you can ignore the effect of the mass holder). Measure the diameter of the wire at several points along its length. Calculate an average value for the diameter d and the cross-sectional area $A = \pi d^2/4$ in m^2. Now work out the approximate value of the force F producing fracture using the tensile strength of copper given above. Proceed cautiously when loading the wire near to this value of F.

g Record the reference position of the mass holder on the metre rule x_0. Add 50 g masses to the holder, each time recording the position of the mass holder x. Tabulate F in N and the extension $e = (x - x_0)$ in m; take $g = 9.8$ N kg^{-1} and do not forget to convert the mass to kg. You are advised to plot a graph of F against e as you increase the load on the wire, so that you can see immediately when the linear region of the graph ends. Otherwise you are liable to fracture the wire suddenly without obtaining all your readings.

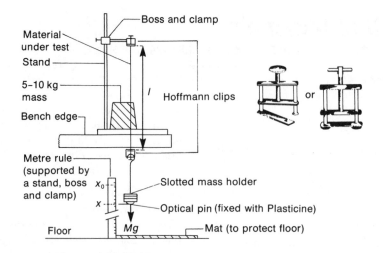

Fig. 6.22 Experimental arrangement for the measurement of the extension $e = (x - x_0)$ of a material subject to a load Mg.

h As soon as the force–extension graph curves towards the horizontal, add masses in 10 g steps. Place these masses on the holder and do not drop them on, as this may be sufficient additional force to cause fracture. Continue adding masses of 10 g until the wire starts to extend without any further addition to the load. Further additions of 5 g masses should cause the wire to fracture.

i If you did not obtain a complete curve for the wire, you can repeat the experiment with a new wire. You will now know the value of the load where the extension increases rapidly.

j From the initial linear section of the force–extension curve determine the slope $\Delta F / \Delta e$. Hence using equation [6.14] determine a value of E for copper. Determine also from your graph the value of F causing fracture and hence calculate the tensile strength of copper. Work out the fractional elongation e/l of the wire at fracture.

k In this experiment it is unlikely that you will be able to obtain the complete force–extension curve for copper (see Fig. 6.23), particularly the plastic and work hardening regions. Suggest a technique for obtaining the complete curve.

NYLON LINE OR MONOFILAMENT

The tensile strength of nylon line or monofilament is 60 MPa.

l Proceed as for copper wire (d)–(f) using nylon line or monofilament.

m Load the filament in steps of 50 g, up to 500 g, recording the value of the load in newtons and the extension $e = (x - x_0)$. Again plot the force–extension curve as the experiment proceeds. Replace the 50 g masses by a single 0.5 kg mass. It is unlikely

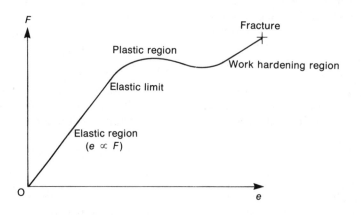

Fig. 6.23 Force–extension curve for a copper wire.

that the reading x will be the same after the replacement and you may need to adjust the metre rule to give the same reading x. Continue to load the nylon with 50 g masses until you reach the plastic deformation region. With an upper limit of about 10 N for the load you may not succeed in breaking the filament.

n Calculate a value for the Young modulus of nylon using the linear region of the force–extension curve.

RUBBER BAND (CROSS-LINKED POLYMER)

The tensile strength of a rubber band (cross-linked polymer) is 5–10 MPa.

o With a rubber band of cross-section 1 mm by 2 mm it is unlikely that you will succeed in breaking the rubber for a load of less than 10 N.

p Set up the cut rubber band so as to measure its extension using the apparatus in Fig. 6.22. Measure the length, width and thickness of the rubber when supporting the 50 g holder. Try to avoid squashing the rubber with the micrometer screw gauge.

q Increase the mass in 50 g steps. Depending on the cross-sectional area of the rubber, you may need to change the smaller masses for a single 0.5 kg mass in order to exceed the elastic limit. Continue to add 50 g masses until the total added mass is 1 kg or until the rubber band breaks. You can try using the larger masses to find out approximately when the rubber breaks.

r From the linear section of the force–extension curve determine E for the rubber band.

NATURAL RUBBER (LINEAR POLYMER CHAINS)

The tensile strength of natural rubber (linear polymer chains) is 5–10 MPa.

s Use a piece of natural rubber strip cut so its width is about 5 mm. If the width is much greater than 10 mm you will need masses up to 1 kg to obtain the complete force–extension curve.

t Follow the procedure in (p) above. Increase the mass in 50 g steps up to 500 g. Plot the force–extension curve as you go along, because you may find

unexpected behaviour at a load of 3–4 N. Note also that because the extension may exceed 1 m, you may have to raise the clamp holding the rubber strip. Do this carefully by supporting the mass holder with one hand, and record the distance through which the clamp is raised.

u From your force–extension curve you should be able to identify two regions which are approximately linear. See if you can explain this behaviour, particularly in contrast to the behaviour of the rubber band.

v If you can distinguish between the two regions in (u), draw the two straight lines and measure their slopes. Hence calculate two values of E for natural rubber.

POLYTHENE

The tensile strength of polythene is 15 MPa.

w Cut a strip of polythene about 1 m in length from a thin polythene bag. Since its thickness will only be about 0.05 mm, you will need to fold several thicknesses to measure the thickness of a single layer using a micrometer screw gauge.

x Measure the extension of the polythene increasing the mass initially in 50 g steps. Depending on the cross-sectional area of the strip, the polythene will extend without any further increase of the load. This should be evident from your force–extension graph. To find an accurate value for the load where this occurs, add 10 g and 5 g masses. As this region ends, you should find that a significant further load is required to produce any further extension.

y From a very short linear region of the force–extension curve determine a value of E for low density polythene.

NOTES

z In your account include a labelled diagram of the apparatus used to produce your force–extension curves. You need not include descriptions of the procedures. It is much more important to present your force–extension curves and to make comparisons of the different types of behaviour of materials under stress. Only one major category of materials is missing, namely, brittle materials such as ceramics. Conclude your account with a table summarising your results for the Young modulus and the tensile strength for those samples that you measured.

6H Elasticity
Measurement of the Young modulus using Searle's apparatus

APPARATUS REQUIRED

- Searle's apparatus including a micrometer screw arrangement (Fig. 6.24) *or* a vernier scale reading to 0.05 mm (Fig. 6.25)
- 2 identical steel wires of diameter about 0.5 mm and 2–3 m in length, fixed to a rigid support
- 2 slotted mass holders (1 kg mass) and slotted masses (10 0.5 kg or 10 1 kg depending on the diameter of the steel wires)
- micrometer screw gauge
- metre rule

PRINCIPLES INVOLVED

a The Young modulus E is a basic property of a material, which describes how the material behaves under stress. It is formally defined as tensile stress/tensile strain, where:

tensile stress
σ = applied force/cross-sectional area of sample
= F/A

and

tensile strain
ε = extension of sample/original length
= e/l

For metals the change in length and cross-sectional area can be considered to be negligible in comparison with l and A.

Thus: $$E = \sigma/\varepsilon = \frac{F/A}{e/l} = \frac{Fl}{Ae} \qquad [6.15]$$

b Up to the elastic limit the tensile strain is usually proportional to the tensile stress and so their ratio E is a constant. In this experiment you will measure the extension of a steel wire for increasing loads F up to the elastic limit of steel. Because the Young modulus of steel is quite high, it is necessary to use a long thin wire in order to obtain easily measurable extensions with reasonable loads (up to 100 N). Extensions of a few mm are measured with a micrometer screw arrangement reading to 0.01 mm. An alternative vernier arrangement reading to 0.05 mm will not give such accurate values for E.

MEASUREMENTS ON A LOADED WIRE

c The apparatus will normally be set up permanently in the laboratory, but you should check that

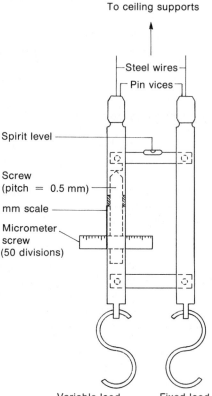

a Front view of Searle's apparatus for the measurement of the Young modulus of a wire.

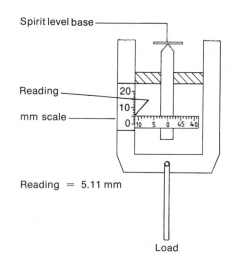

b Detail of micrometer screw arrangement (side view).

Fig. 6.24

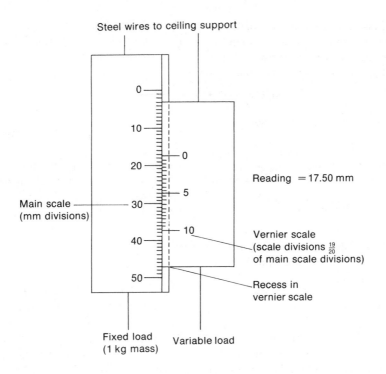

Steel wires to ceiling support

Main scale
(mm divisions)

0

10

20

30

40

50

0

5

10

Reading = 17.50 mm

Vernier scale
(scale divisions $\frac{19}{20}$
of main scale divisions)

Recess in
vernier scale

Fixed load
(1 kg mass)

Variable load

Fig. 6.25 A vernier scale reading to 0.05 mm.

the wire is securely fixed in its pin vices. Add a mass holder to each wire to remove any kinks in the wires.

d   Measure the length of the test wire (with the variable load) l from the bottom of the ceiling support to the top of the pin-vice of the Searle's apparatus or the top of the fixing on the vernier scale. To achieve an error of less than 1%, it is only necessary to measure l to the nearest centimetre. Estimate your uncertainty in l, Δl.

e   Measure the diameter d of the wire at several places along its length and in various orientations using a micrometer screw gauge. Check for any zero error on the gauge. From your readings calculate an average value for d and estimate the error (standard deviation) Δd. As one of the smallest dimensions to be measured, the error Δd has the largest effect on the accuracy of the value of E determined.

f   Before loading the test wire, you should first calculate the maximum load that you can add so as not to exceed the elastic limit of the wire. A wire stretched substantially beyond its elastic limit will be deformed permanently and if you exceed the yield point, the wire is likely to fracture. The yield strength of steel wire is 600 MN m^{-2}, that is, $F/A = 6 \times 10^8$ N m^{-2} at the yield point. Calculate the value of $A = \pi d^2/4$ in m^2, and hence the value of F. Subtract at least 10 N from this value and then work out at what increments you can add masses to obtain between 8 and 10 read-

ings. Obviously you will have to rationalise this, since you only have 0.5 kg and 1 kg masses readily available.

g   Before adding a load adjust the micrometer screw until the bubble is at the centre of the spirit level. Record the micrometer reading x_0 (or the vernier reading if using the alternative apparatus). In adjusting the micrometer take care not to exert any force on the Searle's apparatus, otherwise you will find that the bubble moves from the centre when released.

h   Increase the load in the increments calculated in (f). At each step level the spirit level using the micrometer screw. Record the micrometer reading (or vernier reading) x.

Tabulate the values of the total mass M added and the corresponding extension $e = (x - x_0)$. Leave two further columns for recording the extension for unloading and for the average value of e.

i   As a precaution you should plot a graph of M against e. The graph should be linear but if you exceed the elastic limit or if the wire slips in one of the vices it will start to curve.

j   Continue to take readings of M and e until you reach the upper limit calculated for the load.

k   Unload the wire in the same increments as used for loading and record $(x - x_0)$ for each step.

l If you have kept within the elastic limit of the wire, the corresponding values of e for loading and unloading should be the same within experimental error. Calculate the average value of e. If the two values are markedly different check your force–extension graph for linearity. If the graph is linear then it is suggested that you use only the readings for loading.

m Plot a graph of M (ordinate) against e (abscissa). Hence using equation [6.15] and the slope s of your graph calculate a value for E; take $g = 9.8 \text{ N kg}^{-1}$. Estimate Δs in the slope of your graph by drawing extreme straight lines.

n You can now calculate the uncertainty in E, ΔE. The maximum fractional error $\Delta E/E$ can be determined from equation [6.15]:

$$\frac{\Delta E}{E} = \frac{\Delta l}{l} + \frac{\Delta A}{A} + \frac{\Delta s}{s} \qquad [6.16]$$

Now since $A = \pi d^2/4$, the fractional error in A, $\Delta A/A = 2\Delta d/d$, that is, twice the fractional error in the diameter. The measurement of d is therefore one of the most important in determining the accuracy of E. Substitute your estimates of the errors in equation [6.16]. From your value for E calculated in (m) work out a value for ΔE.

NOTES

o Your account should include a labelled diagram of the apparatus, details of the procedure, the graphical analysis leading to a value for E and an estimate of the uncertainty in E. You should also explain why two wires were used (other than the obvious reason that two wires are needed to support the apparatus).

FURTHER WORK

p You can calculate the energy stored in the wire when subject to its maximum load by working out the area under the force–extension curve. Since this graph is a straight line the stored energy $= \frac{1}{2}Fe = \frac{1}{2}Mge$. However, the loss in gravitational potential energy of the load is Mge. Try to explain where the difference in energy is lost.

61 Viscous Forces
Measurements on falling spheres in a liquid

APPARATUS REQUIRED

- Perspex tube closed at one end, length about 1 m and internal diameter about 50 mm, filled with glycerol
- large rigid stand to hold the tube vertically
- 2 small rubber bands or small strips of adhesive paper
- steel ball-bearings sorted in sizes from 1.5 to 8 mm in diameter
- magnet (to retrieve steel ball-bearings)
- tweezers
- cloth for cleaning ball-bearings
- metre rule
- micrometer screw gauge
- vernier callipers
- balance reading to 0.1 g
- stopwatch reading to 0.1 s
- 0–50 °C thermometer

PRINCIPLES INVOLVED

a Any body moving through a fluid (liquid or gas) will experience a retarding force or viscous force. Under certain conditions this force is proportional to the speed v with which the object moves through the fluid, that is, $F_v = kv$. The constant k depends on the shape and dimensions of the body, and the nature of the fluid. For a sphere of radius r, the constant k has a value of $6\pi\eta r$, where η is defined as the viscosity of the medium through which the body moves. η has units of N s m^{-2}.

b Consider a sphere falling through a viscous medium (Fig. 6.26). The forces acting on the sphere are the viscous force $kv = 6\pi\eta rv$, the upthrust $U =$ weight of fluid displaced, and the weight of the sphere $= mg$. The resultant force downwards can be used to calculate the acceleration a and the velocity of the sphere at any time t during its motion down the fluid:

$$\text{resultant force} = ma = mg - U - F_v \qquad [6.17]$$

As the velocity of the sphere increases, the viscous force increases. Thus in equation [6.17] the acceleration a decreases from its initial value of about g for a sphere released from rest to zero. The sphere then reaches a terminal velocity v_t for $a = 0$. The way in which a and v vary with t is shown in Fig. 6.27; the corresponding variations of a and v with distance fallen x are similar (but *not* identical).

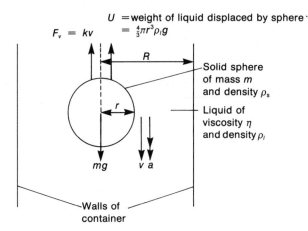

$$F_v = kv$$

U = weight of liquid displaced by sphere
$= \frac{4}{3}\pi r^3 \rho_l g$

Solid sphere
of mass m
and density ρ_s

Liquid of
viscosity η
and density ρ_l

mg v a

Walls of
container

Fig. 6.26 Forces acting on a sphere of radius r falling through a liquid of viscosity η.

c When the sphere reaches its terminal velocity equation [6.17] can be simplified by setting ma to zero. If the density of the material of the sphere is ρ_s then $mg = \frac{4}{3}\pi r^3 \rho_s g$. For a liquid of density ρ_1, $U = \frac{4}{3}\pi r^3 \rho_1 g$. Thus equation [6.17] becomes:

$$0 = \frac{4}{3}\pi r^3 g(\rho_s - \rho_1) - 6\pi\eta r v_t$$

or:

$$v_t = \frac{2(\rho_s - \rho_1)gr^2}{9\eta} \qquad [6.18]$$

d Equation [6.18] can be used as a basis for measuring the viscosity of a liquid. v_t can be measured for spheres of various radii and, since ρ_s, ρ_1 and g are known, η can be determined. In fact, although you will determine a value for η, the main purpose of this experiment is to investigate deviations from equation [6.18] as the sphere size is increased.

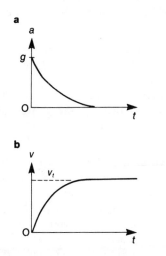

Fig. 6.27 **a** Acceleration and **b** Velocity of an object falling through a viscous medium. v_t is the terminal velocity of the object.

e Equation [6.18] is derived using the following assumptions concerning the viscous force:

(i) the medium is of infinite extent, that is, the dimension R in Fig. 6.26 is large compared with r, and edge effects can be neglected.

(ii) the flow of liquid past the sphere is streamline and not turbulent (see Fig. 6.28).

Both these factors are likely to be more significant for the larger diameter spheres.

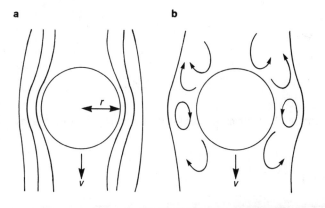

Fig. 6.28 Liquid layer lines for **a** Streamline and **b** Turbulent flow of the liquid past the sphere.

MEASUREMENTS ON THE VARIATION OF v_t WITH r (Fig. 6.29, overleaf)

f First measure the diameters of each of the ball-bearings using a micrometer screw gauge. Calculate an average value of r for each size of ball-bearing. Tabulate these values of r leaving five further columns for v_t and data analysis.

g Determine the density of the steel of the ball-bearings. Measure the mass of at least ten of the largest bearings. Hence calculate the average value of the mass. ρ_s can be determined from mass/volume of the sphere.

h Place two horizontal markers on the tube, the first about 0.2 m from the top and the second a further 0.4 m down the tube. By the time the ball-bearing passes the first marker it should have reached its terminal velocity. Elastic bands are easier to use than adhesive strips because they can be more easily adjusted to be horizontal. Sighting along the elastic band ensures that you do not incur a parallax error as the sphere passes the marker. Measure the distance d between the markers using a metre rule.

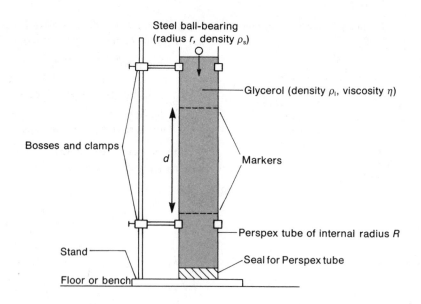

Fig. 6.29 Experimental arrangement for measuring the fall of steel ball-bearings in glycerol.

Steel ball-bearing
(radius r, density ρ_s)

Glycerol (density ρ_l, viscosity η)

Bosses and clamps

d

Markers

Perspex tube of internal radius R

Stand

Seal for Perspex tube

Floor or bench

i Check that the tube is vertical. Using the tweezers, drop a small ball-bearing down the centre of the column of liquid. By the time the ball-bearing reaches the second marker it should not be more than 5 mm from the centre. If there is a significant tilt of the tube then you will have to adjust the clamp and/or use spacers under the base of the stand.

j Starting with the smallest sphere, measure its time of fall t between the two markers. Avoid air bubbles on the sphere, particularly with the smallest spheres, as this may significantly affect the motion of the sphere. This is best achieved by smearing the spheres in glycerol and placing the sphere in the liquid rather than dropping it from above. Repeat the measurement of the time of fall several times and calculate an average value for the terminal velocity $v_t = d/t$. Add this value of v_t to your table.

k Remove the spheres from the bottom of the tube using a magnet. This avoids the problem of mixing up spheres of different diameters. You will have to be patient as small spheres take several minutes to extract. Collect the spheres on a cloth and clean them. Return them to their marked container.

l Repeat the measurements of v_t for the other sizes of ball-bearings and add these results to your table.

CALCULATIONS ON THE RELATIONSHIP BETWEEN v_t AND r

m From equation [6.18] it would be expected that a graph of $v_t/\text{m s}^{-1}$ (ordinate) against $r^2/10^{-6}\ \text{m}^2$ (abscissa) would be a straight line of slope $2(\rho_s - \rho_l)g/9\eta$. Calculate the values of r^2 and enter them into your table. Plot the graph.

n You should find that the initial part of the graph is a straight line through the origin curving towards the horizontal for larger values of r^2. Draw the best straight line through the points for small r^2 values and measure its slope. Now calculate a value for η, using $\rho_l = 1260\ \text{kg m}^{-3}$ and $g = 9.8\ \text{N kg}^{-1}$.

o Your graph clearly indicates that the values for the terminal velocities v_t for large values of r are too low. There are three possible reasons: (i) edge effects, (ii) turbulence and (iii) the spheres had not reached their terminal velocity. Of these three, only (iii) is the factor that can be readily checked experimentally.

p Move both markers a further 0.1–0.2 m down the tube. How far you move them depends on the depth of the liquid column. Do not have the lower marker closer than 0.1 m to the bottom, otherwise edge effects could affect your result. For just two extreme sizes of ball-bearing measure v_t and compare the values with those already tabulated. If v_t is more than 10% larger then you have found a significant factor affecting your experimental results.

q In (p) it is only a terminal effect if you measured a larger change for the larger ball-bearing. Although the viscous force does increase with the radius of the ball-bearing (proportional to r), its effect, in comparison with the weight of the ball-bearing (proportional to r^3), actually decreases. Thus it is expected that the larger ball-bearings will reach their terminal velocity much later than the smaller spheres.

r Empirically the effect on v_t as a result of the sphere falling in a finite medium of extent R is determined by the Ladenburg factor $(1 + 2.4r/R)$. To see if this effect is significant calculate this factor for each of your values of r. Determine the internal radius R of the tube using vernier callipers. Add these values to your table of results. Since edge effects are likely to impede the fall of the spheres, you should multiply all your values of v_t by the corresponding Ladenburg factor.

s Draw a new graph of the corrected values for v_t against r^2. This should have a much longer linear section than the graph drawn in (m). Measure its slope and determine a new value for η. If you drew the original straight line correctly, you should find that the new value of η is not significantly different from that determined in (n). However, you do have the satisfaction of explaining the original deviations from equation [6.18].

t If you are satisfied that you have explained any deviations from linear behaviour for even the largest sphere, then you do not need to consider the final factor, namely, turbulence, which occurs when the terminal velocity exceeds a certain value. The factor indicating whether or not turbulence has occurred is the Reynolds number (Re). For a sphere moving in a viscous medium (Re) = inertial force/viscous force = $\rho_l r v_t / \eta$. Calculate the Reynolds number for each sphere size using the value of the viscosity determined in (s). The condition for streamline flow is that (Re) should be significantly less than one. This may explain any remaining deviations from equation [6.18], since turbulence leads to low values for v_t.

NOTES

u In your account describe the simple procedure by which you measured the viscosity of glycerol. Record the temperature at which you measured η, since η is very sensitive to temperature changes. Include your final table and a short discussion of the factors that affected the linearity of the graph of v_t against r^2. Explain why the method would be difficult to use to determine the viscosity of water (about 0.001 N s m^{-2}).

7 OSCILLATIONS AND WAVES

This section includes experiments on oscillatory systems: simple harmonic motion of a loaded spring (experiment 7A), damped vibrations of a moving-coil galvanometer (experiment 7B) and forced vibrations of a moving-coil galvanometer (experiment 7C). There are four experiments on stationary waves: stationary waves in free air (experiment 7D), stationary waves in an air column (experiment 7E), stationary waves on a stretched wire using a standard sonometer (experiment 7F) and stationary waves on a stretched wire carrying an alternating current in a magnetic field (experiment 7G).

7.1 MEASUREMENT OF THE PERIOD OF OSCILLATION

In most of the systems that you will encounter the period of the oscillations will be between 0.5 and 2 seconds. Clearly, using hand timing, you could not expect to determine the period to an accuracy of better than ±0.05 s if you measured the time for only one complete oscillation. This would then represent an experimental uncertainty of between 2.5% and 10%. This is an uncertainty that can be reduced by simply recording the total time for a large number of oscillations, between 20 and 50. Suppose you decide that you wish to reduce the uncertainty in the period to 0.1%. Assuming a timing error of 0.05 s, the minimum time to use is 50 s. For a period of around 2 s this would require the timing of 25 oscillations. Clearly other errors in the experiment may not justify such precision, but usually you should aim to reduce the experimental uncertainty in the period to less than 1%. You must, of course, be careful not to make a counting error; you can reduce the probability of such an error by making two measurements of the time. When counting oscillations, a counting down is recommended: 5, 4, 3, 2, 1, 0 as the vibrating system passes a reference point, starting the stopwatch at 0. Normally the amplitude of an oscillation decreases with time as a result of damping. Fortunately, for light damping as encountered in most mechanical systems, the period of the oscillation is virtually independent of the amplitude of the oscillation. The only effect is an exponential decay of the oscillation. This means that you normally do not have to worry about the effect of damping on the period of oscillation.

7A Simple Harmonic Motion
Investigation of the extension and vibrations of a loaded spring

APPARATUS REQUIRED

- spring of unextended length 0.1–0.3 m (force constant 15–20 N m^{-1})

- 9 slotted masses and holder (50 g)

- metre rule

- stopwatch reading to 0.1 s

- 1 stand, 2 clamps and 2 bosses

- 2 wooden blocks for supporting the upper end of the spring

- optical pin and Plasticine

- G-cramp for securing stand base to bench or a 5 kg mass

PRINCIPLES INVOLVED

a   Provided that the elastic limit of a spring of natural length l_0 is not exceeded, the extension e is proportional to the load Mg (Fig. 7.1). The constant of proportionality k in the equation:

$$Mg = ke \qquad [7.1]$$

is called the force constant or stiffness of the spring.

k can be simply determined by measuring the increase in length of the spring as Mg is increased. There is only one slight problem: most springs are produced with a slight compression of the turns. Thus for small loads no extension will be registered; it is therefore necessary to place a small load (about 0.5 N) on the spring to remove this compression.

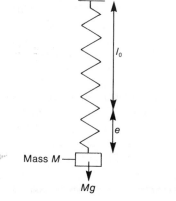

Fig. 7.1   Extension e of a spring of natural length l_0 subject to a force Mg.

b   If a mass which produces an extension e is displaced vertically from its equilibrium position by a small amount, the mass executes simple harmonic motion because the restoring force is proportional to the displacement. The period of oscillation T is then given by:

$$T = 2\pi \sqrt{\frac{M}{k}} \qquad [7.2]$$

There are two limitations on the validity of this equation: (i) the spring must not be extended beyond its elastic limit and   (ii) the initial further displacement of the spring downwards must not exceed e otherwise the spring will be compressed at the top of its oscillation. Both these factors invalidate equation [7.2].

MEASUREMENT OF THE EXTENSION OF THE SPRING

c   Set up the apparatus as shown in Fig. 7.2 (overleaf). Make sure that the spring is firmly held at its upper end. There should be a loop or ring at the lower end of the spring to support the mass holder. Fix the optical pin on the base of the holder with Plasticine.

d   Record the reading x_0 indicated by the optical pin on the metre rule when the spring supports the holder alone.

e   From this reference point increase M in 50 g steps and record the reading x on the metre rule. Hence calculate the extension $e = (x - x_0)$ for a total mass M (excluding the mass of the holder). Plot a graph of M against e as you load the spring; this will enable you to check that the elastic limit of the spring has not been exceeded.

f   From the linear section of your graph, use equation [7.1] to calculate a value for k. Take $g = 9.8$ N kg^{-1} and do not forget to convert M to kilograms.

MEASUREMENT OF THE VIBRATIONS OF A LOADED SPRING

g   You may remove the optical pin from the mass holder.

h   In measuring the period of oscillation of the loaded spring, you should choose the number of oscillations to be timed so that your timing error of the period is less than 1%. Remember also that the appropriate mass to take is the total mass, including the holder (see equation [7.2]).

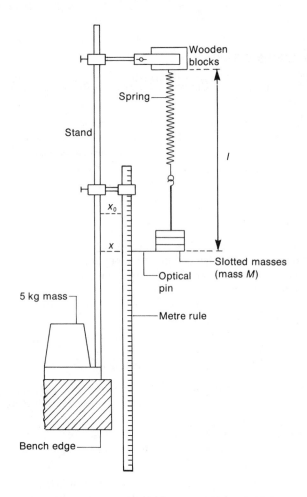

Fig. 7.2 Apparatus for measuring the extension of a spiral spring. The extension for a load Mg is determined from $e = (x - x_0)$.

l Your account should include a brief description of the experiments, the analysis leading to two values for k. Comment also on any deviations from linearity in the graphs produced in (f) and (k).

m In principle the combined results from the two experiments above can be used to determine a value for g. Substituting for k from equation [7.1] in equation [7.2] $T = 2\pi\sqrt{e/g}$. Thus a graph of T^2 against e should be a straight line of slope $4\pi^2/g$. In practice there is the problem of finding corresponding values of e and M because of the initial compression of most springs.

n In space it is impossible to monitor the 'weight' of an astronaut using normal balances, because the astronaut is in free fall with the space vehicle. A normal spring balance would not register a reading. Thus an ingenious way to measure the astronaut's mass was found: the period of oscillation of the astronaut in a chair supported by springs is measured. Equation [7.2] depends only on the existence of a restoring force proportional to the extension of the spring.

FURTHER WORK

o You can examine in more detail the phenomenon encountered in (j), where the vibrations change from those of a spring to those of a pendulum. Place the mass M for which this occurred on the spring. Measure approximately the periods of the two types of oscillations, as the spring changes from one mode to the other.

p You might expect the periods of vertical (T_v) and horizontal (T_h) oscillations to be the same if you were observing a resonance phenomenon. In a resonance phenomenon the natural frequency of the pendulum of length l would be the same as that of the vibrating spring. Since the frequency of a vibration $= 1/$the period, the periods would be the same. However, you will have found that T_h is significantly greater than T_v.

q If the sideways motion corresponds to that of a simple pendulum, then its period should be $2\pi\sqrt{l/g}$, where l is the total length of the system. See if your value of T_h is consistent with this equation. If T_h is consistent with the motion of a simple pendulum, try to explain why it is impossible for T_h to be equal to $T_v (= 2\pi\sqrt{e/g}$ from (m)); take $l = l_0 + e$, where l_0 is the effective length of the unextended spring system.

i Starting with the mass holder alone, determine the period of vertical oscillation T. Draw up a table of M (in kg) and T; leave a further column for data analysis.

j Increase M in 50 g steps and determine T for each value of M. Note that for one particular value of M, you may find it impossible (or difficult) to measure T because the spring alternates quite rapidly between vertical oscillations and horizontal swings (as for a simple pendulum). The periods of these two motions are not the same. If this occurs ignore that reading. You can consider the reasons for this phenomenon in the Further work section.

k From equation [7.2], plot an appropriate graph in order to determine a second value k.

7B Damped Free Vibrations
Investigation of the free oscillations of a moving-coil galvanometer

APPARATUS REQUIRED

- light-beam galvanometer (switched to short before moving)
- 2 V accumulator
- resistance box 0–10 000 Ω
- mounted variable resistor 10–110 kΩ + 0–1 MΩ with 4 mm terminals
- mounted double-throw, single-pole switch with 4 mm terminals
- mounted capacitor 0.47 µF with 4 mm terminals
- plug key
- connecting wire
- stopwatch reading to 0.1 s

PRINCIPLES INVOLVED

a　In this experiment you will investigate the effect of damping on the oscillations of a light-beam galvanometer. Here the electromagnetic damping of the galvanometer is altered by varying the resistance values connected across the galvanometer on its direct (or ballistic) setting.

b　For light damping the oscillations are sinusoidal with an amplitude that decreases exponentially with time (Fig. 7.3a). The period of oscillation T does not change with time.

As the damping is increased critical damping is reached, where the oscillation decays to zero displacement in a time of approximately $T/4$ (Fig. 7.3b). Further increase of the damping leads to overdamping, where the displacement of the system returns to zero only very slowly (Fig. 7.3c).

QUALITATIVE OBSERVATIONS ON DAMPING

c　Set up the circuit shown in Fig. 7.4 (overleaf). Here the double-throw, single-pole switch is used as a single-throw switch (first two terminals only). Only the 0–1 MΩ variable resistor (R_p) is used (second two terminals only). Before switching the galvanometer to direct check that the dial of the variable resistor is turned fully clockwise. Set the resistance box (R_d), which provides the electromagnetic damping, to 3000 Ω. With the switch open, centre the pointer of the galvanometer to zero.

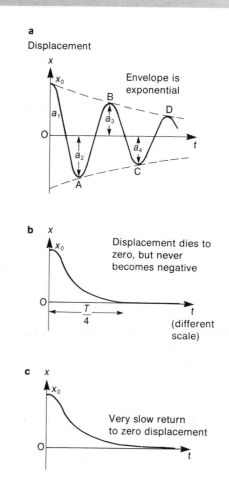

Fig. 7.3　Oscillations of a system subject to **a** light damping, **b** critical damping, **c** heavy damping.

d　Close the switch. The deflection of the pointer should be about 50 mm to the right. Carefully increase the deflection by decreasing R_p until the deflection is full scale.

e　Now open the switch and observe the oscillations of the light beam as they gradually decay. Close the switch again and allow the deflection to settle down to full scale. This normally takes some time; the time can be decreased by switching the galvanometer to its ×1 scale until the deflection is steady and then switching back to direct.

f　Open the switch again and record the displacement of the oscillations at points such as A, B, C, D, etc. in Fig. 7.3a. Hence sketch a graph of displacement

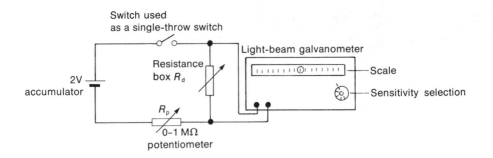

Fig. 7.4   Circuit diagram for a qualitative investigation of the electromagnetic damping of a light-beam galvanometer.

against time for light damping of the galvanometer. You can determine the time axis from the period of oscillation of the light beam. If you miss any of the deflections, you can repeat the measurements by closing the switch again.

g   Increase the damping of the galvanometer by decreasing R_d to about 120 Ω*. Adjust R_p to obtain a full scale deflection. When the switch is opened you should find that the displacement decreases to zero rapidly. Determine the approximate time taken for this to occur. Hence draw a rough graph of the displacement curve for critical damping.

h   The electromagnetic damping is increased further by decreasing R_d to 14 Ω. With this shunt resistance across the galvanometer, you will need to reduce R_p to obtain a full scale deflection again. Open the switch. The deflection now decreases very slowly to zero. Draw a graph of the displacement by measuring the time to decrease to 0.75, 0.5, 0.25 and 0.1 of the initial displacement. This curve corresponds to heavy damping.

QUANTITATIVE MEASUREMENTS ON A LIGHTLY DAMPED SYSTEM

i   Set up the circuit shown in Fig. 7.5. The switch is now used as a double-throw switch. In position A the capacitor C is charged by the accumulator. In position B the capacitor C discharges through the galvanometer and R_d. This discharge of the capacitor is virtually instantaneous and provides an impulse to the deflection system of the galvanometer. The rate at which the subsequent oscillations decay will depend on the value of R_d. R_p now consists of both variable resistors to give a finer adjustment on this protective resistance. R_p should initially be set to its maximum value.

If you have any doubts about the connections in your circuit,

The exact value of the critical resistance is usually marked on the back of the galvanometer.

then ask for it to be checked. A direct connection of the accumulator to the galvanometer will damage the galvanometer.

Close the plug key.

j   Initially set R_d to infinity; if the resistance box does not have this setting, just disconnect it from the circuit. The only damping of the galvanometer will be air damping. Move the switch to A to charge the capacitor. When the switch is moved to B, the capacitor will discharge through the galvanometer. Because the value of R_p is large the impulse will be extended over about 0.5 s. Provided that the light beam oscillates with a reasonable amplitude on scale, you can now decrease R_p towards its minimum value of 10 kΩ. This low value for R_p will not significantly extend the time of the instantaneous impulse. The oscillations can be stopped by switching the galvanometer from direct to ×1. It can then be switched back to direct again for the measurement of the oscillations. Check that the rest position of the light beam is at the centre of the galvanometer scale.

k   Charge and discharge the capacitor and record the amplitudes of as many swings either side of the zero as you can. Do not expect to get them in one set. Provided that the galvanometer coil is stationary when given its impulse, the readings are quite reproducible. So you can gradually build up the complete set of amplitudes such as shown in Fig. 7.6. Remember that you can cut down the waiting time between sets of results by switching from direct to ×1.

l   Plot a graph of the amplitude a (ordinate) against the number of the swing n (abscissa); all values of a are taken as positive irrespective of the direction of the swing (Fig. 7.7).

m   Introduce some electromagnetic damping into the galvanometer circuit by setting R_d to 3000 Ω. Check the zero setting of the galvanometer. Repeat

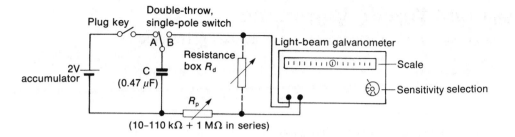

Fig. 7.5 Circuit diagram for producing oscillations of a light-beam galvanometer.

steps (k) and (l). The graph should be plotted on the same axes as the one for air damping alone.

n As the swings to both sides have been numbered (n), the period T is represented on the horizontal axis by the interval between two successive odd (or even) values of n. Since oscillations were started at the centre, the first swing occurs $\frac{1}{4}$ of the way through the first oscillation, the second swing occurs $\frac{3}{4}$ of the way through the first oscillation, and the first oscillation is complete midway between $n = 2$ and $n = 3$. Draw a second scale on the horizontal axis of Fig. 7.7 showing the number of the oscillation N. The relationship between N and n is $N = (\frac{n}{2} - \frac{1}{4})$.

o The *damping factor* or *decrement* δ is defined as the ratio of any amplitude a_N to the amplitude a_{N+1} exactly one oscillation later:

$$\delta = \frac{a_N}{a_{N+1}} \qquad [7.3]$$

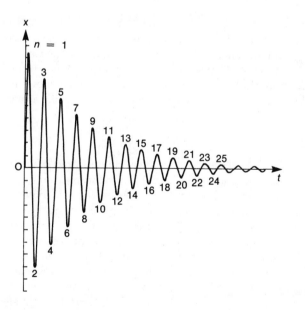

Fig. 7.6 The displacements required to characterise the damping of the light-beam galvanometer.

From this definition of the decrement, an equation can be derived relating the amplitude a_N to the amplitude in the absence of damping a_0 and δ. Using equation [7.3]:

$$a_N = a_0/\delta^N = a_0\delta^{-N} \qquad [7.4]$$

You never have the opportunity to measure a_0, corresponding to $N = 0$. By the time that your first reading is made ($N = \frac{1}{4}$ or $n = 1$) damping has already dissipated some of the oscillation energy. The value of a_0 is usually quite important, since it does represent the amplitude of the system in the absence of damping.

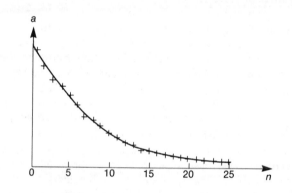

Fig. 7.7 A graph of the 'maxima' of displacement against n.

p From equation [7.4] plot a suitable graph in order to determine a_0 and δ from both sets of your results. Both sets of results should lead to the same value a_0, although the second value for δ should be larger to indicate an increase in damping.

NOTES

q Your account should include a description of the different types of damping and the detailed analysis of the results for a lightly damped system. Details of the circuit diagrams are not required, but you should include a brief description of the method used to produce damped oscillations of a moving-coil galvanometer.

7C Damped Forced Vibrations
Investigation of the forced oscillations of a moving-coil galvanometer

APPARATUS REQUIRED

- light-beam galvanometer (switched to short before moving)

- signal generator, frequency range 0.1–10 Hz, ÷100 attenuation

- resistance box 0–10 000 Ω

- mounted variable resistor (potentiometer) 0–1 MΩ

- connecting wire

- stopwatch reading to 0.1 s

PRINCIPLES INVOLVED

a   Any system displaced from equilibrium will vibrate with a natural frequency f_0. If a system is forced to vibrate by an externally applied force of frequency f, then the system will also vibrate with a frequency f. The amplitude of this forced vibration will be small unless the applied force has the same frequency as the natural frequency of the system f_0. When $f = f_0$ resonance occurs and the amplitude of the vibrations of the system can be very large. The amplitude of the forced vibration at resonance depends on the magnitude of damping in the system. In theory, if the damping is zero, the amplitude at resonance is infinite; in practice damping is always present in a mechanical system so the amplitude of vibration is finite. Fig. 7.8 shows the type of curves obtained for the amplitude response of a mechanical system subject to varying amounts of damping. For light damping the frequency of the resonance peak is almost identical to f_0, but as the damping of the system increases to critical damping the resonance peak is displaced to lower frequencies, as shown by the dashed line in Fig. 7.8.

b   In this experiment the vibrations are produced in a light-beam galvanometer (set on its ballistic range) by applying an alternating electrical signal to the coil of the galvanometer. Damping of the galvanometer system is controlled by varying the electromagnetic damping in the electrical circuit. Because of the limited scale of the galvanometer, it is really only possible to investigate the amplitude response of the galvanometer for a small range of damping. If the circuit is set to record the response with very low (air) damping, the resonance curve for light (electromagnetic) damping corresponds to only a very small scale deflection.

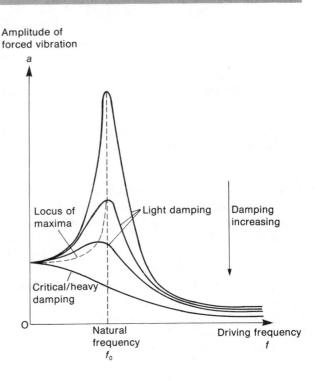

Fig. 7.8   The amplitude response curves for a mechanical system subject to damping.

MEASUREMENT OF THE AMPLITUDE RESPONSE

c   Connect up the circuit shown in Fig. 7.9. The high impedance output of the signal generator is used, with the attenuation set to ÷100 initially. The variable resistance R_v is set to its maximum value (knob turned fully clockwise). The resistance R_d, which allows the electromagnetic damping to be varied, is set to a value of 3000 Ω.

d   Turn the galvanometer on to its direct scale. Set the frequency of the signal generator to about 0.5 Hz and turn the output up slowly so as to obtain a reasonable amplitude of oscillation of the light beam; if necessary reduce R_v. Disconnect the galvanometer from the circuit, and measure its natural frequency of oscillation f_0 by timing 20 complete oscillations. This now gives you a fairly accurate value for the resonance frequency of the system. The oscillation can be stopped by turning the galvanometer to its ×1 scale; when the pointer reaches zero, you can turn back to the direct scale.

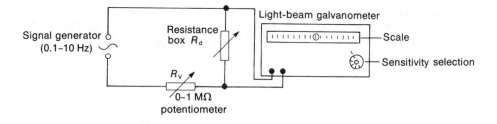

Fig. 7.9 Circuit diagram for determining the amplitude response curves of a light-beam galvanometer subject to forced vibrations.

e Before reconnecting the galvanometer centre the pointer on the scale. Now adjust the frequency of the signal generator to f_0 as determined in (d). If the frequency scale is accurate this should correspond to the resonance of the galvanometer system. If the calibration is in error, slight adjustments will be required to obtain resonance. Unfortunately after any adjustment of the frequency, the output of the signal generator or the value of R_v, the oscillations of the galvanometer beam do not settle down to their 'steady state' until at least ten oscillations have been completed. You will therefore need patience as you make the adjustments required to obtain the amplitude response curves. Adjust the frequency of the signal generator so as to obtain the maximum amplitude of oscillation (resonance). Adjust R_v until this amplitude corresponds to the full range of the galvanometer scale. The exact position of resonance will be difficult to obtain because a change in f of less than 0.01 Hz can cause a 20% change in the amplitude of oscillation. Having made all the adjustments to obtain resonance and a full scale deflection, R_v and the signal generator output should remain unaltered for the remainder of the experiment. Only f will be varied.

f Decrease f to 0.1 Hz. Since the oscillations take a long time to decay to the low value expected for this frequency, turn the galvanometer sensitivity to ×1 and then back to direct when the oscillations cease. Record the amplitude of oscillation a for this frequency. Increase f in 0.1 Hz steps up to 0.4 Hz. Remember to allow time for the oscillations to build up to their 'steady state' amplitude before recording a. As the response curve increases rapidly from 0.4 Hz, amplitude readings should be determined at smaller intervals in f from 0.4 to 0.6 Hz. Return the interval in f to 0.1 Hz up to frequencies of 2 Hz.

g Plot the amplitude response curve for $R_d = 3000\ \Omega$. See if your curve shows any evidence of a second maximum in amplitude at $f = 2f_0$: this second resonance is theoretically expected in a mechanical system.

h Reset the value of R_d to 500 Ω; this increases the electromagnetic damping of the galvanometer system by a factor of about five. Starting at 0.1 Hz, determine the response curve for this setting of R_d. Find as accurately as you can the frequency at which resonance occurs. Is it significantly different from the previous value ($R_d = 3000\ \Omega$)?

i Plot the amplitude response curve for this value of R_d on the same axes as the $R_d = 3000\ \Omega$ curve.

j Finally confirm that for the critical resistance of the galvanometer* (R_d about 120 Ω), there is no significant resonance maximum.

NOTES

k Your account should include a brief description of the method for obtaining the amplitude response curves, and the curves obtained. Comment on whether there was any significant change in the resonant frequency as the damping increased.

l The amplitude response curves are important in the design of mechanical systems: (i) in designing buildings and bridges the natural frequency of vibration must be significantly different from the frequencies of forced vibrations arising from winds. (ii) a car suspension system must have a natural frequency significantly different from that of the forced vibrations caused by irregularities in the road surface; alternatively the suspension can be critically or heavily damped so there is no significant amplitude resonance. (iii) a car stuck in the mud can be effectively removed by bouncing the rear end; if the downward pushes are timed correctly, the amplitude of the vibrations of the rear of the car increase sufficiently to remove the car from the mud.

*The exact value for the critical resistance of the galvanometer is usually marked on the back of the galvanometer.

m Electrical resonance occurs in a tuned circuit consisting of a capacitor, an inductor and a resistor. In this type of circuit charge resonance corresponds to amplitude resonance in a mechanical circuit. Current resonance does in fact correspond to velocity resonance in a mechanical system (see experiment 13C, page 176). The resistive component is the electrical equivalent of damping.

7D Stationary Waves in Free Air
Identification of nodes and antinodes along a stationary wave in free air

APPARATUS REQUIRED

- signal generator, frequency range 500–3000 Hz, 0–4 V on low impedance output
- loudspeaker 8/16 Ω impedance
- microphone, crystal (piezoelectric) type
- cathode ray oscilloscope with a sensitivity of at least 50 mV/div (or mV/cm)
- sheet of aluminium or wood, about 20 cm by 20 cm, with a stand
- leads (preferably screened) from microphone to CRO, at least 1 m long
- leads from signal generator to loudspeaker
- metre rule
- mercury-in-glass thermometer 0–50 °C

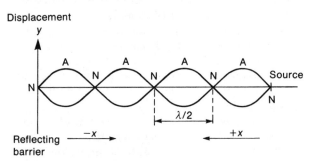
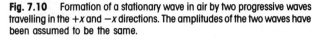

Fig. 7.10   Formation of a stationary wave in air by two progressive waves travelling in the $+x$ and $-x$ directions. The amplitudes of the two waves have been assumed to be the same.

b   One of the simplest ways of observing a stationary wave in air is to reflect sound waves from a barrier (Fig. 7.10). As a microphone is moved along a line joining the source and screen, a series of maxima (A) and minima (N) in the sound intensity will be detected. In Fig. 7.10 it has been assumed that the two progressive waves have the same amplitude; in practice the reflected wave would have a smaller amplitude and so the minima in intensity would not be zero.

c   The distance between successive minima (N) is equal to $\lambda/2$, where λ is the wavelength of the original sound wave. Since the frequency f is known, the speed c of the sound wave in air can be determined using $c = f\lambda$. An average value for c can be determined by measurements on the standing wave patterns for a range of frequencies f. The assumption here is that the speed of sound in a medium is independent of its frequency, that is, there is no dispersion as occurs for light waves in a medium; this is certainly true for sounds in the audible range, up to 20 000 Hz.

PRINCIPLES INVOLVED

a   When two progressive waves of the same frequency f travelling in opposite directions are superimposed, a stationary wave can be formed. In a stationary wave certain points along the wave, called nodes, are displacement minima, whilst other points along the wave, called antinodes, are displacement maxima. If the amplitudes a of the two progressive waves are equal, the displacement at the nodes will be zero at all times, whereas the displacement at the antinodes will vary with time between $+2a$ and $-2a$.

MEASUREMENTS ON STANDING WAVES IN AIR

Note: at high frequencies the sound from the loudspeaker can be unpleasant, so try to keep the volume down to a minimum and take your measurements quickly.

d Set the loudspeaker and reflecting barrier 1 metre apart on a bench (Fig. 7.11). You can sometimes obtain better results by placing these two components on stools 1 metre apart; this does cut down the reflections of sound waves from the surroundings such as the bench. Connect the microphone to the Y-plates of the CRO and place it near to and facing the barrier, and on the line defined by the metre rule; the Y-plate sensitivity should be about 50 mV/div and the time base set to about 1 ms/div. Connect the low impedance output of the signal generator to the loudspeaker.

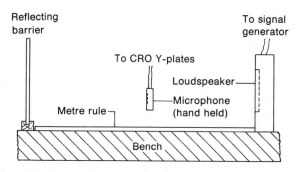

Fig. 7.11 Apparatus for detecting the nodes of the stationary wave formed by the superposition of the wave from the loudspeaker and the wave formed by reflection from the barrier.

e Set the frequency f of the signal generator to 1000 Hz. Adjust its output until the amplitude of the trace on the CRO screen is about 2 cm. The trace, which represents the time variations of the signal from the microphone, will not be exactly sinusoidal; the microphone will detect stray sounds around the laboratory. Check that as you move the microphone along the metre rule, the amplitude of the trace varies between the expected maxima and minima. If necessary increase the sensitivity of the Y-plates.

f Move the microphone away from the barrier and note the position x_0 of the first minimum. As you move the microphone along towards the loudspeaker note the number of minima n shown on the CRO trace. As you approach the loudspeaker it will become more difficult to distinguish the minima from the background intensity of the sound. Record the position x corresponding to the nth minimum.

g The distance between the first and the nth minima $(x - x_0)$ can now be used to calculate λ from $(n - 1)\lambda/2 = (x - x_0)$. Tabulate the values for f and λ. You can estimate the uncertainty in λ by noting the uncertainties in x and x_0 as you attempt to detect the minima.

h Increase f in 500 Hz steps up to 3000 Hz and repeat steps (f) and (g). As f increases you should be able to detect an increasing number of minima n.

i Decrease f to 500 Hz and see if you can detect any minima. Should you be successful, comment on whether you think that the measurement is reliable and suggest a reason as to why measurements should start at $f = 1000$ Hz.

j From your results for f and λ plot a suitable graph so as to obtain a value for c. From your graph estimate the error in c.

k Record room temperature. Hence correct your value for c to the value at 0 °C assuming that c is proportional to the square root of the absolute temperature; take $T(\text{K}) = \theta(\,°\text{C}) + 273$.

NOTES

l Your account should include a detailed description of the formation and detection of stationary sound waves in air. Include the measurements leading to a value for c. Compare your result with the accepted value for c.

m The formation of a stationary wave on a line between two sound sources is a particular example of interference. At certain points between the sources the phase difference between the two waves is an odd multiple of π, leading to destructive interference. If the phase difference between the two waves is a multiple of 2π, then constructive interference will occur. The distance between two successive positions of destructive interference is $\lambda/2$.

n The formation of standing waves in air is often used to suppress high levels of noise from a generator. The noise from a generator is detected and produced as a sound wave from a loudspeaker. The loudspeaker can be positioned so that there is an interference minimum in the region around the generator. Of course, this does mean that elsewhere there will be maxima in the sound intensity.

o Interference between radio waves (long wavelength electromagnetic waves, $\lambda \approx 100$ m) can be used as a navigational aid. As a ship moves between two similar radio stations, its receiver will detect maxima and minima in the signal; the distance between minima (say) can be used to compute the position of the ship, provided that the positions of the two radio stations (and the frequency of the radio waves) are known.

7E Stationary Waves in an Air Column
Investigation of the harmonics of a vibrating column of air of variable length

APPARATUS REQUIRED

- resonance tube assembly on a floor stand (see Fig. 7.13 for two versions)
- metre rule
- set of tuning forks (256–512 Hz frequency)
- striking pad or cork bung for striking tuning forks
- beaker of water for topping up resonance tube
- 0–50 °C thermometer

PRINCIPLES INVOLVED

a A tuning fork held above the open end of a tube, as in Fig. 7.12, will result in a longitudinal sound wave travelling down the tube. This wave will be reflected at the closed end of the tube. The superposition of these two waves will establish a stationary wave in the tube. Resonance will only occur for those waves whose wavelengths λ are correctly matched to the length of the air column. Then the reflected rarefaction at the open end enters the column at the same instant as the rarefaction from the tuning fork to give constructive superposition. Such waves will give a sound wave of constant intensity.

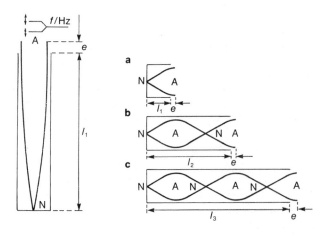

Fig. 7.12 Displacement curves for an air column subject to forced vibrations: **a** first, **b** second and **c** third resonances.

b The boundary conditions at the open end of the tube must correspond to a pressure node and hence a displacement antinode. The boundary conditions at the closed end of the tube correspond to a displacement node and hence a pressure antinode.

c A small length of air outside the tube is also set in vibration. The effective length of the vibrating air column exceeds the length of the tube by e, the end correction. e is approximately equal to 0.6 times the tube radius.

d For the first resonance, Fig. 7.12a, the length of the air column $(l_1 + e) = \lambda/4$. Thus if the speed of the sound wave in the column is c:

$$c = 4f(l_1 + e) \qquad [7.5]$$

for a tuning fork of frequency f.

Equation [7.5] can be used to investigate the relationship between f and the first resonance length l_1, and to determine a value for the speed of sound in damp air.

e Further resonances can be obtained for vibrating air columns of length $\frac{3}{4}\lambda$ (Fig. 7.12b) and $\frac{5}{4}\lambda$ (Fig. 7.12c). Thus for the first three resonances:

$$\left.\begin{aligned} l_1 + e &= \tfrac{1}{4}\lambda \\ l_2 + e &= \tfrac{3}{4}\lambda \\ l_3 + e &= \tfrac{5}{4}\lambda \end{aligned}\right\} \qquad [7.6]$$

Subtraction of any of these two equations can be used to find a value for λ, eliminating the end correction e. A further value for c can then be calculated.

INVESTIGATION OF THE RELATIONSHIP BETWEEN f AND THE LENGTH l₁

f Set the apparatus up as shown in Fig. 7.13, ensuring that the tube is as near vertical as possible. The procedure given for finding the resonances applies to the apparatus with the movable tube. The procedure for the other version is similar but greater care has to be taken with adjusting the length of the air column.

g For the highest frequency tuning fork ($f = 512$ Hz) calculate an approximate value for l_1 using $c = 300$ m s^{-1}. Set l_1 to about 3 cm shorter than this length.

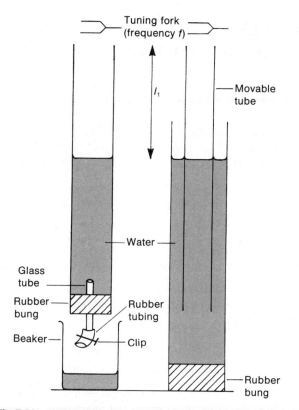

Fig. 7.13 Measurement of the resonances of a column of air. Two versions of the apparatus are shown.

h Carefully adjust the height of the movable tube so as to obtain a maximum in the sound intensity when the 512 Hz tuning fork is struck on its pad and held near to the open end of the tube. Do not strike the fork too hard otherwise it will not vibrate at a single frequency. Measure the length of the air column l_1 with a metre rule. Also estimate the uncertainty in l_1 by finding the range over which l_1 can be varied without significantly altering the sound level.

i Tabulate f and l_1 (preferably in metres). Leave a further column for data analysis.

j Repeat the measurements for a range of frequencies down to 256 Hz. Plot a graph of l_1 against f as the experiment proceeds. This will help to identify any doubtful experimental points.

k From equation [7.5] choose an appropriate graph to plot so as to obtain a straight line relationship. From this graph determine a value of c from the slope and a value of e from an appropriate intercept. (Hint: If you plot l_1 as one of your variables you will need to leave room for a small negative intercept on the l_1 axis.)

l Correct your value for c to the value of c at 0 °C assuming that c is proportional to the square root of the temperature of the air in kelvin. $(T(K) = \theta(°C) + 273)$.

Comment on whether the value of c you determined is likely to be lower or higher than the value for dry air.

INVESTIGATION OF THE FIRST THREE RESONANCES OF AN AIR COLUMN

m Because of the limit on the maximum length of the air column (about 1 m) and the decreasing intensity of the resonances, it is only possible to find l_1, l_2 and l_3 for the highest frequency tuning fork $(f = 512 \text{ Hz})$.

n Gradually increase the length of the air column and determine the positions of the first three resonances.

o Using equation [7.6] determine three values for λ by using the equations in pairs. Calculate the average value for λ together with an estimate in its uncertainty from your range of λ values.

p Calculate a value for c from $c = f\lambda$ and correct this value of c to the value for 0 °C as in (l).

NOTES

q Your account should include a detailed account of the measurement of the first resonance for a range of frequencies, and the analysis leading to the value for c. Compare your value of c with the accepted value for c in dry air at 0 °C.

r Comment on whether the value of c determined graphically in (k) is likely to be more reliable than the value determined in (p).

s The principal application of resonance in closed columns of air is in tuning wind instruments to produce notes of a particular frequency.

t In principle this experimental arrangement could be used to determine the speed of sound waves in a gas, particularly a gas that is denser than air.

7F Stationary Waves on a Wire (I)
Investigation of the transverse stationary waves on a stretched wire undergoing forced vibrations at the fundamental frequency

APPARATUS REQUIRED

- sonometer: box or board with attached steel wire and pulley
- 2 bridges (one of which may be fixed)
- slotted masses: 9 1 kg masses and a 1 kg holder *attached securely* to the steel wire
- set of tuning forks (256–512 Hz frequency)
- striking pad or cork bung for striking tuning forks
- metre rule (unless sonometer has its own scale)
- micrometer screw gauge
- G-cramp
- a mat or scrap piece of wood (to protect the floor should the steel wire break)

PRINCIPLES INVOLVED

a   Dimensional analysis can be used to predict the form of an equation relating physical quantities. For example, it can be used to show that the speed c at which transverse waves travel along a wire depends on the tension P and the mass per unit length μ of the wire. Dimensional analysis will not predict the value of any dimensionless constant required to turn the relationship into an equation. The purpose of both parts of this experiment is to test the relationship predicted by dimensional analysis and to find the value of the constant.

b   Dimensional analysis shows that the speed of transverse waves is proportional to $\sqrt{P/\mu}$. Hence:

$$c = k\sqrt{\frac{P}{\mu}} \qquad [7.7]$$

where k is the dimensionless constant to be determined.

c   In practice it is not possible to determine c directly. Instead the wavelength λ of the stationary wave set up on the wire by forced vibrations of frequency f is determined. Then c can be calculated from $c = f\lambda$.

d   When a stretched wire is forced to vibrate at a particular frequency f, a stationary wave pattern is formed, whose wavelength $\lambda = c/f$. If the length of the wire is an integral number of half wavelengths, then resonance occurs, where the nodes and antinodes are well defined. In this experiment you will only be concerned with the first mode of vibration at the fundamental frequency. For the fundamental frequency or first

harmonic the length of the wire l_0 must be exactly half a wavelength long. A node then exists at each end and a single antinode occurs at the centre, as shown in Fig. 7.14.

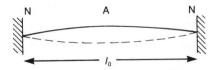

Fig. 7.14   Fundamental mode of vibration of a stretched wire showing the nodes N and antinode A.

e   For the fundamental frequency equation [7.7] can be rewritten in terms of $l_0 = \lambda/2$ and f as:

$$f = \frac{k}{2l_0}\sqrt{\frac{P}{\mu}} \qquad [7.8]$$

f   A change of either the forcing frequency f or tension P affects the wavelength of the stationary wave pattern. The length l_0 must be adjusted until it is once more one half-wavelength long.

g   For resonance to occur, giving a maximum displacement at the centre of the wire, the frequency of the forcing system must equal the natural frequency of the forced system (the wire in this experiment). Adjusting the length of the wire changes its natural frequency of vibration. When its length is one half-wavelength, the wire's natural frequency is matched to the forcing frequency. In this experiment the forcing frequency is one of several standard tuning forks.

VARIATION OF l_0 WITH FREQUENCY f (FOR A CONSTANT TENSION P)

h   The sonometer is fitted with a single steel wire secured very firmly at one end. Tension is applied to the wire by hanging masses from the other end over the pulley. Ensure that the loop for attaching the mass holder is secure; the whiplash from a steel wire suddenly released from tension can be dangerous. Although the total length of the steel wire is constant, a variable length can be made to vibrate between two bridges.

i   Place the sonometer at the end of a bench as shown in Fig. 7.15. The pulley should be positioned far enough over the bench edge so that the masses are freely suspended. To ensure that the sonometer does not topple when fully loaded, you are advised to use a G-cramp to secure the sonometer to the bench. Do not

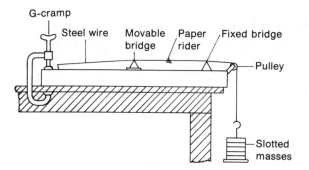

Fig. 7.15 *The sonometer: general arrangement.*

over-tighten the cramp. Use a mat or a scrap piece of wood to protect the floor from falling masses should a disaster occur.

j In the experiments that follow, the wire under tension $P = Mg$ is forced to vibrate at a particular frequency f by a tuning fork. The length of the wire l_0 must be adjusted to obtain resonance. The simplest technique is to sound the tuning fork by striking it on a cork pad (not the bench, which will not give a single frequency), and then to hold the stem of the fork on one of the bridges. The fork will set the wire vibrating. Resonance can be detected by watching a small strip of paper folded over the centre of the wire, whilst the other bridge is used to vary the vibrating length of the wire. The large amplitude of vibration at the antinode causes the paper rider to move. At resonance, this movement should be sufficient to throw the paper rider off the wire. Alternatively, if you have a good musical ear, you may be able to tune the wire audibly whilst both are vibrating separately at their natural frequencies. Hold the tuning fork near to one ear and pluck the sonometer wire at its centre. Adjust the length of the wire between the bridges until the two notes are the same. Both methods achieve the same result.

k Measure the diameter d of the sonometer wire at several places along its length using a micrometer screw gauge.

l Attach a mass M of 10 kg to the wire and find the length l_0 for which resonance occurs with the tuning fork of frequency 256 Hz. Unless the sonometer has its own scale, use a metre rule to measure l_0. (Hint: if d is just less than 0.5 mm, then l_0 will be about 0.5 m; for other values of d assume that l_0 is proportional to $1/d$). Tabulate f and l_0 (preferably in metres). Leave a further column for data analysis.

m Repeat the measurements of l_0 for tuning forks up to a frequency of 512 Hz. For each frequency you should be able to estimate the correct length using your first measurement in (l) and equation [7.8].

n Equation [7.8] predicts that l_0 is proportional to $1/f$. Plot a suitable graph to confirm this relationship. Since you are attempting to confirm proportionality (not just linearity) you should include the origin of coordinates on your graph.

o Measure the slope of the graph and hence determine a value for the constant k. The other quantities involved in the expression for the slope can all be determined: $P = Mg$ taking $g = 9.8$ N kg^{-1}, and the mass per unit length μ = mass of 1 metre of wire, taking the density of steel to be 7800 kg m^{-3}.

VARIATION OF l_0 WITH TENSION P (FOR A CONSTANT FREQUENCY f)

p For this part of the experiment use only the lowest frequency tuning fork ($f = 256$ Hz). Check your original determination of l_0 for $M = 10$ kg. Tabulate l_0, M and $P = Mg$; leave a further column for data analysis.

q Repeat the measurement of l_0 for M decreasing in 1 kg steps down to 2 kg.

r According to equation [7.8] l_0 should be proportional to $\sqrt{P}$. Plot a suitable graph to confirm this relationship. You should again include the origin of coordinates if you wish to verify proportionality.

s Measure the slope of the graph. Hence determine a second value for k.

NOTES

t Your account should include a labelled diagram of the sonometer, a description of the method used to determine l_0, and the analysis leading to the confirmation of equation [7.8].

u Study the two graphs you obtained and the distribution of points on them. Hence comment on which value of k is more reliable.

v The main purpose of this experiment was to investigate the validity of an equation. It could have been used to determine the speed of a transverse wave on a wire from $c = f\lambda = 2fl_0$. Further, from these results it is possible to show that c is independent of frequency for transverse waves on a wire.

w Confirming the relationship between c and μ is in principle possible by using wires of varying diameter d. Equation [7.8] predicts that l_0 is proportional to $1/\sqrt{\mu}$ for fixed values of f and P. Hence l_0 should be proportional to $1/d$. In practice this would be a difficult experiment to perform on a standard sonometer.

7G Stationary Waves on a Wire (II)
Investigation of the harmonics of a stretched wire carrying a current in a magnetic field

APPARATUS REQUIRED

- sonometer: box or board with attached steel wire and pulley
- 2 bridges (one of which may be fixed)
- slotted masses: 9 1 kg masses and a 1 kg holder *attached securely* to the steel wire
- signal generator: 0–5 V output on the low impedance output, capable of sustaining a current of 1 A in the sonometer wire
- 4 magnadur magnets fitted on a yoke
- connecting wires with 4 mm terminals and crocodile clips
- ammeter, 0–5 A a.c. (or an avometer/multimeter switched to its a.c. range)
- metre rule (unless sonometer has its own scale)
- micrometer screw gauge
- G-cramp
- a mat or scrap piece of wood (to protect the floor should the steel wire break)

PRINCIPLES INVOLVED

a A wire carrying a current experiences a force F when placed in a magnetic field as shown in Fig. 7.16. If an alternating current of frequency f is used, the force F will alternate with the same frequency. The wire will then execute transverse vibrations with a frequency f.

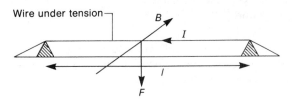

Fig. 7.16 The force F acting on a current carrying wire in a magnetic field of flux density B.

b Depending on where the magnetic field is applied along the wire, various modes of vibration are possible. If the field is applied near to the centre of the wire, the wire will vibrate such that there is an antinode (A) at its centre as shown in Fig. 7.17a and c. If the field is applied about one-third along the length of the wire, other modes of vibration are possible, as shown in Fig. 7.17b.

c Resonance will occur when the frequency of the force F is equal to the natural frequency of vibration of the wire, as obtained when the wire is plucked.

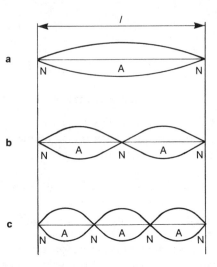

Fig. 7.17 The first three modes of vibration of a stretched wire fixed at its ends, showing nodes N and antinodes A. **a** Fundamental (1st harmonic), **b** 1st overtone (2nd harmonic), **c** 2nd overtone (3rd harmonic).

d The speed c of a transverse wave along a wire under tension P can be shown to be:

$$c = \sqrt{P/\mu} \qquad [7.9]$$

where μ is the mass per unit length of the wire; $\mu = \pi r^2 \rho$ for a wire of radius r and density ρ.

e For the first mode of vibration, the first harmonic, the length l of the wire corresponds to one-half of a wavelength λ. Hence using $c = f\lambda$, the frequency of vibration of the wire will be given by:

$$f = \frac{1}{2l}\sqrt{\frac{P}{\mu}} \qquad [7.10]$$

Using this equation you will investigate how l varies with the frequency of vibration f.

f With this experimental arrangement it is relatively easy to investigate the harmonics of a vibrating wire. For the nth harmonic, the length of vibrating wire $l = n\lambda/2$. The relationship between f and l then becomes:

$$f = \frac{n}{2l}\sqrt{\frac{P}{\mu}} \qquad [7.11]$$

This equation will be used to investigate how f varies with the harmonic n for a fixed length of wire.

VARIATION OF *l* WITH FREQUENCY *f* FOR THE FIRST HARMONIC (*P* IS CONSTANT)

g   The sonometer is fitted with a single steel wire secured very firmly at one end. Tension is applied to the wire by hanging masses from the other end over a pulley. Ensure that the loop for attaching the mass holder is secure; the whiplash from a steel wire suddenly released from tension can be dangerous.

h   Although the total length of the steel wire is constant, a variable length can be made to vibrate between two bridges.

i   Place the sonometer at the end of a bench as shown in Fig. 7.18. The pulley should be positioned far enough over the bench edge, so that the masses are freely suspended. To ensure that the sonometer does not topple when fully loaded, you are advised to use a G-cramp to secure the sonometer to the bench. Do not over-tighten the cramp. Use a mat or a scrap piece of wood to protect the floor from falling masses should a disaster occur.

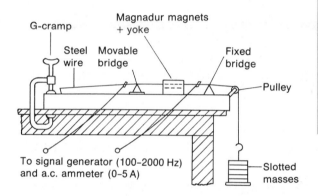

Fig. 7.18 The sonometer: the general arrangement, showing the connections to the a.c. supply and the position of the magnet for the fundamental mode of vibration.

j   Arrange the magnadur magnets in pairs on their yoke; ensure that the magnets on opposite sides of the yoke correspond to 'north' and 'south' poles, otherwise the wire may not vibrate with a large amplitude. Place the magnet at the centre of the wire between the two bridges. Make two connections to the ends of the wire using crocodile clips and connect the wires from the clips to the a.c. ammeter and signal generator placed in series. Adjust the output of the signal generator to give a current of about 1 A; the exact value is not important, nor does it matter that this current varies as the frequency of the signal generator is varied.

k   Place a total mass of 10 kg on the end of the wire. This will provide a fixed tension *P* of 98 N. Set *l* to 0.6 m.

l   Slowly increase the frequency of the signal generator from 100 Hz and find the frequency *f* at which the amplitude at the centre of the wire is a maximum for the first harmonic; it should be between 150 and 250 Hz. Take care not to increase the frequency too rapidly, otherwise you could find the third harmonic instead. Detecting the resonance should not be difficult either from the visual appearance of the vibrating wire or from the audible sound produced by the vibrating wire. Tabulate *f* and *l* (preferably in metres). Leave a further column for data analysis.

m   Decrease *l* in 0.05 m steps down to *l* = 0.1 m. If the sonometer has two movable bridges, these can be moved by equal amounts, leaving the magnet at the centre. If one bridge is fixed, you should recentre the magnet each time. Determine the resonant frequency *f* for each value of *l*.

n   Disconnect the crocodile clips from the wire and measure its diameter *d* at several places along its length using a micrometer screw gauge.

o   From equation [7.10] plot a suitable graph so as to obtain a straight line. Measure its slope and hence determine a value for the mass per unit length of the wire μ. Compare your value for μ with the theoretical value for the wire, taking the density of steel to be 7800 kg m^{-3}.

MEASUREMENTS ON THE HARMONICS OF A VIBRATING WIRE (*P* AND *l* CONSTANT)

p   Reconnect the signal generator to the sonometer wire. Reset *l* to 0.6 m.

q   Check your value for the frequency of the first harmonic f_1. Now determine the frequencies for the second and subsequent harmonics, f_2, f_3, f_4, f_5. These are expected to be simple multiples of f_1. You should decide where to move the magnet to for each harmonic in order to obtain the appropriate stationary wave (see Fig. 7.17). Tabulate f_n and *n*.

r   Plot a suitable graph to show the linear relationship between f_n and *n*. From the slope of the graph determine a second value for μ, using equation [7.11].

NOTES

S   Your account should include a labelled diagram of the apparatus, the principle used to determine the frequency of the vibrating wire, and the analysis leading to two values for the mass per unit length of the wire.

T   In this experiment you investigated only how f varied with l and n. This experimental arrangement could also have been used to investigate how f varies with the tension P and the mass per unit length of the wire μ. The latter is not very easy to do as it means using several wires of widely differing diameters; P would have to be chosen on the basis of the maximum tension that the thinnest wire could sustain before breaking.

U   This experiment could also have been used to confirm that the speed of transverse waves along a wire is independent of their frequency, that is, $c = f\lambda = 2fl$ (for the first harmonic) is constant.

V   If you have completed experiment 7F using the sonometer and tuning forks, compare this experiment with it, listing any advantages and disadvantages that you can see.

8 GEOMETRICAL AND PHYSICAL OPTICS

In this section you will measure the refractive index of a transparent solid and a liquid using Snell's law (experiment 8A). You will also use a prism spectrometer to measure the refractive index of the prism material (experiment 8D), although the main application of this spectrometer is for the measurement of the wavelengths of the light emitted by solids, liquids and gases. Basic optical measurements, relevant to the design of optical instruments, are included in the measurement of the focal lengths of lenses (experiment 8B) and mirrors (experiment 8C). Interference of light in a thin film will be used to measure very small distances of the order of 10–100 μm (experiment 8E). The diffraction grating spectrometer is used for the accurate measurement of the wavelengths of light emitted by a vapour lamp (experiment 8F).

8.1 LOCATING IMAGES BY THE USE OF NO PARALLAX

Probably the most common way of finding the position of an image formed by a lens or mirror is to use a light source and a screen to observe the focused image. However, there is a simpler method using mounted optical pins and the method of no parallax between the image and a locating pin. This method can also be used to locate virtual images, unlike the light source–screen method which can only be used to locate real images.

The principle of no parallax is quite simple: if you look at two objects (such as two fingers) at differing distances from your eyes, then as you move your head from side to side one of the objects will appear to move relative to the other. Only if the two objects are exactly the same distance from your eyes will there appear to be no relative movement as you move your head.

In order to illustrate the principle, consider finding the radius of curvature of a concave mirror (Fig. 8.1). You will probably know that if an object is placed exactly at the centre of curvature of the mirror, then an image the same size as the object will be formed at the same position as the object, as shown in Fig. 8.1a. With the pin in any position outside the focal point, you should be able to see an inverted image of the pin. Generally, as you move your head from side to side, you will see a relative movement between the pin and its image, as shown in Fig. 8.1b. Only when the image is coincident with the pin will there be no relative movement, as shown in Fig. 8.1c.

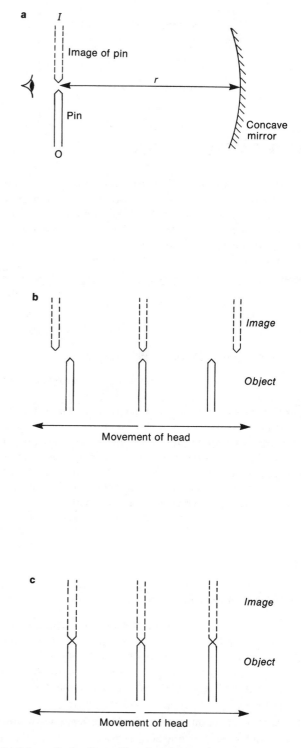

Fig. 8.1 a Finding the position of an image using the method of no parallax; b incorrect position, c correct position of pin.

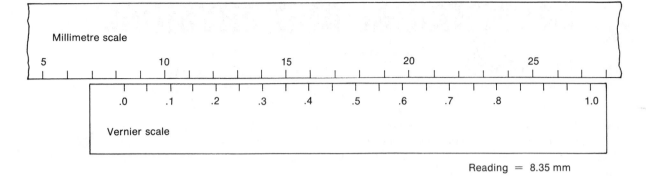

Fig. 8.2 Using a vernier scale reading to 0.05 mm.

8.2 SPECIAL VERNIER SCALES

In order to measure small distances accurately it is usual to use a travelling microscope with a vernier reading to 0.05 mm as in experiments 8A and 8F. Accurate measurements of refractive index (experiment 8D) and wavelengths (experiment 8F) require an angular vernier scale reading to one minute of arc; 60 minutes (60′) of arc are equal to 1 degree (1°) of arc.

a) TRAVELLING MICROSCOPE VERNIER (Fig. 8.2)

As in most vernier scales, the vernier scale slides along a main scale marked in millimetres or centimetres. The vernier scale is marked with 0.1 mm divisions, although sometimes the decimal point is omitted; the intermediate divisions correspond to 0.05 mm. As with a normal vernier find the lowest reading on the main scale corresponding to the zero on the vernier scale, 8 mm in Fig. 8.2. Then look along the vernier until one of the vernier divisions coincides with a scale division on the main scale, 0.35 mm in Fig. 8.2. The final reading is then 8.35 mm.

b) ANGULAR VERNIER (Fig. 8.3)

The main scale is marked in $\frac{1}{2}°$ divisions, but it is often only numbered at 10° intervals. This makes the scale very difficult to read particularly without a magnifying glass. The vernier is marked in intervals of 1′ but is usually only numbered at 10′ intervals. When set to a particular angle, read the main scale to the nearest $\frac{1}{2}°$ corresponding to the zero on the vernier scale, $29\frac{1}{2}°$ in Fig. 8.3. Then follow the vernier scale until one of its divisions coincides with a main scale division, 19′ or 20′ in Fig. 8.3. Thus the reading is 29° 49′, which converts to 29.82° in decimals.

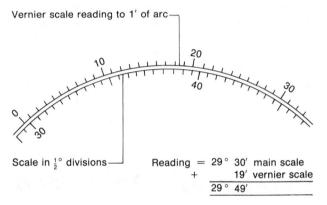

Fig. 8.3 Using an angular vernier reading to 1 minute of arc.

8.3 SPECTROMETER ADJUSTMENTS (Fig. 8.4)

Whether the spectrometer is used with a prism or with a diffraction grating, there are two common adjustments: a) adjusting the telescope to focus parallel light on the cross-wires of the eyepiece, b) adjusting the collimator to produce parallel light from the light source.

a) ADJUSTMENT OF THE TELESCOPE

Take the spectrometer outside with a chair, stool or desk to mount it on. Unclamp the telescope and point it towards a distant object. The eyepiece is first adjusted so that the telescope is in normal adjustment, that is, the final image is formed at infinity. Adjust the eyepiece by sliding it in and out of its tube, until the cross-wires are clearly seen with one eye, whilst a distant object is viewed directly with the other eye. The image of the cross-wires is then effectively at infinity. The telescope can now be set to receive parallel light by adjusting the knob on the telescope until a distant object is in focus. *Do not* make any subsequent adjustments to the telescope.

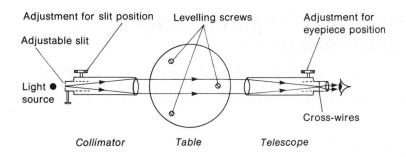

Fig. 8.4 The adjustments of a spectrometer: the collimator is adjusted to give parallel light and the telescope is adjusted to receive parallel light.

b) ADJUSTMENT OF THE COLLIMATOR

Return to the laboratory and set the spectrometer up in a darkroom or use a black cloth to screen out daylight. Set up a sodium source (with its control unit) so that it is aligned with the slits of the collimator. Rotate the telescope so as to view the light from the collimator. If you cannot see an image of the slit, even when fully open, check that the slit shutter has not been left in the closed position.

Adjust the position of the slit using the knob on the collimator until its image is focused. The collimator is now producing parallel light. Finally, adjust the slit width so as to obtain a fine image of the slit. Sometimes a worn pair of slits will prevent you from obtaining a fine slit image of uniform width. The collimator should not be readjusted, despite a temptation just to improve the image – you could end up by having to adjust the spectrometer from the beginning again.

8A Refraction at a Plane Boundary
Simple measurements of refractive index

APPARATUS REQUIRED

Because of its diversity this will be listed under the separate experiments.

PRINCIPLES INVOLVED

a   The refractive index $_1n_2$ for a wave travelling from medium 1 to medium 2 is simply the ratio c_1/c_2 of the speeds of the wave in these two media.

b   From this definition, simple geometry can be used to show that $_1n_2 = \sin i/\sin r$, where i and r are respectively the angles of incidence and refraction, as shown in Fig. 8.5.

This forms the basis of one method for measuring refractive indices of transparent media.

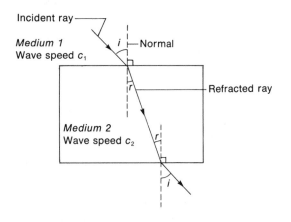

Fig. 8.5   Measuring refractive index using Snell's law. i is the angle of incidence and r is the angle of refraction.

c   Assuming that c_1 is greater than c_2, there is a maximum angle for r, which is the critical angle θ_c corresponding to grazing incidence, $i = 90°$, in Fig. 8.6. Then $_1n_2 = 1/\sin \theta_c$. Thus the measurement of a single angle is sufficient to give a value for the refractive index. This method can also be adapted to measure the refractive index of a small quantity of liquid smeared on to the flat side of the D-block shown in Fig. 8.6. Of course, this measurement gives the refractive index for a wave travelling from the liquid into the solid $_1n_s$, but if the refractive index for the solid is known from (b) for a wave travelling

from air to the solid, then the refractive index of the liquid can be found from:

$$_an_l = {_an_s}/{_1n_s} \qquad\qquad [8.1]$$

where:

$$_1n_s = 1/\sin \theta_c \qquad\qquad [8.2]$$

and θ_c is now the critical angle for a wave travelling from liquid to solid.

There is one limitation: the refractive index of the liquid must be less than that of the solid, otherwise there is no critical ray.

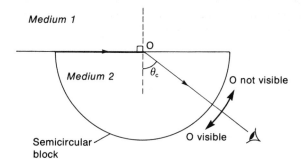

Fig. 8.6   Measuring refractive index using the critical angle θ_c.

d   The third method uses real and apparent depth for an object viewed through a transparent medium. From Fig. 8.7 it is easy to show that $h_r/h_a = \tan i/\tan r$. Provided that the angle of incidence is small, $\sin i \approx \tan i$ and $\sin r \approx \tan r$. Then from (b), $_1n_2 \approx h_r/h_a$. It is very easy to ensure that i is very small by viewing the object from directly above using a travelling microscope; the approximation then results in an error of less than 0.1% for angles of incidence less than 2°.

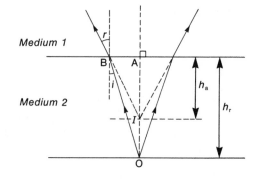

Fig. 8.7   Measuring refractive index using real depth h_r and apparent depth h_a.

The measurement of refractive index using sin i/sin r (Snell's law)

APPARATUS REQUIRED

- Perspex or glass rectangular block
- 4 optical pins
- fibre board
- white card, about 0.2 m by 0.2 m, and drawing pins
- protractor

---

e Pin a sheet of white card to the fibre board and place the block at the centre. Draw around the glass block with a fine pencil point. Place two pins P_1 and P_2 as shown in Fig. 8.8, so as to define a ray with an angle of incidence of about 70°. Looking through the block, place pins P_3 and P_4 so that all four pins appear to be in a straight line.

f Remove the block. Draw the two normals to the block at P_1 and P_3 and then construct the ray path $P_2P_1P_3P_4$. Measure both sets of values for i and r. Tabulate these angles, together with their average values. Leave two further columns for data analysis.

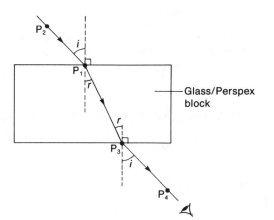

Fig. 8.8 Finding the ray path through a block using pins P_1, P_2, P_3 and P_4.

g Replace the block accurately within its outline. Repeat the procedure in (e) for values of i decreasing in about 10° intervals down to 20°. Measure the pairs of angles i and r and add these to the table of results.

h Plot a suitable graph from your results so as to obtain a straight line and from its slope determine a value for the refractive index $_an_s$.

i From the variations in i and r for a particular ray estimate an uncertainty in the value of $_an_s$.

The measurement of refractive index using real and apparent depth

APPARATUS REQUIRED

- 2 Perspex or glass rectangular blocks (as used previously)
- lycopodium powder in a dispenser
- travelling microscope

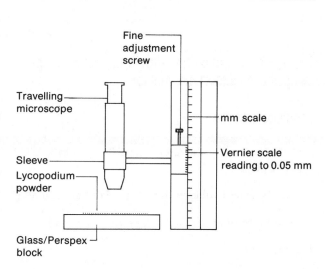

Fig. 8.9 Measurement of refractive index of a block using real and apparent depth.

j Place one block on a sheet of white card and sprinkle a thin layer of lycopodium powder on the top of the block. Focus the travelling microscope on the lycopodium powder, as shown in Fig. 8.9. If you move the microscope in its sleeve so as to focus on the powder, do not subsequently use this method for refocusing; always use the vernier scale movement. When approximately in focus clamp the microscope and use the fine adjustment screw of the microscope. Record the scale reading d_1 using the vernier scale (see section 8.2(a)).

k Place the second block on top of the first. Unclamp the microscope and refocus on the lycopodium powder. When approximately in focus, clamp the microscope and use the fine adjustment to obtain an accurate focus. Record the scale reading d_2.

l Sprinkle a fine layer of lycopodium powder on top of the second block. Focus the microscope on this layer of powder. Record the scale reading d_3.

m From the readings above the real depth $h_r = d_3 - d_1$ and the apparent depth $h_a = d_3 - d_2$. Calculate the value of $_a n_s$ and compare this value with the previous value determined using Snell's law.

n Note that this method is very sensitive to errors in determining d_1, d_2 and d_3 because these quantities appear as differences in the equation for $_a n_s$.

The measurement of the refractive index of a liquid using the critical angle method

APPARATUS REQUIRED

- D-shaped block of the same material as the blocks used previously

- small beaker of liquid: water, glycerol or liquid paraffin

- small piece of graph paper (20 mm by 10 mm)

- optical pin

- fibre board

- white card, about 0.2 m by 0.2 m, and drawing pins

- protractor

o Pin the sheet of cardboard to the fibre board. Place the block near to the centre and draw its outline with a fine pencil point. Mark the position of the centre of the flat face. Cut a strip of graph paper about 2 mm wide and of length equal to the thickness of the block; include on the strip the main grid line or draw a fine but clear vertical line, as shown in Fig. 8.10.

p Smear the marked side of the graph paper with the liquid and stick it to the centre of the block, so that the line is vertical. Whilst viewing the line through the block, move the optical pin along the curved surface of the block until the image of the line just disappears. This corresponds to the critical ray.

q Remove the block and draw the normal to the flat face. You can now draw the critical ray and measure the angle θ_c.

r Repeat the measurement of θ_c four more times and calculate an average value and an estimate of the uncertainty in the angle. Take care not to allow the liquid to dry out, as you may end up with the critical angle for air to the block, and not the value for liquid to solid.

s Using equations [8.1] and [8.2] calculate $_a n_1$. From the uncertainty in the value of θ_c estimate the uncertainty in this refractive index.

t Explain why the refractive index of the liquid must be less than that of the material of the block for the method to work.

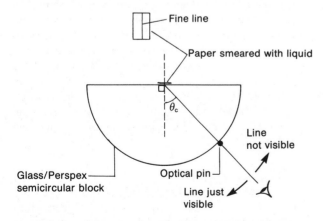

Fig. 8.10 Measurement of the refractive index of a small quantity of liquid using the critical angle method.

Measurement of the refractive index of a liquid using an air cell

APPARATUS REQUIRED

- air cell consisting of two glass plates with a small air gap (1–2 mm) between them (see Fig. 8.11)
- sufficient quantity of liquid to fill the air cell container
- ray box fitted with a fine slit
- 12 V power supply for the ray box
- board for raising the ray box to the correct height
- optical pin or reference mark on the air cell container

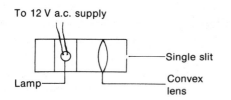

Fig. 8.11 Using an air cell to measure the refractive index of a liquid.

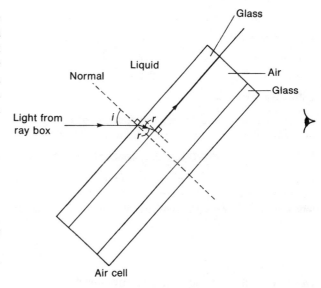

Fig. 8.12 Principle of the air cell: $i = \theta_c$ for the critical ray shown.

U   Fill the air cell container with liquid, so that the air cell is covered completely. Set up the ray box on a board and adjust the position of the lamp or convex lens so as to obtain a parallel beam of light; place the slit in its slot. Align the light box and air cell as shown in Fig. 8.11, with the air cell normal to the parallel beam from the light box. Place a vertical reference mark on the container of the air cell or use the optical pin.

V   Whilst keeping your eye in line with the slit and the reference mark, rotate the air cell until the image of the slit just disappears when the cell is rotated clockwise. Read the angle θ_1 on the scale of the cell. Now rotate the cell in the anticlockwise direction and determine the second position where the image of the slit disappears. Measure this angle θ_2. Repeat the measurements several times so as to obtain an estimate of the uncertainty in determining the extinction positions.

W   The angle $(\theta_2 - \theta_1)$ or $(\theta_1 - \theta_2)$ is equal to twice the critical angle θ_c for light travelling from air to liquid. Hence calculate a value for the refractive index of the liquid and estimate its error.

X   Explain why the critical angle measured is independent of the refractive index of the material used to form the air cell. You may find Fig. 8.12, drawn for the critical ray, of assistance.

NOTES

Y   Your account should include a description of the methods used to measure the refractive indices of solids and liquids. Where relevant you should compare the methods and discuss any advantages and disadvantages. Summarise your results at the end of the account.

Z   Note that you have measured an average value for the refractive index, because you used white light. The refractive index of a medium depends on the frequency of the light (dispersion), but this variation is quite small, about 0.02, for the complete range of the visible region of the electromagnetic spectrum.

8B Converging and Diverging Lenses
Measurements of the focal lengths of lenses

APPARATUS REQUIRED

- converging (convex) lens of focal length 0.10–0.15 m on a stand
- diverging (concave) lens of focal length about 0.15 m on a stand
- light box with a fine gauze grid or cross-wires
- mounted optical pin
- plane mirror on a stand
- screen (about 50 mm by 50 mm) on a stand
- metre rule

PRINCIPLES INVOLVED

a For converging lenses the focal length f can be determined by focusing parallel light on to a screen.

b The most accurate measurements of the focal length are based on the use of the lens equation for a thin lens and paraxial rays (rays with small angles of incidence):

$$\frac{1}{f} = \frac{1}{v} + \frac{1}{u} \qquad [8.3]$$

where u is the distance between the object O and the centre of the lens, and v is the distance between the image I and the centre of the lens (Fig. 8.13).

Clearly this equation can only be used directly for real images, which can be formed on a screen. Thus it is limited to converging lenses with the object placed outside the focal point.

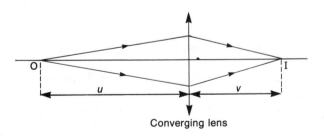

Fig. 8.13 Refraction by a converging lens. u is the object distance and v is the image distance.

c Equation [8.3] can be used to measure f for a diverging lens, provided that a converging lens is used to produce a convergent beam, as shown in Fig. 8.14. If the

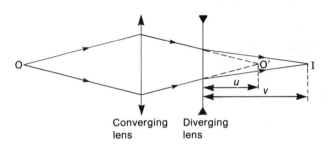

Fig. 8.14 Principle used to form a real image with a diverging lens. O' acts as a virtual object for the diverging lens and produces a real image I.

converging lens alone produces a real image at O', then a real image can be produced at I with the combined lens system. Mathematically the image at O' can be considered to act as a virtual object for the diverging lens, and produces a real image at I. In the lens equation the sign of u is negative and the sign of v is positive if you are using the 'real is positive' sign convention.

APPROXIMATE MEASUREMENT OF THE FOCAL LENGTH OF A CONVERGING LENS

d An estimate of f can be obtained by focusing light from a distant object, such as a window, on to a piece of card. The distance between the lens and the focused image is approximately f.

e A more accurate single determination of f can be made using the apparatus shown in Fig. 8.15. A plane mirror is placed behind a converging lens, which is illuminated by a light box.

f Adjust the orientation of the plane mirror, so that the reflected light forms an image on the light box. Move the converging lens on a line between the light box and plane mirror until a focused image of the grating or cross-wires is obtained on the light box. The distance between the light source and the centre of the lens is equal to the focal length of the lens. Measure f and estimate its uncertainty by finding the range over which the image can be considered in focus.

g Explain the principle by which the distance measured in (f) can be taken to be equal to f. You may like to confirm that the distance measured is independent of the position of the plane mirror, provided that the mirror is well aligned with the axis of the optical system.

h Although more tedious, a more accurate determination of f can be made using the same principle with an optical pin. Replace the light box with the mounted optical pin. Adjust the height of the pin until you can see an image of the pin when looking towards the mirror. Move the pin along the axis of the lens, until the pin and its image coincide using the method of no parallax (see section 8.1). Measure the distance between the pin point and the centre of the lens. Record this value for f.

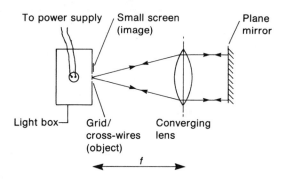

Fig. 8.15 Measuring the focal length f of a converging lens using a plane mirror.

MEASUREMENT OF THE FOCAL LENGTH OF A CONVERGING LENS USING THE LENS FORMULA

i Set up the optical system shown in Fig. 8.16 placing the lens at about $(f + 0.02 \text{ m})$ from the light source. This should give a real image on the screen about 1 m from the light box. If it is significantly more than 1 m, adjust the position of the lens (away from the source). Record u and v, measured to the centre of the lens and screen. Tabulate u and v. Leave two further columns for data analysis.

j Increase u in steps that produce changes in v of at least 0.05 m. Continue taking readings until it is difficult to judge whether the diminished image is in focus. Add the values of u and v to your table of results.

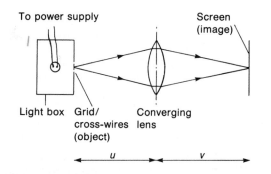

Fig. 8.16 Determining the focal length of a converging lens using the lens formula.

k Based on the lens formula, equation [8.3], there are several ways of determining f using different graphs. Only two will be used.

l Plot a graph of u against v. Determine the point on your curve corresponding to $u = v$. Hence determine a value for f.

m A straight line graph can be obtained using equation [8.3]. Plot this graph and determine two values of f from the appropriate intercepts; measure the slope of the straight line.

n Comment on whether you consider the values of f from (l) or (m) to be more reliable.

MEASUREMENT OF THE FOCAL LENGTH OF A DIVERGING LENS USING THE LENS FORMULA AND AN AUXILLARY CONVERGING LENS

o Place the converging lens about $2f$ from the light source and obtain a focused image on the screen. Mark the position of the screen or simply measure its distance from a reference point such as the centre of the converging lens.

p Place the diverging lens about halfway between the converging lens and screen (Fig. 8.17). Move the screen away from the lens until a focused image is obtained. Record the position of the screen as in (o).

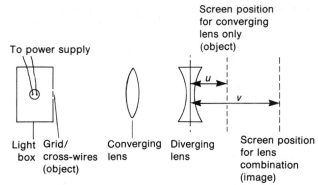

Fig. 8.17 Measuring the focal length of a diverging lens by using a converging lens to produce a final real image.

q You can now work out u and v for the diverging lens, either by measuring the distances of your marks from the centre of the diverging lens, or from the distances from your reference point (after subtracting the distance between your reference point and the diverging lens). Tabulate these values of u and v.

r Occasionally difficulty is found in obtaining a focused image with the diverging lens added after the converging lens image is first obtained. Should this be so, try to obtain a focused image on the screen with both lenses in place. With the screen placed about 1 m from the light box, move the lenses independently until a focused image is obtained. This will give you a value of v first. Note the position of the diverging lens and remove it. A focused image can now be obtained by moving the screen towards the converging lens. You can now measure u with reference to the previous position of the diverging lens.

s Move the diverging lens farther away from the converging lens than in part (p) and readjust the position of the screen so as to obtain a focused image. Obtain four further pairs of values for u and v.

t Plot a suitable graph so as to obtain a value for f. Remember that values for u are negative, and that any intercepts relating to f must also be negative for a diverging lens.

NOTES

u Your account should include a description of the methods used to determine f for converging and diverging lens, together with any graphical analysis used to determine f.

v In the design of optical systems, such as camera lenses, telescopes and microscopes, it is important to have a method for accurately measuring the focal lengths of the component lenses. In practice most of the designing is done by using the lens maker's formula:

$$\frac{1}{f} = (n-1)\left(\frac{1}{r_1} - \frac{1}{r_2}\right)$$

where n is the refractive index (relative to air) of the material used to make the lens, and r_1 and r_2 are the radii of curvature of the lens surfaces.

FURTHER WORK

w If the lens is inaccessible, the methods detailed above cannot be used to measure f. Then an alternative method can be used based on the use of conjugate images.

Provided that the distance between the object and image is at least $4f$, two positions of a converging lens can be found where a real image is formed (Fig. 8.18). Measurements of the distance between the object and image l and of the distance moved by the lens between the two images d can be used to determine f.

If a is the distance between the lens and the image for one position:

$$\left.\begin{array}{l} u = d + a = \frac{1}{2}(l+d) \\ v = a \quad\quad = \frac{1}{2}(l-d) \end{array}\right\} \qquad [8.4]$$

These values of u and v can be substituted into the lens equation [8.3] to give:

$$f = \frac{l^2 - d^2}{4l} \qquad [8.5]$$

Note that it does not matter which image is chosen, since the lens equation is symmetrical in respect of interchanging u and v.

x Set up the optical system shown in Fig. 8.18, with $l = (4f + 0.1 \text{ m})$. Determine the two positions of the images. Note that since you only require the distance d moved by the lens, you can measure d from the front or back of the stand. This is often easier than estimating the position of the centre of the lens. Repeat the measurements of d for l values increasing in steps of about 0.05 m up to about 1 m. Tabulate your values of l and d.

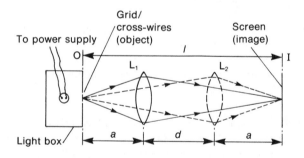

Fig. 8.18 Measuring the focal length of a converging lens using conjugate images.

y From equation [8.5] plot a suitable graph so as to obtain a value for f from the slope.

z Equation [8.5] can also be used to show that the minimum value of l for forming a real image from a converging lens is $4f$. (Hint: take the minimum value for d to be zero.)

8C Converging and Diverging Mirrors
Measurements of the focal lengths of mirrors

APPARATUS REQUIRED

- converging (concave) mirror of focal length about 0.15 m on a stand
- diverging (convex) mirror of focal length about 0.15 m on a stand
- converging (convex) lens of focal length about 0.15 m on a stand
- light box with a fine gauze grid or cross-wires
- mounted optical pin
- screen (about 50 mm by 50 mm) on a stand
- metre rule

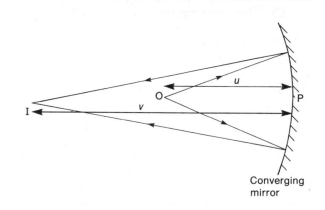

Fig. 8.20 Principle of finding the focal length f of a converging mirror using the object distance u and image distance v.

PRINCIPLES INVOLVED

a The simplest method for measuring the focal length f of converging mirrors is to determine the centre of curvature of the mirror, and hence its radius of curvature r. Rays from an object O placed at the centre of curvature of a mirror will be incident normally on the mirror and these rays will then be reflected back along the original path (Fig. 8.19). Then the object and its image will be coincident. For paraxial rays (small angles of incidence) $f = \frac{1}{2}r$.

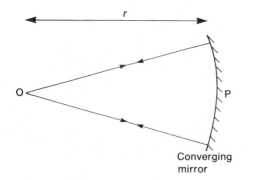

Fig. 8.19 Principle of finding the radius of curvature r of a converging (concave) mirror.

b The most accurate measurements of focal length are based on the use of the mirror equation for paraxial rays:

$$\frac{1}{f} = \frac{1}{v} + \frac{1}{u} \qquad [8.6]$$

where u is the distance from the object O to the pole of the mirror P, and v is the distance between the image I and the pole of the mirror P (Fig. 8.20).

c Measuring the focal length of a diverging mirror requires a convergent beam. This is produced using a converging lens, as shown in Fig. 8.21. When the convergent beam is incident normally on the mirror, the beam is reflected back along its original path. Thus a focused image is produced by the converging lens alone at C. The mirror is then added and moved until the image I and object O coincide. The distance between C and the pole of the mirror P is then r.

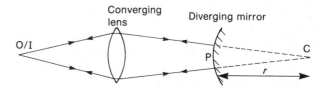

Fig. 8.21 Principle of finding the radius of curvature r of a diverging (convex) mirror.

MEASUREMENT OF THE FOCAL LENGTH OF A CONVERGING MIRROR FROM ITS RADIUS OF CURVATURE

d Set up the optical system shown in Fig. 8.22 (overleaf). Simply move the mirror until the image of the source is focused on the light box. Measure the distance r between the light box and the centre of mirror. Repeat the measurement to obtain an estimate of the uncertainty in the measurement of r. Calculate f and its uncertainty.

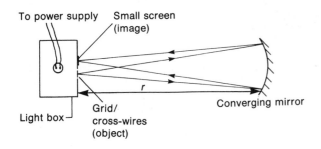

Fig. 8.22 Measuring the radius of curvature r of a converging mirror.

e r can also be measured using an optical pin and the method of no parallax (see section 8.1). Replace the light box by the mounted optical pin. Move the pin until it is coincident with its inverted image as determined by no parallax. Measure the distance between the point of the pin and the centre of the mirror r. Calculate f and estimate its uncertainty.

MEASUREMENT OF THE FOCAL LENGTH OF A CONVERGING MIRROR USING THE MIRROR EQUATION

f Set up the optical system shown in Fig. 8.23. It is not possible to have the source and screen in the same straight line on the axis of the mirror. The mirror should be rotated slightly so as to form an image on the screen. Try to minimise this rotation, since the mirror equation is strictly valid for paraxial rays and small angles of incidence.

g Set the distance between the light box and mirror to be about $(f + 0.02\ \text{m})$. Starting with the screen near to the mirror, move the screen towards the light box. Rotate the mirror slightly so as to keep the image on the screen. Move the screen until a focused image is obtained; this is likely to be about 1 m from the mirror. Measure and tabulate u and v. Leave two further columns for analysis.

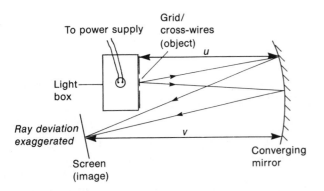

Fig. 8.23 Measuring the focal length of a converging mirror using the mirror formula.

h Increase u in steps that produce changes in v of about 0.05 m. Continue taking readings of u and v until it is difficult to judge whether the diminished image is in focus. Add these values of u and v to your table of results.

i Based on the mirror formula, equation [8.6], there are several ways of determining f using different graphs. Only two will be used.

j Plot a graph of u against v. Determine the point on your curve corresponding to $u = v$. Hence determine a value for f.

k A straight line graph can be obtained from equation [8.6]. Plot this graph and determine two values of f from the appropriate intercepts; measure the slope of the straight line.

l Comment on whether you consider the values from (j) or (k) to be more reliable.

MEASUREMENT OF THE FOCAL LENGTH OF A DIVERGING MIRROR USING AN AUXILLARY CONVERGING LENS

m Use a converging lens to form an image on the screen. The distance between the lens and the screen should be about 0.5 m. Measure the distance between the lens and screen a (Fig. 8.24).

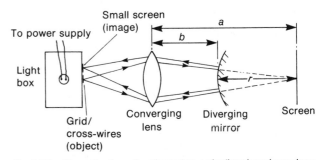

Fig. 8.24 Measuring the radius of curvature r of a diverging mirror using a convex lens to produce a converging beam of light.

n Place the mirror between the lens and screen. Adjust the position of the mirror until a focused image of the source is obtained on the side of the light box and close to the grid/cross-wires. Measure the distance b between the centres of the lens and mirror.

o Calculate $r = a - b$ and $f = \frac{1}{2}r$.

p Repeat the measurements of a and b using a different initial position of the lens. Remember that the distance between the lens and the screen must be at least equal to r for the second part of the experiment to work successfully.

NOTES

q Your account should include a description of the methods used to determine r and f, together with relevant graphical analysis. You should include a summary of your results for the two types of mirror.

r The mirrors most commonly used in schools are spherical mirrors. However, these types of mirror are seldom used in optical instruments. This is because parallel rays some distance off axis will not be brought to a common focus on the axis; a caustic is produced. So in optical instruments, such as reflecting telescopes, parabolic mirrors are used. These mirrors have the property that all parallel off-axis rays are brought to a common focus. If you are an expert in conic sections, you should have little difficulty in proving this geometrically.

s Accurate parabolic surfaces are quite difficult to produce. There has been a very interesting suggestion as to how to produce such a surface: when a container of liquid is rotated about a vertical axis through its centre, the liquid surface forms a parabolic profile. Thus a large container of mercury can be rotated at the appropriate angular velocity so as to obtain a mirror of the correct curvature. There are evident engineering problems in implementing this idea.

8D Deviation by a Prism
Use of the prism spectrometer to measure the angle of minimum deviation leading to the refractive index of the material of the prism

APPARATUS REQUIRED

- spectrometer
- prism with a prism clamp to fix it to the spectrometer table
- sodium lamp and control unit (transformer)
- magnifying glass for reading spectrometer scale

PRINCIPLES INVOLVED

a From measurements of the refracting angle A of a prism and the angular deviation D produced by the prism it is possible to measure accurately the refractive index of the material of the prism. Monochromatic light is used since the refractive index depends on the frequency of the light.

b The principle of measuring A is shown in Fig. 8.25. Parallel light is incident on the sides of the prism defining A. The angle between the reflected beams of light from the two faces is $2A$.

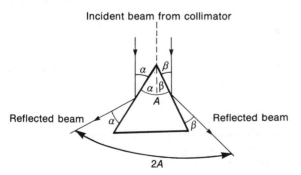

Fig. 8.25 Principle of measuring the refracting angle A of a prism.

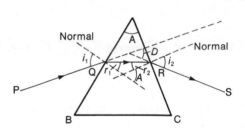

a The ray path through a prism.

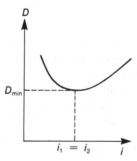

b How the angle of deviation D of the ray varies with the angle of incidence i_1.

Fig. 8.26

c The deviation of a ray of light through a prism is shown in Fig. 8.26a. The angle of deviation $D = (i_1 - r_1) + (i_2 - r_2)$. As the angle of incidence i_1 is decreased from an initial large value, D decreases until it reaches a minimum value D_{min}; as i_1 is decreased further D starts to increase, as shown in Fig. 8.26b. At minimum deviation $i_1 = i_2$, so that the ray passes symmetrically through the prism. It is this position of the prism that is well defined and D_{min} can be measured using a prism spectrometer.

d Using the definition of refractive index $_an_p = \sin i_1/\sin r_1$, i_1 and r_1 can be replaced by the two measurable quantities A and D_{min}. At minimum deviation $i_1 = i_2$ and $r_1 = r_2$, so $D_{min} = 2i_1 - 2r_1$. From the geometry of Fig. 8.26a $A = r_1 + r_2 = 2r_1$. Thus:

$$2r_1 = A$$

and:

$$2i_1 = A + D_{min}$$

in the equation for the refractive index $_an_p$:

$$_an_p = \frac{\sin\left(\dfrac{A + D_{min}}{2}\right)}{\sin\left(\dfrac{A}{2}\right)} \qquad [8.7]$$

SPECTROMETER ADJUSTMENTS

e The adjustment of the telescope is given in section 8.3(a).

f The adjustment of the collimator is given in section 8.3(b). Following this adjustment you should leave the spectrometer set up.

g The final adjustment is levelling the table. The exact procedure will depend on the design of the spectrometer, and so only guidelines are given here. The telescope should be unclamped.

h Choose one of the three corners of the prism as the refracting angle A. Mark the top of the prism with a small piece of Sellotape. If the prism has a ground face, A will usually be opposite to this face. Clamp the prism on to the table with the refracting angle A facing the collimator. You can adjust the height of the table so that the prism is at the correct height. Now you should be able to approximately level the table by eye using the three adjustment screws S_1, S_2 and S_3 shown in Fig. 8.27. See if you can locate the two reflected images of the collimator slit from faces AC and AB using the telescope. If you cannot see one of these images, it is likely that the prism table is at the incorrect height or the table is some way from the horizontal. If this is so try to locate the images by eye without using the telescope; you should then be able to adjust correctly the height of the table.

i Turn the telescope to position T_1 shown in Fig. 8.27 and centre the telescope cross-wires on the slit image. Use the levelling screws S_1 and S_2 (which tilt face AB) until the slit image is centred.

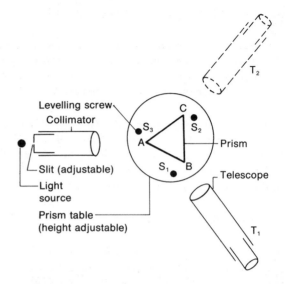

Fig. 8.27 Measuring the refracting angle A of a prism.

j Turn the telescope to position T_2 shown in Fig. 8.27 and centre this image on the telescope cross-wires. Use levelling screw S_3 (which tilts face AC) until the image is centred.

k Repeat steps (i) and (j) to refine the adjustment of the table.

l Leave the spectrometer set up in this way because it can be used to measure the refracting angle A without further adjustments.

MEASUREMENT OF THE REFRACTING ANGLE OF THE PRISM

m Rotate the telescope to position T_1 so that the slit image is approximately centred on the cross-wires. Clamp the telescope and use the fine adjustment screw to centre the sodium orange line exactly on the cross-wires. Read the circular vernier (see section 8.2(b)) and record the angle θ_1.

n Unclamp the telescope and rotate the telescope to position T_2. Repeat step (m) and record the angle θ_2.

o You can calculate the angle $2A$ from $(\theta_2 - \theta_1)$ or $(\theta_1 - \theta_2)$. If the angular scale passed through the 360° mark you should make allowances for this: for example if $\theta_1 = 290°$ and $\theta_2 = 50°$, $2A$ should be calculated from $(360° - (\theta_1 - \theta_2)) = 120°$ and not $(\theta_1 - \theta_2) = 240°$. Looking at the prism will enable you to distinguish clearly between these two possibilities.

MEASUREMENT OF THE ANGLE OF MINIMUM DEVIATION

p   Rotate the table so that the light from the collimator is incident at a large angle i on the face AB of the prism, as shown in Fig. 8.28a. As you rotate the prism table so that i decreases, you should be able to see (without the aid of a telescope) the orange image of the slit start to move in one direction and then reverse direction of movement. The position where the direction of movement changes corresponds to minimum deviation. Leave the prism set at this approximate position of minimum deviation.

q   Unclamp the telescope and rotate it to the position where you observed minimum deviation. As you rotate the table by a few degrees (from a larger value of i to a smaller value of i) in the anticlockwise direction, the image of the collimator slit should move as shown in Fig. 8.28b. Clamp the telescope and adjust the position of the telescope using the fine adjustment screw until the position of minimum deviation for the sodium orange line occurs exactly on the vertical cross-wire of the telescope. Read the position of the telescope θ_1 on the circular vernier scale.

r   If you have set up the spectrometer very carefully and if the collimator slit is in good condition, you may resolve the two sodium orange lines (wavelengths 589.0 and 589.6 nm). Often only a single line will be seen.

s   Remove the prism, unclamp the telescope and rotate the telescope to observe the light directly from the collimator. Clamp the telescope and use the fine adjustment screw to centre the slit image. Record the angle θ_2.

t   Calculate D_{min} from $(\theta_1 - \theta_2)$ or $(\theta_2 - \theta_1)$. Note whether the telescope has passed through the 360° mark (see (o)).

u   Calculate the refractive index of the material of the prism using equation [8.7]. From estimates of the uncertainties in A and D_{min} calculate the maximum uncertainty in the value of the refractive index.

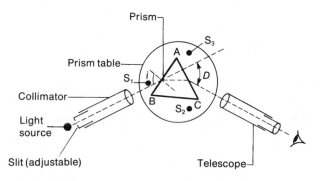

a Measuring the angle of deviation D produced by a prism.

NOTES

v   Your account should include a brief reference to the adjustments of the prism spectrometer, a description of the measurements of A and D_{min}, the calculation of $_a n_p$ and an estimate of its uncertainty.

w   In principle the spectrometer could be used to determine the refractive index of a liquid by using a thin-walled hollow prism to hold the liquid.

x   The spectrometer could be used to determine how the refractive index of the material varies with the wavelength, or more exactly the frequency, of the light. A lamp emitting a series of wavelengths is used and the angle D_{min} determined for each wavelength.

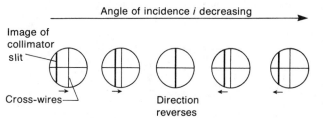

Angle of incidence i decreasing

Image of collimator slit

Cross-wires

Direction reverses

b Finding the position of minimum deviation.

Fig. 8.28

y   Although this experiment has only been concerned with the measurement of refractive index, a prism spectrometer is normally used to determine the wavelengths of light emitted (or absorbed) by a sample. In this application the prism spectrometer could be calibrated to produce a graph of wavelength λ against D_{min} using a series of standard spectral lines.

8E Thin Film Interference

Investigations of the interference produced in a wedge film, and the measurement of the radius of curvature of the surfaces of a converging lens using Newton's rings

APPARATUS REQUIRED

- monochromatic source: sodium lamp and control unit (transformer)
- glass plate (about 0.1 m by 0.1 m), preferably mounted at 45° in a stand
- travelling microscope
- 2 stands, clamps and bosses
- wooden blocks of various sizes, or two laboratory jacks
- sheet of black paper
- converging lens with a focal length of about 0.1 m, in a stand to be used with source
- wedge film made from two glass slides and a piece of aluminium foil
- plano–convex or biconvex lens, radius of curvature about 1 m
- optical flat or thick glass plate
- vernier callipers
- micrometer screw gauge

PRINCIPLES INVOLVED

a   Interference effects can be produced with light either by division of wavefront or by division of amplitude. In interference by division of wavefront the wave from the source is used to produce two coherent sources by using two slits (Young's two slit experiment), reflection (Lloyd's mirror) or refraction (Fresnel's biprism). In interference by division of amplitude a single source is used and interference is produced by the reflection of the light from two surfaces. Depending on the path difference between these two surfaces constructive or destructive interference occurs. This experiment is concerned with interference by division of amplitude.

b   The first example of interference by division of amplitude is interference in a wedge film. An air wedge is formed by two glass slides separated at one end by a piece of aluminium foil (Fig. 8.29). Interference occurs as a result of the path difference between light reflected at the lower face B of the first slide and light reflected at the upper face C of the second slide. The path difference depends on the thickness of the air film and it is expected that constructive interference will occur whenever the distance traversed in the air film $2d$ is an integral number of wavelengths $n\lambda$. The interference fringes observed should consist of a series of equidistant lines perpen-

dicular to the plane of the paper, provided that the surfaces of the slides B and C are optically flat to within a fraction of a wavelength.

c   Before looking at the mathematics of the interference in the air film, one problem should be cleared up: why interference occurs only between light reflected from B and C in Fig. 8.29, and not between other reflected light such as that from A and B. Interference of this type does occur but its effect on your observations will not be significant. Consider, firstly, the interference in the air film, which has a thickness of about only 10 μm. Although the angles have been exaggerated in Fig. 8.29, the interference between ① and ② does actually occur near to B or just outside the air film. These fringes are therefore observed by focusing the travelling microscope on surface B. Secondly, consider the interference in the glass slide, which has a thickness of about 1 mm. The interference occurs between light reflected at the top and bottom surfaces of the slide, as shown in Fig. 8.30. Since the two rays, ① and ②, are parallel, interference occurs effectively at infinity; in practice a microscope would be used to produce interference fringes by focusing the reflected light onto the cross-wires of the eyepiece. So if you focus on the lower surface of the first slide, the interference fringes formed as a result of reflections at the first glass slide are unlikely to be focused.

There is a second reason why the two fringe systems cannot be confused: the slide thickness is about 1 mm and so the optical path difference between light reflected from A and B is very large (approximately equal to the refractive index of the glass × twice the thickness of the slide t_g). The fringes will therefore be very closely spaced, and they cannot be clearly resolved by the travelling microscope.

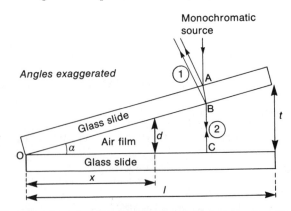

Fig. 8.29   Formation of localised interference fringes in an air wedge by the interference of light reflected from B and from C.

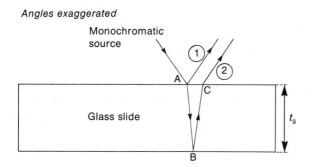

Angles exaggerated

Monochromatic source

Glass slide

Fig. 8.30 Formation of non-localised interference fringes in a glass slide by the interference of light reflected at A and B.

d The mathematics of interference is complicated by one factor: light reflected at a less to more (optically) dense boundary is subject to a phase change of π, equivalent to a path difference of $\lambda/2$. This occurs at boundary C in Fig. 8.29. Thus the condition for constructive interference is:

$$2d = (n + \tfrac{1}{2})\lambda \qquad [8.8]$$

Since the angle of the wedge α is small, the distance of the nth fringe from O is $x_n = d/\alpha$. Thus:

$$x_n = (n + \tfrac{1}{2})\lambda/2\alpha \qquad [8.9]$$

In practice it is impossible to count the fringes from O, and it is usual to measure the fringe separation $\Delta x = x_n - x_{n-1}$. From equation [8.9]:

$$\Delta x = \lambda/2\alpha \qquad [8.10]$$

From equation [8.10] the angle of the wedge α (in radians) can be determined. If the total length of the slide l is measured, it is now possible to determine the thickness t of a small object from $t = \alpha l$.

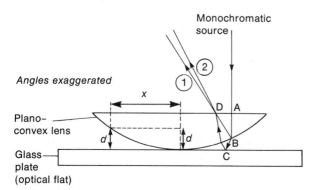

Angles exaggerated

Monochromatic source

Plano-convex lens

Glass plate (optical flat)

Fig. 8.31 Formation of localised interference fringes in an air gap formed by a plano–convex lens and a glass plate.

e If a converging lens is laid on a flat glass plate, interference fringes can be formed from the curved air film formed between the lower surface of the lens and the glass plate, as shown in Fig. 8.31. The interference occurs between light reflected from B and C. The fringes are localised near to the air film, as with the wedge film. Because of the exaggerated angles in the diagram, the

location of interference is at D, much farther away from the air film than in reality. Because the thickness of the air film is constant at any particular distance x from the centre of the lens, it is expected that the fringe system will consist of concentric circles. The circles will not be equally spaced because of the curved surface of the lens: they are expected to be more closely spaced as x increases.

f From previous analysis constructive interference will occur whenever $2d = (n + \tfrac{1}{2})\lambda$. The distance x of a fringe from the centre cannot, as in the wedge film, be simply related to d. To obtain this relationship, it is necessary to look at the geometry of the circle, and in particular, the intersecting chord theorem (Fig. 8.32). The theorem applied to Newton's rings simply states that:

$$x \times x = d \times (2R - d) \qquad [8.11]$$

where R is the radius of curvature of the lower (reflecting) surface of the lens. Since R is much larger than d, $(2R - d)$ can be taken to be $2R$.

Thus in equation [8.8] $2d$ is replaced by x^2/R from equation [8.11], so that:

$$x_n^2 = R\lambda(n + \tfrac{1}{2}) \qquad [8.12]$$

for the nth fringe from the centre of the lens.

In the ideal case, when the centre of the lens is in contact with the glass plate $(d = 0)$, there would be a dark fringe at the centre. In practice it is likely that the centre of the lens will not be in perfect contact with the glass plate and it is then impossible to determine the absolute value for n. This is not important because it will be systematically wrong by a constant amount p. Equation [8.12] becomes:

$$x_n^2 = R\lambda n + R\lambda(p + \tfrac{1}{2}) \qquad [8.13]$$

Thus a graph of x_n^2 against the nominal (counted) value of n should be a straight line of slope $R\lambda$; the intercept on the n axis will be $-(p + \tfrac{1}{2})$. Equation [8.13] can then be used to determine λ or R. In this experiment R will be measured, although this is not a particularly important application of Newton's rings (see Notes section).

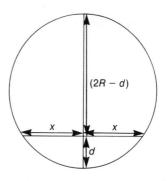

Fig. 8.32 The intersecting chord theorem.

MEASUREMENTS ON INTERFERENCE FRINGES OBTAINED FROM A WEDGE FILM

g The air wedge should be made placing a single thickness of aluminium foil between two glass slides. Ensure that the piece of foil used is flat. You may use Sellotape to fix the ends of the slides together but try not to buckle the slides, otherwise the fringes will not be equally spaced or parallel.

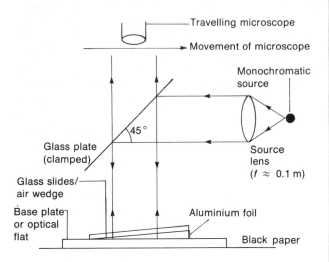
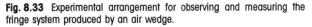

Fig. 8.33 Experimental arrangement for observing and measuring the fringe system produced by an air wedge.

h Set up the experimental arrangement shown in Fig. 8.33. The wedge film is placed on top of the optical flat. A sheet of black paper placed underneath assists the observation of the fringes. Arrange the reflecting glass plate a few centimetres above the wedge, so that the light is reflected on to the wedge from the sodium lamp. The illumination of the wedge should in principle be collimated using the source lens clamped a distance f from the light source. In practice, if you have difficulty in aligning the optical system, you can dispense with the lens and just remove the shield from the light source. Provided that the source is a reasonable distance (0.2 m) from the reflecting glass plate, you should obtain good quality interference fringes. Arrange the travelling microscope directly above the wedge film, so that you can not only focus on the wedge but also traverse a reasonable distance (0.02 m) parallel to the wedge. It is almost certain that you will need to use the wooden blocks and/or laboratory jacks to achieve this. As an aid to focusing place a sheet of graph paper underneath the wedge.

i If you look directly down on to the wedge you should be able to see interference fringes, even if they are not very uniform.

j Focus the microscope on the fringes and traverse the wedge, with the microscope movement unclamped. There are several possible observations: the fringes are not perpendicular to the direction of traverse; the fringes are bent; the fringes are not uniformly spaced. Assuming that you have aligned the travelling microscope to travel parallel to the wedge, the most likely reason for these observations is buckled slides. Try pressing gently on the top slide to see what effect this has on the fringe system. If you cannot produce reasonably straight and parallel fringes, it is worth making up another wedge, perhaps with thicker glass. Often it is impossible to obtain equally spaced fringes over the whole wedge film. If this is so, make your measurements on the region where the fringe spacing is largest; this is likely to correspond to the smallest wedge angle α.

k If you have any doubts about the quality of your experimental arrangement, simply replace the wedge by the lens you intend to use to produce Newton's rings. You should see a ring pattern even without the aid of a microscope. This will reassure you about the correctness of your alignments, and the most likely source of failure is the wedge.

l Unclamp the travelling microscope movement, and turn the fine adjustment screw to one end of its thread; this will give you the maximum traverse of the fringes on the fine adjustment. Clamp the microscope. Adjust the screw until the cross-wires of the microscope are centred on a bright fringe. Read the vernier scale of the travelling microscope (see section 8.2(a)). As you turn the fine adjustment count the fringes until you reach the other end of the screw thread. Read the vernier scale. Calculate the average fringe spacing Δx.

m Without moving the microscope, unclamp the microscope movement, and reset the screw to the other end of its thread. Repeat the measurements in (l) and obtain a further value for Δx. If these values differ significantly then you know that the wedge is far from uniform and only an estimate of the wedge angle α can be obtained.

n Measure the length t of the slide using the vernier callipers.

o From equation [8.10] calculate a value for the wedge angle α using $\lambda = 589.3$ nm. Then calculate the thickness of the foil from $t = \alpha l$. You can easily check whether the value for t is an overestimate by taking a piece of the foil and folding it so as to obtain about 16 thicknesses of foil. Measure the thickness of this with a micrometer screw gauge and hence calculate t.

p Replace the wedge by the plano–convex or biconvex lens. If the lens is plano–convex make sure that you have the curved surface in contact with the glass plate. You should observe the circular fringe system even without the aid of a microscope. It will usually just be a matter of moving the lens and/or microscope carefully until you have the central fringe (a fairly large disc) near to the centre of your field of view. Check that the travelling microscope moves along a diameter of the fringe system.

q For measurements on the fringes, it is more accurate to measure the diameters of the rings by traversing from one side of the ring system to the other. However, it is very easy to lose count or miscount rings. So here the rings are measured from the centre to the outer rings. Move the microscope to the centre of the fringe system, turn the screw mechanism fully in one direction and then clamp the movement. Make a fine adjustment to centre the cross-wires of the microscope. Read the vernier corresponding to $n = 0$. Now move the fine adjustment until you reach the fifth ring ($n = 5$) and read the vernier again. (If you are working in pairs it is quite useful for one of you to look down the microscope continuously, whilst the other one reads the vernier and notes down the vernier reading and n). Continue counting rings in intervals of five until you reach the end of the screw thread or the rings become too closely spaced for accurate counting. If you reach the end of the fine adjustment, you can unclamp the microscope and reset the screw adjustment to the other end. This has to be done carefully because the microscope can move slightly during this operation.

r Calculate the ring radii x_n from the vernier reading for the nth ring and the initial vernier reading ($n = 0$). Tabulate x_n and n. It is recommended that x_n is converted to metres to avoid any subsequent problems with units.

s Plot a graph of x_n^2 (ordinate) against n (abscissa). Allow for a small (10) negative intercept on the n-axis. Measure the slope of the graph and any intercept on the n-axis. Using a value for the mean wavelength of the sodium orange lines of 589.3 nm (5.893×10^{-7} m), calculate the radius of curvature R of the lens surface used to form the air film (see equation [8.13]).

NOTES

t Your account should include a brief description of how the interference occurs in thin films and the measurements made on the fringe systems. Include only those equations directly relevant to the measurement of the wedge angle and the foil thickness, and the equation used to determine the radius of curvature of the lens surface.

u The wedge film can certainly be used to measure the dimensions of very small objects with linear dimensions of only a few micrometres. However, one of its most useful applications is the measurement of surface irregularities and other distortions of transparent materials. From the nature of the fringes these irregularities and distortions can be identified and measured accurately. Similarly Newton's rings can be used to measure the uniformity of a lens surface. Any non-uniformities will be indicated by the ellipticity of the ring system, or variations in the ring spacing along different directions. This application is only important in designing precision optical systems where the lens surface must be uniform to within a fraction of a wavelength.

v Newton's rings can also be used as the basis for the accurate measurement of the Young modulus of a transparent material such as glass (Cornu's method). A glass slide is supported on two knife edges and is subject to a tensile stress by loading each end with a small weight (0.2–0.5 N). The plano-convex lens is rested on the material under test, as shown in Fig. 8.34.

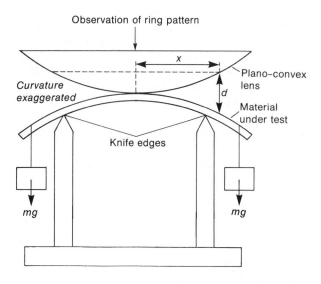

Fig. 8.34 Using Newton's rings to measure the Young modulus of a transparent material such as glass.

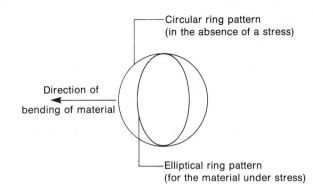

Circular ring pattern
(in the absence of a stress)

Direction of
bending of material

Elliptical ring pattern
(for the material under stress)

Fig. 8.35   The change in the ring pattern as the material is subject to a stress.

The ring pattern formed as a result of interference between light reflected from the material under test and the bottom surface of the lens will now consist of ellipses (Fig. 8.35). Measurement of the differences between the major and minor axes of the ellipses can be used to measure the curvature of the material under stress. From the theory of bending beams, the linear dimensions of the material and the value of the weights mg, this curvature can be used to calculate the Young modulus of the material.

Note that Fig. 8.35 is a simplified representation, because there is also a stress at right angles to the direction of bending shown in Fig. 8.34.

8F Diffraction Grating Spectra
Use of the diffraction grating spectrometer to measure the wavelength of light

APPARATUS REQUIRED

- spectrometer fitted with a diffraction grating holder
- diffraction grating, 300–600 lines mm^{-1} (7500–15 000 lines per inch)
- sodium lamp and control unit (transformer)
- mercury lamp and control unit (transformer)
- magnifying glass for reading spectrometer scale

PRINCIPLES INVOLVED

a   A diffraction grating effectively consists of a series of opaque and transparent lines. The transparent sections, which are much narrower than the opaque sections, diffract the light. The diffracted light from the transparent sections interferes to give the characteristic diffraction grating maxima, whose angular separation depends on the separation of the transparent sections d and the wavelength of the light λ.

b   In Fig. 8.36 parallel light is diffracted at an angle θ by the diffraction grating. Constructive interference will occur if the path difference x between light diffracted from successive transparent sections is a multiple n of the wavelength λ. Thus:

$$x = d \sin \theta = n\lambda \qquad [8.14]$$

n is called the order of the diffraction maximum; the maximum number of orders observed for a given wavelength will be determined by d. The value of d is not usually given; instead the number of lines per millimetre $N = 1/d$ is given.

c   In this experiment you will firstly determine d for the diffraction grating using light of a known wavelength; the value for N marked on the grating is not sufficiently accurate for spectrometry. You will then use the grating spectrometer to measure the wavelengths of the light emitted by a mercury lamp.

SPECTROMETER ADJUSTMENTS

d   The adjustment of the telescope is given in section 8.3(a).

e   The adjustment of the collimator is given in section 8.3(b). Following this adjustment the spectrometer should be left set up with the sodium lamp in place.

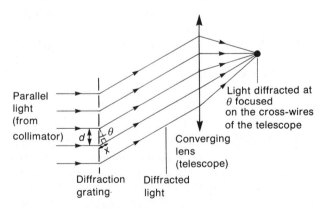

Parallel light (from collimator)

Light diffracted at θ focused on the cross-wires of the telescope

Converging lens (telescope)

Diffraction grating

Diffracted light

Fig. 8.36   How a diffraction grating spectrum is produced. The grating spacing is d and the diffraction angle is θ.

f Screw on the diffraction grating holder. Place the diffraction grating in the holder and set the grating normal to the light from the collimator. There is a standard procedure for this adjustment, but in practice it is sufficiently accurate to make this setting by eye. Any error in this setting of the grating is reduced by measuring the angular separation 2θ of a given diffraction maximum either side of the zero (centre) order, as shown in Fig. 8.37.

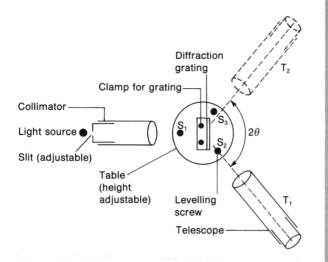

Fig. 8.37 Using a diffraction grating spectrometer to measure the angle of diffraction θ.

g Unclamp the telescope and see how many diffraction orders you can observe either side of the zero. It will only be about two for a fine grating but it may be four or more for a coarse grating.

h If the spectrometer has been set up correctly and the collimator slit is in good condition, you should be able to resolve the two sodium orange (D) lines corresponding to $\lambda = 589.0$ nm and 589.6 nm. If you cannot resolve two lines, take the mean wavelength to be 589.3 nm.

i If the lines are too high or too low you will need to move the table. If the lines progressively move up or down as you rotate the telescope in the anticlockwise direction, you will need to level the table. First check by eye that it is approximately level. Rotate the telescope to position T_1 in Fig. 8.37 and centre the cross-wires of the telescope on the highest diffraction order. Adjust screw S_2 to centre the line. Now rotate the telescope to position T_2 and centre the cross-wires on the corresponding diffraction order. Adjust screw S_3 to centre the line. Return to position T_1 and check that the line is still centred. If it is not, repeat the adjustments of S_2 and S_3. It is possible that the grating is tilted towards or away from the collimator, but provided that you can obtain good diffraction maxima you should not need to adjust screw S_1.

CALIBRATION OF THE DIFFRACTION GRATING

j Rotate the telescope so as to centre the cross-wires on the highest diffraction order on the left-hand side. Clamp the telescope and use the fine adjustment screw to centre one of the sodium D lines on the cross-wires of the telescope. Note which line you used. Read the position of the telescope using the vernier scale (see section 8.2(b)), record the angle θ_1 and the order of the maximum n. Tabulate n and θ_1. Leave four further columns in the table, one for the angle θ_2 on the other side of the zero order and three for the calculation of θ and d.

k Unclamp the telescope and rotate it anticlockwise to the next diffraction order. Clamp the telescope and measure the diffraction angle θ_1 for this order. Repeat the measurements for all the diffraction orders on the left-hand side of the zero order. Ensure that you always make the measurements of θ_1 on the same sodium D line, if both lines are resolved.

l Now measure the angles θ_2 corresponding to the diffraction maxima on the right-hand side of the zero order. Add these results to your table.

m Calculate 2θ from $(\theta_1 - \theta_2)$ or $(\theta_2 - \theta_1)$. If the angular scale passed through the 360° mark you should make allowances for this: for example if $\theta_1 = 290°$ and $\theta_2 = 50°$, 2θ should be calculated from $(360° - (\theta_1 - \theta_2)) = 120°$ and not $(\theta_1 - \theta_2) = 240°$. Common sense will usually tell you if you have neglected this factor.

n Calculate θ for each diffraction order, and, using equation [8.14] calculate the values for d. These should be constant. Calculate the average value of d and estimate its uncertainty, either from the spread of your results or from the standard deviation. Remember to use the appropriate value for the wavelength as given in (h). Convert your value of d to the equivalent number of lines per millimetre.

MEASUREMENTS ON THE SPECTRAL LINES OF MERCURY VAPOUR

o Replace the sodium lamp by the mercury lamp. View the spectrum through the telescope. You should be able to see the violet, blue, green and yellow lines. The latter is a doublet corresponding to a wavelength difference of only 2 nm, and so you may not resolve both lines. You will also notice that the diffraction orders for particular wavelengths overlap: for example the fourth order blue line will be close to the third order yellow line. For this reason it is easier to measure the diffraction angles for each spectral line separately.

p Starting with the yellow line(s) measure the values for 2θ for as many orders as possible. Tabulate the values for n, 2θ and θ. Hence using the value for d determined in (n), calculate the wavelengths corresponding to the yellow line(s) from equation [8.14]. You should calculate the average wavelength of each line and estimate the uncertainty from the spread of values of λ.

q Repeat the measurements in (p) for each of the spectral lines. Because the violet line is very weak, you may only be able to measure the first order maximum.

r Summarise your results for the wavelengths of the light emitted by mercury vapour together with an estimate of the uncertainties in these wavelengths.

NOTES

s Your account should include a brief description of the alignment procedure for the grating spectrometer, the calibration of the diffraction grating, and the measurements on the mercury spectrum. Compare your values for the wavelengths with the accepted values in Table A3.8 of appendix 4 (page 309).

t Transmission gratings cannot normally be used in the ultraviolet region of the electromagnetic spectrum. For this reason most spectrometers use reflection gratings. The principle of operation is the same as the transmission grating, but they can be used in the far ultraviolet region, where many interesting electronic transitions occur to or from the ground state of atoms and molecules. Usually the reflection grating is made in the form of a concave mirror. In this way the spectra are focused on a detector, such as a photomultiplier.

u The best transmission gratings are usually made by ruling glass with a diamond knife on a precision-made machine. These gratings are usually blazed so that the light is diffracted only into the first order spectrum; this maximises the light intensity to be measured with a detector.

v The smallest wavelength difference $\Delta\lambda$ that a diffraction grating can resolve is determined by the total number of lines illuminated N_t and the order of the spectrum n:

$$\frac{\Delta\lambda}{\lambda} = \frac{1}{N_t n}$$

For a typical diffraction grating spectrometer this ratio is less than 10^{-4} for $n = 1$. Thus for $\lambda = 500$ nm, $\Delta\lambda \approx 0.05$ nm. This is seldom achieved with the diffraction gratings used in schools because of the non-uniformities of replica gratings.

9 THERMAL PROPERTIES OF MATTER

In this section you will complete experiments illustrating the use of a cooling correction in calorimetry (experiment 9A) and the use of continuous flow calorimetry to reduce the effects of energy losses (experiment 9E). The thermal conductivity of a material is a most important property in the design of efficient heat insulation and heat transfer. Its measurement depends on whether the material is a good conductor of heat (experiment 9B) or a poor conductor of heat (experiment 9C). Experiment 9D is an investigation of the behaviour of a vapour and the measurement of the saturated vapour pressure of a liquid.

9.1 NEWTON'S LAW OF COOLING

In all calorimetry experiments it is necessary to minimise the effect of energy losses (or energy gains at low temperatures). These losses usually result in too high a value for a thermal property, such as the specific heat capacity or specific latent heat of vaporisation. At temperatures normally used in calorimetry (20 to 100 °C), the energy loss is mainly by convection of the surrounding air. It is expected that the rate at which energy is lost from a surface will depend on the temperature θ of the body above the surroundings, the surface area A exposed and the nature of the surface, characterised by an emissivity ε.

The precise relationship between the rate of energy loss and θ depends on the convection conditions:

a) Forced convection (a draught)

The rate of energy loss, dQ/dt, is proportional to the excess temperature θ. This is an empirical relationship and it is usually called Newton's law of cooling. Thus:

$$\frac{dQ}{dt} = -\varepsilon A \theta \qquad [9.1]$$

The minus sign just indicates that Q is decreasing as t increases. Since the internal energy Q of the body is related to its mass m, its specific heat capacity c and θ, by $Q = mc\theta$, equation [9.1] can be rewritten as:

$$\frac{d\theta}{dt} = -k\theta \qquad [9.2]$$

where $k = (\varepsilon A)/(mc)$ is a constant for a particular body.

Equation [9.2] can be integrated to give the value of the excess temperature θ at time t for a body initially at an excess temperature of θ_0 as:

$$\theta = \theta_0 \exp(-kt) \qquad [9.3]$$

This simple law then enables a correction to be applied to Q, or more usefully to θ during a heating experiment, for convection losses.

b) Convection in still air

The rate of energy loss is now found to be related to $\theta^{5/4}$. This equation can also be integrated as for Newton's law of cooling, but it is far more difficult to apply this cooling law to obtain a correction for heat losses or a correction to θ in a heating experiment. You may therefore adopt one of two approaches: either perform heating experiments under which equation [9.1] is valid, or assume that for small temperature rises (20–40 K) the differences between the two cooling laws is not significant. The latter assumption is not really valid, as a simple calculation will show. The ratio of the rate of energy losses at excess temperatures of 40 K and 20 K is 2.0 according to Newton's law of cooling, and $(2)^{1.25} = 2.4$ for the $\theta^{5/4}$ law. The first alternative is therefore preferred in experiment 9A.

9A Calorimetry

Determination of the specific heat capacity of a metal block including a cooling correction based on Newton's law of cooling

APPARATUS REQUIRED

- solid aluminium block (or calorimeter)
- insulating board (to protect bench)
- 50 W, 12 V immersion heater to *fit* the block
- mercury-in-glass thermometer for 0–100 °C (preferably reading to 0.5 °C)
- glycerol
- power supply 0–12 V d.c.
- voltmeter 0–10 V d.c.
- ammeter 0–5 A d.c.
- rheostat 0–10 Ω (at least 5 A maximum current)
- switch
- connecting wires
- stopwatch or stopclock
- hair dryer (set to blow cool air)
- clamp, boss and stand to support hair dryer

PRINCIPLES INVOLVED

a The specific heat capacity c of a solid of mass m is normally determined by measuring its temperature rise θ when a quantity of energy Q is supplied to the solid. In this experiment Q is supplied electrically using an immersion heater switched on for a time t:

$$IVt = mc\theta \qquad [9.4]$$

where I is the current flowing and V is the potential difference across the heater.

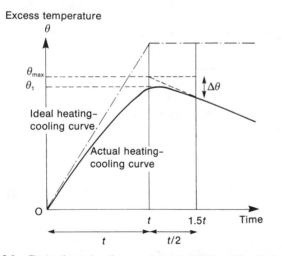

Fig. 9.1 The heating and cooling curve for a metal block, and the calculation of the cooling correction $\Delta\theta$.

b Equation [9.4] represents the perfect situation assuming no heat losses to the surroundings. The ideal heating curve corresponds to the dashed line ($-\cdot-\cdot$) shown in Fig. 9.1. The actual heating curve will correspond to the continuous line. Thus the measured temperature rise θ_1 after time t will be too low and the calculated value of c too high.

c The metal block will usually reach its maximum temperature (as registered by a thermometer) after the electrical heating has been switched off. The maximum temperature rise θ_{max} at the time t, when the electrical heating has been switched off, can be obtained by extrapolating back the cooling curve to time t as shown in Fig. 9.1.

d The correction $\Delta\theta$ to the temperature θ_{max} for energy losses to the surroundings can also be found from the heating–cooling curve assuming Newton's law of cooling is valid. At a constant rate of heating it can be assumed that the average rate of energy loss is proportional to the average excess temperature, $\frac{1}{2}\theta_{max}$. After the electrical heating has been switched off the rate loss of energy is proportional to θ_{max} initially. Thus in a time $t/2$ the block will lose approximately the same amount of energy as it lost in a time t during the heating period. Thus the temperature fall from θ_{max} in a time $t/2$ will give a value for the cooling correction $\Delta\theta$.

THE HEATING–COOLING CURVE OF A METAL BLOCK

e Measure the mass m of the metal block using a balance.

f Connect the electrical circuit as shown in Fig. 9.2. Before inserting the immersion heater into the block, close the switch and adjust the power supply and the rheostat to give a potential difference V of about 10 V. Open the switch.

g Place the heater and thermometer in the block as shown in Fig. 9.2. A few drops of glycerol should be used in the thermometer hole to improve thermal contact; it is not usually necessary to do this for the immersion heater, which should be a fairly tight fit with good metal to metal contact.

h Place the hair dryer a few metres from the block, so that a steady stream of cool air is blown towards the block. If you do not have access to a hair dryer you

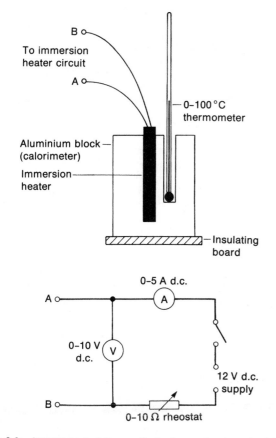

a

B ○—

To immersion
heater circuit

A ○—

— 0–100 °C
thermometer

Aluminium block —
(calorimeter)

Immersion —
heater

— Insulating
board

b

0–5 A d.c.

A ○—(A)

0–10 V (V)
d.c.

12 V d.c.
○ supply

B ○—

0–10 Ω rheostat

Fig. 9.2 Measurement of the specific heat capacity of an aluminium block: **a** apparatus and **b** circuit diagram.

CALCULATION OF THE SPECIFIC HEAT CAPACITY

m　An approximate value for c can be calculated using equation [9.4] and the value of θ_{max} determined from your graph (see (c)).

n　A more accurate value of c can be obtained by adding to θ_{max} the cooling correction $\Delta\theta$ as described in (d).

o　You can also calculate the average rate of energy loss from the block during heating. It is approximately equal to half the value of the rate of energy loss during the initial cooling period, $-mc(d\theta/dt)_{\theta_{max}}$; $(d\theta/dt)_{\theta_{max}}$ is the slope of the $\theta - t$ cooling curve at $\theta = \theta_{max}$. Since the graph is nearly linear, you can estimate this slope and hence calculate the average rate of energy loss. What fraction of the total energy supplied to the block does this represent?

NOTES

p　Your account should include a brief description of the experiment, the heating–cooling curve, the calculation of c with and without the cooling correction, and your estimate of the average rate of energy loss during heating.

FURTHER WORK

q　You may use the results from the $\theta - t$ cooling curve to assess the validity of Newton's law of cooling. It may aid this analysis if you redrew the cooling curve on an enlarged temperature scale.

r　Assuming that the rate of energy loss is proportional to θ^n, the slope of the cooling curve $(d\theta/dt)$ should be proportional to θ^n. The slope of the cooling curve can be determined by drawing a tangent to the curve. Select four temperatures on your cooling curve, draw tangents to the curve at these points and measure their slopes s (ignore the negative sign). Draw up a table of θ and s. Decide what graph you should plot in order to determine a value for n.

s　Drawing tangents to curves and measuring their slopes is a notoriously inaccurate procedure for most experimental results. So a more reliable method of analysis (but more limited) is to see if the $\theta - t$ cooling curve follows an exponential law, equation [9.3]. t must be measured from the time at which the heater was switched off; the first part of the curve should be ignored because for a short time the temperature is actually rising because the effect of the energy supplied to the centre of the block is not registered by the thermometer until some time later (thermal lag). Plot a suitable graph to see if your cooling curve conforms to equation [9.3].

should carry out the experiment in the best draught available, and assume that Newton's law of cooling is valid.

i　Measure the initial temperature θ_R of the block. This temperature should be subtracted from all subsequent measurements to give the excess temperature θ.

j　Close the switch and start timing. Record V and I. Record the temperature of the block at 1 minute intervals. Continue heating until the temperature rise is about 40 K (about 20 minutes). Observe the voltmeter and if necessary adjust the rheostat so as to keep V constant.

k　Open the switch and continue to record the temperature every minute. If you only wish to calculate the cooling correction you will only need the cooling curve for $t/2$ (about 10 minutes). If you wish to check the validity of Newton's law of cooling (see Further work section) you should record the cooling curve until the temperature has fallen to at least 20 K below the maximum temperature of the block.

l　Plot a graph of the excess temperature θ (ordinate) against t (abscissa).

9B Thermal Conductivity (I)
Measurement of the thermal conductivity of a good conductor (Searle's bar)

APPARATUS REQUIRED

- lagged copper bar fitted with an immersion heater (50 W, 12 V)

- 4 0–50 °C mercury-in-glass thermometers reading to 0.2 °C

- measuring cylinder 0–500 ml or 500 ml beaker

- power supply 0–12 V d.c.

- rheostat 0–10 Ω (maximum current at least 5 A)

- ammeter 0–5 A d.c.

- voltmeter 0–10 V or 0–15 V d.c.

- connecting wire

- supply of cold water (preferably from a constant head apparatus)

- stopwatch or stopclock

- vernier callipers

PRINCIPLES INVOLVED

a   The rate of energy transfer dQ/dt through a thin section Δx of a material by conduction (Fig. 9.3) is given by:

$$\frac{dQ}{dt} = \lambda A (\theta_2 - \theta_1)/\Delta x \qquad [9.5]$$

where $(\theta_2 - \theta_1)$ is the temperature difference and A is the cross-sectional area of the material. λ is called the thermal conductivity of the material. The term $(\theta_2 - \theta_1)/\Delta x$ is called the temperature gradient, $d\theta/dx$, along the material. Thus equation [9.5] becomes:

$$\frac{dQ}{dt} = -\lambda A \frac{d\theta}{dx} \qquad [9.6]$$

The minus sign only indicates that θ decreases as x, the distance from the heat source, increases.

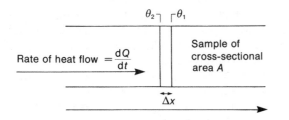

Fig. 9.3   Heat flow through a sample of uniform cross-sectional area A.

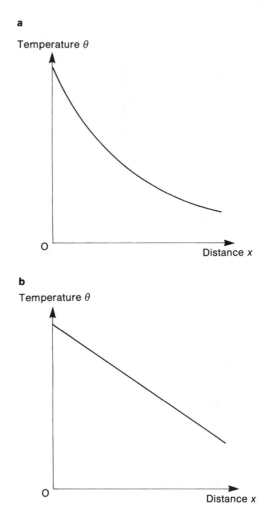

Fig. 9.4   Temperature distribution along   **a** unlagged and   **b** lagged samples.

b   In principle λ could be determined by measuring the rate of energy transfer and the temperature gradient along the sample. However, if the material was in the form of an unlagged bar, energy would be lost from the sides of the bar and the value of dQ/dt would decrease along the bar. Thus from equation [9.6] you can see that the temperature gradient would decrease; the temperature distribution along the bar would be as shown in Fig. 9.4a. Clearly a curve for the temperature gradient poses practical problems; it would at the very least require the measurement of θ at many points along the bar in order to determine the shape of the curve. A much simpler solution for a good conductor is to lag the bar with an insulator. Assuming that no energy is lost from the sides of the bar, dQ/dt is constant along the bar and therefore the temperature gradient is constant. The temperature variation along the bar is then linear as shown in Fig. 9.4b. The temperature gradient can be determined by measuring the temperature at any two points along the bar separated by a distance l; the temperature gradient is then $-(\theta_2 - \theta_1)/l$.

c For an accurate determination of λ the temperature difference $(\theta_2 - \theta_1)$ should be as large as possible. From equation [9.6] it is seen that this can be achieved for metals ($\lambda \approx 100$ W m^{-1} K^{-1}) by using a long bar with a small cross-sectional area. There are limits on the values of l and A. If the bar is too long the energy losses from the surface of the bar may become significant. Also the time taken for the bar to reach thermal equilibrium, and hence constant temperature, would be far too long. The lower limit on A is set by the disturbance of the linear energy flow through the bar by the presence of two thermometers registering $(\theta_2 - \theta_1)$. Normally mercury-in-glass thermometers are used, but ideally a calibrated thermocouple should be used to measure the temperature difference directly.

d Finally, if an insulated metal bar was used without any form of cooling at one end, the far end of the bar would eventually reach a temperature not very far below θ_2. To ensure the establishment at equilibrium of a reasonably large temperature gradient, cooling water is circulated at one end of the bar.

e The use of cooling water actually allows a second determination of λ to be made. Two independent values of dQ/dt can be measured using (i) the energy supplied to the electrical heater at one end of the bar and (ii) the energy absorbed by the water at the other end of the bar. Energy losses from the sides of the bar can also be determined from the differences in the two values of dQ/dt.

MEASUREMENTS OF THE ENERGY FLOW ALONG THE BAR

f If the bar is accessible measure its diameter d and the distance between the two thermometer holes along the bar (l) using vernier callipers. If the bar is permanently lagged these values will be given to you.

g Set up the electrical heating of the bar and the water cooling of the bar as shown in Fig. 9.5. Check that there is mercury in the thermometer holes along the bar so that thermal contact between the thermometers and bar is improved. Make sure that the thermometers used to measure the water temperature are securely fitted, so that no water leaks out of the apparatus.

h Since the temperature differences to be measured are quite small, you should check that each pair of thermometers (θ_1 and θ_2, θ_3 and θ_4) read the same as each other before you commence heating the bar. If not you should make a note of the difference; this difference must be added or subtracted as appropriate from the final temperature difference.

i Set the potential difference across the electrical heater to between 10 and 12 V. Record the values for the current (I) and the potential difference (V). These values should be kept constant throughout the experiment by adjustment of the power supply output or rheostat.

j The adjustment of the flow rate of water is critical. If it is too fast the temperature difference ($\theta_4 - \theta_3$) will be too small for accurate measurement. If the rate of flow is too slow the temperature gradient along the bar

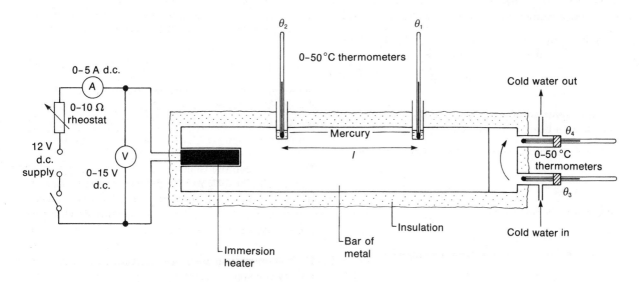

Fig. 9.5 Searle's method for the measurement of the thermal conductivity of a good conductor.

will be too low. A rate of flow of about 100 ml a minute should make a good starting point. Remember that if you change the rate of flow of water, it will take several minutes for the water to reach thermal equilibrium again.

k   After about 20 minutes the bar should have reached a steady state. Check that the temperatures (or more particularly the temperature differences) are constant (to within 0.2 K) over a further time of about 5 minutes.

l   Determine the time taken to collect 500 ml of water in the measuring cylinder. You can now calculate the mass m of water flowing in each second taking the density of water to be 998 kg m^{-3}. Alternatively measure the mass of water collected directly in a measuring cylinder or beaker of known mass.

m   Record the four temperatures θ_1, θ_2, θ_3 and θ_4.

n   Calculate a value for λ using the rate of energy transfer IV from electrical heating, $A = \pi d^2/4$ and the value of $(\theta_2 - \theta_1)/l$.

o   Calculate a second value for λ using the internal energy gained by the water in a second, $mc(\theta_4 - \theta_3)$, A and the temperature gradient. Take the specific heat capacity of water to be 4180 J kg^{-1} K^{-1}.

p   Using the results calculated in (n) and (o) what is the most likely value for λ?

q   Calculate the rate of energy losses from the surface of the bar.

NOTES

r   Your account should include a description of the experiment, the details of the calculation of two values for λ and your estimate of the energy losses from the bar.

s   This method would be unsuitable for a poor conductor ($\lambda \approx 1$ W m^{-1} K^{-1}). The bar would have to be extremely short for equilibrium to be established in a reasonable time; the distance between the thermometers would be small and therefore the value of l could not be measured accurately; finally the energy losses from the sides would be significant, since the sample and its insulation would have comparable thermal conductivities.

9C Thermal Conductivity (II)
Measurement of the thermal conductivity of a poor conductor (Lees' disc)

APPARATUS REQUIRED

- Lees' apparatus consisting of a steam chamber and a brass plate supported by three wires from a stand
- samples in the form of a disc the same diameter as the brass plate and 1–4 mm in thickness
- steam generator (kettle, Bunsen burner, tripod and rubber tubing)
- rubber tubing from the steam chamber to the sink or into a large beaker of cold water
- 2 0–100 °C mercury-in-glass thermometers to fit Lees' apparatus
- petroleum jelly
- micrometer screw gauge
- vernier callipers
- cloth or towel (to handle steam chamber)
- stopwatch or stopclock

PRINCIPLES INVOLVED (Fig. 9.6)

a   Provided that the energy losses from the sides of a sample are negligible, the rate of energy transfer by conduction dQ/dt through the sample is given by:

$$\frac{dQ}{dt} = \lambda A (\theta_2 - \theta_1)/x \qquad [9.7]$$

where A is the cross-sectional area of the sample and x the thickness, across which there is a temperature difference of $(\theta_2 - \theta_1)$. λ is the thermal conductivity of the material.

b   If the sample is an insulator then lagging its sides will not significantly reduce the energy losses. Therefore the sample must be in the form of a thin disc, whose cross-sectional area A ($= \pi r^2$) is much greater than the area of the exposed edge ($= 2\pi rx$).

c A must also be large to produce a large rate of energy transfer across the sample. x must also be small otherwise it would take a long time for the sample to

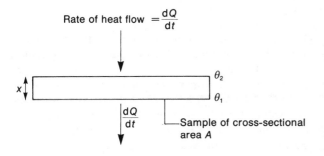

Rate of heat flow $= \dfrac{dQ}{dt}$

θ_2
θ_1
x
$\dfrac{dQ}{dt}$

Sample of cross-sectional area A

Fig. 9.6 Heat flow through a thin sample of thickness x and cross-sectional area A.

reach the steady state, where the temperature θ_1 is constant.

d The problem of measuring the temperature difference across a sample only 1–4 mm thick is solved in a quite ingeneous way. The disc is sandwiched between two brass plates, in which the two thermometers are placed. Since the thermal conductivity of brass is several hundred times that of the sample, the temperature of each brass plate is virtually identical to the face of the disc with which it is in contact.

MEASUREMENT OF THE TEMPERATURE GRADIENT

e This experiment takes a long time to reach equilibrium, so you should start heating the kettle immediately and connect it to the steam chamber (Fig. 9.7). Ensure that the outlet of the steam chamber is passed into cold water so as to condense the steam produced.

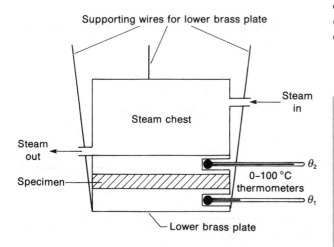

Supporting wires for lower brass plate

Steam chest

Steam in

Steam out

Specimen

Lower brass plate

θ_2
0–100 °C thermometers
θ_1

Fig. 9.7 Lees' method for the measurement of the thermal conductivity of a poor conductor.

f Measure the mass m of the lower brass plate. Use a micrometer screw gauge to measure the thicknesses x of the samples and vernier callipers to measure

their diameters d. These measurements can be made later but are far easier to make whilst the samples are cold.

g Assemble the whole apparatus as shown in Fig. 9.7. To ensure good thermal contact between the brass plates and the sample, smear the faces of the sample with a very *thin* layer of petroleum jelly. Even an air gap as small as 0.01 mm can cause an error of 25% in the value of λ.

h The temperature of the upper brass plate of the apparatus will rapidly rise to near to 100 °C once the steam passes into the steam chamber. However, the lower brass plate will take about 20 minutes to reach a steady temperature. Record θ_1 at two-minute intervals until it changes by less than 1 K between two intervals. Record θ_1 and θ_2.

i In equation [9.7] all the information required to calculate λ is available with the exception of the rate of energy transfer dQ/dt. This is determined by a separate experiment in which the rate of cooling of the lower brass plate is determined.

MEASUREMENT OF THE HEAT FLOW RATE

j In order to find the rate of energy transfer through the sample, a cooling curve for the lower brass plate (insulated on its top surface) is determined. During cooling the brass plate is losing energy under the same conditions as it was in the main experiment above. Thus as the temperature passes through θ_1, the rate of energy loss will be equal to the value of dQ/dt required to calculate λ. For a brass plate of mass m and specific heat capacity c, the rate of energy loss is obtained by differentiating $Q = mc\theta$ with respect to time:

$$\frac{dQ}{dt} = mc\frac{d\theta}{dt} \qquad [9.8]$$

k Heat the lower brass plate directly using the steam chamber. Hold the steam chamber with a cloth and carefully remove the sample. When the lower brass plate has reached a temperature about 10 K above θ_1 remove the steam chamber and place an insulator (or several samples) on the top surface of the plate. Record the temperature θ of the lower brass plate at one-minute intervals until its temperature is about 5 K below θ_1.

l Plot the cooling curve and determine its slope at $\theta = \theta_1$ by drawing a tangent at θ_1 (Fig. 9.8). Hence calculate dQ/dt taking $c = 370$ J kg^{-1} K^{-1} for brass, and using the mass m determined in (f).

m Calculate λ for the sample using equation [9.7].

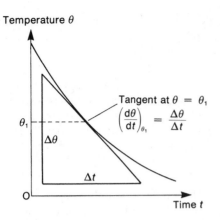

Fig. 9.8 Measurement of the rate of temperature fall for the lower brass plate.

n If there is sufficient time repeat the measurements (g) and (h) for a different sample. You should also measure the thickness x of the sample. If you are fortunate, the cooling curve determined in (k) and (l) can be used to determine the rate of cooling, and hence dQ/dt, for the new value of θ_1. Calculate the value of λ for this sample.

NOTES

o Your account should include a complete description of the experiment and the details of the calculation of θ for the samples used. Also include an estimate of the error resulting from the neglect of energy losses from the sides of the sample and comment on the validity of the assumption that the temperatures of the brass plates correspond to the temperatures of the faces of the specimen (λ for brass is 110 W m^{-1} K^{-1}).

p This apparatus can also be used to measure the thermal conductivity of liquids. The disc sample is replaced by an annulus with thin walls. The liquid is contained in the annulus. It is important to heat the liquid from above to reduce the effects of energy transfer through the liquid by convection.

FURTHER WORK

q Estimate the error resulting from a thin layer of air, about 0.01 mm in thickness, between the sample and the brass plates. Take the thermal conductivity of air to be 0.03 W m^{-1} K^{-1}.

9D Saturated Vapour Pressure
Variation of the saturated vapour pressure with temperature

APPARATUS REQUIRED

- capillary tube containing a coloured water index with attached scale
- 0–100 °C mercury-in-glass thermometer
- tall beaker (for capillary tube)
- Bunsen burner
- wire gauze and tripod
- ice

PRINCIPLES INVOLVED

a The air enclosed by a liquid index as shown in Fig. 9.9 will be saturated with the vapour of the particular liquid. Assuming that the total pressure (air + saturated vapour) is equal to atmospheric pressure P_A, the saturated vapour pressure (SVP) can be calculated from $P_A - P_T$, where P_T is the partial pressure of the air enclosed by the index at temperature T(K) or θ(°C). Clearly if the variation of P_T with temperature T (or θ) could be measured, the variation of SVP p_T with temperature could be calculated.

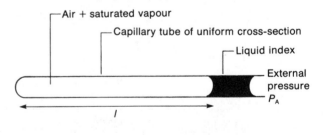

Fig. 9.9 The principle of the measurement of the pressure exerted by a saturated vapour (SVP).

b It is usually assumed that the air obeys the perfect gas equation $PV = \mu RT$ or $PV/T =$ constant. In order to calculate P_T for the air at any temperature, its value is required at one particular temperature. The assumption is therefore made that at 0 °C (273 K) the SVP of water is zero; the value of P_T at 0 °C is then taken to be equal to P_A. The SVP of water is 600 Pa (equivalent to 4.6 mm mercury) at 0 °C as compared with its SVP of 70 kPa (530 mm mercury) at 90 °C; so the error involved is less than 1% at the highest temperature that you will use. Thus P_T is calculated from:

$$\frac{P_T V_T}{T} = \frac{P_A V_0}{273} \qquad [9.9]$$

V_0 is the volume of the air column at 273 K. Since the capillary tube is of uniform cross-sectional area, the volume is simply proportional to the length of the air column, l_T. Then P_T is calculated from:

$$P_T = \frac{P_A l_0}{273} \times \frac{T}{l_T} \qquad [9.10]$$

c   Unfortunately the SVP at or near to the boiling point of the liquid cannot be measured using this method. The liquid index disappears near to its boiling point.

MEASUREMENTS ON A SATURATED VAPOUR

d   In order to reduce the evaporation of the liquid index, the capillary tube will usually be sealed with a piece of rubber tubing and a clip. Remove the clip; you should not try to pull the rubber tubing and clip together off the capillary tube because the sudden change in pressure may cause the liquid index to break up.

e   Use a barometer to determine the atmospheric pressure. If one is not available assume that $P_A = 760$ mm of mercury. Convert this pressure to pascals using $g = 9.81$ N kg^{-1} and the density of mercury = 13550 kg m^{-3} at 20 °C.

f   Prepare a mixture of ice and water in the tall beaker. Immerse the capillary tube with its scale into the mixture (Fig. 9.10). Note that the scale may be made from a broken thermometer, so that the length l of the column has no particular units. Check that the zero of the scale does in fact correspond to the bottom end of the capillary tube; if it does not you will have to add or subtract a correction for all scale readings.

g   Record the value of $l = l_0$ at $\theta = 0$ °C.

h   Place the beaker on a tripod and wire gauze and commence heating the ice–water mixture using a Bunsen burner. Obtain values for $l = l_T$ at temperature intervals of about 10 °C up to 60 °C, then at 5 °C intervals up to about 90–95 °C. In order to obtain reliable readings for l_T you will need to carefully adjust the Bunsen flame and stir the water so as to maintain θ constant. Take care as you approach 100 °C because the SVP increases rapidly and there is

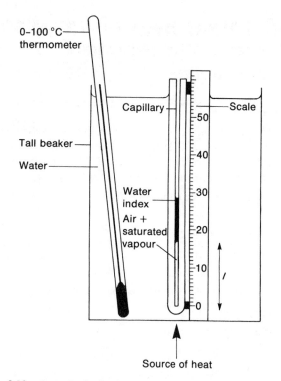

Fig. 9.10   Apparatus for the measurement of the SVP of water.

a danger of the liquid index either being pushed out of the tube or boiling away.

i   Tabulate θ and l_T. Leave three further columns for the analysis of the data.

CALCULATION OF THE SATURATED VAPOUR PRESSURE

j   Calculate the values of T, the temperature in kelvin, corresponding to the values of θ in your table. Using equation [9.10] calculate the partial pressure P_T of the air. Complete the table with the values of the SVP $p_T = P_A - P_T$.

k   Plot a graph of p_T (ordinate) against θ (abscissa) to show the relationship between these quantities.

NOTES

l   Your account should include a brief description of the experimental procedure, the analysis leading to values of the SVP and a comment on the limitations of the method. Explain why the total pressure of the air and saturated vapour is only approximately equal to the atmospheric pressure.

m   This method can be used to find the saturated vapour pressure of any liquid from a temperature just above its freezing point to about 5 °C below its boiling point.

113

9E Latent Heat of Vaporisation
Measurement of the specific latent heat of vaporisation of a liquid using continuous flow calorimetry

APPARATUS REQUIRED

- flask fitted with a vapour jacket, bung, heating coil (about 50 W, 20 V), tube and funnel as shown in Fig. 9.11. Alternatively an inverted Dewar flask may be used instead of the flask with a vapour jacket
- Liebig condenser connected to a supply of cold water
- 2 100 ml beakers
- power supply 0–25 V d.c.
- ammeter 0–5 A d.c.
- voltmeter 0–50 V d.c.
- rheostat 0–10 Ω (maximum current at least 5 A)
- connecting wire
- stopwatch or stopclock
- liquid: distilled water (not tap water), ethanol or methanol

PRINCIPLES INVOLVED

a   The simplest method of determining the specific latent heat of vaporisation of a liquid is to measure the amount of liquid vaporised in a given time using a constant rate of heating. If the energy is provided electrically using a potential difference V and a current I, then the mass of liquid m vaporised in a time t is given by:

$$IVt = mL_v \qquad [9.11]$$

where L_v is the specific latent heat of vaporisation of the liquid.

b   Equation [9.11] will usually give a very high value for L_v unless precautions are taken to reduce energy losses and a correction is applied for these energy losses. The reduction of the energy losses to a minimum is achieved in this experiment by using a vapour jacket. When the liquid is boiling steadily, it is surrounded by vapour at the same temperature as the boiling liquid. Energy losses by conduction (which depend on the temperature difference between the liquid and its surroundings) are therefore virtually zero.

c   In principle a correction can be applied for any residual energy losses. The experiment can be performed twice using different rates of heating. If m_1 and m_1 are the amounts of liquid vaporised in the same time t using heating rates I_1V_1 and I_2V_2 respectively, then:

$$\left.\begin{array}{l} I_1V_1t = m_1L_v + ht \\ I_2V_2t = m_2L_v + ht \end{array}\right\} \qquad [9.12]$$

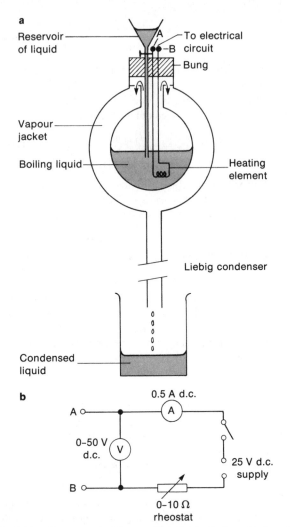

Fig. 9.11   Measurement of the specific latent heat of vaporisation of a liquid: **a** apparatus and   **b** circuit diagram.

The rate of energy loss h is the same in both experiments because the liquid is boiling at a constant temperature.

Eliminating h from equations [9.12]:

$$L_v = \frac{(I_1V_1 - I_2V_2)t}{(m_1 - m_2)} \qquad [9.13]$$

Whilst this may seem to be an ideal way of eliminating the effects of energy losses, great care has to be taken in practice because of experimental errors. Even if the errors in individual quantities are quite small, the uncertainties in their differences can represent large fractional (or percentage) errors. One consequence is that, if the energy losses are small, the value of L_v calculated using equation [9.13] is inferior to that calculated using equation [9.11]. At the very least you should ensure that the differences in the above equation are quite large.

MEASUREMENT OF L_v

d Connect up the circuit diagram as shown in Fig. 9.11. Ensure that the liquid used covers the heating coil. Also check that the heating coil is not too near the bottom of the flask, otherwise the coil can become very hot and melt. In the version of the apparatus shown, the liquid can be added from a funnel as its level in the flask decreases. If you use a Dewar flask, you will have to fill it well above the level of the filament but below the level of the outlet tube.

e In this experiment the mass of liquid vaporised is measured by condensing the vapour. It is therefore necessary to use a Liebig condenser with a flow rate of about 5 ℓ min^{-1} to ensure that all the vapour is condensed.

f Adjust the rheostat to obtain a potential difference of about 20 V across the heater. Record I_1 and V_1. Maintain these values constant during the experiment by adjusting the rheostat.

g Place one beaker to collect the condensed vapour. Measure the mass of the second beaker. When the liquid has been boiling steadily for about 5 minutes collect about 50 ml of liquid in the second beaker over a measured time t. Hence determine the mass m_1 of liquid vaporised.

h Decrease V so as to obtain about half the previous rate of heating. Record the values I_2 and V_2 and check that their product is approximately half the value of $I_1 V_1$.

i Dry the second beaker and check its mass. After about 5 minutes the liquid should be boiling at its new rate. Collect the condensed vapour for exactly the same time as recorded in (g). Measure the mass of liquid m_2.

j Using equation [9.11] calculate two independent values for L_v, using the results of the two different heating rates.

k Now you can decide whether you will obtain any improvement on either of these values by using

equation [9.13]. At the lower rate of heating energy losses should be more significant. Therefore the value of L_v should be significantly higher for the second (and lower) rate of heating. If in your opinion the difference between the two values of L_v is within experimental error (e.g. they differ by less than 2% of the value of L_v), then you are likely to obtain an inferior result to either of your values if you use equation [9.13]. If the difference is significant (and in the right direction) calculate a value for L_v from equation [9.13]. Use this revised value of L_v to calculate h from either of the equations [9.12].

NOTES

l Your account should include a complete description of the experiment together with your analysis leading to two values of L_v. Comment on whether the correction for energy losses was required; if so give a revised value for L_v and an estimate of the fractional (or percentage) energy loss.

m The other notable experiment on continuous flow calorimetry to determine the specific heat capacity c of a liquid uses a similar principle to eliminate the effect of energy losses. In experiment 1 liquid flows at a rate m_1 over a heating coil; the temperature difference $(\theta_2 - \theta_1)$ between the inlet and outlet liquid flow is recorded. Thus:

$$I_1 V_1 = m_1 c (\theta_2 - \theta_1) + h \qquad [9.14]$$

In a second experiment the rate of electrical heating is decreased to $I_2 V_2$ and the flow rate of the liquid m_2 is adjusted to give the same temperature difference as in experiment 1. Provided that the mean temperature of the liquid is the same in both experiments, the rate of energy loss is the same. Thus:

$$I_2 V_2 = m_2 c (\theta_2 - \theta_1) + h \qquad [9.15]$$

These equations can be solved to eliminate h. However, as in the L_v experiment, unless the rates of liquid flow are significantly different, the value for c can be inferior to the value calculated using only equation [9.14]. In fact there is an additional problem in this experiment, of adjusting the flow rate m_2 to obtain the same temperature difference as in experiment 1; the temperature difference can be as small as 5 K.

10 CURRENT ELECTRICITY

10.1 ELECTRICAL CIRCUITS

10.1.1 General circuit principles

All the experiments in this section involve circuits around which steady, direct currents (d.c.) flow. Later sections deal with alternating currents (a.c.) (13) and electronics (15 and 16), for which many of the notes that follow are relevant.

Cells and batteries are ideal power supplies for the circuits studied in this section, but, like most electrical components, they are easily damaged through misuse. A key or switch symbol is shown in practical circuit diagrams, and you should certainly include some form of switch next to the battery in all the circuits that you assemble, though a flying lead that can be easily connected and disconnected will suffice if a switch or key is not available. A specific instruction to switch a circuit on or off is given in the text only where the risk of serious damage to a component exists. See notes (f) and (g).

The following general procedure should be observed when connecting up and using a circuit.

a) Arrange the components in a logical order on the bench and connect them together tidily, using short leads. Leave the main key or switch open (off).

b) Check for short-circuits and omitted components by following round each loop of the circuit.

c) Set any rheostats, potential dividers or resistance boxes to produce small initial currents.

d) Close the key to switch on the circuit and check that the pointers of any meters move in the correct direction across their scales, but not too far.

e) Adjust variable resistors to check that currents and voltages can be varied over expected ranges.

f) Switch off as often as possible between measurements to preserve batteries.

g) Switch off before changing or reconnecting components.

10.1.2 Electric cells

In a cell, or battery of cells, chemical energy is stored which can be converted into electrical energy when the cell is allowed to drive a current. The chemical changes that occur establish an electromotive force (e.m.f.) between the electrodes, which are connected directly to the terminals of the cell. A primary cell contains chemicals that must be replaced when the e.m.f. of the cell has fallen; its cell action is irreversible. But a secondary cell, or accumulator, can be recharged by driving a reverse current through it; its cell action is reversible.

There are many types of primary and secondary cell; each type has its own advantages that make it suitable for particular applications. Cells that you might encounter in the laboratory and elsewhere include those listed below. Note that the symbols (+) and (−) refer to the polarity of the terminals connected to the electrodes named. This means that the electrode marked (+) is the cathode and the one marked (−) is the anode.

PRIMARY CELLS

a) The *Leclanché cell* consists of carbon (+) and zinc (−) electrodes in an electrolyte of ammonium chloride. Its e.m.f. is 1.5 V. The ordinary zinc–carbon dry cell commonly used in torch and radio batteries is a Leclanché cell in which the electrolyte is in a dry (paste) form.

b) The *alkaline cell* consists of manganese dioxide mixed with graphite (+) and zinc (−) electrodes in an electrolyte of potassium hydroxide. Its e.m.f. of 1.5 V allows it to be used as an alternative to the zinc–carbon dry cell, over which it has the advantages of greater energy stored per unit volume, better discharge characteristics, longer shelf life and much less risk of damage due to leaking.

c) The *Weston cadmium cell* consists of mercury (+) and mercury–cadmium amalgam (−) electrodes in an electrolyte of cadmium sulphate. Its e.m.f. of 1.0186 V, which varies only slightly with temperature, is used as a standard for laboratory measurements of e.m.f. To ensure that this e.m.f. is maintained, you must never allow the cell to drive currents of more than a few microamps, and even currents within this recommended range should not be allowed to flow continuously for more than a few seconds.

d) The *Daniell cell* consists of copper (+) and zinc (−) electrodes in an electrolyte of dilute sulphuric acid. Its e.m.f. of 1.08 V may be used as a standard, but the e.m.f. of the Weston cell is far more reliable.

SECONDARY CELLS

a) The *lead–acid accumulator* consists of lead oxide (+) and lead (−) electrodes in an electrolyte of dilute sulphuric acid. Its e.m.f. of around 2.0 V remains constant for some time while current is drawn from it, provided the cell has not been freshly charged. It will drive very large currents, a property that makes it ideal for use in a car battery, which consists of six cells in series.

b) The *nickel–iron* (*nife*) *cell* consists of nickel oxide (+) and iron (−) electrodes in an electrolyte of potassium hydroxide. Its e.m.f. is about 1.2 V. It can be charged quickly and is therefore used in battery powered vehicles like milk floats.

c) The *nickel–cadmium* (*nicad*) *cell* consists of nickel oxide (+) and cadmium (−) electrodes in an electrolyte of potassium hydroxide. Its e.m.f. is about 1.2 V. For storing a given amount of energy, the nicad cell is lighter (though much more expensive) than either of the other two secondary cells. It is used in dry rechargeable batteries for shavers, cassette players, etc.

INTERNAL RESISTANCE

The current driven by a cell must pass through the chemicals inside the cell, which inevitably have a resistance – the internal resistance of the cell. The internal resistance of a lead–acid accumulator is only a few hundredths of an ohm, while that of a dry cell is about an ohm. The internal resistance of a cell determines the largest current that the cell can drive. This is the short-circuit current. Measurement of internal resistance forms part of two of the experiments in this section. An experiment designed to reveal and measure genuine internal resistance can involve quite large currents that would severely curtail the life of the cell. (It might be decided to investigate, and thereby sacrifice, one from a batch.) For this reason, the cells under investigation here incorporate concealed series resistors that increase their effective internal resistance. These artificial increases of internal resistance ensure that currents are kept at or below reasonably low values, and they provide short-circuit protection. You are not, therefore, investigating real cells, but at least the cells will survive your experiment and those of several others.

10.2 METERS

10.2.1 Moving-coil galvanometer

Most conventional electrical meters are based on a moving-coil galvanometer, in which the deflection of the pointer is proportional to the current flowing through the coil. The meter may then be adapted to register currents or voltages up to a particular maximum by connecting it to a suitable shunt (parallel resistance) or multiplier

(series resistance). On most meters coloured terminals are used to indicate polarity: the positive terminal is red and the negative terminal is black.

10.2.2 Meter adaptions

For a reasonably precise measurement of a current or voltage the meter should cover an appropriate range. Ideally, full-scale deflection (f.s.d.) of the meter should just exceed the largest value of the quantity that is likely to be encountered during the experiment. Many different ammeters and voltmeters might be needed in a laboratory, but it is more economical to stock several shunts and multipliers for use with one type of basic galvanometer. Special meter systems have been designed on this principle for sixth-form laboratories.

The scale on the meter of such a system is usually marked with a series of numbers, but without units. However, the value of current or voltage marked on the shunt or multiplier that you connect to the galvanometer allows you to interpret the deflection of the pointer. This marked value always represents f.s.d., i.e. the value of the current or voltage that moves the pointer right across the scale. If the meter carries two (or more) scales, choose the more appropriate one.

In some systems shunts and multipliers are mounted so that they can simply be plugged in to the basic galvanometer. A shunt or multiplier consists only of a single resistor, so it is quite common to find two or three, each with its own marked terminal, mounted on one adaptor unit. One other terminal, which can be either positive or negative, is used as a common terminal.

These ideas are illustrated in Fig. 10.1 (overleaf). Fig. 10.1a shows a basic galvanometer, on which the deflection can be interpreted using the information marked on the left-hand side: a current of 100 μA produces full-scale deflection of 10 (on the upper scale), so the deflection indicated of 7.4 (on the same scale) represents a current of 74 μA. Note that the resistance of the galvanometer is marked (1000 Ω), which allows the p.d. between the terminals to be calculated: $V = IR = 74$ mV. The basic galvanometer illustrated is simultaneously an ammeter covering the range 0–100 μA and a voltmeter covering the range 0–100 mV. If the ammeter adaptor unit shown in Fig. 10.1b were plugged into the galvanometer and connections made to the two terminals marked with arrows, the meter would be adapted so that a current of 1.0 A produced a full-scale deflection of 10 on the upper scale. The deflection indicated in Fig. 10.1a of 7.4 on the same scale would therefore represent a current of 0.74 A. Similarly, the voltmeter adaptor unit shown in Fig. 10.1c would adapt the meter so that a p.d. of 50 V produced a full-scale deflection of 5 on the lower scale. The deflection indicated of 3.7 on the same scale would therefore represent a p.d. of 37 V. Note the choice of whichever of

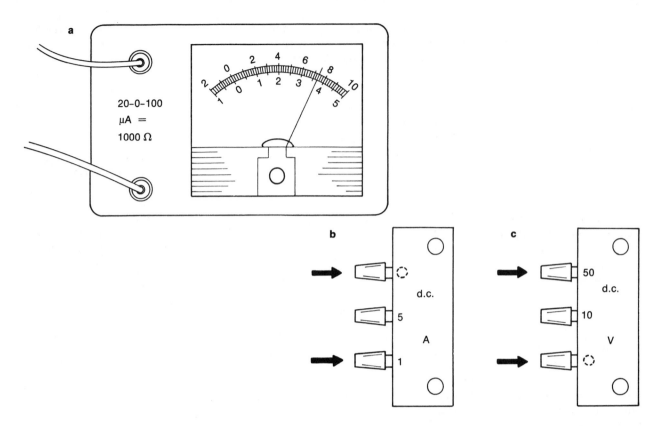

Fig. 10.1 A popular meter system designed for A-level experiments: **a** the basic galvanometer in use; the small screw below the scale is used to zero the pointer; **b** adaptor for converting the galvanometer to read currents up to 1 A or 5 A; **c** adaptor for converting the galvanometer to read p.d.s up to 10 V or 50 V.

the two scales seems more appropriate: the lower scale, marked 0–5, would be chosen to interpret currents and voltages when the meter has been adapted for f.s.d.s of 50 mA, 500 mA, 500 mV, 5 V, etc., while the upper scale, marked 0–10, would be chosen for f.s.d.s of 1 mA, 10 mA, 100 mA, 1 V, 10 V, etc.

10.2.3 Multimeters

A multimeter contains shunts and multipliers that are connected internally by means of range-setting switches. A good multimeter is a very versatile instrument, covering a wide range of currents and voltages, direct and alternating. It can also be used to measure resistance directly; a battery inside the meter drives a current through the resistance, which is registered on the scale. Since this current is large when the resistance is small, the resistance scale has its zero on the right-hand side. See Fig. 10.2a, which shows also that the resistance scale is not linear. When using a multimeter, observe carefully the following points.

a) Place it with its scale uppermost, i.e. the needle should move in a horizontal plane.

b) Check when making connections to it that you are using the correct pair of terminals; for most applications the same two are always used, but special terminals may

be provided for high voltage connections or high current connections, or both.

c) Before switching on the circuit to make a measurement, set a high value range, then turn down the setting to increase sensitivity as required.

d) Zero adjusters for the resistance ranges are usually provided. Having selected an appropriate range, short out the two terminals of the meter and use the adjuster, or adjusters, to zero the pointer at the right-hand end of the scale.

e) To preserve the battery inside, never leave the multimeter set on one of its resistance ranges for longer than necessary.

Electronic digital multimeters (Fig. 10.2b) are now cheaper, and more accurate, more sensitive and more reliable than their moving-coil ('analogue') counterparts, which eventually they may completely replace. Their other main advantages include:

i) A very high resistance, of several megohms, on all voltage ranges, compared with several kilohms for moving-coil meters.

ii) Alternating currents and voltages of high frequency are measured accurately; the performance of moving-coil meters adapted for a.c. deteriorates as frequency increases, though at mains frequency (50 Hz) there are usually no problems.

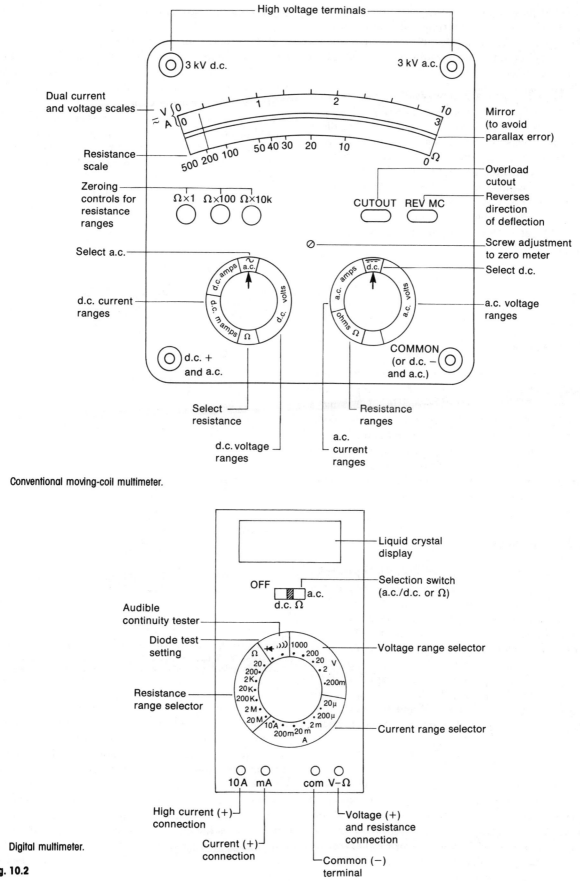

a Conventional moving-coil multimeter.

b Digital multimeter.

Fig. 10.2

iii) Direct display of the measured quantity, eliminating the possibility of reading the wrong scale; however, units and their prefixes (μ, m, k, M) must still be determined from the position of the range-setting switch, except on auto-ranging meters.

Many different types are now available, some with function and range set by rotary switches (Fig. 10.2b) and some by push-button combinations. Additional facilities such as direct measurement of capacitance and transistor parameters are provided on the more advanced models. Most digital multimeters are fitted with internal fuses that give adequate overload protection, making them virtually free from the effects of accidental misuse. But they are battery powered, so remember to turn off after use. See also note (b), page 118, concerning correct connection of terminals.

10.3 RESISTORS

10.3.1 Resistance

Resistors of one form or another are included in nearly every experimental electrical circuit. In most applications it is essentially the resistor's property of having a particular p.d./current ratio that is required. This ratio is, of course, the resistor's resistance, measured in Ω. Resistance is an electrical quantity that applies to every type of component, not just resistors. Resistance values encountered in the laboratory range from about one to several million ohms.

10.3.2 Fixed resistors

Every resistor is rated to carry currents up to a particular value, and you must ensure that this current is not exceeded. Overheating due to large power dissipation may cause not only a temporary change of resistance from the nominal value, but also permanent damage to insulation or to the resistor itself. Usually either the maximum current or the maximum power dissipation is specified, depending on the type of resistor and the application for which it is intended. Use any of the following expressions relating current I, p.d. V, power P and resistance R to determine safe maximum values of I or V, as appropriate:

$$P = I^2R = \frac{V^2}{R} = VI$$

The stated resistance of a fixed resistor should always be used in conjunction with its tolerance, normally expressed as a percentage. The stated value is only nominal; the actual value lies between limits determined by the tolerance. For example, if the tolerance of a 100 Ω resistor is 5%, its resistance is guaranteed by the manufacturer to lie between 95 Ω and 105 Ω.

10.3.3 Variable resistors

In all the experiments in this chapter you will use some form of variable resistor as a means of varying either current or voltage. Most variable resistors have three terminals: connections are made to the two ends of a resistor, which is usually either a carbon film or a long wire wound as a coil, and the third terminal is connected to a sliding contact, sometimes called a wiper, that can be moved to any position along the resistor. Two common types of variable resistor are shown in Fig. 10.3.

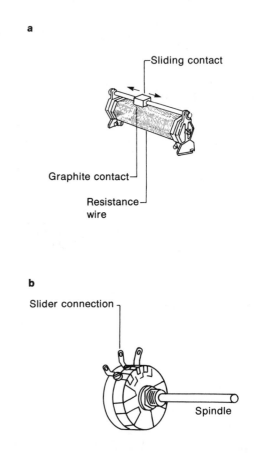

Fig. 10.3 Variable resistors: **a** high-current type, in which the resistance wire is coiled on an open tube, with the slider at the top; **b** low-current radio type, in which the coiled resistance wire and the slider are concealed.

Of the two ways of connecting a variable resistor, a rheostat, used to vary the current around a circuit, is probably the more familiar. See Fig. 10.4. Note that only two of the three terminals are connected; one of them must be that of the slider, but it is possible to use either of the two end terminals. However, with the rheostat connected as shown, movement of the slider to the right decreases the resistance between the terminals and therefore increases the current, which might seem to be the more logical alternative. Similarly, a radio type might be connected so that clockwise rotation of the slider increases current.

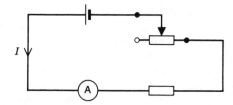

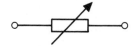

a Variable resistor connected as a rheostat to control a current *I*.

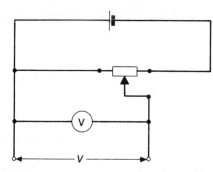

b Standard symbol for a rheostat.

Fig. 10.4

A variable resistor can also be connected as a potential divider (sometimes called a potentiometer) to provide a variable voltage between two points. All three terminals of the variable resistor are then used, as shown in Fig. 10.5. It is convenient to connect the potential divider so that the p.d. *V* is increased either by movement of the slider to the right (as in Fig. 10.5) or by clockwise rotation of the slider of the radio type.

Fig. 10.5   Variable resistor connected as a potential divider (or potentiometer) to control a p.d. *V*.

10.3.4 Resistance boxes

In some experiments you need to know the value of the resistance set on a variable resistor. Where only a few predetermined values are required, the appropriate resistors may be assembled for you in a box complete with some form of setting switch. But if many values are required, or if values cannot be predetermined, a resistance box is used. This contains many standard resistors, a combination of which is set to give a total resistance of known value. In the plug-key type a resistance is set by removing the key that otherwise shorts it out. In the decade type a ten- or eleven-way rotary switch is used for each decade (0–1 Ω, 0–10 Ω, 0–100 Ω, etc.). The stated values of standard resistances of the type normally connected in resistance boxes are accurate to within 1% (i.e. their tolerance is 1% or better).

The resistors in a resistance box are, of course, subject to limits of power dissipation as in section 10.3.2. In general it is therefore advisable to set a high value of resistance before switching on the circuit. See section 10.1.1(c). However, beware also of setting the resistance to zero (or some other very low value that might lead to an excessive current) during the course of an experiment. This is easily done accidently when a setting is altered. On the plug-key type of resistance box you should therefore remove the necessary plugs for the new setting before replacing those of the old one. On the decade type you should switch new resistances in before turning any of the decade switches back to zero. Alternatively, the circuit can be switched off while alterations are made.

10.4 THE POTENTIOMETER

10.4.1 General principles

The potentiometer circuit is used for comparing potential differences, but adapted with other components it can be used to measure voltages, currents and resistances. In principle, it is used instead of a voltmeter, over which it has the advantages of greater precision, accuracy and versatility, and of causing absolutely no disturbance to the circuit to which it is applied. Such disturbance arises in the case of a voltmeter from the current that it draws. However, the potentiometer is cumbersome to use and it does not give direct readings of any electrical quantities.

A basic potentiometer circuit is shown in Fig. 10.6. AB is a length of uniform resistance wire stretched out over a rule or scale. A cell connected across the wire drives a constant current *I* along it. The p.d. *V* under investigation is applied to the connections X and Y, with the polarity indicated. X is connected directly to the end A of the wire, and Y is connected through a centre-zero galvanometer to a contact maker, sometimes called a jockey, that allows electrical contact to be made on the wire anywhere between A and B.

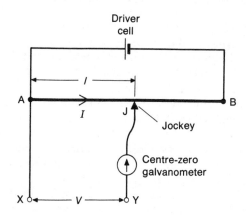

Fig. 10.6   The potentiometer circuit.

If the jockey is placed on the wire near the end A, a p.d. of approximately V drives a current down through the galvanometer. If the jockey is now placed on the wire near B, the net p.d. of approximately $(V_{AB} - V)$ around the lower loop drives a current up through the galvanometer. These two currents produce deflections in opposite directions on the galvanometer. At some point J along the wire the jockey can be placed such that no current flows through the galvanometer, in which condition the potentiometer is said to be balanced: the potential drop V_{AJ} along the wire between A and J balances (i.e. equals) V. As the wire is uniform, and the current that flows along it is the same at all points, the balance length l is proportional to V. If balance lengths l_1 and l_2 are determined for two p.d.s V_1 and V_2 applied in turn to the connections XY, it follows that:

$$\frac{V_1}{l_1} = \frac{V_2}{l_2} \qquad [10.1]$$

Hence the ratio of two p.d.s equals the ratio of their balance lengths.

Note that the conditions that lead to the derivation of equation [10.1] apply only when the potentiometer is balanced. If the jockey is placed anywhere on the wire other than J, a current flows through the galvanometer, and the currents in the two sections of the wire are not then equal (an application of Kirchhoff's first law). Different potential gradients are established in the two sections, and the potential drop along the wire is no longer proportional to length. Note also that no current is drawn from the source of p.d. only when the potentiometer is balanced. An off-balance current through the galvanometer may disturb the value of V, as would certainly be the case if the source is a cell. The analysis of the unbalanced potentiometer circuit and its effects is complex, but fortunately our concern is with the condition of the circuit only when a balance point has been found; analysis is then straightforward, and the p.d. under investigation suffers no disturbance.

10.4.2 The practical potentiometer

The e.m.f. $\mathcal{E}_D$ of the driver cell determines the greatest value of p.d. for which a balance point can be found, since V must be less than V_{AB}, the p.d. between A and B, which is approximately $\mathcal{E}_D$. The most important property of the driver cell is its ability to drive a current that remains constant during the course of the experiment. Of all the cells listed in section 10.1.2 the lead–acid accumulator is the most suitable for use as the driver cell. The precise value of its e.m.f. (around 2.0 V) varies from one cell to another, but the e.m.f. of any one lead–acid accumulator does remain constant for some time during use, provided that it has not been freshly charged. The current I that it drives along the potentiometer wire and V_{AB} are therefore also constant.

The length l_{AB} of the potentiometer wire is usually either 50 cm or 1 m, though on some types the wire is split into sections, and l_{AB} might be 2 m or even 4 m. The precision of a potentiometer measurement for which $V_{AB} \approx \mathcal{E}_D \approx 2$ V and $l_{AB} = 1$ m would be comparable with that of a voltmeter covering the range up to 2 V, whose scale is marked with 1000 divisions! The accuracy of potentiometer measurements depends largely on the uniformity of the wire. Try to avoid scraping or striking the wire with the jockey, actions that produce local variations of the wire's cross-sectional area. Accuracy also depends on how close the connection at A from X is made to the point at the left-hand end of the wire from which balance lengths are measured. The wire is either heavily soldered there or clamped beneath a metal block, against which the zero mark on the scale is placed.

Accuracy and precision of comparisons of p.d. made on the potentiometer are greatest when both p.d.s. are just less than V_{AB}; balance points are then near the end B of the wire. Balance lengths for small p.d.s might be too short to be measured accurately. For example, if a 2 V accumulator is used as the driver cell with a potentiometer wire 1 m long, the potential drop across each millimetre of wire is about 2 mV. The balance length for a p.d. of 10 mV would be only 5 mm, but since this can be determined only to the nearest millimetre, the measurement has an uncertainty of about 20%. Balance lengths are increased by connecting a variable resistance R_v in series with the potentiometer wire to reduce V_{AB} (Fig. 10.7). The required value of R_v depends on the resistance R_{AB} of the potentiometer wire, whose length is effectively increased by the inclusion of R_v. For example, to reduce R_{AB} to 20 mV, R_v would be chosen such that the 2 V accumulator produces across it a p.d. of 2.00 V–0.02 V= 1.98 V, for which it would need to be about 99 times R_{AB}. The arrangement is then equivalent to a potentiometer wire 100 m long, of which only 1 m is actually accessible. A very sensitive galvanometer, such as a light-beam type, is necessary to detect the small off-balance currents that flow in a potentiometer circuit that has been modified in this way.

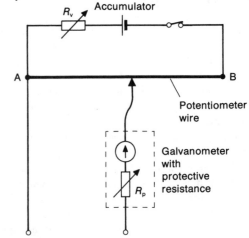

Fig. 10.7   The practical potentiometer.

10.4.3 Galvanometers

The precision with which balance points can be located depends largely on the sensitivity of the galvanometer. Unfortunately, the more sensitive the galvanometer is, the more vulnerable it is to damage from off-balance currents. It is usual, therefore, to connect a large series resistance R_p, of several kilohms, that reduces off-balance currents to within safe limits. As the balance point is approached, R_p is reduced, either by shorting it out completely if it is of fixed value, or gradually if it is variable; R_p protects the galvanometer, but it also acts as a sensitivity control. In circuit diagrams it is shown as a variable resistor incorporated with the galvanometer (Fig. 10.7). A light-beam galvanometer does not require a separate protective resistance; its movement is protected by resistors switched in by the sensitivity control. Note that the accuracy of the galvanometer affects neither the precision nor the accuracy of potentiometer measurements: the galvanometer is used only to detect currents, or rather their absence; certainly not to measure them. Even a zero error on the galvanometer should have no effect. Positive location of a balance point is made only when tapping the jockey lightly on and off the wire at that point produces absolutely no movement of the galvanometer's pointer (or light spot), whatever its position. Some galvanometer movements are undamped and take a long time to settle down once disturbed. The oscillating movement of such a galvanometer can be quickly brought to rest by briefly shorting it out.

10.4.4 Connection, testing and fault finding

A complete circuit that includes a potentiometer is complicated and takes time to assemble. You are recommended to connect first the potentiometer loop, then the connections to X and Y (one of which includes the galvanometer) and finally the circuit or device containing the p.d. under investigation. Turn the galvanometer's protective resistance up to its maximum value and test the circuit by placing the jockey on the wire first near the end A and then near B. If the deflections on the galvanometer θ_A and θ_B are in opposite directions, the circuit is correct and a balance point exists somewhere on the wire, which you may then proceed to locate. A fault may be identified, if any other result is obtained, as follows:

a) If both deflections are in the same direction, with $\theta_A < \theta_B$, either the driver cell or the p.d. under investigation is connected the wrong way round.

b) If both deflections are in the same direction, with $\theta_A > \theta_B$, the p.d. under investigation exceeds V_{AB}; turn down any series resistance that has been included with the driver cell.

c) If both deflections are virtually the same, and this same deflection is also obtained wherever the jockey is placed

on the wire, a bad connection exists in the potentiometer loop.

d) If no deflections are obtained at all, a bad connection exists in the leads between the potentiometer and X and Y.

10.4.5 Calibration

The potentiometer can only be used to compare p.d.s, but balance lengths may be converted directly to voltages if the potentiometer is calibrated by measuring the balance length that corresponds to a known p.d. A standard cell, which has an e.m.f. with an uncertainty of less than 0.1%, is used for this purpose. The Weston cadmium cell is normally used as the laboratory standard (see section 10.1.2(c)). The Weston cell must always be protected by a large series resistance of several hundred kilohms, which can be reduced to a safe minimum of several kilohms as the balance point is approached. Accordingly, the standard cell is shown in circuit diagrams incorporating fixed and variable resistors. A very sensitive galvanometer, such as a light-beam type, is required to detect the small off-balance currents limited by these large protective resistors.

10.5 THE METRE BRIDGE

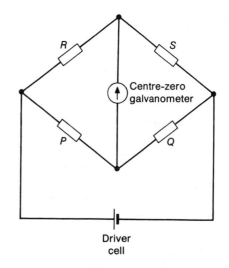

Fig. 10.8 The Wheatstone bridge network.

10.5.1 The Wheatstone bridge

The metre bridge circuit is a practical adaptation of the Wheatstone bridge network, a circuit used primarily for the comparison of resistances. A simple Wheatstone bridge network is shown in Fig. 10.8. Four resistances P, Q, R and S are connected in a loop. A cell is connected between two opposite corners of the loop and a centre-zero galvanometer between the other two. One or more of the resistances is varied until no current flows through the galvanometer, in which condition the bridge is said to be *balanced,* and the relationship between the four resistances is then given by:

$$\frac{P}{Q} = \frac{R}{S} \qquad [10.2]$$

10.5.2 The metre bridge

If an unknown resistance R is to be compared with a standard S, equation [10.2] may be rearranged to give

$$R = \frac{P}{Q} \times S$$

in which it can be seen that the *ratio* (P/Q) must be known, but the individual values of P and Q need not be. In the metre bridge circuit P and Q are formed by the two sections of a length AB of a uniform resistance wire, stretched over a rule or scale (Fig. 10.9). A cell, such as an accumulator, is connected across the ends of the wire. The two resistances R and S are connected in the top arm of the bridge, between terminals linked by a copper or brass strip of minimal resistance. The point between R and S is connected through a centre-zero galvanometer to a contact maker (jockey) that allows electrical contact to be made on the wire anywhere between A and B.

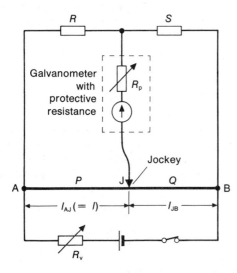

Fig. 10.9 The metre bridge circuit; when the bridge is balanced

$$\frac{R}{S} = \frac{P}{Q} = \frac{l_{AJ}}{l_{JB}}$$

At some point J along the wire the jockey may be placed to balance the bridge. As the wire is uniform, the ratio of resistances P/Q equals the ratio l_{AJ}/l_{JB} of the lengths of the two sections, whose sum is constant and equal to the total length l_{AB} of the wire. If l is the balance length measured between A and J $(l = l_{AJ})$, we have:

$$R = \left(\frac{l}{l_{AB} - l}\right) \times S \qquad [10.3]$$

Note that the balanced condition is not affected if the e.m.f. of the driver cell varies.

The precision with which balance points can be located depends on the sensitivity of the galvanometer. A series resistance R_p is included to protect the galvanometer and to act as a sensitivity control (see section 10.4.3).

The length l_{AB} is usually 1 m, as the name of the circuit suggests, but half-metre and two-metre bridges are quite common. The accuracy with which measurements are made on the metre bridge depends partly on the uniformity of the resistance wire, so the practical precautions detailed in section 10.4.2 apply here. R and S should always be connected with short, thick leads. Contact and lead resistances render the metre bridge unsuitable for the comparison of very low resistances $(< 0.1\ \Omega)$.

The standard resistance S is chosen to be of comparable value with the unknown R so that the balance point lies as close as possible to the centre of the wire. If the balance point is close to one end, one or other of the two lengths l and $(l_{AB} - l)$ is too short to be measured accurately.

10.5.3 Testing and fault finding

Set R_p to its maximum value and test the circuit by placing the jockey on the wire, first near the end A, and then near B. If the deflections of the galvanometer pointer are in opposite directions, the circuit is correct and a balance point exists somewhere on the wire, which you may then proceed to locate. Reduce R_p as the balance point is approached. If there is no deflection when the jockey is placed at one of the ends, a bad connection exists in the top arm of the bridge; for example, if no deflection is obtained when the jockey is placed at A, there is either an open circuit at S or a short-circuit across R. If the galvanometer shows no deflections at all, there may be a fault in the connections of either the cell or the galvanometer.

10A Diode Characteristics
Investigation of the variation of current with potential difference for diodes made from silicon and germanium

APPARATUS REQUIRED

- silicon diode labelled S
- germanium diode labelled G
- 2 V accumulator (or equivalent d.c. supply)
- 2 digital multimeters
- variable resistor, maximum resistance about 100 Ω
- fixed resistor, resistance 1.2 kΩ
- key (or switch)
- thermometer to read room temperature
- connecting wires

PRINCIPLES INVOLVED

a The ideal diode has zero resistance when it is forward-biased, i.e. when a potential difference is applied across the diode in its normal conducting (forward) direction. When reverse-biased, its resistance is infinite. Real diodes behave rather differently. In this experiment you will investigate the variation of current with p.d. in the forward direction for two diodes, made from different semiconducting materials: silicon and germanium. This variation is known as the *I–V* characteristic of a diode.

b The theoretical variation of current *I* with p.d. *V* for a semiconductor diode is given by the exponential relationship (the 'rectifier equation'):

$$I = I_0 \left[\exp\left(\frac{eV}{kT} \right) - 1 \right]$$

in which I_0 is a constant current, e is the electronic charge, T is the absolute temperature of the diode and k is the Boltzmann constant. Since $(eV/kT) \gg 1$, even when V is small, the rectifier equation can be simplified and becomes:

$$I = I_0 \left[\exp\left(\frac{eV}{kT} \right) \right] \qquad [10.4]$$

I_0 is the small leakage current that flows through the diode when reverse-biased. Its value is more or less independent of V.

c If you are using unmounted diodes, you will need to examine them closely to establish their polarity. Fig. 10.10a shows the outlines of common forms of diode, from which the cathode end may be identified as the one that is marked in some way, usually with a band. In the forward direction current flows from anode to cathode. Note that the bar of the diode symbol shown in Fig. 10.10b represents the cathode.

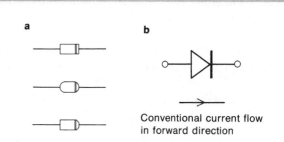

Fig. 10.10 **a** Diode outline shapes; the cathode end of each one is identified by a band. **b** Diode symbol.

d For many electrical devices the relationship between *V* and *I* is adequately expressed by the quantity resistance $R(= V/I)$, which may or may not be constant. For a device whose resistance is not constant, such as a diode, it is sometimes useful to refer to the rate of change of *V* with *I*. Thus *dynamic resistance r* is defined by:

$$r = \frac{\mathrm{d}V}{\mathrm{d}I}$$

r equals the reciprocal of the slope of the *I–V* characteristic, and is often therefore called the *slope resistance*. Like *R*, *r* is measured in ohms.

SILICON DIODE

e The circuit to be used during the experiment is shown in Fig. 10.11. The variable resistor R_V is connected as a potential divider across the accumulator. The fixed resistor R_S limits the current that can flow through the diode to just over 1 mA, and thereby prevents its temperature from rising appreciably. Digital multimeters are used as an ammeter and a voltmeter to measure *I* and *V*.

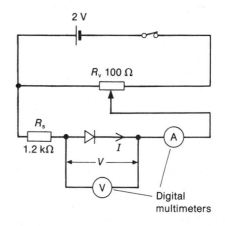

Fig. 10.11 Measuring the characteristics of a diode.

f Connect up the circuit as in Fig. 10.11 with the silicon diode S in position. Close the key and increase V until the ammeter starts to register a current. Increase V to obtain a set of corresponding values of V and I up to the point where $I = 1.0$ mA; increments of V of about 20 mV are suitable. Tabulate your readings (recording I in μA).

g Plot the I–V characteristic of the diode – I (ordinate) and V (abscissa) – using axes that include the origin. Note how current flow commences only when V exceeds about 0.4 V, but thereafter a small further increase of V produces a large increase in I. Mark on your graph a line that represents ideal diode behaviour. Determine R and r for the diode when $I = 500$ μA.

h Measure the room temperature $\theta(°C)$ and use the relationship $T = \theta + 273$ to calculate the absolute room temperature $T(K)$. Refer to equation [10.4], in which I_0, e, k and T are regarded as constants. Plot a suitable linear graph and use it to determine k and I_0, given that $e = 1.60 \times 10^{-19}$ C. Examine your graph and note whether or not it curves at its upper end. Why might non-linear behaviour be expected there?

GERMANIUM DIODE

i Repeat (f) with the germanium diode G in position. Plot the I–V characteristic of this diode on the graph prepared in (g) so that the characteristics of the two diodes can be compared. Note the different p.d.s at which the two diodes start to conduct. Determine R and r for this diode when $I = 500$ μA. Repeat (h) to determine I_0 for this diode and obtain a second value of k.

NOTES

j Your record should include a labelled circuit diagram.

k The two principal differences between silicon and germanium as suitable semiconducting materials should be evident from your results. A germanium diode conducts in the forward direction at a lower p.d. than a silicon diode and is therefore more suitable for the rectification of small signal voltages. On the other hand, a silicon diode has a much smaller leakage current. Silicon also has better thermal stability and withstands higher voltages before breaking down and is generally the better material.

10B Meter Connections
Measurement of resistance with an ammeter and a voltmeter, and investigation of the errors that the meters introduce

APPARATUS REQUIRED

- matched ammeter and voltmeter under investigation (values of quantities that are given in the text are appropriate for Unilab grey meters adapted as 0–1 mA ammeter and 0–1 V voltmeter)
- decade resistance box covering the range up to 10 000 Ω
- 2 V accumulator
- 2 variable resistors, maximum resistance of each about 100 Ω
- key (or switch)
- connecting wires

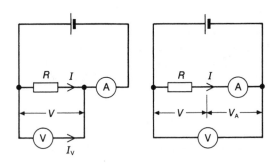

Circuit X   *Circuit Y*

Fig. 10.12   The two ways of connecting a voltmeter and an ammeter to measure a resistance R.

PRINCIPLES INVOLVED

a Resistance R can be determined simply by measuring the potential difference V across the resistance and the current I that flows through it. Thus $R = V/I$. A voltmeter and an ammeter can be used to measure V and I. Consider the alternative circuits shown in Fig. 10.12. In circuit X the voltmeter indicates the true p.d. V across R, but the ammeter indicates the sum of the current I flowing through R and the small current I_V drawn by the voltmeter. The apparent resistance R_X calculated from the meter readings is therefore less than the true value of R. In circuit Y the ammeter indicates the true current I flowing through R, but the voltmeter indicates the sum of the p.d. V across R and the small p.d. V_A across the ammeter. The apparent resistance R_Y calculated from the meter readings is therefore more than the true value of R. We have therefore $R_X < R < R_Y$. In this experiment you will determine R_X and R_Y (by using both circuits) for a series of known values of R.

CIRCUIT X

b The circuit to be used during the experiment is shown in Fig. 10.13. The known resistance R is set on the decade resistance box. One of the variable resistors is connected as a potential divider across the accumulator, and the other as a rheostat, to provide respectively coarse and fine controls for setting suitable currents and voltages. The voltmeter is shown connected directly across R, producing the arrangement that represents circuit X. Only one lead need be reconnected, as indicated, to produce the arrangement that represents circuit Y.

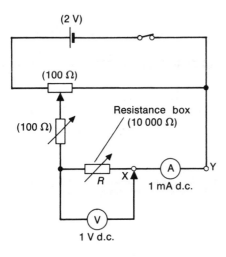

Fig. 10.13 Using a voltmeter and an ammeter to measure resistance for comparison with the true value.

c Connect up the circuit of Fig. 10.13, with the voltmeter lead connected to the point X. Measure the p.d. V and the current I_X indicated on the meters for twelve values of R given by $R/\Omega = 300, 390, 500, 640, 800, 1000, 1250, 1600, 2000, 2500, 3200$ and 4000. For each value of R adjust the two variable resistors to produce the largest possible meter deflections, i.e. either the ammeter or the voltmeter should have a full-scale deflection. Tabulate your readings (Table 1). Allow space for six more columns.

d Calculate and record in a fourth column $\log_{10} R$ for each value of R. Calculate also $R_X(=V/I_X)$ and $\log_{10} R_X$ for each set of corresponding values of R, V and I_X, and record your results in the fifth and sixth columns.

CIRCUIT Y

e Change the voltmeter connection from X to the point Y shown in Fig. 10.13. Measure the p.d. V_Y and the current I indicated on the meters for the same twelve values of R listed in (c). Tabulate your readings separately (Table 2, in which also space should be left for six more columns).

f Copy the fourth column of Table 1 ($\log_{10} R$) into a fourth column of Table 2. Calculate $R_Y(=V_Y/I)$ and $\log_{10} R_Y$ for each set of corresponding values of R, V_Y and I, and record your results in the fifth and sixth columns.

COMPARATIVE ANALYSIS

g Draw a graph of $\log_{10} R_X$ (ordinate) against $\log_{10} R$ (abscissa). On the same graph plot $\log_{10} R_Y$ against $\log_{10} R$, and also plot the straight line $\log_{10} R$ against $\log_{10} R$, with which the other two can be compared. Label the three lines. Which circuit is more suitable for measuring (i) small resistances and (ii) large resistances?

h Calculate and record in a seventh column of Table 1 the error $e_X(=(R_X-R))$ introduced by circuit X. If $R_X < R$, e_X is negative. Calculate also the fractional error expressed as a percentage $(=(e_X/R) \times 100)$, and $\log_{10} |e_X|$, where $|e_X|$ is the magnitude or modulus of e_X. Record your results in the eighth and ninth columns. Similarly, calculate and record in the seventh, eighth and ninth columns of Table 2 the error $e_Y(=(R_Y-R))$ introduced by circuit Y, the fractional error expressed as a percentage $(=(e_Y/R) \times 100)$ and $\log_{10} |e_Y|$.

i Draw two graphs to show how the percentage errors (ordinate) vary with $\log_{10} R$ (abscissa). Allow for positive and negative values of percentage error between $+40\%$ and -40%.

j Draw two more graphs to show how $\log_{10} |e_X|$ and $\log_{10} |e_Y|$ (ordinate) vary with $\log_{10} R$ (abscissa).

k Estimate from both pairs of graphs the value of R for which $|e_X| = |e_Y|$. State the value of the common percentage error for this value of R.

l Comment on the variation of e_Y with R; you have plotted $\log_{10} |e_Y|$ against $\log_{10} R$ but try to estimate how e_Y itself varies. Refer to the first few values of e_Y recorded in Table 2.

m Your record should include labelled diagrams of both circuits.

n If particular moving coil meters are to be used to measure a resistance R, the value of R determines which of the two circuits, X or Y, is more suitable. However, the need for circuit Y is virtually eliminated if digital meters are used. A digital voltmeter has such a high resistance (usually several megohms) that the current I_X in circuit X that it would draw is negligible, and the reading on the ammeter is virtually that of the true current I flowing through R.

o Given that the resistance R_a of the 0–1 mA ammeter is 100 Ω and the resistance R_v of the 0–1 V voltmeter is 10 kΩ, tabulate a series of theoretical values of R_X and R_Y for about half the values of R that you used in the experiment; cover the full range from 300 Ω to 4000 Ω. (R_X consists of R and R_v in parallel, and R_Y consists of R and R_a in series.) Calculate values of $\log_{10} R$, e_X, e_Y, the fractional errors expressed as percentages, $\log_{10}|e_X|$ and $\log_{10}|e_Y|$. Hence plot theoretical curves on your graphs of (i) and (j) and compare them with your experimental results. Explain any significant deviations.

10C Energy Transfer

Investigation of the efficiency with which energy is transferred from a source of e.m.f. to a load resistance

APPARATUS REQUIRED

- source of e.m.f. under investigation: battery of 3 dry cells with added artificial 'internal' resistance
- 0–100 mA d.c. ammeter
- decade resistance box(es) covering range up to 200 Ω
- key (or switch)
- connecting wires

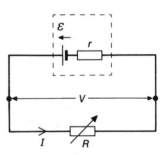

Fig. 10.14 The current I that is drawn from a cell depends on the load resistance R and the cell's internal resistance r.

PRINCIPLES INVOLVED

a A source of e.m.f. $\mathcal{E}$ is shown in Fig. 10.14 connected across a variable load resistance R. The internal resistance r of the source is shown as a separate component, though since r arises within the source, of which it forms an integral part, it can never be removed. The power P supplied by the source to R, i.e. the rate at which electrical energy is converted to internal energy in R, depends upon the value of R. Consider the two extreme values.

(i) If $R = 0$ (short circuit), the current I is large (limited only by r), but since the p.d. $V(= IR)$ across R must be zero, $P(= VI)$ is also zero.

(ii) If $R = \infty$ (open circuit), I is zero, so P is zero again, although now $V = \mathcal{E}$.

b For all values of R between 0 and ∞, P is greater than zero. In this experiment you will investigate how P, V and I vary with R, and verify the prediction of the maximum power theorem, which states that the maximum value of P occurs when $R = r$. You will also investigate the efficiency of the circuit: not all of the chemical energy that is converted into electrical energy inside the source is supplied to R.

VARIATION OF I WITH R

c The circuit to be used is shown in Fig. 10.15. The source of e.m.f. incorporates a battery of three regular 1.5 V dry cells with a concealed series resistor to increase its effective internal resistance. The total internal resistance r, whose value you will determine during the experiment, is therefore the sum of the real internal resistance (probably about 1 or 2 Ω) and the added resistance. See section 10.1.2.

d Connect up the circuit of Fig. 10.15. Set $R = 0$, switch on, and use the ammeter to measure the current I in the circuit. This particular value of I is the short-circuit current and will be the largest one that you have to measure. If it exceeds the upper limit of the range of the ammeter, increase R until a reading can be taken.

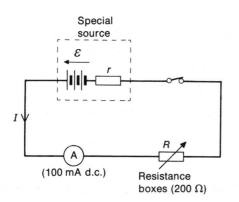

Fig. 10.15 Measuring the current drawn from a cell for various load resistances.

e Now measure I for a series of increasing values of R up to 200 Ω. Use roughly 5 Ω increments up to about 30 Ω, 10 Ω increments up to 100 Ω and 20 Ω increments thereafter, to obtain at least 20 corresponding readings of R and I. If you are using a moving-coil ammeter, the most convenient way of taking reasonably precise measurements is to set R at a desired value, then to adjust it by a few ohms until the pointer of the ammeter lies over one of the scale divisions (though this may not be possible when R is small and I is large). Tabulate your readings; in addition to columns for R and I, three more will be required.

f Refer to Fig. 10.14. The relation between $\mathcal{E}$ and I is obtained by applying Kirchhoff's second law (the loop equation):

$$\mathcal{E} = I(R + r)$$

which can be rearranged to give:

$$\frac{1}{I} = \frac{R}{\mathcal{E}} + \frac{r}{\mathcal{E}} \qquad [10.5]$$

in which r and $\mathcal{E}$ are constants.

g Use equation [10.5] to plot a suitable linear graph, and from it determine r and $\mathcal{E}$. You will need to use one of the three extra columns of your table.

VARIATION WITH R OF I, V, P AND EFFICIENCY

h Calculate and record in the fourth column of your table the p.d. $V(= IR)$ across R for each set of corresponding values of R and I. Calculate also the power $P(= I^2R)$ developed in R, and record your results in the fifth column.

i On one graph plot the variations of I, V and P (ordinates) with R (abscissa). Choose suitable scales for the three y-axes and include the origin of each one.

j The efficiency η of any system in which energy is transferred can be defined by:

$$\eta = \frac{\text{power output}}{\text{power input}}$$

For the circuit of Fig. 10.14 η might therefore be expressed as:

$$\eta = \frac{\begin{array}{c}\text{rate at which electrical energy is converted}\\\text{to internal energy in } R\end{array}}{\begin{array}{c}\text{rate at which chemical energy is converted}\\\text{to electrical energy in the source}\end{array}}$$

$$\eta = \frac{VI}{\mathcal{E}I}$$

$$\eta = \frac{V}{\mathcal{E}}$$

Efficiency is conveniently expressed as a percentage.

Thus:
$$\eta = \frac{V}{\mathcal{E}} \times 100$$

Since $\mathcal{E}$ is constant, η is clearly proportional to V and approaches 100% as V approaches $\mathcal{E}$. A graph of η against R would have the same form as your graph of V against R and therefore need not be drawn; the two graphs would actually be identical if 100% coincided with $\mathcal{E}$ on the two appropriate y-axes.

k Examine your graphs to answer the following questions:

(i) What is the value of R when P is maximum? Refer to the value of r that you obtained in (g) and comment on whether or not your results confirm the prediction of the maximum power theorem.

(ii) What is the value of V when P is maximum? Relate this to the value of $\mathcal{E}$ that you obtained in (g) and deduce the value of η when P is maximum.

(iii) Comment on the value of P as η approaches 100% and on the feasibility of using circuits of high efficiency.

NOTES

l Your record should include a labelled circuit diagram and a note about the artificially increased internal resistance of the source.

m No account has been taken of the resistance R_a of the ammeter, which will have been included in the value of r that you obtained in (g). You may be able to calculate R_a from information marked on the meter and its shunt; typically its value might be about 1 Ω.

n The maximum power theorem has important applications for the matching of electronic components.

Usually it is desirable to achieve maximum power transfer from one component to the next, and high efficiency is less important. For the varying voltages and currents found in many electronic circuits, the quantity *impedance* is more appropriate than resistance; both are measured in ohms. Thus the impedance of a loudspeaker (the load) should equal the output impedance of the amplifier (the source) that drives it. (If the amplifier is regarded as a source of e.m.f., its output impedance is equivalent to internal resistance.) Such an arrangement is only 50% efficient, but it produces the loudest sound!

FURTHER WORK

○ Estimate the uncertainties in the values of r and $\mathcal{E}$ that you obtained in (g).

10D Potentiometer (I)
Comparison of the e.m.f. of a cell with that of a standard cell, and measurement of the cell's internal resistance

APPARATUS REQUIRED

- cell under investigation: dry cell with added artificial 'internal' resistance
- Weston standard cell incorporating series protective resistors
- light-beam galvanometer (switch sensitivity to SHORT before moving)
- decade resistance box covering the range up to 100 Ω
- slide-wire potentiometer with jockey
- galvanometer with suitable sensitivity control
- 2 V accumulator
- 2 keys (or switches)
- connecting wires

PRINCIPLES INVOLVED

a When a balance point is obtained along a potentiometer wire, no current flows in the leads connecting the potentiometer to the source of potential difference that is being measured. It therefore provides an ideal means of making a precise comparison of the true e.m.f.s of two cells. In the first part of the experiment you will compare the e.m.f. $\mathcal{E}$ of the dry cell with that of a standard cell. In the second part a variable resistance R is connected across the dry cell, as shown in Fig. 10.16, and the potentiometer is used to balance the terminal p.d. V of the cell. When a balance point has been found, the same current I flows through both the dry cell and R. Applying Kirchhoff's second law to this loop we have:

$$\mathcal{E} = I(R + r) \qquad [10.6]$$

where r is the internal resistance of the cell.

E.M.F. COMPARISON

b Connect up the circuit of Fig. 10.17a ensuring that the Weston standard cell is adequately protected by suitably large series resistances. When all

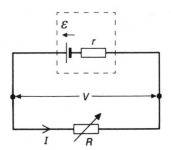

Fig. 10.16 The terminal p.d. V of a cell depends on the resistance R and the internal resistance r of the cell.

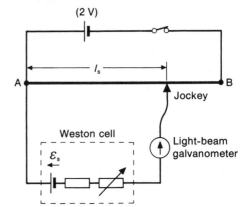

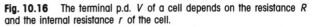

a Balancing the e.m.f. of the Weston standard cell.

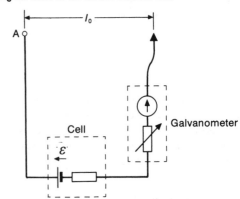

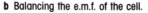

b Balancing the e.m.f. of the cell.

Fig. 10.17 Determining the e.m.f. of a cell with a potentiometer.

130

components are in position, switch the sensitivity of the light-beam galvanometer from SHORT to ×1, in which condition the galvanometer is very sensitive, though its movement is well damped and will come to rest in a very short time. The large series resistances protect both standard cell and galvanometer. Switch on. Find a balance point along the wire and record the balance length l_s.

c Now replace the standard cell and its protective resistor by the dry cell under investigation, and replace the light-beam galvanometer by the less sensitive galvanometer with its own protective resistor. See Fig. 10.17b. Find a balance point along the wire and record the balance length l_0.

d Modify equation [10.1] to suit the quantities involved here, and hence calculate $\mathcal{E}$, given that the e.m.f. $\mathcal{E}_s$ of the standard cell is 1.019 V.

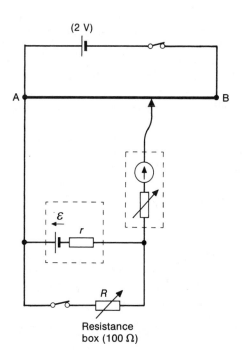

Fig. 10.18 Balancing the terminal p.d. of the cell on the potentiometer.

VARIATION OF V WITH R

e The circuit to be used for this part of the experiment is shown in Fig. 10.18. To the circuit of Fig. 10.17b is added the resistance box connected across the dry cell. The key helps to preserve the dry cell, but its use is not essential. The dry cell incorporates a concealed series resistor to increase its effective internal resistance. The total internal resistance r is therefore the sum of the real internal resistance (less than 1 Ω) and the added resistance. See section 10.1.2. Note that this artificial increase of r will have had no effect on the result obtained in (d): when no current flows through a cell (as when balance points were found in (b) and (c)) there can be no p.d. across any resistance in series with the cell, including its own internal resistance. The true e.m.f. therefore appears at the terminals of the cell.

f The terminal p.d. V of the dry cell, which equals the p.d. IR across R, is balanced by the p.d. along a length l of the potentiometer wire. Equation [10.1] may be used to relate l to the balance length l_0 found in (c):

$$\frac{l_0}{l} = \frac{\mathcal{E}}{V}$$

Since $V = IR$, it follows that:

$$\frac{\mathcal{E}}{I} = \frac{Rl_0}{l}$$

Rearranging equation [10.6] we have:

$$\frac{\mathcal{E}}{I} = (R + r)$$

Equating these two expressions for $\mathcal{E}/I$ gives:

$$R\left(\frac{l_0}{l} - 1\right) = r$$

which, on rearranging, gives:

$$R = \frac{rl}{(l_0 - l)}$$

so:

$$\frac{1}{R} = \frac{l_0}{rl} - \frac{1}{r} \qquad [10.7]$$

g Connect up the circuit in Fig. 10.18 and measure the balance length l for ten values of R given by $R/\Omega = 100, 40, 20, 14, 10, 8, 6, 5, 4$ and 3. Tabulate your measurements and add to them the value of l_0 found in (c), which corresponds to $R = \infty$.

h Refer to equation [10.7], in which l_0 and r are constants. Plot a suitable linear graph and use it to calculate r.

i State two requirements of the potentiometer circuit that must be met if balance lengths along the wire are to be proportional to the p.d.s that are applied, and describe briefly simple tests that you might make to check these requirements.

NOTES

j Your record should include labelled circuit diagrams where appropriate, a derivation of equation [10.7], and a note about the artificially increased internal resistance of the cell.

k Had there been the e.m.f.s of several cells to measure in (c) and (d), it would have been convenient to calculate the *potential gradient* along the potentiometer wire. This can be used as a calibration constant for the potentiometer circuit (your particular combination of driver cell, potentiometer wire and connecting leads), which effectively adapts the scale of 100 cm to register voltages. If a length l_s of wire corresponds to the e.m.f. $\mathcal{E}_s$ of the standard cell, then unit length of wire (e.g. 1 cm) corresponds to a p.d. of $\mathcal{E}_s/l_s$; a suitable unit for this potential gradient is V cm^{-1}. Any balance length (in cm) may then be multiplied by the potential gradient to convert it to a voltage.

FURTHER WORK

l Estimate the uncertainties in the values of $\mathcal{E}$ and r that you obtained in (d) and (h).

m Carry out the tests that you suggested in (i).

n Repeat (c) and (d) for as many cells as you can find in the laboratory to calculate their e.m.f.s. See section 10.1.2.

10E Potentiometer (II)
Measurement of resistance by comparison of the potential differences across two resistances carrying the same current

APPARATUS REQUIRED

- 4 unknown resistances labelled A, B, C and D
- wire labelled W, about 1.2 m long
- 1 Ω, 10 Ω and 100 Ω standard resistances
- terminals mounted on a block (or other means of conveniently holding W)
- variable resistor, maximum resistance about 20 Ω
- slide-wire potentiometer with jockey
- galvanometer with suitable sensitivity control
- 2   2 V accumulators
- 2 keys (or switches)
- micrometer screw gauge
- metre rule
- connecting wires

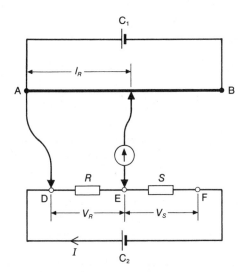

Fig. 10.19 Comparing resistances with a potentiometer.

PRINCIPLES INVOLVED

a The ratio of two resistances may be found by comparing the potential differences across them when they carry the same current, and the potentiometer circuit is ideally suited for making such a comparison. The most straightforward means of ensuring that the two resistances do carry the same current is, of course, to connect them in series in a circuit. The general form of the circuit to be used is shown in Fig. 10.19. Cell C_1 drives a steady current along the potentiometer wire, and cell C_2 drives a steady current I through the two resistances: the unknown R and the known standard S. The potentiometer connections are made first to terminals D and E, and a balance length l_R is obtained that represents the p.d. V_R across R. The potentiometer connections are then made to terminals

E and F, and a new balance length l_S is obtained that represents the p.d. V_S across S. Thus:

$$\frac{V_R}{V_S} = \frac{IR}{IS} = \frac{R}{S}$$

Combining this with equation [10.1] we have:

$$R = \frac{l_R}{l_S}S \qquad [10.8]$$

The ratio of the two resistances therefore equals the ratio of the two balance lengths. When a balance point has been obtained, no current flows in the leads connecting the potentiometer circuit to the lower circuit, which contains two resistances. This is why we are able to assume that the same current I flows through R and S during measurements of both l_R and l_S.

b To obtain the greatest precision from potentiometer measurements, we try to ensure that balance lengths are as long as possible; i.e. balance points should be near the end B of the potentiometer wire. This implies that l_R and l_S should be comparable, which in turn implies that the standard resistance S should be of similar value to the unknown R. You are provided with three standards. You will measure the resistances of four unknowns, labelled A, B, C and D, and a length of wire, firstly estimating each one, and then selecting the most appropriate standard for a more precise, second measurement.

INITIAL ESTIMATES OF R

c Connect up the two parts of the circuit of Fig. 10.20 for the comparison of the unknown resistance R_A with the 10 Ω standard S. Omit R_V from your circuit. Connect the potentiometer across R_A, as shown, find the balance point along the wire, and measure the balance length l_R. Now connect the potentiometer across S and measure the balance length l_S. Use equation [10.8] to calculate R_A.

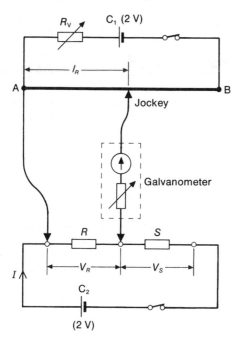

Fig. 10.20 Practical potentiometer circuit for comparing resistances.

d Repeat (c) for the other three labelled unknown resistances R_B, R_C and R_D.

e Use the micrometer screw gauge to measure the diameter of the sample of wire labelled W in several places along its length. Calculate the mean diameter d. Connect a measured length L (about 1.0 m) of the wire between the mounted terminals and repeat (c) to estimate its resistance R_W. Disconnect the terminals from the circuit, but do not yet remove or alter the wire between them.

MORE PRECISE MEASUREMENTS OF R

f The five results obtained so far should be regarded only as estimates, since no attempt was made to use the most appropriate standard; this may now be chosen for a precise determination of each unknown. The aim is to obtain balance lengths l_R and l_S that are comparable. S should therefore be chosen so that the ratio R/S (or S/R) is as close as possible to unity.

g If the two cells C_1 and C_2 in Fig. 10.20 are of the same type, and R and S are comparable, we would expect V_R and V_S each to be about half the total p.d. V_{AB} across the potentiometer wire. The balance lengths l_R and l_S occupy therefore only the left-hand half of the wire. Slightly improved precision can be obtained if V_{AB} is reduced to increase both l_R and l_S, and this is achieved by incorporating a variable resistance R_V in series with the driver cell C_1, as shown in Fig. 10.20. R_V should be increased until the *greater* of the two balance lengths can just be obtained on the wire (with a balance point near the end B of the wire). Once set, R_V must not be altered between measurements of l_R and l_S, otherwise a true comparison of V_R and V_S cannot be made.

h Decide which standard resistance is the most appropriate for each unknown, including R_W. Hence use the circuit of Fig. 10.20 to make a more precise measurement of all five resistances in turn. Include the variable resistance R_V in your circuit, turning it up to improve the sensitivity of the potentiometer as necessary. Remember that R_V must not be altered between corresponding measurements of l_R and l_S.

i Tabulate your results to show both initial estimates and precise values for each unknown. Calculate the resistivity ρ of the wire material, given by:

$$\rho = \frac{R_W A}{L}$$

where $A\,(= \pi d^2/4)$ is the cross-sectional area of the wire.

NOTE

j Your record should include a labelled circuit diagram that shows all components used, a short explanation of the principle of comparing resistances with a potentiometer, and a note on the use of the variable resistance R_V.

FURTHER WORK

k Estimate the uncertainties in the values of the five resistances that you obtained in (h).

10F Potentiometer (III)
Calibration of an ammeter by measurement of the potential difference across a standard resistance in series

APPARATUS REQUIRED

- ammeter under investigation, reading up to 1 A d.c.
- 2 Ω standard resistance
- Weston standard cell incorporating series protective resistors
- light-beam galvanometer (switch sensitivity to SHORT before moving)
- variable resistor, maximum resistance about 25 Ω
- slide-wire potentiometer with jockey
- galvanometer with suitable sensitivity control
- 2   2 V accumulators
- 2 keys (or switches)
- connecting wires

PRINCIPLES INVOLVED

a   An unknown current I can be determined by passing it through a known standard resistance S, across which the potential difference V is then measured using the potentiometer circuit.

Thus:
$$I = \frac{V}{S}$$

If S is connected in series with an ammeter, the current I_m indicated by the ammeter can be compared with the true current I. In this experiment you will compare I and I_m over the full range of the ammeter's scale, thereby *calibrating* the ammeter. When a balance point has been found along the potentiometer wire, no current flows in the leads connecting the potentiometer circuit to the circuit containing the standard resistance and the ammeter, which we are therefore able to assume both carry the same current I at all times. This would not be true if a conventional voltmeter were used to measure V, since the voltmeter itself would draw a small current.

b   As I_m is increased, a series of balance lengths is found that show how V is varying, but values of V cannot be calculated unless the potentiometer is calibrated with a standard cell. This then allows balance lengths on the potentiometer to be converted directly to voltages.

POTENTIOMETER CALIBRATION

c   Connect up the circuit shown in Fig. 10.21, ensuring that the Weston standard cell is adequately protected by suitably large series resistances. When all components are in position, switch the sensitivity of the light-beam galvanometer from SHORT to ×1, in which condition the galvanometer is very sensitive, though its movement is well damped and will come to rest in a very short time. The large series resistances protect both standard cell and galvanometer. Switch on, find a balance point along the wire and record the balance length l_s. Calculate the potential gradient ($= \mathcal{E}_s/l_s$) along the wire, given that the e.m.f. $\mathcal{E}_s$ of the standard cell is 1.019 V.

CURRENT MEASUREMENT

d   The circuit to be used for this part of the experiment is shown in Fig. 10.22. The light-beam galvanometer is replaced by the less sensitive galvanometer with its own protective resistor. The standard cell and its protective resistors are replaced by a loop around which the accumulator drives the current I. This can be set to any value by adjusting the variable resistance R_V.

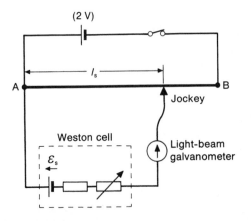

Fig. 10.21   *Calibrating the potentiometer with a standard cell.*

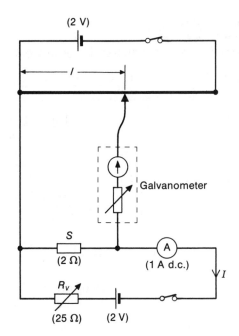

(2 V)

I

Galvanometer

S
(2 Ω)

(A)
(1 A d.c.)

I

R_V
(25 Ω)   (2 V)

Fig. 10.22 Potentiometer circuit for calibrating an ammeter.

e   The p.d. V across S is balanced by the p.d. along a length l of the potentiometer wire.

Thus:
$$V = l\frac{\mathcal{E}_s}{l_s}$$

Note that this expression also follows from equation [10.1]. Since $I = V/S$, we have:

$$I = \frac{l}{S}\frac{\mathcal{E}_s}{l_s} \qquad [10.9]$$

f   Connect up the circuit of Fig. 10.22 and measure the balance length l along the potentiometer wire for about ten different values of indicated current I_m, covering the entire range of the ammeter. Try to read the ammeter to a greater degree of precision than you would normally do. If one division on the scale represents 20 mA, estimate I_m to the nearest 4 mA. Such precision can be justified here because what are being investigated in this experiment are consequences of the ammeter's defects, which would normally invalidate readings other than to the nearest scale marking. If possible, adjust R_V such that the ammeter's pointer lies exactly over a scale marking, though this will not be easy for larger currents. Before attempting to find the balance point ensure that I_m is steady. After recording the balance length, check the reading of the ammeter; if it has changed, record the later value. Tabulate your measurements of I_m and l.

g   Calculate and record in a third column the true current I, using equation [10.9]. The greatest source of uncertainty here arises from the uncertainty in the

value of S. Try to find out the tolerance of S and record your calculated values of I with an appropriate number of significant figures: you must be aware of the uncertainty in I.

AMMETER CALIBRATION CHART

h   Calculate and record the difference $(I - I_m)$ between the true and indicated currents. When $I_m < I$, record the difference as a negative quantity.

i   Display your results as a calibration chart for the ammeter: plot a graph of $(I - I_m)$ (ordinate) against I_m (abscissa).

j   Does $(I - I_m)$ vary in a random manner, or does your chart reveal any trends? Suggest possible causes for such trends. Comment on the reliability of your chart: are there any regions of it where the uncertainty in $(I - I_m)$ is greater than 100%?

NOTES

k   Your record should include a labelled circuit diagram and a clear statement of how I is calculated.

l   Your calibration chart only applies to the particular combination of galvanometer and shunt that you have used as the ammeter. A current I_m indicated on this ammeter should have added to it a correction $(I - I_m)$, which can be obtained from the chart.

10G Potentiometer (IV)
Adaptation of a potentiometer circuit to measure the small e.m.f. of a thermocouple

APPARATUS REQUIRED

- copper–constantan thermocouple
- 5 Ω standard resistance
- Weston standard cell incorporating series protective resistors
- light-beam galvanometer (switch sensitivity to SHORT before moving)
- 2 decade resistance boxes each covering the range up to 1000 Ω (×1 Ω)
- slide-wire potentiometer with jockey
- metre bridge
- galvanometer with suitable sensitivity control
- 2 V accumulator
- 2 keys (or switches)
- 2 beakers
- Bunsen burner, tripod and gauze
- ice and water
- connecting wires

PRINCIPLES INVOLVED

a The potential difference across a normal potentiometer is approximately equal to the e.m.f. of the driver cell. A lead–acid accumulator used with a wire of length 1 m produces a potential gradient of about 2 mV mm^{-1}, and a small e.m.f. of about 5 mV would therefore be balanced by the potential drop across only 2.5 mm of wire! The sensitivity of the potentiometer can be increased by connecting a large resistance R, which reduces the current I that flows along the wire to around 1 or 2 mA (Fig. 10.23). The p.d. V_{AB} across the wire is then only a few mV. (Alternatively, the same sort of sensitivity is obtainable from a potentiometer wire over 300 m long!) In this experiment you will modify a potentiometer in this way and use it to measure the e.m.f. $\mathcal{E}_\theta$ of a thermocouple, which arises when the junctions between wires of two different metals are maintained at different temperatures.

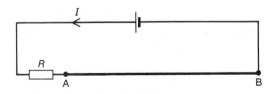

Fig. 10.23 Increasing the sensitivity of a potentiometer by connecting a series resistance.

b The potentiometer circuit can only be used to *compare* potential differences. An e.m.f. that has been balanced on the wire cannot be calculated unless the potentiometer has been calibrated, i.e. unless the potential gradient along the wire has been determined. Usually this is done by balancing a known p.d. on the wire, for which a standard cell is used. But the e.m.f. of the standard cell normally available in laboratories (the Weston cell) is 1.019 V. If the potentiometer circuit has been modified to balance p.d.s up to only a few mV, it would not be possible to find a balance point for the Weston cell. The e.m.f.s of nearly all cells lie in the range 1.0 to 2.0 V, so there are no other cells that might be more suitable.

c In the circuit shown in Fig. 10.23:

$$V_{AB} = IR_{AB} \qquad [10.10]$$

where R_{AB} is the resistance of the potentiometer wire. The calibration procedure with the Weston cell leads to a determination of I, but to calculate V_{AB} and hence the potential gradient it is also necessary to know R_{AB}, which you will measure as accurately as possible in the first part of the experiment.

MEASUREMENT OF R_{AB}

d Any uncertainty in the final value of the thermocouple's e.m.f. that you calculate is determined mainly by the uncertainty in R_{AB}. It would be desirable to limit the uncertainty in R_{AB} to ±1%. This sort of precision is not obtainable from the resistance ranges on a conventional moving-coil multimeter. However, you may have access to a digital multimeter, with which direct resistance measurements can be made to an accuracy of ±0.1%, but before using it check that this accuracy applies to small resistances. (R_{AB} probably lies in the range 2–10 Ω.)

e If a direct reading multimeter is not available, the most accurate means of measuring R_{AB} is by comparison with a standard resistance S, for which the metre bridge circuit can be used. The metre bridge is a practical adaptation of the Wheatstone bridge network (on which the next three experiments in this section are based; see also section 10.5). The two resistances are connected in the arms of the bridge as shown in Fig. 10.24. When the bridge is balanced:

$$\frac{R_{AB}}{S} = \frac{l_R}{l_S} \qquad [10.11]$$

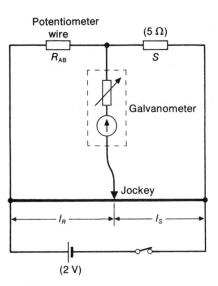

Fig. 10.24 Using a metre bridge circuit to measure the resistance R of the potentiometer wire.

f Connect the potentiometer that you will be using during the remainder of this experiment in the left-hand arm of the metre bridge and the 5 Ω standard resistance S in the right-hand arm. (One of the resistance boxes, on which 5 Ω has been set, can be used for this purpose.) Use short, thick connecting leads of minimal resistance. Connect up the remainder of the circuit shown in Fig. 10.24. Balance the bridge and measure the balance lengths l_R and l_S. Use equation [10.11] to calculate R_{AB}. Alternatively, measure R_{AB} directly using a digital multimeter.

BALANCING $\mathcal{E}_\theta$ ON THE POTENTIOMETER

g To reduce V_{AB} to a value that is just greater than $\mathcal{E}_\theta$ two resistance boxes are connected in series with the potentiometer wire, as shown in Fig. 10.25. The total resistance $(R_1 + R_2)$ that is eventually set on them is then maintained for the remainder of the experiment, so that the current I along the potentiometer wire is kept constant. $\mathcal{E}_\theta$ is to be balanced against the p.d. across a length l_θ of the wire. The potential gradient along the wire is V_{AB}/l_{AB}, where l_{AB} is the length of the wire.

Hence:
$$\mathcal{E}_\theta = \frac{V_{AB}}{l_{AB}} \times l_\theta \qquad [10.12]$$

h Start heating a beaker of water over the Bunsen burner and prepare a mixture of ice and water. Connect up the top part of the circuit of Fig. 10.25, setting a combined value $(R_1 + R_2)$ of about 100 Ω on the two resistance boxes. Now connect the lower part of the circuit, and place the two junctions of the thermocouple in their respective beakers as far apart as possible. Switch the sensitivity of the light-beam galvanometer from SHORT to $\times 0.01$. When the water boils, turn down the burner a little and locate the

approximate position of the balance point along the wire, near the end A, increasing the galvanometer's sensitivity as necessary.

i Estimate by how much your balance length must be increased to shift the balance point into the right-hand half of the wire (aim to make the balance length about three-quarters of l_{AB}). Increase the combined resistance $(R_1 + R_2)$ by the same proportion, rounding the value to be set up or down to the nearest 100 Ω. If you need to set $(R_1 + R_2)$ above 1800 Ω (necessary if R_{AB} is greater than about 6 Ω) you will require resistance boxes with ranges above 1000 Ω. If these are not available, limit $(R_1 + R_2)$ to 1800 Ω. Once you are satisfied that $\mathcal{E}_\theta$ can be balanced against the p.d. across a reasonable length of wire, measure the balance length l_θ and note the value of $(R_1 + R_2)$.

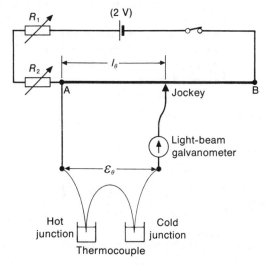

Fig. 10.25 Balancing the e.m.f. of a thermocouple on the potentiometer.

POTENTIOMETER CALIBRATION

j Calibration is achieved by connecting the standard cell and the galvanometer across R_2 as shown in Fig. 10.26 (overleaf). R_1 and R_2 are adjusted, maintaining their combined value $(R_1 + R_2)$, until the galvanometer shows no deflection. The p.d. V_2 across R_2 then balances the e.m.f. $\mathcal{E}_s$ of the standard cell. Provided that the combined resistance $(R_1 + R_2)$ eventually set in (i) has been maintained, the current I that flowed around the potentiometer circuit when $\mathcal{E}_\theta$ was balanced on the wire now flows through R_2 and is given by:

$$I = \frac{V_2}{R_2} = \frac{\mathcal{E}_s}{R_2} \qquad [10.13]$$

k Connect the standard cell and the light-beam galvanometer to your potentiometer circuit, as shown in Fig. 10.26. Ensure that the standard cell is adequately protected by suitably large series resistances. Switch the sensitivity of the galvanometer from SHORT to $\times 1$,

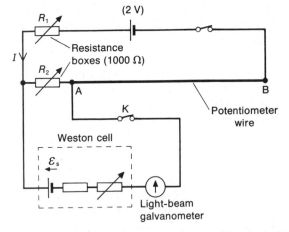

Fig. 10.26 Calibrating the adapted potentiometer with a standard cell.

in which condition the galvanometer is very sensitive, though its movement is well damped and will come to rest in a short time. The large series resistances protect both standard cell and galvanometer. Adjust R_1 and R_2, keeping $(R_1 + R_2)$ constant, to balance V_2 against ε_s; close the key K for only a few seconds at a time. Use equation [10.13] to calculate I, given that $\varepsilon_s = 1.019$ V.

CALCULATION OF ε_θ

l Calculate V_{AB} from equation [10.10], using the values of I and R_{AB} that you found in (k) and (f).

m Hence calculate ε_θ from equation [10.12], using the value of l_θ that you measured in (i).

NOTE

n Your record should include labelled circuit diagrams, where appropriate, and clearly set out calculations.

FURTHER WORK

o Use the thermocouple to measure room temperature. Keep the cold junction in the ice/water mixture so that the hotter junction then becomes the thermometer probe. You may assume that the e.m.f. generated between the junctions is proportional to their temperature difference. (You are, in fact, thereby defining a temperature scale based on the thermoelectric e.m.f. as the thermoelectric property.)

10H Metre Bridge (I)
Measurement of the resistance of specimens of wire to determine the resistivity of the material

APPARATUS REQUIRED

- material under investigation: 2 wires of different diameters labelled X and Y (both about 1 m long)
- 5 Ω standard resistance
- metre bridge with jockey
- galvanometer with suitable sensitivity control
- 2 V accumulator
- key (or switch)
- connecting wires
- micrometer screw gauge
- metre rule

PRINCIPLES INVOLVED

a The resistance R of a wire made from a material of resistivity ρ is given by:

$$R = \frac{\rho L}{A}$$

where L and A are the wire's length and cross-sectional area respectively. ρ is defined by this equation. For a wire having a circular cross-section of diameter d:

$$A = \frac{\pi d^2}{4}$$

and:

$$R = \frac{4\rho L}{\pi d^2}$$

In this experiment you will use a metre bridge circuit to compare the resistances of various lengths of two wires, made from the same material but of different diameters, with a standard resistance. Since both L and d are to be varied, it is convenient to combine them by regarding (L/d^2) as one variable quantity.

Thus:
$$R = \frac{4\rho}{\pi}\left(\frac{L}{d^2}\right) \qquad [10.14]$$

VARIATION OF R WITH (L/d^2)

b   Use the micrometer screw gauge to measure the diameters of the two wires in several places. Calculate for each wire the mean diameter d.

c   Connect a precisely measured length L (about 0.75 m) of the thinner wire X in the left-hand arm of the metre bridge and the 5 Ω standard resistance S in the right-hand arm (Fig. 10.27). Remember to connect S with short, thick leads of minimal resistance. Connect up the remainder of the circuit. Balance the bridge, and measure the length l along the bridge wire.

d   Repeat (c) for four more decreasing values of L down to about 0.15 m. Tabulate your measurements of L and l.

e   Repeat (c) and (d) using the thicker wire Y for five decreasing values of L between 1.00 m and 0.20 m. Record all measurements in one table, but indicate clearly which ones apply to which wire.

f   Use equation [10.3] to calculate the value of R for each set of corresponding values of L and l, and record your results in a third column of your table. Calculate also values of the quantity (L/d^2) and record your results in a fourth column. Ensure that you use the appropriate value of d in each case. Think carefully about units.

g   On one set of axes draw graphs of R (ordinate) against L/d^2 (abscissa). All ten points should theoretically lie on one line; but unless you think that they are colinear, distinguish one set of five points from the other and draw two lines. Refer to equation [10.14] and use your graph(s) to determine ρ.

h   What would cause your two graphs to have different slopes? What would cause the two graphs to be separate though parallel?

i   Explain why it is important to take decreasing values of L for each wire.

NOTE

j   Your record should include a labelled circuit diagram.

FURTHER WORK

k   Estimate the uncertainty in the value of ρ that you obtained in (g).

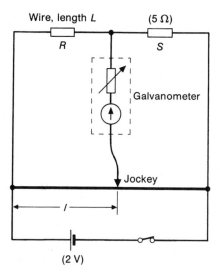

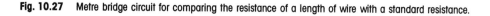

Fig. 10.27   Metre bridge circuit for comparing the resistance of a length of wire with a standard resistance.

10I Metre Bridge (II)
Investigation of the variation of resistance of a metal with temperature

APPARATUS REQUIRED

- metal under investigation: coil of enamelled copper wire mounted in glycerol-filled test tube
- 5 Ω standard resistance
- metre bridge with jockey
- galvanometer with suitable sensitivity control
- 2 V accumulator
- key (or switch)
- connecting wires
- −10–110 °C thermometer
- tall beaker
- Bunsen burner, tripod and gauze
- retort stand, clamp and boss
- ice and water

PRINCIPLES INVOLVED

a A wire of uniform cross-sectional area A and length L has a resistance R given by:

$$R = \frac{\rho L}{A}$$

where ρ is the resistivity of the material from which the wire is made, and which is defined by this equation. For metals ρ increases linearly with $\theta\,(°C)$ according to the equation:

$$\rho = \rho_0(1 + \alpha\theta)$$

in which ρ_0 is the resistivity of the metal at 0 °C, and α is the temperature coefficient of resistivity of the metal. α is numerically equal to the increase in ρ caused by a temperature increase of 1 K. In this experiment you will use a metre bridge circuit to compare the resistance of a specimen of copper wire at temperatures between 0 °C and 100 °C with a standard resistance. If changes of L and A are negligible then $R \propto \rho$, and so:

$$R = R_0(1 + \alpha\theta) \qquad [10.15]$$

where R_0 is the resistance of the specimen at 0 °C.

VARIATION OF R WITH θ

b Prepare a mixture of ice and water in the beaker and immerse the test tube containing the coiled specimen of copper wire. Stand the beaker on the tripod and gauze. Connect the coil in the left-hand arm of the metre bridge with thick leads that are long

enough to keep the coil away from other parts of the circuit, so that they are not affected by the Bunsen, which will be used to heat the beaker and its contents. Loop these leads over the clamp on the retort stand to keep them clear of the Bunsen flame. You may also be able to use the stand to hold the test tube just off the bottom of the beaker. Connect the 5 Ω standard resistance S in the right-hand arm of the bridge using short, thick leads, and connect up the remainder of the circuit shown in Fig. 10.28. Measure the temperature θ of the mixture; don't assume that it is 0 °C. Balance the bridge, and measure the length l along the bridge wire.

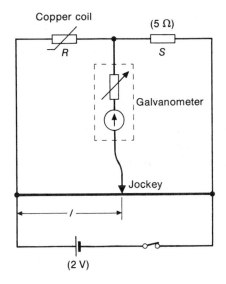

Fig. 10.28 Metre bridge circuit for comparing the resistance of a copper coil with a standard resistance.

c Remove the ice, top up the beaker if necessary and start heating. Stir the water continuously, and when its temperature is about 10 °C remove the Bunsen. Balance the bridge, measure the length l, and then immediately re-measure the temperature θ of the water. Tabulate your measurements of θ and l. Note that the temperature may alter while you are balancing the bridge; this is why the value of θ that you record should be the one measured just *after* you have balanced the bridge, and not the one measured before.

d Repeat (c) for nine more increasing values of θ up to the temperature at which the water boils. To maintain the higher temperatures while you balance the bridge, do not remove the Bunsen, but turn down its flame. Stir the water frequently.

e Use equation [10.3] to calculate the value of R for each set of corresponding values of θ and l, and record your results in a third column of your table.

f Refer to equation [10.15], in which R_0 and α are constants. Plot a suitable linear graph and use it to determine R_0 and α. Assume that θ is the temperature of the coil.

g Explain why the specimen of copper wire has to be thin and very long. What property (or properties) of glycerol makes it a suitable liquid with which to fill the test tube containing the coil? Why is the test tube immersed in a beaker of water?

NOTE

h Your record should include a labelled circuit diagram.

FURTHER WORK

i Estimate the uncertainty in the value of α that you obtained in (f).

j Repeat (b), (c), (d), (e) and (f) using a specimen of constantan wire, but for only about five different values of θ. Comment on the suitability of constantan as an alloy from which to manufacture standard resistances.

10J Metre Bridge (III)
Investigation of the variation of the resistance of a semiconductor with temperature

APPARATUS REQUIRED

- semiconductor under investigation: thermistor type TH-7
- 10 Ω standard resistance
- metre bridge with jockey
- galvanometer with suitable sensitivity control
- 2 V accumulator
- key (or switch)
- connecting wires
- −10–110 °C thermometer
- beaker
- Bunsen burner, tripod and gauze
- retort stand, clamp and boss
- ice and water

PRINCIPLES INVOLVED

a The resistance of a semiconductor decreases as its temperature increases. As in metals, a temperature rise increases the amplitude of vibration of the atoms in the crystal structure (the lattice), which therefore collide more frequently with the moving charge carriers. But the effect of this, which tends to increase resistance, is overwhelmed in semiconductors by the effect of the release of more and more charge carriers as the temperature increases. In metals the concentration of charge carriers is hardly affected by temperature.

b The resistance R of a pure semiconductor theoretically varies with absolute temperature T according to the exponential relationship:

$$R = R_0 \exp\left[\frac{E_g}{kT}\right] \qquad [10.16]$$

in which R_0 and E_g are constants for the semiconductor and k is the Boltzmann constant. E_g is known as the width of energy gap in the semiconducting material and represents the amount of energy a charge carrier must acquire before it can contribute to the process of conduction. k is a universal constant related to the temperature dependence of the energy of individual atoms; its precise definition will not be considered here.

c In this experiment you will use a metre bridge circuit to compare the resistance of a thermistor at temperatures between 0 °C and 100 °C with a standard resistance. The thermistor is made from a small piece of semiconducting material.

VARIATION OF R WITH θ

d Prepare a mixture of ice and water in the beaker and stand it on the tripod and gauze. Immerse the thermistor and connect it in the left-hand arm of the metre bridge with thick leads that are long enough to keep the coil away from other parts of the circuit, so that they are not affected by the Bunsen, which will be used to heat the beaker and its contents. Loop these leads over the clamp on the retort stand such that the thermistor is suspended in the water, well above the bottom of the beaker. Keep the leads clear of the Bunsen flame. Connect the 10 Ω standard resistance S in the right-hand arm of the bridge using short, thick leads, and connect up the remainder of the circuit shown in Fig. 10.29. Measure the temperature θ (°C) of the mixture; don't assume that it is 0 °C. Balance the bridge, and measure the length l along the bridge wire.

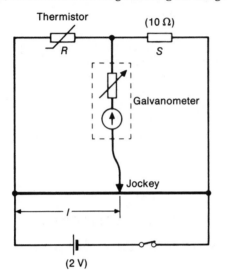

Fig. 10.29 Metre bridge circuit for comparing the resistance of a thermistor with a standard resistance.

e Remove the ice and start heating. Stir the water continuously, and when its temperature is about 10 °C remove the Bunsen. Balance the bridge, measure the length l, and then immediately re-measure the temperature θ of the water. Tabulate your measurements of θ and l. Note that the temperature may alter while you are balancing the bridge; this is why the value of θ that you record should be the one measured just after you have balanced the bridge, and not the one measured before.

f Repeat (e) for nine more increasing values of θ up to the temperature at which the water boils. To maintain the higher temperatures while you balance the bridge, do not remove the Bunsen, but turn down its flame. Stir the water frequently.

g Use equation [10.3] to calculate the value of R for each set of corresponding values of θ and l, and record your results in a third column of your table.

h Draw a graph of R (ordinate) against θ (abscissa), which can be assumed to be the temperature of the thermistor. Does the form of your graph suggest that R decreases exponentially with temperature, as predicted by equation [10.16]?

i Use the relationship $T = \theta + 273$ to calculate values of the absolute temperature T of the semi-conductor and record your results in a fourth column. Refer to equation [10.16], in which R_0, E_g and k are constants. Plot a suitable linear graph and use it to determine E_g given that the Boltzmann constant $k = 1.38 \times 10^{-23}$ J K^{-1}.

j Express E_g in electron-volts (eV), given that 1 eV $= 1.60 \times 10^{-19}$ J, and compare your result with the energy gaps in pure germanium (0.67 eV) and pure silicon (1.14 eV).

k Suggest a practical use for a thermistor of the type that you have used.

NOTES

l Your record should include a labelled circuit diagram.

m In most semiconducting devices, including transistors and integrated circuits, temperature effects are a nuisance, and they are therefore made from materials in which E_g is relatively high. Integrated circuits, for example, are formed on chips of silicon rather than germanium. Thermistors, on the other hand, are made from material in which E_g is low, since it is intended that they respond to temperature variations.

FURTHER WORK

n Estimate the uncertainty in the value of E_g that you obtained in (i).

11 ELECTRIC AND MAGNETIC FIELDS

This section includes experiments on the Hall effect in extrinsic semiconductors (experiment 11A), the measurement of magnetic fields using a search coil (experiments 11B and 11C), an investigation of the mutual induction of two coils (experiment 11D) and measurements on electrons moving in electric and magnetic fields (experiments 11E and 11F). In order to make a more substantial experiment of 11B, which uses a search coil and ballistic galvanometer to measure a steady magnetic field, an experiment on the comparison of capacitances using a ballistic galvanometer is also included.

11.1 ACCELERATION OF CHARGED PARTICLES

If a particle of charge q is accelerated through a potential difference of V_A, then it gains kinetic energy equal to the electrostatic potential energy qV_A. Thus for a particle of mass m starting from rest, the velocity v is given by:

$$\tfrac{1}{2}mv^2 = qV_A \qquad [11.1]$$

11.2 DEFLECTION OF A CHARGED PARTICLE IN AN ELECTRIC FIELD

Consider a positively charged particle q with velocity v in the x-direction entering an electric field E in the y-direction as shown in Fig. 11.1. The particle experiences no force in the x-direction and a force $F_y = qE$ in the y-direction. Thus the trajectory of the charged particle in the electric field will be a curve as shown. After leaving the field the particle will travel in a straight line. By considering independently the horizontal and vertical motions of the particle, an equation relating the vertical distance y to the horizontal distance x travelled by the particle can be found.

If the particle travels a distance x in time t, then

$$x = vt \qquad [11.2]$$

In the vertical direction, the acceleration of the particle a_y can be calculated from $ma_y = qE$. Thus in time t, the particle travels a vertical distance y given by:

$$y = 0 + \tfrac{1}{2}a_y t^2 \qquad [11.3]$$

Substituting in equation [11.3] for a_y and for t from equation [11.2] gives:

$$y = \left(\frac{Eq}{2mv^2}\right)x^2 \qquad [11.4]$$

This is the equation of a parabola.

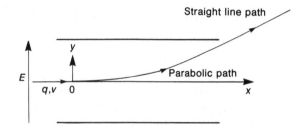

Fig. 11.1 The deflection of a particle, positive charge q and velocity v, in an electric field E. The deflection for a negatively charged particle will be in the opposite direction.

11.3 DEFLECTION OF A CHARGED PARTICLE IN A MAGNETIC FIELD

If a particle travelling with velocity v enters at an angle θ to a magnetic field of flux density B, it experiences a force F of magnitude $Bqv \sin \theta$ perpendicular both to the direction of travel of the particle and to B. In general this will produce a helical path for the charged particle. However if $\theta = 90°$, the force $F = Bqv$ of constant magnitude and always perpendicular to v produces a circular trajectory of the particle (Fig. 11.2 overleaf). Thus the acceleration $a = v^2/r$ for a particle travelling in a circle of radius r is related to the centripetal force Bqv by:

$$\frac{mv^2}{r} = Bqv \qquad [11.5]$$

11.4 A CHARGED PARTICLE IN CROSSED ELECTRIC AND MAGNETIC FIELDS

The velocity of a charged particle can be determined from equation [11.1]. Alternatively it can be determined by using a combination of an electric field E and a magnetic field B to produce zero resultant deflection of the

143

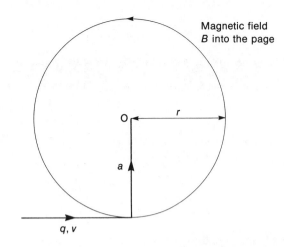

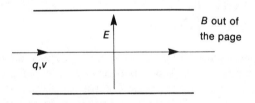

Fig. 11.2 The trajectory of a particle, positive charge *q* and velocity *v*, injected perpendicular to a magnetic field of flux density *B*. The trajectory would be the same for a negative particle with *B* out of the page.

particle. In Fig. 11.3 the electric field E will produce a deflection in the vertical direction, whereas the magnetic field B will produce an opposite vertical deflection. For a zero deflection in the combined fields:

$$Eq = Bqv \qquad [11.6]$$

So particles with a velocity $v = E/B$ will travel in a horizontal straight line. Thus by adjusting E or B to obtain zero deflection of the particle in the fields, v can be measured.

Fig. 11.3 The use of crossed electric and magnetic fields to produce zero deflection of a charged particle.

11.5 THE SEARCH COIL AND ELECTROMAGNETIC INDUCTION

The search coil can be used to measure either a steady magnetic field or an alternating magnetic field. To measure a steady field the total charge Q flowing through a ballistic galvanometer, when the magnetic flux through the search coil is changed, is measured. Measurement of an alternating magnetic field is achieved by measuring the e.m.f. induced in the search coil using a cathode ray oscilloscope.

11.5.1 Measurement of a constant magnetic field using a search coil

Fig. 11.4 shows a search coil of N turns and average cross-sectional area A placed with its plane normal to the magnetic field of flux density B. If the coil is rapidly removed from the field then an e.m.f. $\mathcal{E}$ will be induced that is directly related to the rate of change of magnetic flux $\varPhi = BA$. Thus:

$$\mathcal{E} = -\frac{\mathrm{d}}{\mathrm{d}t}(N\varPhi) = -NA\left(\frac{\mathrm{d}B}{\mathrm{d}t}\right) \qquad [11.7]$$

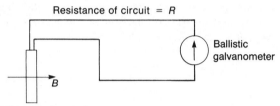

Fig. 11.4 The measurement of a constant magnetic field B using a search coil and ballistic galvanometer.

The negative sign in equation [11.7] will be ignored since we are interested only in the magnitude of $\mathcal{E}$. Clearly the current $I = \mathcal{E}/R$ flowing in the search coil circuit will depend on the rate at which the coil is removed from B. But if a ballistic galvanometer is used to measure the charge flow Q, it can be shown that Q is independent of this rate of removal. Integrating:

$$I = \frac{NA}{R}\frac{\mathrm{d}B}{\mathrm{d}t}$$

with respect to t gives:

$$Q = \frac{NAB}{R} \qquad [11.8]$$

The assumption is that the time for which Q flows through the ballistic galvanometer is significantly less than the period of oscillation of its suspension; otherwise Q cannot be considered to provide an instantaneous impulse.

Alternatively, if there is sufficient room in the magnetic field, the search coil may simply be rotated through 180° in the field. It is easy to show that the total magnetic flux change through the coil is doubled and the charge flow Q is double the value given by equation [11.8].

11.5.2 Measurement of an alternating magnetic field using a search coil

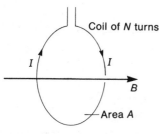

Coil of N turns

I I

B

Area A

Fig. 11.5 The use of a search coil to measure a time varying magnetic field B.

Fig. 11.5 shows a search coil with its plane perpendicular to a time varying magnetic field $B = B_0 \sin (2\pi ft)$ of frequency f. This alternating field is provided by an alternating current supply in a conductor. The e.m.f. induced in the search coil will depend on the rate of change of magnetic flux NAB through the coil. The e.m.f. $\mathcal{E}$ will have the same frequency f as that of the field, but its magnitude will also depend on f. As can be seen from Fig. 11.6, the rate of change of B, and therefore the magnetic flux, will be doubled if the frequency f is doubled. Thus a large e.m.f. of several volts can be induced in the search coil by using a suitably high frequency power supply connected to the conductor.

This can be more formally shown from the mathematical analysis. Using equation [11.7]:

$$\mathcal{E} = NA \frac{d}{dt} [B_0 \sin (2\pi ft)]$$

$$\mathcal{E} = NAB_0 \times 2\pi f \cos (2\pi ft)$$

Thus the peak value of $\mathcal{E}, \mathcal{E}_0$, is given by:

$$\mathcal{E}_0 = 2\pi fNAB_0 \qquad [11.9]$$

This e.m.f. can be measured using a cathode ray oscilloscope (CRO – see appendix 1, page 290) and the value for B_0 determined at any point along the conductor.

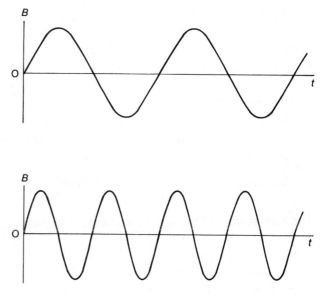

Fig. 11.6 The effect of changing the frequency of the magnetic field B.

11A Hall Effect

Investigation of the Hall effect and measurement of the charge carrier density in an extrinsic semiconductor

APPARATUS REQUIRED

- Hall effect wafers (p- and n-type)
- 6 V battery unit/power supply
- 0–100 mA d.c. ammeter
- 0–100 mV d.c. voltmeter with a resistance of at least 1000 Ω
- 0–1000 Ω resistance box to limit the current through the Hall slice to 50 mA
- permanent magnet with a known value of B ($\approx$ 0.1 T)

For the optional experiment to measure the magnetic field due to a current carrying conductor you will require:

- pair of Helmholtz coils or a circular coil
- 6 V d.c. power supply providing a coil current of about 1 A
- 0–1 A d.c. ammeter
- 0–6 V a.c. supply, preferably with a range of frequencies
- CRO with a voltage sensitivity of 100 mV div^{-1}
- op-amp based amplifier with a gain of −100, with its power supplies (+15 V, 0 V, −15 V)
- Hall slice with screened leads to the amplifier
- clamp, boss and stand

PRINCIPLES INVOLVED

a   When a magnetic field B is applied across a slice of a conductor or doped semiconductor carrying a current I, an electric field E is set up between the faces X and Y (Fig. 11.7). Thus a potential difference $V_H = Ea$ is produced across the slice. The magnitude of the Hall voltage V_H depends on the number of charge carriers (electric charge q) per unit volume n, the physical dimensions of the slice, the current I and the magnetic flux density B. V_H for conductors is very much smaller than for doped semiconductors, and so it is the latter that are usually used to measure magnetic fields.

b   By considering the force exerted by B on the charge carriers, it can be shown that the electric field set up across XY is given by:

$$E = \frac{BI}{Anq} \qquad [11.10]$$

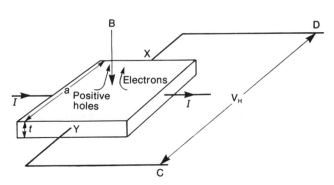

Fig. 11.7   The Hall effect for a slice of semiconductor of thickness t.

where $A = ta$ is the cross-sectional area of the slice perpendicular to the direction of current flow. Thus V_H can be determined from:

$$V_H = \frac{BI}{tnq} \qquad [11.11]$$

The direction of the electric field E, and hence V_H, depend on the type of charge carriers. In n-type semiconductors the majority charge carriers are electrons ($q = -e$) and so the electric field set up is in the direction Y to X. In p-type semiconductors the majority charge carriers are positive holes ($q = +e$) and the electric field will be from X to Y. Thus the two types of semiconductor will give Hall voltages of opposite sign, with C at a positive potential with respect to D for an n-type semiconductor.

c   The Hall voltage can be used to measure n (if B is known), B (if n is known) or to determine the type of semiconductor (if the direction of B is known). The magnitude of the Hall voltage for a semiconductor is about 100 mV for a magnetic field flux density of about 0.1–0.2 T, but only about 1 mV for a typical magnetic field of 1 mT for a current carrying conductor. Whereas a voltage of 100 mV can be measured accurately with a high resistance galvanometer (at least 1000 Ω), a voltage of 1 mV is very difficult to measure. It is tempting to use a light-beam galvanometer on one of its more sensitive scales, but unfortunately its resistance is only about 10 Ω, in comparison to the resistance of the Hall slice of about 100 Ω. Thus the galvanometer would not measure the true Hall voltage, since an appreciable current would flow through the galvanometer and the measured value of V_H would be far too low (see experiment 10B). There are several alternatives including the use of a potentiometer to measure a small e.m.f. (see experiment 10G) or operational amplifier with a gain of about 100 (see experiment 15B) to increase the output voltage to about 100 mV. The latter forms part of the optional experiment given in the Further work section.

d   The main part of the experiment involves the determination of n and the type of doped semiconductor using a known magnetic field derived from a permanent magnet.

MEASUREMENT OF THE HALL VOLTAGE

e   Set up the circuit shown in Fig. 11.8. The potentiometer for zeroing the Hall voltage is usually an integral part of the Hall slice. The resistance box should be set to its maximum value and slowly decreased until the recommended value for I is registered. You must not exceed this value because the semiconductor slice can easily be damaged by electrical heating which causes its resistance to decrease rapidly. You may find that a battery unit will give only the recommended current with the resistance box taken out of the circuit. Record the value of I. The terminals marked V_H should be connected to a 0–100 mV meter. A digital meter may be used, but if one is not available a 0–100 μA ammeter with a resistance of 1000 Ω will give a full scale deflection of 100 mV.

f   In the absence of a magnetic field, adjust the potentiometer of the Hall slice until V_H is zero. This adjustment is quite difficult and if you find it impossible to obtain exactly zero, record the reading and adjust subsequent readings as appropriate.

g   The reason for the non-zero value of V_H in the absence of a magnetic field is the electric field set up across the semiconductor when a current flows through it. Only a small effect of about 50 μV is expected from the earth's magnetic field.

h   Place the Hall slice in the magnetic field so that B is perpendicular to the Hall slice. You may need a stand, clamp and boss to hold it in position. If you are using a digital voltmeter, it will not matter which Hall slice you use, since the meter can register a negative value of V_H. A moving-coil meter must be correctly connected, and so if you obtain a negative deflection, just reverse the meter connections to obtain a positive deflection. Record V_H making any necessary corrections for the initial meter reading. Note the direction of V_H and B.

i   Repeat the measurement in (h) using the second Hall slice.

DETERMINATION OF THE SEMICONDUCTOR TYPE AND THE CHARGE CARRIER CONCENTRATION n

j   In order to determine the semiconductor type refer to Fig. 11.7 and the signs of the Hall voltages that you measured.

k   The calculation of n from equation [11.11] requires the values of B and t. The value of B will be given and t is usually 1 mm. Take $q = e = 1.6 \times 10^{-19}$ C. Using your data calculate the value of n for each Hall slice.

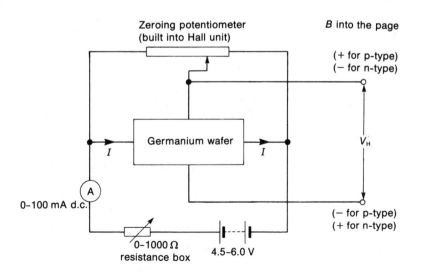

Fig. 11.8   Circuit used to measure the Hall voltage produced by a semiconductor.

NOTES

l Include in your account a description of the Hall effect, the circuit diagram for the Hall slice and a summary of your results for the type of semiconductor and n values. Against each set give the identifying mark, usually a coloured dot, for the slice.

m A Hall slice can be used to determine the uniformity of magnetic fields in large instruments such as a cyclotron or nuclear magnetic resonance scanning instrument. Remember that for reliable measurements the slice must be set perpendicular to the direction of B.

FURTHER WORK

n You will be investigating the problems involved in measuring a small magnetic field using one of the Hall slices. As a suitable investigation you can measure the magnetic field along the axis of a pair of Helmholtz coils and confirm that the field is uniform in the region between the coils. Alternatively you may just measure the variation of the magnetic field along the axis of a circular coil.

o Initially, try to measure the magnetic field produced by a pair of Helmholtz coils connected to a 6 V d.c. supply as shown in Fig. 11.9. Support the Hall slice with the stand, boss and clamp so that it is parallel to the plane of the coils. Connect the V_H terminals of the Hall slice to the input of the 741 operational amplifier (Fig. 11.10) using screened leads. The 741 should be connected to its power supplies: $+V_s$ to $+15$ V, $-V_s$ to -15 V; the 0 V of the power supply

should be connected to the common earth. V_{out} may be connected to a 0–100 mV digital meter or a CRO set to a sensitivity of about 50 mV div^{-1}; the CRO should be switched to d.c. with the time base off.

p With the Helmholtz coils disconnected from their power supply, zero the voltmeter or centre the line on the CRO screen. This may be impossible to do because the adjustment of the potentiometer on the Hall slice is quite coarse. However, if you are successful you may now measure the variation of V_H on the axis of the Helmholtz coils with a current of about 0.5–1.0 A flowing in the coils. If V_H decreases to zero near to the mid-point between the coils, it is most likely that the coils have not been connected correctly so as to obtain the current flowing in the same sense around the coils. Record a series of values of V_H at approximately 40 mm intervals along the axis of the coils. Take the Hall slice out of the system and note how rapidly V_H decreases with distance. Hence using the information from (k) and equation [11.11], plot a graph showing the variation of B along the axis of the coils. Remember to correct V_H for the amplification factor of the 741.

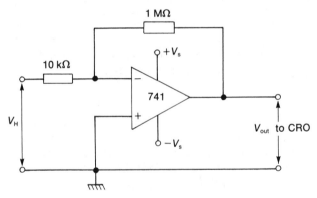

Fig. 11.10 A simple operational amplifier circuit with a gain of 100 used for measuring a very small Hall voltage.

q Sometimes it is quite impossible to reduce the amplified value of V_H to near zero. If this is so, try an alternative method for measuring V_H. Replace the d.c. supply to the coils by an a.c. supply and set the CRO to a.c. Now any residual and constant value of V_H will not affect the measured voltage. Only the Hall voltage produced as a result of the alternating magnetic field in the coils should be observed. You should check that this is a genuine Hall voltage and not a 50 Hz signal picked up from the mains and amplified by a factor of 100. This is checked simply by using an a.c. supply with a frequency significantly higher than 50 Hz, say 100 Hz. With the CRO time base switched on you should be able to confirm that the frequency of V_H is the same as that of the a.c. supply and not 50 Hz.

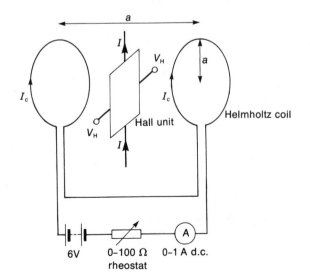

Fig. 11.9 The measurement of the magnetic field on the axis of a pair of Helmholtz coils.

11B Ballistic Galvanometer

(I) Comparison of capacitors

APPARATUS REQUIRED

- mirror-lamp moving coil galvanometer with a charge sensitivity of about 80 mm μA^{-1}
- 100 kΩ protective resistor mounted on a terminal block
- single-pole, double-throw switch
- standard capacitor (0.5 μF)
- unknown capacitor (less than 1 μF)
- 1.5 V battery unit
- 0–5 V d.c. voltmeter
- connecting wires

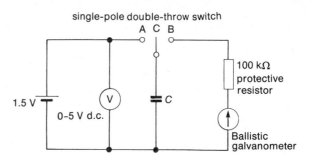

Fig. 11.11 Circuit diagram for the comparison of capacitances using capacitor discharge through a ballistic galvanometer.

PRINCIPLES INVOLVED

a   If a capacitor C is charged using a potential difference V, then the charge $Q = CV$ on the capacitor plates can be measured by discharging it through a ballistic galvanometer. Provided that the duration of the charge flow is much less than the period T of oscillation of the galvanometer suspension, the deflection x is proportional to Q.

b   In principle the deflection of the galvanometer should be corrected for damping effects using the procedure given in experiment 7B, but this is less important because you will be comparing capacitors. Thus the ratio of two capacitances C_1/C_2 will be equal to the ratio of the two deflections x_1/x_2 provided that the two capacitors are of a similar magnitude.

COMPARISON OF TWO CAPACITORS

c   Before moving the galvanometer check that it is switched to 'short', otherwise you may damage its suspension.

d   Set up the circuit shown in Fig. 11.11 using the standard capacitor C_1 for C. Switch the galvanometer to a low sensitivity scale. Charge the capacitor by placing the switch in position A and then discharge it by moving the switch to B. If this is satisfactory, increase the sensitivity until the galvanometer is set on its 'direct' scale. In this position the galvanometer suspension will only be subject to air damping and it will oscillate for some time after the capacitor is discharged. These oscillations can always be stopped by switching the galvanometer from 'direct' to '×1' and back to 'direct'.

e   Note that the protective resistor is required to limit the maximum current through the galvanometer to less than about 20 μA. If the capacitor is discharged directly through the galvanometer, an initial transient current as high as 0.2 A could flow through the galvanometer; this could damage the galvanometer. Provided that the time constant of the capacitor–galvanometer circuit RC is much less than T, the presence of the protective resistor will not affect the assumption that the discharge provides an instantaneous impulse to the galvanometer. For the values of R and C used, RC is only about 50 ms as compared with a typical value for T of 2 s.

f   Centre the galvanometer pointer and discharge the capacitor through the galvanometer. Record the maximum deflection $x_1 = a_1$ in Fig. 11.12. If you wish to make a correction for damping following the procedure in experiment 7B (k), (n), (o), (p), you should record successive maxima $a_1, a_2, a_3 \ldots$ If you do not obtain all the readings in one discharge, you should repeat the charging and discharging operations.

g   Replace the standard capacitor by the unknown capacitor C_2 and repeat the measurements in (f).

h   Calculate the ratio C_1/C_2 from the ratio of the respective deflections. C_2 can be calculated if the value of C_1 is known.

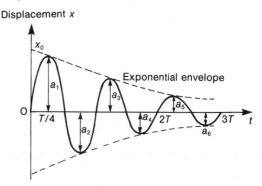

Fig. 11.12 Damping of the oscillations of the galvanometer.

i Your account should include a circuit diagram and an analysis of your results leading to a ratio for the two capacitances.

j This method for comparing capacitors can be used to measure the relative permittivity of a dielectric between the plates of a capacitor. A parallel plate capacitor of a suitable design can be filled with a liquid dielectric; the deflections of the galvanometer are measured with and without the dielectric in place. Since the geometry of the capacitance is unaltered, x_2/x_1 is equal to the relative permittivity of the dielectric.

(II) Use of the search coil to measure magnetic fields

APPARATUS REQUIRED

- mirror-lamp galvanometer as used in part I
- range of mounted resistors (10 kΩ–100 kΩ)
- permanent magnet such as an Eclipse magnet or magnadur magnets on a yoke
- lateral search coil of known resistance (see Fig. 11.13)
- solenoid with about 1000 turns per metre
- 0.5-metre rule
- longitudinal search coil of known resistance (see Fig. 11.14)
- 0–12 V d.c. power supply
- 0–5 A d.c. ammeter
- 0–20 Ω rheostat (current at least 2.5 A)
- connecting wires

PRINCIPLES INVOLVED

k When a search coil of resistance R_s and N turns of mean cross-sectional area A is removed from a magnetic field of flux density B, the charge Q flowing in the search coil circuit is NAB/R_s (equation [11.8]). The coil must be placed in the field so that its plane is perpendicular to B.

l In order to use a ballistic galvanometer to measure Q, the resistance of the search coil circuit will often have to be increased according to the value of B and the charge sensitivity of the galvanometer. You will need to find a suitable value for the additional resistance R to be added to R_s in equation [11.8]. You can do this by trial and error or by calculation from an estimate of B. The charge sensitivity can be obtained from the previous experiment using the known values of $Q_1 = C_1 V$ and the deflection x_1; that is, x_1/Q_1 in mm μC^{-1}. Alternatively its value may be marked on the galvanometer.

MEASUREMENT OF B FOR A PERMANENT MAGNETIC FIELD

m Set up the circuit shown in Fig. 11.13. If you are using trial and error use the largest value for the additional resistance R and note the deflection of the galvanometer, when the search coil is removed from the field. Decrease R until the first throw of the galvanometer is on scale. If you do have an estimate of B, you can calculate R and then choose the appropriate resistor. First calculate the maximum charge Q_{max} that can be measured using the charge sensitivity and the maximum scale deflection. Then calculate the resistance of the search coil circuit $(R + R_s) = NAB/Q_{max}$. Values for N and A will be given.

n Measure the maximum deflection of the galvanometer when the search coil is removed. Take several readings and hence calculate an average value for the deflection. Calculate the value for B using the total resistance value for the search coil circuit.

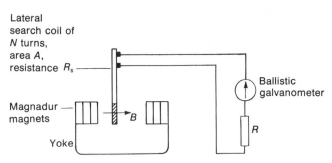

Lateral search coil of N turns, area A, resistance R_s

Fig. 11.13 The measurement of a permanent magnetic field using a search coil and ballistic galvanometer.

MEASUREMENT OF B FOR A SOLENOID

o Set up the circuit shown in Fig. 11.14 using the longitudinal search coil to ensure that B is still perpendicular to the plane of the coil. Adjust the rheostat to obtain a current of about 2 A, or the maximum value recommended for the solenoid. You should not need any additional resistance R in the search coil circuit, but you should confirm this by estimating B using $B = \mu_0 nI$, for a solenoid with n turns per metre carrying a current I.
$\mu_0 = 4\pi \times 10^{-7}$ H m^{-1}.

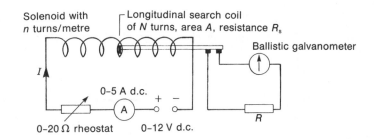

Solenoid with
n turns/metre

Longitudinal search coil
of N turns, area A, resistance R_s

Ballistic galvanometer

I

0–5 A d.c.

A

0–20 Ω rheostat   0–12 V d.c.

R

Fig. 11.14 The circuit diagram and arrangement for measuring the magnetic field inside a solenoid using a search coil and ballistic galvanometer.

p You can now measure how the magnetic field varies along the length of the solenoid. Place the search coil at one end of the solenoid and break the solenoid circuit. Record the deflection of the galvanometer. Push the search coil along the solenoid using the 0.5-metre rule to measure the distance d from one end. Hence record galvanometer deflections for increments in d of about 20 mm, making and breaking the solenoid circuit for each d setting. Remember that you can reduce the waiting time between readings by switching the galvanometer from its 'direct' setting to '×1'.

q From the results obtained in (p), calculate B as a function of d. Plot a suitable graph to show the variation of B along the solenoid. See if your results confirm that B at the centre of the solenoid is twice the value at either end. Also comment on the uniformity of B within the solenoid.

NOTES

r Your account should include the appropriate circuit diagrams and a brief description of the measurements taken. Also include the graph showing the variation of B along a solenoid.

Make sure that you switch the galvanometer to 'short' before moving it after you have completed the experiments.

11C Alternating Magnetic Fields
Use of the search coil to investigate the magnetic field produced in a solenoid

APPARATUS REQUIRED

- 'slinky' spring free from kinks
- 2 pieces of hardboard and clamps to hold the 'slinky' extended
- signal generator, 0–6 V on its low impedance output, frequency range 500–10 000 Hz
- cathode ray oscilloscope
- 0–1 A a.c. ammeter
- search coil (lateral) with a known N and A
- metre rule
- connecting wires, with crocodile clips for connections to the 'slinky'

PRINCIPLES INVOLVED

a An e.m.f. $\mathcal{E} = NAB_0 \times 2\pi f \cos(2\pi ft)$ will be induced in a search coil of N turns of average area A, when it is placed with its plane perpendicular to an alternating magnetic field of amplitude B_0 and frequency f. The peak value of $\mathcal{E}$, $\mathcal{E}_0 = 2\pi f NAB_0$, equation [11.9].

b The alternating field is produced from an alternating current passing through a solenoid. The induced e.m.f. is measured from the CRO trace of $\mathcal{E}$. Thus it is possible to measure how $\mathcal{E}_0$ and hence B_0 varies along a solenoid.

THE VARIATION OF ε WITH THE FREQUENCY OF THE ALTERNATING FIELD

c Set up the circuit shown in Fig. 11.15 (overleaf). Place the two hardboard sheets so as to separate about 100 turns of the 'slinky'. Stretch the 'slinky' to a length of 0.5 m between the hardboard pieces and clamp them firmly. Ensure that the turns are evenly spaced, otherwise the number of turns n per unit length of the solenoid will vary. Check that the lateral coil will fit between the loops of the solenoid.

d Set the frequency of the signal generator to 500 Hz and adjust the output to give a current value of about 0.5 A r.m.s. You should be able to obtain this current provided you connect the signal generator across only the turns between the hardboard sheets.

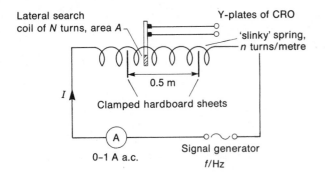

Fig. 11.15 Circuit diagram and arrangement for measuring an alternating magnetic field using a search coil and CRO.

e Using long leads connect the search coil to the Y-plates of a CRO. You will need to use an initial voltage sensitivity of 0.1 V div^{-1} and a time base setting of about 100 μs div^{-1} to 1 ms div^{-1} (see appendix 1, page 290, for the use of the CRO). You should cee a slightly distorted sine wave when the search coil is placed in the centre of the solenoid with its plane perpendicular to B. You may find that you have to push the coils apart to make the measurement, because of the attractive forces between the turns of the solenoid.

f Measure the value peak-to-peak of ε_0 from the value on the CRO trace, as shown in Fig. 11.16.

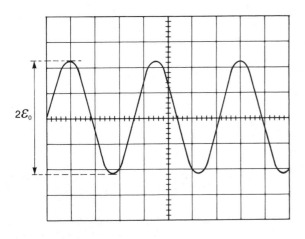

Fig. 11.16 A CRO trace showing the voltage waveform from the search coil. ε_0 is the peak value of the induced e.m.f.

g Repeat the measurements of ε_0 for frequency values up to 5000 Hz in increments of 500 Hz. You will need to change both the Y-plate voltage sensitivity and the time base setting as f is increased.

h From these results you may now confirm that ε_0 is directly proportional to f. Plot a suitable graph to confirm this proportionality, and from the slope of the graph determine B_0.

i Check the value of B_0 by calculating the theoretical value using $B_0 = \mu_0 n I_0$. n can be determined by counting the number of turns between the hardboard pieces and $I_0 = \sqrt{2} I_{r.m.s.}$. $\mu_0 = 4\pi \times 10^{-7}$ H m^{-1}.

MEASUREMENT OF THE VARIATION OF THE MAGNETIC FIELD ALONG A SOLENOID

j Set the signal generator to a fixed frequency of 5000 Hz and use a Y-plate voltage sensitivity of 1 V div^{-1} with the time base set to between 10 and 100 μs div^{-1}.

k Measure the variation of ε_0 as a function of d from one end of the solenoid, using increments in d of about 50 mm. Hence produce a table of the variation of B_0 with d.

l Draw a graph of the variation of B_0 with d and confirm that the magnetic flux at the centre of the solenoid is one-half of its value at either end. Comment also on the uniformity of the magnetic field; state this result in terms of the distance from one end for which B_0 is 0.95 of its maximum value.

NOTES

m Your account should include a circuit diagram, the results confirming the relationship between the induced e.m.f. and the frequency of the alternating magnetic field, and the results showing the variation of the magnetic field along the axis of a solenoid.

n There is an interesting contrast between the results obtained for the search coil inside a solenoid and those obtained for the induced e.m.f. for a pair of coils of similar size close to each other as in a transformer (see experiment 11D). In the latter situation it is found that the e.m.f. induced in the secondary coil is almost independent of the frequency of the voltage (and hence magnetic field) of the primary coil. But as you will have found in this experiment, the e.m.f. induced in the 'secondary' search coil is proportional to the frequency of the magnetic field in the 'primary' solenoid. Can you suggest a reason for this difference in behaviour?

o This use of a search coil to measure an alternating magnetic field is very sensitive. It can, for example, be used to measure stray magnetic fields as low as 10^{-5} T using a CRO sensitivity of 1 mV div^{-1}. Thus a site can be checked as to its suitability for the installation of instruments sensitive to alternating magnetic fields, such as electron microscopes and video recorders.

11D Electromagnetic Induction
Investigation of the mutual induction between two coils

APPARATUS REQUIRED

- 2 small coils of 60 turns each
- 2 small coils of 120 turns each
  or 2 sets of small coils with 60 and 120 turn tappings
- dual trace cathode ray oscilloscope
- signal generator, 0–2 V output (low impedance), frequency range 100 Hz–100 kHz
- soft iron cylinder (e.g. from a stand) about 0.5 m in length and 10 mm diameter (to fit the coils)
- half-metre rule
- connecting wires including 2 sets of long leads for CRO–coil connections.

PRINCIPLES INVOLVED

a In this experiment you will investigate the effects of various parameters on the voltage induced in a secondary coil of a transformer (Fig. 11.17). Intuitively you may expect that the voltage induced in the secondary coil V_s would depend on the rate of change of magnetic flux in the primary coil, that is, V_s should be proportional to:

the current I_p in the primary coil,
the number of turns N_p of the primary coil,
the frequency f of the alternating supply.

The magnetic flux through the secondary coil should also be proportional to the number of secondary turns N_s.

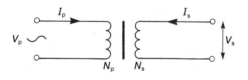

Fig. 11.17 The primary and secondary coils of a transformer.

b However, you will know that $V_s = (N_s/N_p) V_p$ for 100% flux linkage between the primary and secondary coils. V_s is not proportional to N_p and, perhaps more surprisingly, it is independent of the frequency of the primary power supply. It is therefore necessary to examine in more detail the induction processes in these coils. In (a) the situation has been oversimplified. The fact that a current is induced in the secondary coil means that there is a changing magnetic flux in the secondary coil producing an induced e.m.f. in the primary coil. This phenomenon is called feedback, and since it opposes or reduces V_p, it is called negative feedback. Thus the larger

the induced e.m.f. V_s, the larger is the feedback reducing V_p. The mathematics of coupled circuits is outside the A-level syllabus, but the final theoretical result is that V_s is independent of f.

c In this experiment you will investigate whether there is any dependence of V_s on f, verify that V_s depends on the turns ratio N_s/N_p, and see how V_s is affected by the flux linkage between the two coils.

VARIATION OF V_s WITH THE FREQUENCY OF THE POWER SUPPLY

d Place the coils in contact on the metal rod. Using the same number of turns for each coil, connect each coil to a set of Y-plates on the CRO, as shown in Fig. 11.18 with $x = 0$. The signal generator is connected across the primary coil, so that there is a common earth connection for the signal generator and the Y_1-plates of the CRO. See appendix 1, page 290.

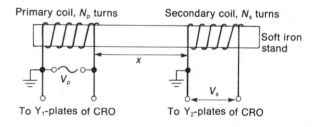

Primary coil, N_p turns   Secondary coil, N_s turns

Soft iron stand

To Y_1-plates of CRO   To Y_2-plates of CRO

Fig. 11.18 Arrangement for measuring the mutual induction of two coils mounted on an iron stand.

e Set the frequency f of the signal generator to 100 Hz and adjust the output to about 1.5 V amplitude or 3 V peak to peak. A suitable sensitivity for both Y-plates is 0.5 V div^{-1} with a time base setting of 1 to 10 ms div^{-1}. You should now see two traces of similar amplitude. Note any phase difference between the traces for V_p and V_s.

f Measure the amplitudes or peak-to-peak values of the signals and calculate V_s/V_p at $f = 100$ Hz.

g Theoretically, it is expected that this ratio should be unity, but the flux linkage between the two coils is unlikely to be 100% even with a soft iron core in place. Without the soft iron core the flux linkage between the two coils is likely to be as low as 50% even with the coils in contact.

153

h Measure the ratio of V_s/V_p at a series of frequencies between 100 Hz and 100 kHz. You will need to adjust the output of the signal generator to maintain V_p constant at its initial value and adjust the time bases to produce stationary traces that can be easily measured. Suitable values for f would be 500 Hz, 1 kHz, 5 kHz, 10 kHz, 50 kHz and 100 kHz.

i Plot a graph of V_s/V_p (ordinate) against f (abscissa) to show how the response of the transformer varies with input frequency. Note that it is usual to use a logarithmic scale for f since it varies over a range of three orders of magnitude. If your curve is not well defined obtain further readings at intermediate frequency values.

j It should be evident from your graph that V_s/V_p decreases with increasing frequency. You should try to explain this behaviour. Also estimate the frequency range over which the output of the transformer is within 50% of its output at low frequencies. This band width is useful in characterising the output of any device.

VARIATION OF V_s WITH THE TURNS RATIO N_s/N_p

k Reset the frequency of the signal generator to 100 Hz. Now compare the ratios V_s/V_p with the turns ratios N_s/N_p for all possible combinations with the coils available.

l You should find that the values for the voltage ratios are low, consistent with the observation in (g) that the flux linkage between the two coils is less than 100%. Making allowance for this factor, confirm that the relationship between the voltage ratio and turns ratio is valid.

VARIATION OF V_s WITH THE SEPARATION OF THE TWO COILS

m You will now measure how the ratio V_s/V_p varies with the separation x of the two coils. f is fixed at 100 Hz and V_p is kept constant at a value of about 1.5 V (amplitude).

n As x is increased in steps of about 0.05 m, measure V_s. You may need to increase the Y_2-plate sensitivity as x increases.

o Clearly, the main reason for the decrease in V_s as x increases is the decrease in the magnetic flux from the primary coil linking with the secondary coil. Using your results you should investigate the form of the relationship between V_s/V_p and x.

p One possibility for this relationship is an inverse law: $V_s/V_p = k/x^n$. Plot a suitable graph to see if this relationship is valid and determine a value for n if a straight line relationship is obtained.

q If your data does not conform to an inverse law, examine the validity of an exponential relationship $V_s/V_p = A \exp(-kx)$. If your results confirm this relationship determine values for the constants k and A.

NOTES

r Your account should include a circuit diagram and summaries of the three sets of results; include any graphical presentations of your results.

11E Specific Charge of an Electron (I)
Use of the fine beam tube to measure e/m_e

APPARATUS REQUIRED

- a room capable of being blacked out
- fine beam tube and stand
- 6.3 V a.c. or d.c. supply for filament
- 0–25 V d.c. supply for focusing electron beam
- 0–300 V d.c. supply for accelerating voltage
- 0–500 V d.c. voltmeter
- 0–50 mA d.c. ammeter (optional)
- pair of Helmholtz coils

- 3   2 V accumulators or a 6 V d.c. supply capable of giving about 1 A
- 0–1 A d.c. ammeter
- 0–100 Ω rheostat (maximum current at least 1 A)
- switch
- connecting wires with 4 mm terminals
- half-metre rule
- stand, clamp and boss

PRINCIPLES INVOLVED

a   An electron injected at right angles to a magnetic field of flux density B will describe a circle of radius r given by:

$$\frac{m_e v^2}{r} = Bev \qquad [11.5]$$

where v is the electron speed. If v is known, the charge to mass ratio or specific charge of the electron e/m_e can be determined.

b   The electron speed can be related to the accelerating voltage V_A using $\frac{1}{2}m_e v^2 = eV_A$ (equation [11.1]). Thus v can be eliminated from equation [11.5] to give:

$$\frac{e}{m_e} = \frac{2V_A}{B^2 r^2} \qquad [11.12]$$

c   Measurements of how the radius r of the electron orbit varies with B or V_A can be used to determine e/m_e from a suitable straight line graph.

SETTING UP THE FINE BEAM TUBE (Fig. 11.19)

d   The fine beam tube will normally be mounted in its stand. If it is not already mounted, you should do this with care; the join between the plastic cap and glass tube is particularly sensitive to handling. Connect up the power supplies and meters as shown; the milli-ammeter for monitoring the electron beam current is optional, but it does assist in deciding whether or not you have any electron beam. Some versions of the fine beam tube have two indirectly heated cathodes; if this is so, ensure that the selection switch is correctly set before switching on the filament heating supply. This is usually fixed at 6.3 V which must not be exceeded, otherwise the cathode may be vaporised and the fine beam tube will have to be replaced. Switch on the heater and allow about a minute for the filament to warm up. Slowly increase the anode voltage V_A to about 100 V. You should see a bluish beam in the vertical direction. If the beam is horizontal then the selector switch is incorrectly positioned; switch off both the heating supply and V_A and alter the switch.

When you have a vertical beam, adjust the potential on the deflector system so as to obtain a parallel electron beam.

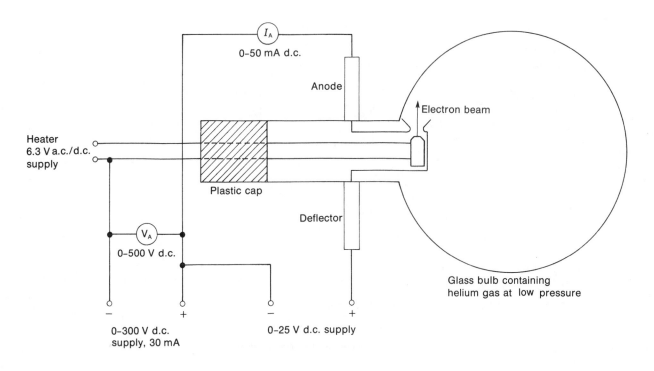

Fig. 11.19   The fine beam tube and the electrical connections required to produce an accelerated electron beam.

PRODUCING THE MAGNETIC FIELD (Fig. 11.20)

e A uniform magnetic field perpendicular to the electron beam is produced using a pair of Helmholtz coils.

f Fit the Helmholtz coils into the slots provided in the stand so that the axis of the fine beam tube and planes of the coils are parallel.

g The circuit shown in Fig. 11.20 should be connected so that the current I flows around both Helmholtz coils in the same direction. The coils are drawn so that if you look along the axis of the fine beam tube (see inset of Fig. 11.20), the coil connections are as shown and the current will flow in the clockwise direction. The magnetic field will then be into the plane of the page. Close the switch and adjust the rheostat so as to obtain a current of about 0.3 A. This should give a circular electron beam with an orbit diameter of about 50 mm. If not, adjust the rheostat to give this orbit diameter. If the beam deflection is zero or small, it is probable that the current is not flowing in the same direction in both coils; then you should exchange the connections to one coil. If the beam is deflected in the wrong direction, then the magnetic field is in the wrong direction; you should reverse the connections to the three accumulators and the ammeter to change the current direction.

MEASUREMENTS OF CIRCULAR ORBITS OF THE ELECTRON BEAM

h The main problem in measuring the diameter of the circular orbit of the electron beam is its inaccessibility. Using a half-metre rule mounted horizontally above the fine beam tube is satisfactory, but you must ensure that you look vertically down on to the beam to avoid parallax errors. Alternatively, you can avoid parallax errors by using a large plane mirror on one side of the fine beam tube, and facing the half-metre rule scale. Then you can line up the images of the half-metre scale and the electron beam in the mirror, as in galvanometers incorporating a mirror behind the pointer.

i Set V_A to 80 V. Adjust the orientation of the Helmholtz coils if necessary to obtain a closed circle for the beam, rather than the helix that is sometimes obtained if B is not exactly perpendicular to the

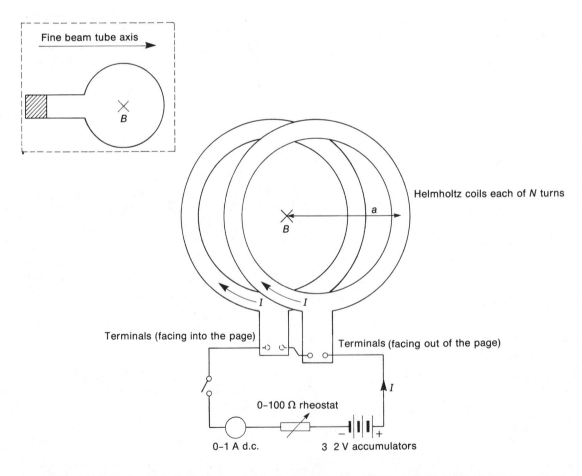

Fig. 11.20 The circuit diagram for the Helmholtz coils. The fine beam tube is omitted for clarity; its direction is shown as an inset.

electron beam. Record the two readings on the half-metre rule defining the diameter of the electron beam orbit (Fig. 11.21). Tabulate the values for V_A, the orbit diameter d and radius $r = d/2$. Leave one further column for data analysis. Note the coil current I.

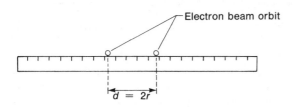

Fig. 11.21 A method for measuring the diameter d of the electron orbit in the fine beam tube.

j Measure the orbit diameters d for a series of values of V_A between 80 and 250 V. Since r^2 is proportional to V_A for a constant B, you should increase the increments in V_A as you approach 250 V. The maximum value for V_A may in fact be limited by the beam striking the top of the fine beam tube and not making a complete orbit.

CALCULATION OF e/m_e

k In equation [11.12], the two quantities varied are V_A and r. B can be calculated from the geometry of the Helmholtz coils and the current flowing in them (see (m)). Plot a suitable graph so as to obtain a linear relationship between the two quantities varied.

l You may find that the graph plotted in (k) deviates from a straight line passing through the origin for the larger values of V_A and r. Although the magnetic field near to the axis of the Helmholtz coils is uniform, near the outer diameter of the coils the field decreases below the expected theoretical value. If this deviation is observed, draw the best straight line through the origin using only the lower values of V_A and r.

m The value of e/m_e can be determined from the slope of your graph using the calculated value for $B = 8\mu_0 NI/(\sqrt{125}a)$. N is the number of turns on one of the Helmholtz coils and a is the mean radius of a coil (see Fig. 11.20). $\mu_0 = 4\pi \times 10^{-7}$ H m^{-1}. Obtain a value for e/m_e and estimate its uncertainty from variations in the slope of your graph.

NOTES

n Your account should include a detailed description of the method for measuring e/m_e. You need not include the circuit diagrams. Detail the analysis leading to a suitable graph from which e/m_e can be determined.

11F Specific Charge of an Electron (II)
Investigation of the deflection of an electron beam in magnetic and electric fields

APPARATUS REQUIRED

- deflection tube and stand
- 6.3 V a.c. or d.c. supply for filament
- 0–5 kV d.c. power supply for the deflecting field and accelerating potential
- 0–2500 V d.c. voltmeter (avometer)
- pair of Helmholtz coils
- 3 2 V accumulators or a 6 V power supply capable of giving about 1 A
- 0–1 A d.c. ammeter
- 0–100 Ω rheostat (maximum current at least 1 A)
- switch
- connecting wires with 4 mm terminals

PRINCIPLES INVOLVED

a In this experiment you will measure the deflection of electrons in an electric field and in a magnetic field. The combined effect of the two fields can then be used to determine the speed v of the electrons. These results can then be combined to determine two values for the charge to mass ratio or specific charge e/m_e for the electron.

b The deflection y of an electron in an electric field E is given by:

$$y = \frac{Ee}{2m_e v^2} x^2 \qquad [11.4]$$

where x is the horizontal distance travelled in the electric field.

c The radius r of the circular orbit of an electron travelling at right angles to a magnetic field of flux density B is given by:

$$\frac{m_e v^2}{r} = Bev \qquad [11.5]$$

Unlike the fine beam tube (experiment 11E), only a part of the circular orbit can be measured in the deflection tube. However, from the geometry of the circle, the measured deflection y can be related to the orbit radius r.

d The speed v of the electron can be determined by using crossed electric and magnetic fields to produce zero deflection of the electron beam:

$$v = E/B \qquad [11.6]$$

e This value of v can be substituted into equations [11.4] and [11.5] to give two values for e/m_e.

CONNECTING UP THE DEFLECTION TUBE (Fig. 11.22)

f The deflection tube will normally be mounted in its stand. If it is not already mounted, you should do this with care; the join between the plastic cap and glass tube is particularly sensitive to handling. Connect up the power supplies and voltmeter as shown. Note that a single power supply is used to provide both the accelerating potential V_A and the deflecting voltage V_d across the plates. This does limit the flexibility of the measurements on the electron beam in the electric field, because the speed of the electrons and the electric field cannot be varied independently. Switch the 6.3 V filament supply on and allow about a minute for the filament to warm up. When the high tension (HT) supply is turned up to about 2000 V, you should see an electron beam describing a parabolic path on the fluorescent screen.

PRODUCING THE MAGNETIC FIELD (Fig. 11.23)

g Switch off the HT and disconnect the deflecting plates from the HT. Take care not to touch any connections to the HT until the voltage has decreased to zero; this may take up to a minute to happen because there are usually several large capacitors in these power supplies.

h A uniform magnetic field perpendicular to the electron beam is produced using a pair of Helmholtz coils.

Fit the Helmholtz coils in the slots provided in the stand so that the axis of the deflection tube and the planes of the coils are parallel. Switch on the HT and set V_A to about 2000 V.

i The circuit shown in Fig. 11.23 should be connected so that the current I flows around both the Helmholtz coils in the same direction. The coils are drawn so that if you look along the axis of the deflection tube (see inset of Fig. 11.23), the coil connections are as shown and the current will flow in a clockwise direction. The magnetic field will then be into the plane of the page and produce a deflection of the electron beam in the opposite direction to that produced by the electric field.

j Close the switch and adjust the current in the coils so as to obtain a vertical deflection of the electron beam comparable to that obtained with the electric field alone (see (f)). If the deflection is zero or much smaller than that obtained in (f), it is likely that the current in the two coils is not flowing in the same direction; then you should reverse the electrical connections to one coil. If the beam is deflected in the same direction as for the electric field, simply reverse the electric field connections.

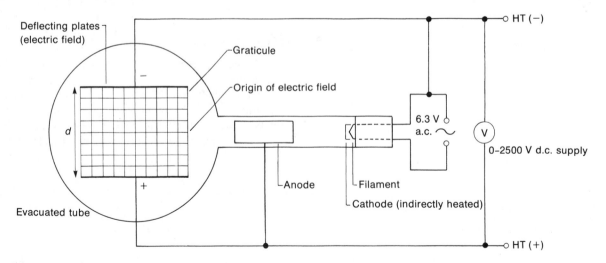

Fig. 11.22 The deflection tube and the electrical connections required to produce an accelerated electron beam. The same power supply (HT) is used to produce the electric field and for deflecting the beam.

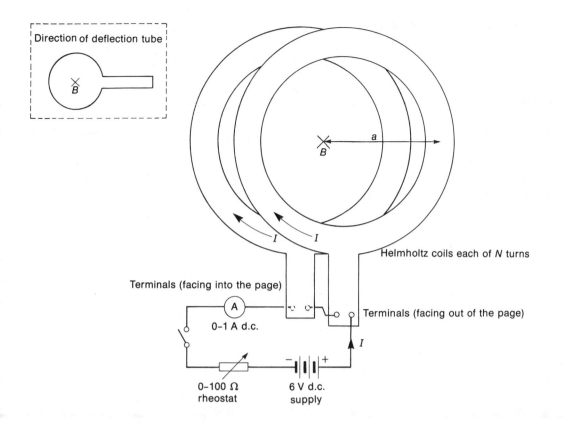

Direction of deflection tube

$\underset{B}{\times}$

$\underset{B}{\times}$ a

Helmholtz coils each of N turns

I I

Terminals (facing into the page)

(A) 0-1 A d.c.

Terminals (facing out of the page)

I

0-100 Ω rheostat

6 V d.c. supply

Fig. 11.23 The electrical circuit for the Helmholtz coils. The direction of the deflection tube relative to the coils is shown as an inset.

MEASUREMENTS ON THE DEFLECTION OF THE ELECTRON BEAM IN AN ELECTRIC FIELD

k Switch off the magnetic field. Switch off the HT and reconnect the deflector plates. Increase the HT to 2500 V.

l Measure the vertical deflection of the electron beam y at a number of convenient values of x (see Fig. 11.24). Usually the electron beam strikes one of the deflector plates before the end of the electric field. Note that the graticule scale does not usually start at $x = 0$, and you should subtract x_0 from all x readings of the graticule. Tabulate your readings for y and x and leave a further column for data analysis.

m Record the values for both V_A and V_d. The electric field E is calculated from V_d/d, where d is the separation of the deflector plates. d can usually be determined to within ± 2 mm from the graticule scale.

n From equation [11.4] a graph of y (ordinate) against x^2 (abscissa) should be a straight line of slope $(Ee/2m_e v^2)$. The unknown quantities are v and e/m_e. Since v will be determined from measurements on the combined effect of electric and magnetic fields (see (t)–(v)), the specific charge of the electron can be determined.

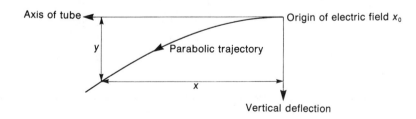

Axis of tube

Origin of electric field x_0

y

Parabolic trajectory

x

Vertical deflection

Fig. 11.24 Measurements on the deflection of the electron beam in an electric field.

MEASUREMENTS ON THE DEFLECTION OF THE ELECTRON BEAM IN A MAGNETIC FIELD

o   Switch off the HT and disconnect the electric field. Switch the HT back on and ensure that V_A is set to its previous value of 2500 V.

p   Switch on the magnetic field and measure the vertical deflection y of the electron beam at a convenient value of x for a coil current I of about 0.1 A. Note that you do not need to correct these values for x, since the graticule scale has been drawn so that the origin of the magnetic field corresponds to $x = 0$ (see Fig. 11.25).

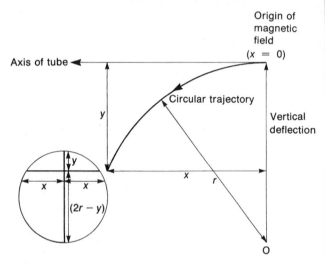

Fig. 11.25   The determination of the radius r of the electron trajectory in a magnetic field.

q   You can calculate the radius r of the electron trajectory from y and x using the intersecting chord theorem for a circle: $x^2 = y(2r - y)$. The value of B can be calculated from the equation $B = 8\mu_0 NI/(\sqrt{125}a)$ for a coil of mean radius a with N turns; $\mu_0 = 4\pi \times 10^{-7}$ H m^{-1}. Tabulate the values for r and B.

r   Make at least three further measurements of r for increasing values of B, corresponding to a maximum current I of about 0.5 A. Add these values of r and B to the table.

s   From equation [11.5], a graph of $1/r$ (ordinate) against B (abscissa) should be a straight line of slope $(e/m_e v)$. The only quantity then required to determine e/m_e is v, which is determined using the procedure described in (t)–(v).

MEASUREMENT OF THE SPEED OF THE ELECTRON BEAM

t   Switch off the HT and reconnect the electric field. Reset V_A to its previous value of 2500 V.

u   Adjust the current in the Helmholtz coils until the electron beam trajectory is as near horizontal as possible. Because of non-uniformities in both the electric and magnetic fields, it may be impossible to obtain an undeflected beam. Find the range of current I for which the beam can be considered to be undeflected (± 1 mm). This will give some indication of the uncertainty in v calculated in (v).

v   Calculate v from E/B and estimate its uncertainty.

CALCULATION OF THE SPECIFIC CHARGE OF AN ELECTRON

w   From the graph of y against x^2 drawn for the electric field in (n) you will have determined a value for $(Ee/2m_e v^2)$. Using the known values of $E = V_d/d$ and v calculate e/m_e.

x   From the graph of $1/r$ against B drawn for the magnetic field in (s) you will have determined a value for $(e/m_e v)$. Using the value of v calculate a second value for e/m_e.

y   Compare the two values of e/m_e and calculate the average value. Use the difference in the two values to estimate the uncertainty in e/m_e.

NOTES

z   You should include in your account an outline of the measurements made to determine e/m_e. It is not necessary to include the circuit diagrams or the detailed arrangement of the Helmholtz coils. Include the analysis leading to two values of e/m_e and give your estimate of the uncertainty in this ratio. Note that you can check the value of v determined in (v) using $\frac{1}{2}m_e v^2 = eV_A$.

12 CAPACITANCE

This section includes experiments in the direct measurement of capacitance (experiment 12A) and two experiments on the charging and discharging of a capacitor through a resistor (experiments 12B and 12C). For an experiment on the comparison of capacitances using a ballistic galvanometer you should refer to experiment 11B part I.

12.1 THE CAPACITOR

A capacitor stores electrical energy. Strictly it does not store electric charge. When a capacitor C is connected to a d.c. power supply electrons will flow until one plate is charged $+Q$ and the other charged $-Q$ (Fig. 12.1a). The total charge on the capacitor is therefore zero. The capacitance C of a capacitor is defined as the ratio of Q/V, when the potential difference across the plates is V. The unit of C is the farad (F) although the practical unit is usually the microfarad ($1\,\mu\text{F} = 10^{-6}$ F) or picofarad ($1\,\text{pF} = 10^{-12}$ F).

The simplest form of capacitor consists of two parallel metal plates separated by an insulator. For two plates separated by a distance d and of common area A (Fig. 12.1b):

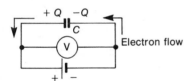

a Charging a capacitor C.

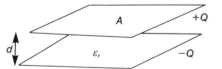

b The parameters affecting the value of the capacitance C.

Fig. 12.1

$$C = \frac{\varepsilon_0 \varepsilon_r A}{d} \qquad [12.1]$$

where

ε_0 = permittivity of free space = 8.85×10^{-12} F m^{-1}

and

ε_r = relative permittivity of the insulator or dielectric.

To obtain the largest values of C for practical use, a large value of A and a small value of d are obtained by rolling up long strips of aluminium separated by a layer of polyester ($\varepsilon_r \approx 4$–5) or paper coated with aluminium oxide ($\varepsilon_r \approx 6$), as in an electrolytic capacitor. The latter can be connected to a voltage supply only in one direction, otherwise the electrolytic process used to form the insulating oxide layer is reversed causing electrical breakdown of the dielectric and subsequent destruction of the capacitor. Small alternating voltages (± 5 V) can be applied to an electrolytic capacitor without causing irreversible damage.

12.2 THE VIBRATING REED SWITCH

Capacitance can be measured simply by finding Q/V, where Q can be found using a ballistic galvanometer of known charge sensitivity (see experiment 11B part I). Alternatively C can be measured by repeatedly charging and discharging a capacitor at a rate of f times a second using a vibrating reed switch (Fig. 12.2a). Although in the conventional sense a continuous current does not flow

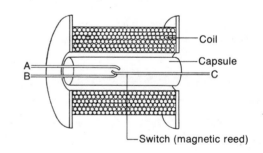

a A vibrating reed switch.

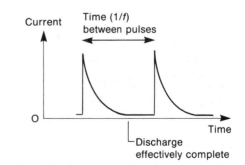

b The discharge of a capacitor by a reed switch vibrating at a frequency f.

Fig. 12.2

between the capacitor plates, the charge–discharge process produces an average current I in the capacitor circuit. Q can then be calculated from $Q = I/f$. The vibrating reed switch consists of a small glass capsule containing the switch inside a coil. Inside the glass capsule are three metal strips, A, B and C (Fig. 12.2a); B is non-magnetic and A and C are magnetic materials. When a large enough current is passed through the coil, A and C are magnetised and C moves to contact A. When the current falls below a certain value, the other pair of contacts (B and C) are closed. If a large enough alternating current of frequency f is passed through the coil, the switch contacts will be continually opening and closing as the current rises and falls. A rectifying diode is connected in series with an alternating current supply, so that current flows during only one half of each cycle. The practical upper limit to the frequency of the supply is set by the response time of the mechanical switch; this is usually about 500 Hz. The current pulses produced by the vibrating reed switch in a charging–discharging circuit (Fig. 12.3) with a capacitor C and resistor R should ideally look like those shown in Fig. 12.2b, that is, the capacitor should be completely discharged between pulses produced by the switch. If the time constant CR of the circuit is too large (see section 12.3), the capacitor may not have completely discharged before the next cycle of charging commences. In practice CR should be chosen to be less than $1/10f$.

In Fig. 12.3 the capacitor C is charged from a source of e.m.f. ε when AC is closed. The circuit equation is (Kirchoff's second law):

$$\varepsilon = V_C + V_R = \frac{Q}{C} + IR \qquad [12.2]$$

Using $I = dQ/dt$, this differential equation can be solved for I:

$$I = I_0 \exp(-t/RC) \qquad [12.3]$$

where $I_0 =$ initial value for the current $= \varepsilon/R$. The current decreases towards zero in a time determined by the time constant CR of the circuit. As can be seen by putting $t = RC$ in equation [12.3], I decreases to $e^{-1} = 1/e\ (= 0.37)$ of its initial value I_0 in a time $t = RC$. At the same time the capacitor charges up according to:

$$Q = Q_0[1 - \exp(-t/RC)] \qquad [12.4]$$

with $Q_0 = \varepsilon C$. Q increases to $[1 - 1/e]\ (= 0.63)$ of its final value of Q_0 in $t = CR$. The curves for Q and I are shown in Fig. 12.4.

Fig. 12.3 Charging and discharging a capacitor C through a resistance R.

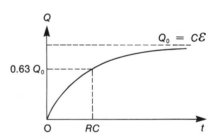

a Charging curve for a capacitor C through a resistor R. The curve for the potential difference V_C across the capacitor has the same shape.

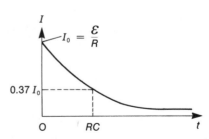

b The current flowing in the circuit. The curve for the potential difference V_R across the resistor has the same shape.

Fig. 12.4

12.3 CHARGING AND DISCHARGING A CAPACITOR C THROUGH A RESISTOR R

Charging and discharging a pure capacitor is of little practical use in electrical circuits. It is more useful to limit the rate of charging and discharging using a resistor R, as for example in smoothing a full-wave rectified alternating signal.

Clearly the potential difference across the capacitor $V_C = Q/C$ varies as shown in Fig. 12.4a, whilst the potential difference across the resistor $V_R = I/R$ varies as shown in Fig. 12.4b.

The capacitor C is discharged through the resistor R by switching the contact C from A to B (Fig. 12.5). The circuit equation is (Kirchoff's second law):

$$0 = V_C + V_R = \frac{Q}{C} + IR \qquad [12.5]$$

The solutions for I and Q are respectively:

$$I = -I_0 \exp(-t/RC) \qquad [12.6]$$

and

$$Q = Q_0 \exp(-t/RC) \qquad [12.7]$$

The negative sign in equation [12.6] simply indicates that the direction of charge flow is opposite to that in the charging circuit.

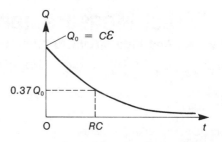

a Discharging curve for a capacitor C through a resistor R. The curve for the potential difference V_C across the capacitor has the same shape.

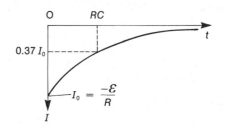

b The current flowing in the circuit. The negative values for I indicate that the charge flows in the opposite direction to that shown in Fig. 12.4b. The curve for the potential difference V_R across the resistor has the same shape.

Fig. 12.5

12A Direct Measurement of Capacitance
Use of a vibrating reed circuit to make a direct measurement of capacitance

APPARATUS REQUIRED

- parallel plate capacitor consisting of two plates (5 mm thick and about 0.25 m × 0.25 m) with holes for 4 mm terminals (Fig. 12.7)
- 1 kg mass for top plate
- 4 polythene spacers (1–2 mm thick) for separating the plates
- 1 sheet polythene or other insulator, of the same dimensions as the plates and 1–2 mm thick
- 0–25 V d.c. supply
- 0–50 V d.c. voltmeter
- vibrating reed switch
- signal generator, $f = 100$–500 Hz and 1 V output on low impedance output
- mirror-lamp galvanometer (current sensitivity about 20 mm μA^{-1} on its ×1 scale)
- 100 kΩ protective resistor for the mirror-lamp galvanometer
- micrometer screw gauge (to measure the spacer thickness)
- half-metre rule
- connecting wires

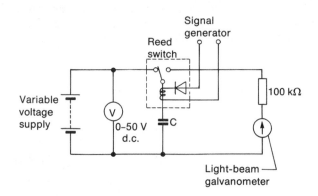

Fig. 12.6 Circuit used to make an absolute measurement of capacitance.

PRINCIPLES INVOLVED

a In the circuit shown in Fig. 12.6 the capacitor is charged and discharged at a frequency f using a vibrating reed switch whose coil is connected to a signal generator. The average current I is measured using a microammeter. A resistor is used to protect the microammeter against accidental connection of the power supply directly across the meter. With a meter resistance of less than 1 kΩ, a direct connection of a 20 V p.d. across the meter could cause a current of more than 20 mA to flow through the meter. Provided that CR is significantly less than $1/f$, the resistor will not affect the average current I measured in the charging–discharging process. In this experiment, $C \approx 10^{-10}$ F so $CR \approx 10^{-5}$ s; provided f is less than 1000 Hz, the resistor will have no effect on I.

b Thus from the definition $C = Q/V = I/fV$, C can be determined from measurements of I and f for a given value of V.

Caution: Do not short-circuit the aluminium plates by contact with each other, otherwise you could damage the vibrating reed switch ($I_{max} \approx 250$ mA).

MEASUREMENT OF THE CAPACITANCE OF AN AIR CAPACITOR

c Separate the two aluminium plates using four identical polythene spacers (see Fig. 12.7). A 1 kg mass is used to hold the upper plate down firmly so that the capacitor plate separation d is equal to the spacer thickness.

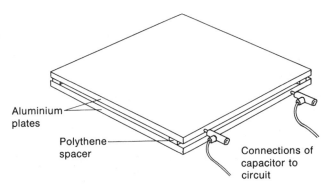

Fig. 12.7 The capacitance used in the circuit of Fig. 12.6.

d Connect the circuit as shown in Fig. 12.6. The mirror galvanometer will be used on its ×1 scale. The direct scale sensitivity is usually marked on the back of the galvanometer. The ×1 sensitivity is usually less than this by a factor which is marked on the instrument (e.g. 0.9). Set the galvanometer pointer reading to zero until you find out the direction of the deflection of the pointer when connected up in the circuit.

e Set the output of the power supply, V, to about 20 V. Record V.

f   The signal generator is set to a frequency f of 100 Hz and an output voltage of about 1 V. You should now hear the vibrating reed switch operating. A constant reading I should now be registered on the galvanometer scale. To use the maximum sensitivity of the scale, the zero should be adjusted to the far left-hand end of the scale when the power supply V is switched off. If the deflection is to the left simply reverse the connections to the galvanometer.

g   Tabulate the frequency f, the deflection x (in mm), the current I (in μA using the current sensitivity), and the charge Q (in nC using $Q = I/f$).

h   Increase the frequency f in steps of about 100 Hz up to 500 Hz and add these readings for f and x to the table you have drawn up in (g). The column labelled Q should, of course, be constant for a fixed value of V.

i C can now be determined by plotting a graph of I (ordinate) against f (abscissa). The slope of the graph CV can be used to calculate C with the known value of V. Note that if I is in μA, C will be in μF.

j   Alternatively, C can be calculated directly from the values of Q/V in your table. Calculate an average value of C and estimate its uncertainty.

CALCULATION OF ε_0

k   For this simple parallel plate capacitor, the value of C can be used to calculate the permittivity of free space ε_0. Since $C = \varepsilon_0 A/d$ you need to measure the area A of one aluminium plate using the half-metre rule and the thickness of one spacer d using a micrometer screw gauge.

l   Use these measurements to determine a value for ε_0. Compare your value with the accepted value.

MEASUREMENT OF THE RELATIVE PERMITTIVITY ε_r

m   Switch off the power supply. Replace the spacers with a sheet of polythene or other suitable insulator of the same thickness as the spacers (1–2 mm). If it is not possible to find an insulator of the same thickness, this can be taken into account subsequently (see (p)).

n   Repeat the measurements (f)–(h) above. Hence determine C_d from a suitable graph.

o   If the insulator thickness is the same as that of the spacers, ε_r is simply the ratio of C_d to the value of C determined in (i) above for an air capacitor.

p   If the insulator thickness is different from that of the spacers, ε_r can be calculated from $C_d = \varepsilon_0\varepsilon_r A/d$ using the value of ε_0 determined in (l) above.

NOTES

q   Your account should include the circuit diagram, an explanation of the principle used to measure Q and the analysis of your results leading to values of C, ε_0 and ε_r.

r   This experiment can be used to verify the expression $C = \varepsilon_0\varepsilon_r A/d$ for a parallel plate capacitance. A can be varied by moving the aluminium plates relative to one another so as to alter the common area of overlap and d can be varied by using a series of spacers. It can then be shown that C is proportional to A, and inversely proportional to d.

s   The value of the relative permittivity of a solid dielectric is not often of more importance than as an indication of the factor by which C can be increased. All practical capacitors include a dielectric. For barium titanate (BaTiO$_3$) ε_r is 150!

t   The relative permittivity of water, particularly in biological systems, is of considerable importance. The way in which ε_r varies with the frequency of the electric field gives information on the shape of biological macromolecules in their natural environment. It has, for example, been used to detect the changes of lipoprotein structure in a person suffering from certain types of cell malfunction. Unfortunately these frequencies are not readily accessible in school laboratories because they are in the range 1 MHz–1 GHz (radio waves–microwaves) and require special screened leads.

FURTHER WORK

u   With reference to (t) above, it is suggested that you measure the relative permittivity of distilled water using the modified parallel plate capacitor system shown in Fig. 12.8. Even distilled water is not a perfect insulator and so some conduction across the plates could occur. To avoid this problem one of the plates is covered with a thin sheet of polythene (e.g. from a polythene bag). To avoid surface tension problems in placing water between the plates, the gap between the plates is increased to 5–10 mm.

V Since the relative permittivity of water is about 80, the setting of V used previously may give a deflection off the galvanometer scale even with $f = 100$ Hz. If this occurs, reduce the sensitivity of the galvanometer to ×0.1 or some other appropriate factor to obtain a deflection on scale. You can also reduce the value of V.

W Calculate $C = I/fV$ using the calibration for I appropriate to the galvanometer sensitivity used. Hence determine ε_r for water using the appropriate values for A and d and the value of ε_0 determined in (l). Note that d may be found using vernier callipers to measure the depth of the Perspex frame.

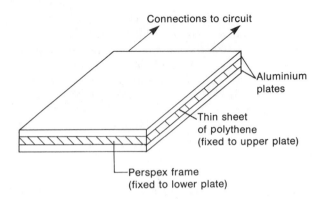

Fig. 12.8 A modified cell for the measurement of the relative permittivity ε_r of a liquid.

12B Charging and Discharging a Capacitor (I)
Investigation of the currents that flow when a capacitor is charged and discharged through a resistor

APPARATUS REQUIRED

- mounted electrolytic capacitor (value given, about 2200 µF)
- mounted electrolytic capacitor (value unknown)
- 0–5 V d.c. voltmeter (resistance about 50 kΩ)
- 2 2 V accumulators (or a 4 V d.c. power supply)
- 2 switches or plug keys
- stopwatch
- connecting wires

PRINCIPLES INVOLVED

a As outlined in section 12.3, when a capacitor C is charged through a resistor R, the potential difference across R, $V_R = IR$ varies with time t as (see equation [12.3]):

$$V_R = V_0 \exp(-t/RC) \qquad [12.8]$$

and that across C, $V_C = Q/C$ varies with time t as (see equation [12.4]):

$$V_C = V_0[1 - \exp(-t/RC)] \qquad [12.9]$$

where $V_0 =$ e.m.f. of the power supply $\mathcal{E}$.

b In principle, in a circuit containing C and R, a voltmeter could be placed across R or C to determine V_R or V_C. But so as to obtain a time variation of V_R or V_C that is easily measured by hand timing, the value of the time constant RC should be about 100 s. So for $C = 1000$ µF, $R \approx 100$ kΩ. Now there would be a problem in using a standard voltmeter to measure V_R or V_C, since its resistance is likely to be comparable to the value of R. Thus such a voltmeter would not indicate a true value for either potential difference. The effect of the voltmeter resistance V_R could be corrected for, but there is a much simpler solution: use the voltmeter as the resistance R in series with C as shown in Fig. 12.9. The voltmeter will then give V_R directly and V_C can be calculated from $V_C = \mathcal{E} - V_R$.

c In capacitor discharge through a resistor the potential differences across the resistor R and the capacitor C are respectively (see equations [12.6] and [12.7]):

$$V_R = -V_0 \exp(-t/RC) \qquad [12.10]$$

and:

$$V_C = V_0 \exp(-t/RC) \qquad [12.11]$$

As in capacitor charging, the voltmeter is used as the series resistor R (see Fig. 12.9).

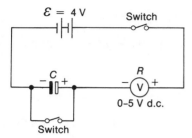

Fig. 12.9 Charging a capacitor C through a resistor R.

CHARGING A CAPACITOR THROUGH A RESISTOR

d The circuit used in this experiment is shown in Fig. 12.9. The capacitor C is an electrolytic capacitor whose polarity must be as shown. The voltmeter V should also be connected with the correct polarity, so as to obtain a positive deflection. The switch in parallel with the capacitor allows the capacitor to be shorted out in order to obtain the initial condition (at $t = 0$) that $V_R = \mathcal{E}$ when the other switch is closed. When the switch across the capacitor is opened the charging of the capacitor will begin.

e With both switches closed, record the initial value of $V = V_R$. As the switch across the capacitor is opened, start the stopwatch. Record values of V_R and the corresponding values of t for at least four minutes or until V_R decreases to about $\frac{1}{10}$ of its initial value. You may find that the simplest procedure is to record t at specific values of V_R rather than at equal time intervals. Tabulate the values of V_R and t. Leave a third column for values of $V_C = \mathcal{E} - V_R$.

f Plot graphs of V_R and V_C (ordinates) against t (abscissa). From these graphs determine approximate values for RC: from the V_R graph determine the value of $t = RC$ for which V_R decreases to $1/e = 0.37$ of its value at $t = 0$; from the V_C graph determine the value of $t = RC$ for which V_C reaches $(1 - 1/e) = 0.63$ of its value at $t = \infty$ (not recorded but theoretically equal to $\mathcal{E}$).

g Using the known value of C, calculate two values for R. If the information is available compare your values with the resistance of the voltmeter. Remember that the tolerance on the value of C may be as large as $\pm 10\%$.

h As an alternative to determining RC from the V_R and V_C curves, the equation for V_R (equation [12.8]) can be used to obtain a straight line graph from which RC can be found from the slope. Plot a suitable graph and determine a value for RC. Calculate a value for R and comment on whether you consider this value to be more reliable than the values determined using the procedure in (f) and (g) above.

DISCHARGING A CAPACITOR THROUGH A RESISTOR

i The circuit used is shown in Fig. 12.10. Note that the voltmeter V is connected with reversed polarity, since V_R has the opposite sign to that recorded in the charging process (see equation [12.10]).

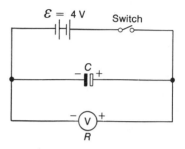

Fig. 12.10 Discharging a capacitor C through a resistor R.

j Charge the capacitor by closing the switch. Record the initial value of V_R at $t = 0$. As the switch is opened start the stopwatch and record values of V_R and the corresponding values of t. Tabulate values of V_R and t. Note that V_R is negative. Add to the table the values of $V_C = -V_R$.

k Plot the curves for V_R and V_C against time t. Since the value of RC has already been determined from the charging curves, it is not necessary to repeat the procedure. Merely note that the time t for V_R and V_C to decrease to $1/e$ of their initial values is equal to RC.

MEASURING AN UNKNOWN CAPACITOR BY DISCHARGE THROUGH A RESISTOR

l Repeat steps (i) to (k) for an unknown capacitor.

m Plot a suitable graph so as to obtain a value of RC from the values of V_C and t. Using the value of R determined in (h), determine the value of C for the capacitor.

NOTES

n Your account should include the circuit diagrams used to charge and discharge the capacitor together with the appropriate curves for V_R and V_C. Summarise your results for the values of R for the voltmeter and the value of C for the unknown capacitor.

12C Charging and Discharging a Capacitor (II)

Use of a CRO to display exponential growth and decay of a potential difference as a capacitor is rapidly charged and discharged through a resistor

APPARATUS REQUIRED

- 0–1 μF variable capacitor (0.1 μF steps)
- 0–10 000 Ω resistance box
- CRO with the time base set to cal (so that it can be used to measure time, see appendix 1, page 290)
- 6 V battery unit or d.c. power supply
- vibrating reed switch
- signal generator, 50–1000 Hz, 1 V on low impedance output

PRINCIPLES INVOLVED

a As outlined in section 12.3, when a capacitor C is charged through a resistor R, the potential difference across C, $V_C = Q/C$ varies with time t as (see equation [12.4]):

$$V_C = V_0 [1 - \exp (-t/RC)] \qquad [12.9]$$

where V_0 = e.m.f. of the power supply $\mathcal{E}$.

The potential difference across a capacitor C discharging through R varies with time t as (see equation [12.7]):

$$V_C = V_0 \exp (-t/RC) \qquad [12.11]$$

b A capacitor C can be rapidly charged and discharged through a resistor R using a vibrating reed switch (see Fig. 12.11). The form of the voltage curve for V_C can be displayed on a CRO. Provided that the CRO time base is set at its calibrated position, the voltage trace can be converted to a V_C–t charging–discharging curve.

c The frequency f of the vibrating reed switch should be chosen so that the capacitor can be effectively charged and discharged in the time interval $1/f$. With $C = 1$ μF and $R = 1000$ Ω, the time constant of the circuit $RC = 1$ ms. Thus the charging–discharging cycle should be effectively complete within $10RC = 10$ ms (see equations [12.9] and [12.11]). Thus a frequency of $f = 100$ Hz would be chosen.

CHARGING AND DISCHARGING A CAPACITOR THROUGH A RESISTOR

d Connect up the circuit as shown in Fig. 12.11. The signal generator should initially be set to a frequency $f = 100$ Hz. Adjust the output voltage of the signal generator to about 1 V, when the vibrating reed should be audible. The CRO Y-plate voltage sensitivity should be set to 1 V div^{-1} or 2 V div^{-1}.

e With appropriate values of C and R you should obtain a trace similar to the one shown in Fig. 12.12c. Adjust the time base setting of the CRO to obtain at least one complete charge–discharge cycle on the CRO screen. If you obtain traces such as those shown in Fig. 12.12a and Fig. 12.12b, then you will need to adjust C or R (or both) or f (remembering that there is an upper limit of about 500 Hz on the effective operation of a vibrating reed switch). If you obtain a trace such as Fig. 12.12a then the value of CR is too small in relation to $1/f$ and the capacitor is charging and discharging too rapidly. If a trace such as Fig. 12.12b is obtained then the value of CR is too large in relation to $1/f$ and the charge–discharge process is too slow.

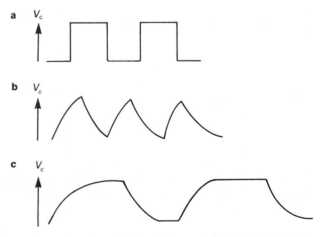

Fig. 12.12 Charging and discharging curves for an RC circuit. The value of RC is **a** too small, **b** too high and **c** correct.

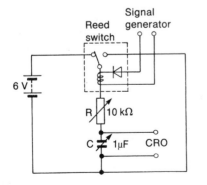

Fig. 12.11 The circuit for charging and discharging capacitor C through a resistor R at a frequency f.

MEASUREMENTS ON THE CHARGING-DISCHARGING CURVES

f When you have obtained a trace similar to that in Fig. 12.12c, adjust the X- and Y-shifts in the CRO to obtain a suitable base line for the measurements of the trace (see Fig. 12.13). Note the time base value (e.g. 1 ms div^{-1}).

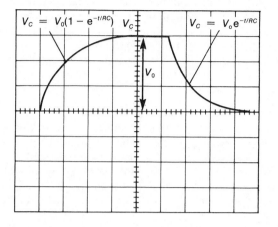

Fig. 12.13 CRO trace of the charging–discharging curve of a capacitor C through a resistor R.

g Read from the trace corresponding values of V_C and t for one complete charge–discharge cycle. Plot these values on a graph.

h On the same graph plot the theoretical curves for V_C using equations [12.9] and [12.11] with the appropriate values of R and C. You can determine the value of V_0 either from the e.m.f. of the d.c. power supply or directly from the CRO trace using the distance between the flat portion of the charging curve and the base line. Take the origin of the discharge curve to correspond to the end of the flat portion of the charging curve.

NOTES

i Your account should include a circuit diagram and the graph of the charging–discharging curve for the value of RC chosen. Sketch also the traces observed for significantly smaller and larger values of RC.

j Clearly these charging–discharging curves (called transients) are relevant to smoothing alternating voltage signals. In rectifying a full-wave rectified signal using a rectifier bridge, RC should be chosen so as to minimise the amount of ripple on the output voltage across C. For example, with a mains frequency voltage (50 Hz) supply, the full-wave rectified voltage has a frequency of 100 Hz. Thus CR should be significantly greater than 10 ms, say 100 ms. If the input resistance of the device operating from a d.c. voltage is known, an appropriate value of C can be chosen.

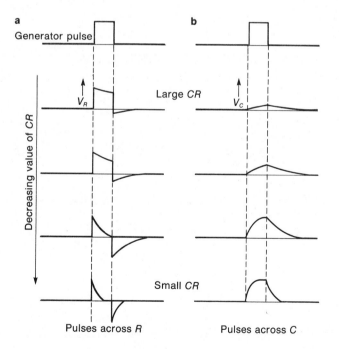

Fig. 12.14 **a** The potential difference across a resistor V_R and **b** the potential difference across a capacitor V_C when a rectangular voltage pulse is applied across R and C in series.

k Another important application of the RC circuit is in differentiating and integrating electrical signals. Fig. 12.14 shows the voltage pulses V_R and V_C across R and C arising from an input square wave V_{in} signal as CR is varied. It can be shown that for small CR values $V_R \approx dV_{in}/dt$, and for large CR values $V_C = \int_0^t V_{in}dt'$.

Such principles can be used to differentiate physical quantities, e.g. the differentiation of velocity–time graphs to obtain acceleration–time graphs if the velocity is input as an analogue electrical signal (see experiment 15F). Integration of differential equations, such as those occurring in simple harmonic motion (both damped and undamped), can be achieved by successive integrations of the acceleration–time and velocity–time curves to give the displacement–time curves (see experiment 15F).

FURTHER WORK

l Observe the voltage signals V_R and V_C on a CRO when a square voltage pulse of frequency f is applied to R and C in series. You can then confirm the differentiating and integrating properties of the circuit as CR is varied.

m As the signal generator is usually earthed, you will have to ensure that the earth connections to the CRO Y-plates and the signal generator are common. Otherwise you will not obtain any signal on the CRO. If you have a dual-trace CRO you can look at the input square wave V_{in} and V_C or V_R at the same time. Unfortunately, because of the common earth problem, you cannot observe V_C and V_R at the same time on the CRO.

n Set f to 100 Hz and the output voltage to about 6 V on the high impedance output. Start with RC less than 0.1 ms (e.g. $R = 1000\ \Omega$, $C = 0.1\ \mu F$), and increase RC to about 1 ms (e.g. $R = 10\,000\ \Omega$, $C = 0.1\ \mu F$). The CRO time base setting should be about 1 ms div^{-1}. Confirm that you obtain voltage traces for V_R and V_C similar to those shown in Fig. 12.14.

13 ALTERNATING CURRENTS

This section includes experiments investigating the relationships between the voltages and currents for an alternating signal of frequency f applied to a capacitor (experiment 13A), an inductor (experiment 13B), an inductor, capacitor and resistor in series – the series resonance circuit (experiment 13C), an inductor and capacitor in parallel – the parallel resonance circuit (experiment 13D). Experiment 13E will include the use of Lissajous' figures to find the phase relationships between the voltages across circuit components and the comparison of frequencies.

13.1 AN ALTERNATING VOLTAGE APPLIED TO A PURE RESISTANCE

When an alternating voltage $V = V_0 \sin (2\pi ft)$ of amplitude V_0 and frequency f is applied to a pure resistance R (Fig. 13.1a), it is easy to show using $V = IR$ that the current I is given by:

$$I = \frac{V}{R} = \frac{V_0}{R} \sin (2\pi ft) \qquad [13.1]$$

Thus the current has the same sinusoidal variation as the applied voltage, as shown in Fig. 13.1b. The ratio of V/I is a constant R, independent of frequency.

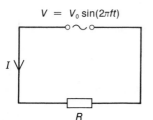

$V = V_0 \sin(2\pi ft)$

a An alternating voltage V of frequency f applied to a pure resistance R.

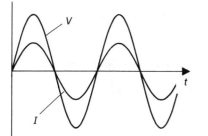

b The relationship between the voltage V and the current I.

Fig. 13.1

13.2 AN ALTERNATING VOLTAGE APPLIED TO A PURE CAPACITANCE

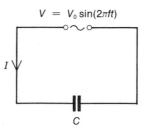

$V = V_0 \sin(2\pi ft)$

a An alternating voltage V of frequency f applied to a pure capacitance C.

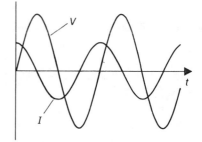

b The relationship between the voltage V and the current I.

Fig. 13.2

When an alternating voltage $V = V_0 \sin (2\pi ft)$ is applied to a capacitor C (Fig. 13.2a), the capacitor plates charge and discharge with frequency f. The current flowing in the circuit can be calculated by differentiating $Q = CV$ thus:

$$I = \frac{dQ}{dt} = 2\pi fCV_0 \cos (2\pi ft)$$

or:

$$I = 2\pi fCV_0 \sin (2\pi ft + \pi/2) \qquad [13.2]$$

Thus the current I has the same frequency as V but it leads V by a phase angle of $\pi/2$ or 90° (Fig. 13.2b).

From equation [13.2] the ratio of the magnitude of V, $|V|$, to that of I, $|I|$, can be seen to be:

$$\frac{|V|}{|I|} = \frac{1}{2\pi fC}$$

171

Thus the **ratio** is a frequency dependent quantity, unlike that for a pure resistor. The ratio of $|V|/|I|$ is called the reactance of the capacitor X_C.

Thus:
$$X_C = \frac{1}{2\pi f C} \qquad [13.3]$$

can be used to calculate the effect of capacitance in a circuit using the equation:

$$|V_C| = |I_C||X_C| \qquad [13.4]$$

The unit of X_C is the ohm.

It is, however, important to remember that in adding voltages across components in a series circuit account must be taken of the phase differences between voltages. For example, in a series circuit consisting of a capacitor C and a resistor R, the size of the total voltage across C and R, $|V|$, is not simply equal to $|V_C|+|V_R|$. Taking account of the result obtained here that V_C is $\pi/2$ out of phase with I for a pure capacitance and that V_R is in phase with I for a pure resistance (see section 13.1), V_R is a phase angle of $\pi/2$ ahead of V_C. Thus the magnitude of the combined voltage V is given by:

$$|V|^2 = |V_C|^2 + |V_R|^2 \qquad [13.5]$$

13.3 AN ALTERNATING VOLTAGE APPLIED TO A PURE INDUCTANCE

When an alternating voltage $V = V_0 \sin(2\pi f t)$ is applied to a pure inductance L (Fig. 13.3a), a back (induced) e.m.f. is produced in the inductance. The current I flowing in the circuit has the same frequency f as V. The current can be calculated using the relationship $V = L \, dI/dt$.

Integrating this equation gives:

$$I = \frac{-1}{2\pi f L} V_0 \cos(2\pi f t)$$

or

$$I = \frac{1}{2\pi f L} V_0 \sin(2\pi f t - \pi/2) \qquad [13.6]$$

Thus the current I has the same frequency as V but it lags behind V by a phase angle of $\pi/2$ or $90°$ (see Fig. 13.3b).

From equation [13.6] the ratio of the magnitude of V, $|V|$, to that of I, $|I|$, is:

$$\frac{|V|}{|I|} = 2\pi f L \qquad [13.7]$$

As for the capacitor, the ratio is seen to be dependent on the frequency f. So the reactance of an inductor X_L, defined as $|V|/|I|$, is:

$$X_L = 2\pi f L \qquad [13.8]$$

This can be used to calculate the effect of inductance in a circuit using:

$$|V_L| = |I_L||X_L| \qquad [13.9]$$

The unit of X_L is the ohm.

Whereas a pure capacitance does exist, most inductors include a significant resistance component R. This factor must usually be taken into account in calculating the voltage across a real inductor. As the voltage across the inductive component V_L is $\pi/2$ out of phase with the voltage V_R across the resistive component, the magnitude of the voltage $|V|$ across a real inductor is calculated from:

$$|V|^2 = |V_L|^2 + |V_R|^2 \qquad [13.10]$$

(see experiment 13B).

Note that subsequently, in order to simplify equations, we shall omit the modulus sign $|\ |$ when referring to the magnitudes of voltages and currents in a.c. circuits. Thus when referring to measurements by voltmeters and ammeters the modulus is implied, since such meters measure only the magnitudes of V and I, or more usually the root mean square values. Only by displaying voltages on a CRO can both the magnitude of V and the phase of V be determined.

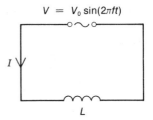

a An alternating voltage V of frequency f applied to a pure inductance L.

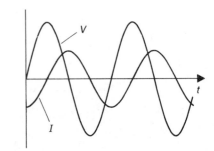

b The relationship between the voltage V and the current I.

Fig. 13.3

13A Capacitive Reactance
Investigation of the variation with frequency of the current through a capacitor

APPARATUS REQUIRED

- mounted capacitor ($C \approx 1\ \mu F$)

- signal generator $f = 100\text{–}1000$ Hz, 5 V output on the low impedance output

- 0–5 V a.c. voltmeter (digital preferred)

- 0–100 mA a.c. ammeter (digital preferred)

- mounted resistor ($R \approx 1000\ \Omega$)

- connecting wires

PRINCIPLES INVOLVED

a As shown in section 13.2, when a capacitor C is connected across an alternating voltage supply of frequency f (Fig. 13.4), the ratio of the magnitudes of the voltage and the current, V/I, is dependent on the frequency f according to:

$$\frac{V}{I} = X_C = \frac{1}{2\pi f C} \qquad [13.11]$$

The reactance X_C of a capacitor therefore decreases as f increases. By measuring V and I as f is varied this dependence of X_C can be confirmed and from a suitable graph C can be determined.

b To see how voltages across components are added when alternating voltages are used, you will investigate a series circuit consisting of a capacitor C and a resistor R (Fig. 13.5). The current I through both components is the same, so from simple d.c. circuit theory you may expect that:

$$V = V_C + V_R$$

or since $\qquad V_C = IX_C \quad \text{and} \quad V_R = IR$

$$V = IX_C + IR$$

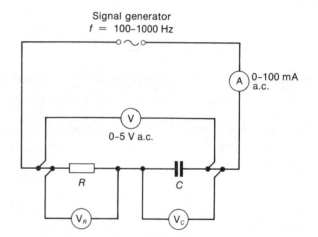

Fig. 13.5 The circuit used to investigate the relationship between the applied voltage V and the voltages across the resistor R and capacitor C, V_R and V_C.

But this does not take account of the relative phases of the voltages V_C and V_R. V_R is clearly in phase with the current I (see section 13.1), whilst V_C is $\pi/2$ out of phase with I (see section 13.2). Thus V_R and V_C may be represented by two vectors which are $\pi/2$ out of phase as shown in Fig. 13.6 (overleaf).

From simple geometry:

$$V^2 = V_C^2 + V_R^2 \qquad [13.12]$$

or

$$V = I\sqrt{\left(\frac{1}{2\pi f C}\right)^2 + R^2} \qquad [13.13]$$

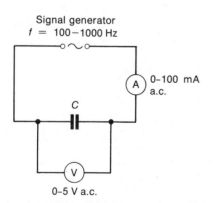

Fig. 13.4 The circuit used to measure the frequency dependence of the reactance of the capacitor C.

In equation [13.13] the ratio V/I for a circuit consisting of reactive and resistive components is referred to as the impedance Z of the circuit.

h To confirm the form of the relationship between X_C and f, equation [13.11], and to determine a value for C, an alternative way of plotting the results is required. Choose the variables to be plotted and hence determine the value of C.

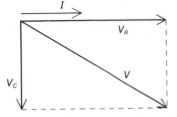

Fig. 13.6 Voltage vector diagram for the series $C-R$ circuit.

MEASUREMENTS OF THE REACTANCE OF A CAPACITOR

c The circuit used is shown in Fig. 13.4. If digital meters are used the correct a.c. ranges should be chosen before they are switched on. Take care also to use the correct input terminals on the digital meters: 'A' and 'COM' for the ammeter, 'V' and 'COM' for the voltmeter. The low impedance output of the signal generator is used.

d Switch on the signal generator and increase the output to about 3 V at $f = 100$ Hz (on the 100 Hz–1000 Hz range). Tabulate f, V, and I; leave two further columns in the table for analysis of the data.

e Increase f in steps of about 100 Hz to 1000 Hz; record f, V and I.

f Note that V may vary as f is changed. You may if you wish adjust the output of the signal generator to maintain V constant at 3 V. But in this experiment this is not important, since you will be calculating the ratio $V/I = X_C$.

g Tabulate values for X_C. Plot a graph to show how X_C varies with f.

ADDING VOLTAGES IN A CIRCUIT CONSISTING OF A CAPACITOR AND A RESISTOR IN SERIES

i Set up the circuit shown in Fig. 13.5. If three (digital) voltmeters are available, all the voltage readings V, V_R and V_C can be recorded at the same time. Otherwise, you will have to connect the voltmeter across the signal generator, the resistor and the capacitor in turn.

j With the frequency of the signal generator set to 100 Hz and V to about 3 V, measure V_R and V_C. Record I. You should satisfy yourself that $V \neq V_R + V_C$ and that the voltages add according to equation [13.12]. Calculate the impedance Z of the circuit from V/I and compare it with the value calculated using equation [13.13].

k Repeat (j) for a frequency of 1000 Hz.

NOTES

l For the capacitor circuit include in your account the graph showing the relationship between the reactance of a capacitor and the frequency; describe how this relationship is used to find a value for C. For the capacitor–resistor circuit include in your account the vector addition of voltages and describe how the impedance of the circuit varies with frequency.

m The series capacitor–resistor circuit can be used as a frequency filter. For low frequencies the reactance X_C will be much greater than R and hence $V_C \gg V_R$. For high frequencies the reverse is true. Thus for a given input signal V, consisting of low and high frequencies, the signal across the capacitor will consist primarily of the low frequencies, whilst the signal across the resistor will consist primarily of high frequencies.

174

13B Inductive Reactance

Investigation of the variation with frequency of the current through an inductor

APPARATUS REQUIRED

- inductor ($L \approx 100$ mH)
- signal generator $f = 10$–1000 Hz, 5 V output on the low impedance output
- 0–5 V a.c. voltmeter (digital preferred)
- 0–100 mA a.c. ammeter (digital preferred)
- connecting wires

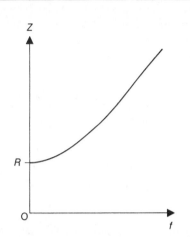

Fig. 13.8 The frequency dependence of the impedance Z of an inductor with a resistive component.

PRINCIPLES INVOLVED

a   As shown in section 13.3, when a pure inductance L is connected across an alternating voltage supply of frequency f (Fig. 13.7), the ratio of the magnitudes of the voltage and current, V/I, is dependent on the frequency f according to:

$$V/I = X_L = 2\pi f L \qquad [13.14]$$

The reactance X_L of an inductor therefore increases linearly with f. Equation [13.14] predicts that $X_L \to 0$ as $f \to 0$.

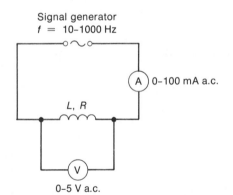

Fig. 13.7   The circuit used to investigate the frequency dependence of the impedance of an inductor L, with a resistive component R.

b   In practice, however, a real inductor has a resistive component R. Since the resistance R of a resistor is independent of frequency, the ratio V/I will not decrease to zero at $f = 0$, but will approach the value of R. Thus a graph of $Z = V/I$ against f should be almost linear for larger frequencies with a slope of $2\pi L$. At low frequencies the graph should curve, approaching R as $f \to 0$ (see Fig. 13.8). Note that for combinations of reactive and resistive components (L and R in this experiment), the ratio V/I is called the impedance Z of the circuit.

c   Although (b) represents a satisfactory way of separating the resistive and inductive components of an inductor, there is an alternative analysis of the impedance results. If the voltage across the inductive component is $V_L = IX_L$, the voltage V across the series combination is calculated using the vector diagram shown in Fig. 13.9:

$$V^2 = V_R^2 + V_L^2$$

Since the current I through both components is the same in a series circuit:

$$V^2 = I^2 R^2 + I^2 (2\pi f L)^2$$

Thus: $$V/I = Z = \sqrt{R^2 + (2\pi f L)^2} \qquad [13.15]$$

Clearly a graph of Z against f is a curve, but if both sides of equation [13.15] are squared a linear relationship can be obtained between Z^2 and f^2:

$$Z^2 = (2\pi L)^2 f^2 + R^2 \qquad [13.16]$$

A graph of Z^2 (ordinate) against f^2 (abscissa) is theoretically a straight line of slope $4\pi^2 L^2$; the intercept on the Z^2-axis, corresponding to $f^2 = 0$, will be R^2. Because of the wide range of Z^2 this intercept cannot be determined accurately unless an expanded Z^2-scale is used for results at low frequencies.

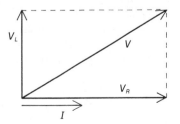

Fig. 13.9   The voltage vector diagram for the L–R series circuit.

175

MEASUREMENT OF THE IMPEDANCE OF AN INDUCTOR

d The circuit used to measure $Z = V/I$ is shown in Fig. 13.7. If digital meters are used, the correct a.c. ranges should be chosen before they are switched on. Take care also to use the correct input terminals on the digital meters: 'A' and 'COM' for the ammeter, 'V' and 'COM' for the voltmeter. The low impedance output of the signal generator is used.

e Switch on the signal generator and increase the output V to about 3 V at $f = 10$ Hz. Tabulate f, V, and I; leave three further columns for the analysis of the data.

f Initially increase f in steps of 10 Hz up to 100 Hz and then in steps of 100 Hz up to 1000 Hz. Record f, V and I.

g Note that V may vary as f is altered. You may if you wish adjust the output of the signal generator to maintain V constant at 3 V. But this is not essential in this experiment, since you will be calculating the ratio $V/I = Z$.

h Tabulate the values of Z. Plot a graph of Z (ordinate) against f (abscissa). From the linear portion of the graph (at high frequencies) determine a value for L. As a guide in analysing this section of the graph, the straight line should extrapolate back to the origin of coordinates. Estimate the value of R by extrapolating the curved section of the graph back to $f = 0$.

i Use the alternative analysis given in (c) to determine another set of values for L and R. Note that it is possible only to determine a reliable value of R by using the low frequency data, with appropriately expanded scales for Z^2 and f^2.

NOTES

j Your account should include a circuit diagram, the two sets of analysis used to determine L and R and a comment on the reliability of these two sets of results for L and R.

13C Series Resonance
Investigation of current and charge resonance in an *L–R–C* series combination

APPARATUS REQUIRED

- inductor ($L \approx 100$ mH)
- resistance box ($R = 0$–1000 Ω)
- capacitor ($C \approx 1$ μF)
- signal generator $f = 100$–1000 Hz, 5 V output on the low impedance output
- 0–5 V a.c. voltmeter (digital preferred)
- 0–20 V a.c. voltmeter (digital preferred)
- 0–100 mA a.c. ammeter (digital preferred)
- connecting wires

PRINCIPLES INVOLVED

a When an alternating voltage V of frequency f is applied across an inductor L, a resistor R and a capacitor C, all in series, the current I varies with frequency in a more complicated manner than for single components. At one particular frequency f_0, called the resonant frequency, the current reaches a maximum value. This maximum value of I depends on the resistive component of the circuit R. This behaviour of the current in the L–R–C series circuit is the electrical equivalent of resonance in a mechanical system subject to a periodic

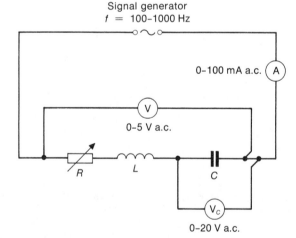

Fig. 13.10 The circuit used to investigate current resonance and charge resonance in an *L–R–C* series circuit.

force of frequency f. The resistive component is the equivalent of damping in a mechanical system. There is one difference: the current resonance curves normally measured are equivalent to velocity resonance in a mechanical system. It is the charge resonance curves, obtained by measuring V_C ($= Q/C$) across the capacitor, that are equivalent to amplitude resonance curves for a mechanical system (see Further work section).

176

b To see how resonance arises, consider the voltage vector diagram, Fig. 13.11, for the circuit shown in Fig. 13.10. The current I through all three components is the same in a series circuit. This diagram takes account of the phase differences between the voltage vectors for an inductor (V_L leads I by $\pi/2$), resistor (V_R is in phase with I) and capacitor (V_C lags behind I by $\pi/2$). Thus the voltage V across the three components is calculated using:

$$V^2 = V_R^2 + (V_L - V_C)^2$$

or using $V_R = IR$, $V_L = IX_L$ and $V_C = IX_C$:

$$V/I = Z = \sqrt{R^2 + (X_L - X_C)^2} \qquad [13.17]$$

The impedance Z of the circuit has a minimum value of R when $X_L = X_C$ in equation [13.17]. Corresponding to this minimum value of Z, the current I will reach a maximum value for any fixed value of V. Since $X_L = 2\pi f L$ and $X_C = 1/2\pi f C$, the frequency at which this occurs is $f_0 = 1/2\pi\sqrt{LC}$. f_0 is called the resonant frequency of the electrical circuit, and for current resonance, f_0 is independent of the resistance of the circuit.

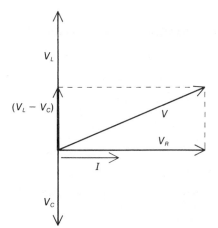

Fig. 13.11 Voltage vector diagram for an L–R–C series circuit.

CURRENT RESONANCE IN AN L-R-C SERIES CIRCUIT

c The circuit used to investigate current resonance is shown in Fig. 13.10. Note that the inductor will include a resistive component R_L. If digital meters are used, the correct a.c. ranges should be chosen before they are switched on. Take care also to use the correct input terminals on the digital meters: 'A' and 'COM' for the ammeter, 'V' and 'COM' for the voltmeter. The low impedance output of the signal generator is used.

d If you are going to investigate both current and charge resonance, you will need to use an additional voltmeter V_C connected in parallel with the capacitor. The charge Q on the capacitor can be calculated from CV_C.

e Set the variable resistor to zero so that $R = R_L$ only. Switch on the signal generator and increase the output V to about 3 V at 100 Hz. As the frequency of the signal generator is varied, its output will change. So as to obtain consistent results for I as f is varied, you should maintain V constant at its initial value.

f Confirm that you obtain a current resonance at frequency f_0 as you vary the frequency f of the signal generator from 100 to 1000 Hz. Now plot the current resonance curve by obtaining pairs of readings I and f. You can decide on the frequency intervals as you proceed with your measurements. Clearly more readings should be taken near to the maximum at f_0. Carefully determine the value of f_0 by scanning the frequencies around the maximum in I. Remember to keep V constant throughout the measurements. If you intend to proceed with the Further work section on charge resonance, record the values of V_C as well.

g From the maximum value of I measured in (f), you can determine the resistance R_L of the inductor. At f_0 $V/I = R_L$, since the impedance Z = resistive component only. The first current resonance curve can be labelled with the value of R_L.

h Note in a table the value of f_0 for this particular value of the resistance.

i Obtain and plot current resonance curves for resistance values of $R = (100 + R_L)\ \Omega$, $(200 + R_L)\ \Omega$, and $(300 + R_L)\ \Omega$. Plot all the current resonance curves on the same set of axes, labelling the curves with the appropriate resistance value.

j From your table of results for f_0 you should be able to confirm that the position of the maximum in the current resonance curve does not vary with R. Compare the experimental value of f_0 with the value calculated from $f_0 = 1/2\pi\sqrt{LC}$.

NOTES

k Your account should consist of a circuit diagram and a labelled set of current resonance curves together with an explanation of how current resonance arises. Include a comparison between the experimental values of the resonant frequencies and the theoretical value.

l Although at resonance $(V_L - V_C) = 0$, this does not mean that V_L and V_C are small. In fact, both can be very large and care must be taken not to touch the terminals of the inductor or capacitor when the resistive component is small. For example, with $C = 1\ \mu F$, $L = 100$ mH and $R = 10\ \Omega$, and with V set to 3 V,

$I_{\text{max}} = V/R = 0.3$ A. Thus $V_C = (1/2\pi f C)I = 95$ V at resonance $(f_0 = 503$ Hz). In this experiment $R \approx 50$ Ω (R_L) and so V_C is unlikely to exceed 20 V.

m The current resonance curves presented in (k) are different in two important details from the amplitude resonance curves obtained in a mechanical system subject to forced vibrations (see experiment 7C). Firstly the current resonance curve passes through the origin (at $f = 0$) and secondly the position of the maximum current is independent of the value of the resistive component (equivalent to the damping term in a mechanical system). The charge resonance curves are in fact the ones to consider when comparing resonance in electrical circuits with amplitude resonance in mechanical systems. This can be seen from comparison of the graphs shown in Fig. 13.12 and Fig. 13.13 with the results obtained in experiment 7C.

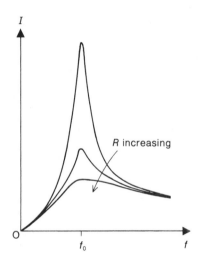

Fig. 13.12 The effect of increasing resistance on current resonance in an L–R–C series circuit. The resonant frequency f_0 is independent of the value of R.

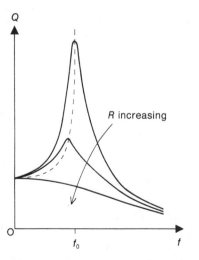

Fig. 13.13 The effect of increasing resistance on the charge resonance in an L–R–C series circuit. The resonant frequency f_0 decreases with increasing resistance R as shown by the dashed line.

FURTHER WORK

n Experimentally it is a simple matter to convert readings of V_C to Q using the known value of C. Then you can plot the charge resonance curves for the series resonance circuit as R is varied. These are similar in appearance to those obtained for the amplitude response of a mechanical system as the damping is varied.

o To see why the comparison should be made between charge resonance and amplitude resonance requires an examination of the differential equations describing the electrical and mechanical systems.

Electrical

$$L\frac{dI}{dt} + RI + \frac{Q}{C} = V_0 \sin (2\pi f t)$$

or

$$L\frac{d^2Q}{dt^2} + R\frac{dQ}{dt} + \frac{Q}{C} = V_0 \sin (2\pi f t)$$

[13.18]

Mechanical

$$m\frac{d^2x}{dt^2} + r\frac{dx}{dt} + kx = F_0 \sin (2\pi f t)$$

[13.19]

inertial force ∝ acceleration	damping force ∝ velocity	restoring force ∝ displacement	periodic force of amplitude F_0

Thus the mechanical displacement x is equivalent to the electrical charge Q, whereas the velocity $v = dx/dt$ is equivalent to $I = dQ/dt$.

p Differential equations such as [13.18] and [13.19] can be solved for Q and x by standard mathematical procedures well outside the normal A-level physics syllabus. However, it is of interest to note that the position of the resonance maximum for Q does depend on R according to the equation:

$$f_0 = \frac{1}{2\pi} \sqrt{\frac{1}{LC} - \frac{R^2}{2L^2}}$$

[13.20]

This predicts that f_0 decreases as R increases. No resonance maximum will be observed for values of:

$$R \geqslant \left(\frac{2L}{C}\right)^{\frac{1}{2}}$$

q See if your results for the charge resonance curves confirm equation [13.20] and that no resonance maximum is observed for the highest resistance value used.

13D Parallel Resonance
Investigation of current resonance in an *L-R-C* loop

APPARATUS REQUIRED

- inductor ($L \approx 100$ mH)
- resistance box ($R = 0{-}1000\ \Omega$)
- capacitor ($C \approx 1\ \mu$F)
- signal generator $f = 100{-}1000$ Hz, 5 V output on the low impedance output
- 0–5 V a.c. voltmeter (digital preferred)
- 0–100 mA a.c. ammeter (digital preferred)
- connecting wires

PRINCIPLES INVOLVED

a   When an alternating voltage V of frequency f is applied across an inductor L with resistive component R in parallel with a capacitor C (Fig. 13.14), the total current in the circuit varies with the frequency in a more complicated way than for single components. At one particular frequency f_0, called the resonant frequency, the current has a minimum value. This minimum value of I depends on the resistive component of the circuit R.

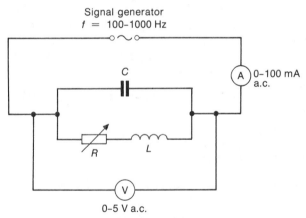

Signal generator
$f = 100{-}1000$ Hz

A 0–100 mA a.c.

0–5 V a.c.

Fig. 13.14   The circuit used to investigate resonance in an *L-R-C* parallel circuit.

b   The analysis of the parallel resonance circuit is quite complicated, since vector additions of voltages and currents have to be made. Firstly V_L and V_R are added to give V, followed by the addition of the currents I_L and I_C to give the total current in the circuit I. (This is considered to be outside the normal A-level physics syllabus.) The main result is that the impedance $Z\ (= V/I)$ of the circuit is a maximum at a frequency f_0 given by:

$$f_0 = \frac{1}{2\pi\sqrt{LC}}\left[\left(\frac{2R^2C}{L}+1\right)^{\frac{1}{2}} - \frac{R^2C}{L}\right]^{\frac{1}{2}} \quad [13.21]$$

For small values of R, $f_0 = 1/2\pi\sqrt{LC}$, as for the series resonance circuit (see experiment 13C).

c   For any fixed value of V, $I = V/Z$ becomes a minimum at f_0. This minimum is theoretically zero at f for a pure inductor–capacitor circuit (see Fig. 13.15). As R increases the minimum decreases in sharpness until there is no noticeable minimum when $R^2 = 2.41L/C$ (see equation [13.21]).

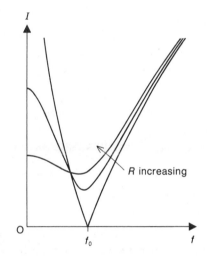

Fig. 13.15   The current response curves for a parallel resonant circuit. The frequency f_0 at which the current I is a minimum decreases as R increases.

d   You may find it strange that the term resonance is used for this parallel circuit, since you will have associated resonance with a maximum response. There is, however, a different way of considering this circuit and that is in terms of voltage resonance. Since $V = IZ$, this circuit gives a maximum value for V across the capacitor (or inductor) at f_0 for a fixed current I from the a.c. power source.

CURRENT RESONANCE IN AN *L-R-C* PARALLEL CIRCUIT

e   The circuit used to investigate current resonance is shown in Fig. 13.14. Note that the inductor will include a resistive component R_L. If digital meters are used, the correct a.c. ranges should be chosen before they are switched on. Take care also to use the correct input terminals on the digital meters: 'A' and 'COM' for the ammeter, 'V' and 'COM' for the voltmeter. The low impedance output of the signal generator is used.

f Set the variable resistor to zero. Thus $R = R_L$ only. Switch on the signal generator and increase the output V to above 3 V at 100 Hz. As the frequency of the signal generator is varied, its output will change. So, to obtain consistent results for I as f is varied, you should maintain V constant at its initial value.

g Confirm that you obtain a minimum value for I at f_0 as you vary the frequency of the signal generator from 100 to 1000 Hz. Now plot the current resonance curve by obtaining pairs of readings of I and f. You can decide on the frequency intervals as you proceed with your measurements. Clearly more readings should be taken in the vicinity of f_0. Carefully determine the value of f_0 by scanning the frequencies around the minimum of I. Remember to keep V constant throughout the measurements. Label the curve with the value of R_L.

h Note the value of f_0 and R $(= R_L)$ in a table. Leave a further column for the theoretical value of f_0.

i Obtain current resonance curves for resistance values of $R = (50 + R_L)$ Ω, $(150 + R_L)$ Ω, $(250 + R_L)$ Ω and $(450 + R_L)$ Ω. Plot these curves on the same set of axes labelling the curves with the appropriate resistance value. Determine carefully the value of f_0 for each resistance value R and add these results to the table in (h) above.

j From your table of results for f_0 and R you should be able to confirm that f_0 decreases according to equation [13.21] as R increases. You should also note whether a significant minimum in I was evident when R approached or exceeded the value of $1.55\sqrt{L/C}$.

NOTES

k Your account should consist of a circuit diagram and a labelled set of resonance curves. Compare the experimental values of the various resonant frequencies with the theoretical values calculated from equation [13.21].

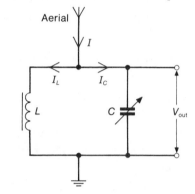

Fig. 13.16 The aerial of a radio receiver: an application of the L–C parallel circuit.

l One important application of the parallel resonance circuit is the tuning unit of a radio receiver (Fig. 13.16). An aerial detects electromagnetic (radio) waves of all frequencies. By adjusting the tuning capacitor C a maximum voltage output V_{out} to the amplifier can be obtained at one particular frequency $f_0 = 1/2\pi\sqrt{LC}$. The alternating magnetic field of the electromagnetic waves induces a current I in the aerial. Although I may be very small at f_0, the component currents I_L and I_C in the inductor L and capacitor C may be comparatively large. Thus V_{out} across the capacitor $(= I_C X_C)$ can be quite large at one particular frequency f_0. Thus for medium wave $(f \approx 800\text{--}150\text{ kHz})$, $LC = (1\text{--}4) \times 10^{-14}\text{ s}^2$. If the aerial circuit has an inductance of 1 mH, C must be variable between 10 and 40 pF.

13E Lissajous' Figures
Investigation of phase relationship and the comparison of frequencies

APPARATUS REQUIRED

- 1 µF capacitor
- 1000 Ω resistor or resistance box (0–1000 Ω)
- signal generator $f = 10\text{--}1000$ Hz, 5 V output on the low impedance output
- dual trace CRO (X–Y mode), or single trace CRO with external X-plate input
- 2 V a.c. supply (mains frequency 50 Hz), or a larger voltage supply used with a rheostat (0–100 Ω, 2 A maximum current) as a potential divider
- connecting wires

PRINCIPLES INVOLVED

a When two sinusoidal oscillations are superimposed at right angles, patterns called Lissajous' figures are obtained. These patterns depend on the phase relationship between the two oscillations and the ratio of their frequencies. The former property is used to investigate the phase relationship between the current I and the voltage V in an a.c. circuit. The latter property is used to calibrate a signal generator using a standard frequency, such as the 50 Hz mains supply.

b Fig. 13.17 shows the Lissajous' figures observed when two oscillations of the same amplitude a and frequency f are superimposed at right angles. Generally the figure is an ellipse. It is easy to show that for a phase difference ϕ of 0 or π the figure is a straight line, whilst for a phase difference of $\pi/2$ the figure is a circle. The figures are observed for electrical signals by applying one electrical oscillation to the X-plates of a CRO and the other electrical oscillation to the Y-plates, with the time base switched off. Measurements of the figures obtained can be used to determine ϕ.

c In practice it is difficult to ensure that the amplitudes a_x and a_y of the x and y signals are identical. Even so, measurements on the ellipse obtained can be used to determine ϕ. Fig. 13.18 shows the general appearance of a Lissajous' figure obtained with a signal of amplitude a_x applied to the X-plates and a signal of amplitude a_y applied to the Y-plates. If the ellipse is correctly centred at the origin of the x- and y-axes, then the intercepts x_0 and y_0 of the ellipse on the x- and y-axes respectively can be used to calculate ϕ:

$$\sin \phi = x_0/a_x \qquad \sin \phi = y_0/a_y \qquad [13.22]$$

a_x and a_y can be determined simply by switching off the y and the x signals respectively.

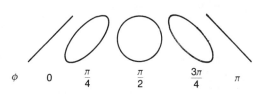

Fig. 13.17 Lissajous' figures obtained by superimposing two oscillations of the same frequency f and amplitude a at right angles. The phase difference between the two oscillations is ϕ (radians).

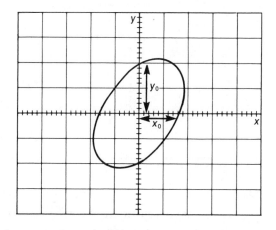

Fig. 13.18 A Lissajous' figure obtained by superimposing two oscillations of the same frequency f and amplitudes a_x, a_y at right angles. The intercepts x_0 and y_0 of the ellipse on the x and y axes can be used to calculate the phase difference ϕ between the two oscillations.

d This method of measuring ϕ is used to determine the phase relationship between the current I and the voltage V in a series circuit consisting of a resistor R and capacitor C (Fig. 13.19). Since the voltage V_R across the resistor is proportional to I, the current can be monitored by connecting the resistor across the X-plates of a CRO. The voltage V is monitored by connecting the Y-plates across the signal generator used to provide the electrical oscillations.

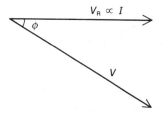

Fig. 13.19 The phase relationship between the current I and applied voltage V in an a.c. circuit can be determined using Lissajous' figures.

e Measuring the ratio of frequencies using Lissajous' figures is an important method of calibrating signal generators. Fig. 13.20 shows the figures observed for simple frequency ratios for f_x (applied to the X-plates) and f_y (applied to the Y-plates) for two alternating signals of the same amplitude. It is not essential to make the amplitudes exactly equal, since it is the number of loops in the figures that are used to find the ratio $f_y:f_x$. For non-integral ratios $f_y:f_x$, the figures are quite complicated and of little practical use (except artistic!). If the frequency f_x is greater than f_y the same types of figures are observed, but rotated through 90°. Thus if $f_y:f_x = 1:2$, a figure of eight (8) is observed. You may find it difficult to obtain stationary patterns such as those shown in Fig. 13.20, because the frequency ratio will not be constant. Thus you will see figures changing shape (and apparently rotating) on the CRO screen. However, these figures always pass through a stage that enables you to identify the number of loops in the Lissajous' figure.

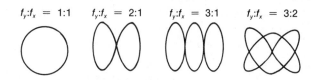

Fig. 13.20 Lissajous' figures obtained by superimposing two oscillations of frequencies f_x and f_y of the same amplitude at right angles.

MEASURING THE PHASE ANGLES IN A C-R SERIES CIRCUIT

f The circuit used is shown in Fig. 13.21. The X-plates of the CRO are connected across the resistor R (set to 1000 Ω) and the Y-plates are connected across the signal generator. Note that the connections to the CRO must be correctly made, with the common earth as shown. Otherwise you may obtain no observable pattern on the CRO.

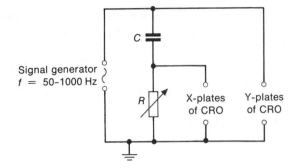

Fig. 13.21 The circuit used to measure the phase relationship between the current in the circuit (proportional to the voltage across R) and the applied voltage.

g   Most modern dual trace CROs have an 'X–Y' setting whereby connections to channel 1 (CH1 or Y_1) are made to a set of X-plates and connections to channel 2 (or CH2 or Y_2) are made to a set of Y-plates (see appendix 1, page 290). The time base is automatically switched off and both the X- and Y-plate sensitivities can be varied to obtain a trace of convenient size. Older dual trace CROs or single trace CROs have separate connections to the X-plates (often at the back of the CRO). If this type of model is used the time base must be switched off. There is usually no possibility of altering the X-plate sensitivity, so you will have to adjust carefully the output of the signal generator to obtain an ellipse of a convenient size. The Y-plate sensitivity can, of course, be varied.

h   Set the X- and Y-plate sensitivities to 2 V div^{-1}. Set the signal generator to a frequency f of 50 Hz and increase its output to obtain an ellipse that fills most of the screen of the CRO.

i   If you do not obtain a figure such as that shown in Fig. 13.18, check that you can separately obtain vertical and horizontal oscillations by either switching off the appropriate channel on the CRO or by disconnecting one of the two signals. Cross earthed connections are the most likely cause of no signal at all. Make sure that the earth terminal of the signal generator is connected to the earth connection on the CRO.

j   To centre the ellipse on the CRO scale, it is usually easier to centre separately the y-signal using the Y-shift and the x-signal using the X-shift. Switch each channel off in turn (or disconnect the signal from the CRO) and centre the resulting straight lines. Whilst you are doing this measure a_y and a_x. Remember that the amplitude is half of the length of the vertical or horizontal straight line. Switch on (or reconnect) both channels and measure the intercepts of the ellipse on the y- and x-axes, y_0 and x_0 respectively. You may find it easier to measure $2y_0$ and $2x_0$ from the distance between both intercepts on the y- or x-axes. Tabulate f, the two values of ϕ obtained from equation [13.22] ($\phi = \sin^{-1}$

or arcsin (x_0/a_x)). Calculate the average value of ϕ. Leave one more column for calculating the theoretical value of ϕ.

k   Repeat (h) and (j) for frequencies $f = 100, 250, 500$ and 1000 Hz to obtain a wide range of values for ϕ. If necessary adjust the signal generator output to maintain an ellipse filling the CRO screen.

l   Compare your results for ϕ with the theoretical values. From the vector diagram (Fig. 13.19), the phase angle between V_R and V is given by $\tan \phi = V_C/V_R$, where V_C is the voltage across the capacitor. Since $V_C = IX_C = I/2\pi fC$ and $V_R = IR$, $\tan \phi = 1/2\pi fCR$. Thus ϕ can be calculated from $\tan^{-1}$ or arctan $(1/2\pi fCR)$. Note any systematic change in the difference between the experimental and theoretical values for ϕ.

CALIBRATION OF A SIGNAL GENERATOR

m   The two circuits required are shown in Fig. 13.22. You will require to use a potential divider for the mains supply only if its output is significantly greater than 2 V or if there is no possibility of altering the X-plate sensitivity (see notes in (g)). Set the X-plate and Y-plate sensitivities to 0.5 V div^{-1}.

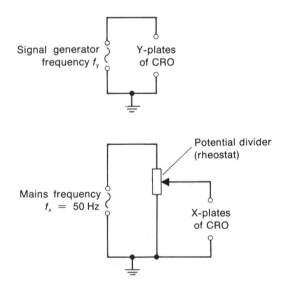

Fig. 13.22 The two circuits used to compare the frequency of the output of a signal generator with mains frequency.

n   Increase the outputs of the signal generator f_y and mains supply f_x so as to obtain a two-dimensional pattern filling the CRO screen. If you do not obtain a two-dimensional trace check the connections to the CRO as detailed in (i).

o Now carefully adjust the frequency dial of the signal generator to obtain an approximately circular pattern $(f_x = f_y)$. This frequency should be 50 Hz. Tabulate the frequency f indicated by the dial and the difference Δf between f and the actual frequency (50 Hz).

p Increase the frequency of the signal generator in steps of 50 Hz and obtain horizontal patterns corresponding to two loops, three loops and so on up to about 20 loops (or the maximum number that you are able to count accurately). You may have to adjust the signal generator output as f is changed. Tabulate f and the difference Δf between f and $n \times 50$ for n loops.

q Produce the calibration curve of Δf (ordinate) against f (abscissa) for the frequency range 100–1000 Hz. Comment on whether the errors are systematic or random.

r Calibrate the signal generator for frequencies of less than 50 Hz. Since $f_x : f_y$ will now be greater than one, the loops will now be vertical. Thus n loops should correspond to a frequency of $50/n$. You may then calibrate the signal generator at 25, 16.7, 12.5 and 10 Hz. Record f and calculate Δf as before.

s Produce a calibration curve for the frequency range 10–100 Hz. Comment on whether the errors are systematic or random.

NOTES

t Include in your account of the measurement of phase angles between I and V in an a.c. circuit, the principle of the method, the circuit diagram and the comparison of the experimental and theoretical values of ϕ.

u The same method could be used to measure ϕ for a series resonance circuit (experiment 13C). This would confirm that at the resonance frequency $f_0 = 1/2\pi\sqrt{LC}$, ϕ is almost zero. (It is not quite zero because the inductor will always have a resistive component.) Either side of the resonant frequency ϕ should vary between $-90°$ $(-\pi/2)$ and $+90°$ $(+\pi/2)$.

v The principal use of the phase angle ϕ is in calculating the power factor $\cos \phi$ in an a.c. circuit. The power dissipated in an a.c. circuit is $I_{r.m.s.} V_{r.m.s.} \cos \phi$, where $I_{r.m.s.}$ and $V_{r.m.s.}$ are the r.m.s. readings normally recorded by an ammeter and voltmeter. Clearly when $\phi = \pm\pi/2$ (that is, a purely inductive or purely capacitive circuit) the power dissipated is zero. Only the resistive component dissipates energy. Both a pure inductance and a pure capacitance return electrical energy to the power supply during one half of the alternating cycle.

w For the signal generator calibration include the principle of the method, the circuit diagram and the calibration curves for the signal generator.

14 ELECTRONS, ATOMS AND NUCLEI

As an introduction to the experiments in this section, guidance will be given on some of the instrumentation and techniques to be used: the d.c. (direct coupled) amplifier (section 14.1), detectors of ionising radiation (section 14.2), counting instruments (section 14.3), counting techniques in radioactivity experiments (section 14.4), and the handling of radioactive sources (section 14.5).

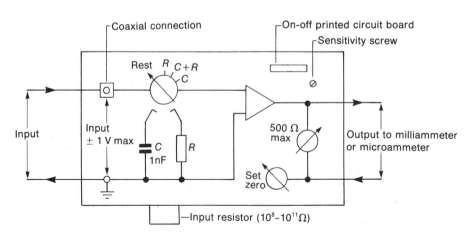

Fig. 14.1 The principle of the d.c. amplifier.

14.1 THE D.C. AMPLIFIER

The d.c. amplifier can be used to measure very small currents in the range 10^{-8} A to 10^{-11} A such as occur in photoelectric emission (experiment 14A) and ionisation currents (experiment 14D). It consists of an amplifier whose stages are directly coupled and are not joined by capacitors as in a normal amplifier. The d.c. amplifier acts as a high resistance voltmeter (resistance about 10^{13} Ω) but it can be adapted to measure current and charge.

A very small direct current is passed through a very high resistance R, which can be varied between 10^8 and 10^{11} Ω using either a resistor unit enclosed in Perspex or glass, or by selecting from a bank of high resistors. The potential difference, about 1 V, is amplified by a battery operated amplifier consisting of a field effect transistor (FET) followed by a multistage amplifier (Fig. 14.1). The current in the output stage, usually in the range 0–1 mA or 0–100 µA, is measured using an external d.c. milliammeter (0–1 mA) or d.c. microammeter (0–100 µA), connected across the terminals O_1 and O_2. The range of the external ammeter is chosen so that if the high resistance R is 10^{11} Ω or 10^8 Ω, the full scale deflection of the milliammeter corresponds to a current through R of 10^{-11} A or 10^{-8} A. In the two experiments in which the d.c. amplifier is used it is not necessary to calibrate the amplifier so that the potential difference across R is exactly 1 V.

The controls of the d.c. amplifier vary according to the model and we shall be considering the Unilab model (Fig. 14.2) mentioning variations as we go along.

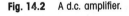

Fig. 14.2 A d.c. amplifier.

184

14.1.1 Power supply

In the Unilab model shown the power supply is included in the unit. The on–off switch takes the form of a printed circuit board labelled *ON* which plugs into a six–way socket on the instrument top panel to make the necessary connections. The battery voltage can be checked by connecting a voltmeter across the outer two printed circuit connections. If this is less than 9 V it will be necessary to recharge the battery, which takes several hours. Remember to take out the *ON* key when you have completed the practical, otherwise the battery will be flat on the next occasion, and you will be most unpopular with a fellow student.

Other forms of d.c. amplifier require an external d.c. power supply.

14.1.2 Calibration

Check the setting of the sensitivity (gain) control (it may have been altered for the photoelectric effect experiment by a student requiring more sensitivity).

Connect a 0–1 mA ammeter (or a 0–100 μA microammeter if appropriate) to the right-hand terminals. Make sure that the meter is correctly set at zero. Set the input switch to 'rest' (top centre) and switch on the amplifier. There should be no input resistor in place.

With the input switch still at 'rest', adjust the 'set zero' control (lower right) on the amplifier to indicate zero on the external meter.

Set the input switch to 'R'. Apply a 1 volt d.c. supply between the inner 4 mm sockets of the screened input (positive) and the lower left earth terminal (negative). Adjust the 'sensitivity' pre-set (upper right) with a small screwdriver so that the external 1 mA or 100 μA meter reads full scale. This sensitivity control consists of a 0–500 Ω variable resistor. Remove the input voltage and set the input switch to 'rest'. Check the 'set zero' adjustment and repeat this procedure until zero and full scale on the meter correspond to 'rest' and 1 volt input respectively. A standard cell (such as a Weston standard cell) may be used for the calibration ($V = 1.019$ V) but take care not to short it by setting the input switch to 'rest' while it is connected.

14.1.3 Measurement of current

With the input switch at 'R', direct currents of 10^{-8} A, 10^{-9} A, 10^{-10} A and 10^{-11} A at full scale can be measured by screwing 10^8 Ω, 10^9 Ω, 10^{10} Ω and 10^{11} Ω input resistances into the front of the unit (or by making the appropriate plug connection).

14.2 DETECTORS OF IONISING RADIATION

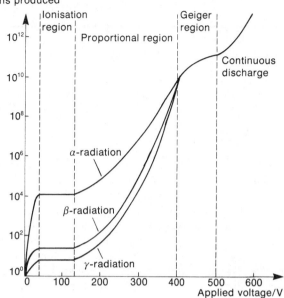

Fig. 14.3 The number of ions produced by α-, β- and γ-radiation in a gas ionisation chamber as the applied voltage is increased.

Radiation can be detected by observing the ionisation it produces in matter, that is, by observing the charges carried by the electrons and the positive ions (Fig. 14.3). Ionisation counters can be used to count α- and β-radiation, but are not very effective in detecting γ-radiations which can pass through the chamber without producing any ionisation. The normal arrangement has argon gas (although in experiment 14D concerning half-life, air is used for experimental convenience) in a cylinder with a fine wire along its axis (Fig. 14.4). When ionisation is produced by radiation a short current pulse results which can be recorded. Depending on the applied voltage V_0, the counter operates in one of three different ways.

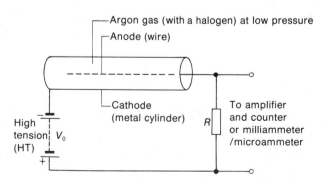

Fig. 14.4 A simplified diagram of a gas ionisation chamber.

14.2.1 Ionisation region (20-100 V)

At small values of V_0 all ions and electrons produced go to the cathode and the anode respectively, producing a small current pulse. The size of the pulse depends on the ionisation properties of the radiation, and therefore distinguishing between α-, β- and γ-radiation requires sensitive equipment and possibly a d.c. amplifier.

14.2.2 Proportional region (100-400 V)

When the voltage V_0 is increased each electron in the original ionisation process acquires sufficient kinetic energy to ionise additional atoms, thus multiplying the original ionisation by 10^3–10^4 times. The total charge in the current pulse is now proportional to the initial amount of ionisation and gives an indication of the energy of α-, β- and γ- radiation entering the detector. Often these pulses are fed to a multichannel analyser, which records the number of pulses versus the total charge in the pulse. This can be used to identify the nuclide producing the radiation. Used in this mode the detector is called a proportional counter.

14.2.3 Geiger region (400-500 V)

If the applied voltage is increased further each electron from the primary ionisation produces secondary electrons which produce more electrons. A current pulse is produced which is large enough to be recorded with very simple circuits. Because ionisation of the gas is complete, the total charge in a pulse is the same for any incident ionising radiation. Therefore it is not possible to distinguish between α-, β- and γ-radiation. An instrument operating in this region is called a Geiger–Müller counter. It will thus detect all forms of radiation but is only about 1% efficient for γ-radiation since most of this passes straight through the chamber without causing any primary ionisation. The Geiger–Müller counter will be used in the β- and γ-radiation absorption experiment (experiment 14C).

14.2.4 Continuous discharge ($V_0 > 500$ V)

If the applied voltage is large enough it will cause the gas to ionise without any ionising radiation and this can damage the tube of the gas ionisation chamber. Never use the instrument in this region.

14.2.5 Geiger-Müller tube connected to a counter (scaler or ratemeter) (Fig. 14.5)

As in the Geiger region described, the ion pair produced by the original radiation consists of an electron which moves towards the anode and a positive ion (from the argon) which moves slowly towards the cathode. An avalanche of electrons builds up through secondary collisions and because the electric field is so large near to the wire a discharge spreads along the whole anode. This means that the charge collected by the wire is of constant value and is independent of the magnitude and location of the initial ionisation. A short duration pulse of constant size results from the initial ionisation. The slower-moving positive ions reaching the cathode could cause more electrons to leave the walls of the Geiger–Müller tube; this would cause further discharges which would lead to spurious pulses. This is prevented by using a quenching gas such as chlorine in the tube.

Following ionisation the instrument is insensitive to the entry of further ionising radiation. In principle corrections can be made to the count to allow for undetected particles entering the chamber during this dead and recovery time (about 100 µs). The great sensitivity of the Geiger–Müller tube makes it suitable for detecting the very low activities from radioactive sources used in schools, but also very susceptible to errors from background radiation, such as cosmic radiation and radiation from the laboratory (see section 14.4).

Once the α- or β-particle enters the tube, the detection efficiency is 100%. The main problem is preventing attenuation by the window and the casing; a thin mica window is used for β-radiation. α-particles are best detected using an ionising chamber. γ detection depends on the conversion of the radiation to electrons in the counter walls, since the production of electrons in the low density gas is very small. Thus the efficiency of detecting γ-radiation depends on the atomic number and thickness of the counter wall. The detection efficiency in the Geiger–Müller tube is only about 1% for γ-radiation. In fact, if a Geiger–Müller tube is used for γ-detection only, it should be used sideways on.

14.2.6 Semiconductor detectors

More recently semiconductors have been used for detecting ionising radiations, particularly those with a low energy. In a $p\,n$ junction diode, electrons and positive holes tend to cancel one another out in the region around the junction and a potential difference is set up across the

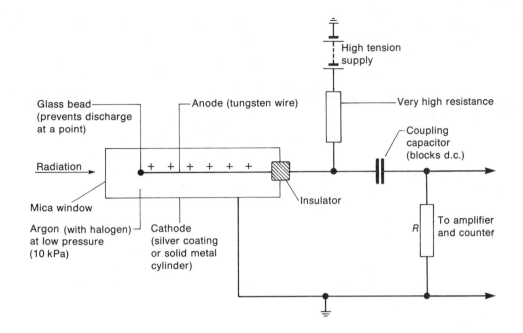

Fig. 14.5 A Geiger–Müller counter.

junction. If the junction is reverse biased (see experiment 10A) so that this potential difference is increased, then any electrons or positive holes produced near to the junction are rapidly swept away. When a charged particle passes across the junction, the electron–hole pairs produced by the particle cause a small detectable pulse in the circuit. This can be amplified and applied to a counter, which will total the number of pulses in a given time.

The energy required to produce an electron–hole pair is only about 3 eV, as compared with 30 eV to produce an ion pair in a gaseous detector. Thus the semiconductor detector is important in low energy work. In addition, they are much more compact than conventional detectors. Semiconductor detectors allow very fast counting rates, without the 'dead time' that limits the count rate of gas ionisation devices. However, like the Geiger–Müller tube, semiconductor detectors are insensitive to γ-radiation.

Semiconductor detectors operate at very low voltages (usually about 10 V) and, since their response is related to the energy deposited at the junction, they allow very fine discrimination between different types of charged particles. For α-particle detection, the junction must be very near to the surface of the $p\,n$ device.

14.3 COUNTING INSTRUMENTS IN RADIATION EXPERIMENTS

The counting apparatus is called a *scaler* if each random ionisation event and the resulting current pulse is recorded as an event on an electrical counting device. A stopwatch is required to find the mean rate of pulse; the ionisation current is then measured in counts per second or counts per minute. If it is operated as a *ratemeter* the counter records the mean rate of occurrence of ionisation events in the Geiger–Müller tube. This can be recorded on the ratemeter dial, often a microammeter, as the equivalent of a current. Various integration times are available to even out fluctuations resulting from the randomness of the ionisation processes.

In the absorption of β- and γ-radiation a scaler is preferred because of the large range of the count rate as the thickness of the absorber is increased from, say, 0.1 mm of aluminium to 10 mm of lead.

The counter usually includes the high voltage supply V_0 required for the Geiger–Müller tube, and is sometimes marked EHT on older counters.

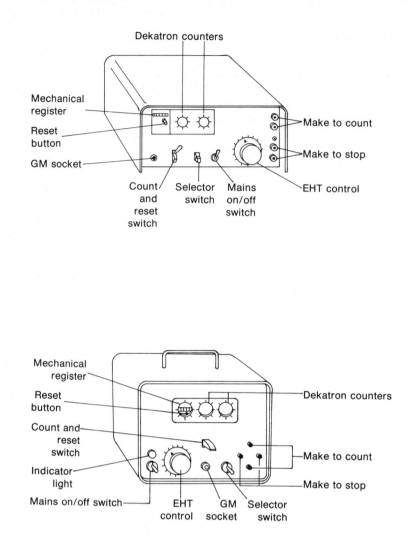

Fig. 14.6   Two types of scaler with mechanical registers and dekatron counters.

14.3.1 Scalers

There are many different versions of scalers: older models use dekatron counters (neon lights) for counts of 0–99 and mechanical registers for counts in excess of 100 (see Fig. 14.6). Modern counters use either LED or LCD displays (see Fig. 14.7). Most scalers can be used for timing experiments using an internal oscillator of frequency 1000 Hz or higher; this facility will not be used here except to test that the scaler is working correctly.

Some modern scalers also include an input terminal with a pre-amplifier for a solid state detector and a circuit for the measurement of frequency.

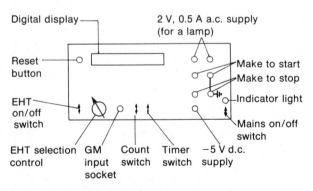

Fig. 14.7   A digital scaler.

14.3.2 Summary of operating procedures

Table 14.1

Controls	Mechanical/dekatron scaler	Digital scaler
a) On/off switch	May have a separate on/off switch for HT/EHT. An indicator light shows that the power supply is on	
b) Setting counters to zero (reset)	Often separate controls for dekatrons and mechanical register	Single reset button
c) Selector switch	Selects pulse from GM tube or from internal oscillator	Separate count and time switches. Latter should normally be off
d) Counting switch	Used to start counting; may be a switch or press button	Counting switch on and reset button is used to start counting
e) GM socket	Screw socket with a coaxial lead to the GM tube	
f) Pair of sockets 'make to count'	Used for timing experiments with mechanical or electrical switches or shutters and for testing the scaler	
g) Pair of sockets 'make to stop'		
h) HT control to vary V_0	This should be set to its minimum value of 250–300 V	
Testing i)	Short circuit 'make to count' using a lead with two 4 mm terminals	
j)	Set selector to select pulses from internal oscillator	Time switch is on Count switch is off
k)	Count switch is on. Check that counter operates at oscillator frequency (usually 1000 Hz or 1000 counts/second)	Check time recorded on display
	Remove 'make to count' lead	
Resetting l)	Move reset switch (which may also be the counting switch) or press reset button. Press reset button beside mechanical counter (sometimes this resets the dekatrons)	Switch on count and press reset button
Geiger–Müller counter m)	Switch off mains and HT or EHT	
n)	Check that the HT or EHT control is set to its minimum value	
o)	Plug in the Geiger–Müller tube, using the knurled ring to screw it home	
p)	Set the HT or EHT control to the voltage required for the Geiger–Müller tube (normally 400–450 V)	
q)	Set the selector switch to the Geiger–Müller position	Time switch should be off
r)	Start and stop counting using the counting switch or button. The centre position of the switch is usually needed to stop counting	Start counting by pressing and releasing the reset button. Stop counting by using the counting switch
s)	Start the stopwatch as the count switch or button is operated	Put the count switch on. Press the reset button and release it as the stopwatch is started. On some scalers the duration of counting can be set automatically from 1–1000 seconds
t)	Reset as in (l)	Reset not required, see (s)

Note that the reason for not using the count switch to initiate the count in a digital meter is the possibility of a pulse being generated which could trigger the digital display. This would result in an initial reading at $t = 0$.

14.4 COUNTING TECHNIQUES IN RADIOACTIVITY EXPERIMENTS

14.4.1 Statistical variation of counts

Radioactive decay is a random process, so the count rate determined in any period of time will vary. The true average disintegration rate can be determined by timing over a long period of time, when such statistical fluctuations are reduced. This method is satisfactory for sources with a long half-life, but to reduce the error to less than 1%, a minimum of 10 000 counts is required and this could take too long (more than 10 minutes) for a low activity source. (Count rates follow a gaussian distribution with a standard deviation, depending on the count N, of $\sqrt{N}$.) Alternatively the time average can be determined by taking a number of readings over shorter time periods and plotting the results on a histogram (Fig. 14.8) or by averaging, but this is a laborious process.

Because of the variations in absorption of β- and γ-radiation the range of count rates can be very wide, from 10^5 to 10 counts/minute.

It is standard technique in nuclear and radiation physics to measure the time taken for a fixed number of counts (say 10^4) and hence to calculate the count rate.

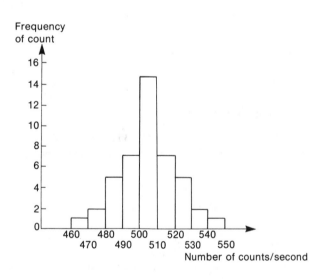

Fig. 14.8 The statistics of counting in radioactivity experiments.

14.4.2 Background count

This consists of cosmic radiation and radiation from the rest of the laboratory. Both are comparable with the radiation from the experimental source and so could seriously affect your results (see Fig. 14.9). Whenever possible record a background count rate and subtract it from all subsequent counts.

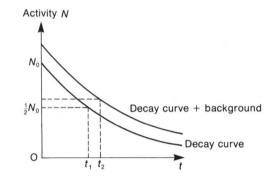

Fig. 14.9 The effect of a background count on the measured half-life of a radioactive source.

14.5 HANDLING OF RADIOACTIVE SOURCES

a) Handle sources only with tweezers or forceps and never pick them up by hand.

b) Do not tamper with radioactive sources. If one appears to be damaged report it to your teacher.

c) Never hold a source near to you, and particularly not near to your eyes. If in doubt as to the identification use a magnifying glass or ask your teacher.

d) Always return a radioactive source to its lead box after completing an experiment.

e) If the radioactive source is a gas (as in experiment 14D) do not pump any into the air. A radioactive source (no matter how short lived) in the respiratory system is not recommended.

f) As a precaution, wash your hands before leaving the laboratory.

190

14A The Photoelectric Effect
Investigation of photoemission and the measurement of the Planck constant

APPARATUS REQUIRED

- Unilab photoelectric unit (potassium cathode) with coaxial lead
- filter holder
- d.c. amplifier, input resistance value 10^{11} Ω
- 0–100 μA d.c. ammeter (centre reading preferred), a 0–1 mA ammeter will suffice but is not really sensitive enough
- 0–1 V d.c. voltmeter
- connecting wire with 4 mm terminals

and

- mercury vapour lamp and power supply
- single wavelength filters (Chance-Pilkington 0V1 + 0Y10, Ilford 806, 807, 808)

or

- white light source
- standard set of filters (wavebands given – Ilford 601, 602, 603, 605, 607)

PRINCIPLES INVOLVED

a   If light of sufficiently high frequency f is incident on a clean metal surface, the emission of electrons can occur and a photoelectric current I can be measured (Fig. 14.10). However, there is a lower limit to f, f_0, below which no photoemission can occur. f_0 depends only on the surface of the metal and is independent of the intensity of the light.

b   The simplest explanation of the photoelectric effect is that light is emitted and absorbed in *quanta* of energy $E = hf$, where h is the Planck constant. Only if hf exceeds the minimum energy required to remove an electron from the surface of the metal will photoemission occur. This minimum energy is called the work function W.

c   The difference between hf and W gives the emitted electrons a maximum kinetic energy $\frac{1}{2}mv_{max}^2$, where:

$$hf = W + \tfrac{1}{2}mv_{max}^2$$

d   Photoemission can be prevented (for $hf > W$) by applying a stopping potential V_s using the potential divider circuit shown in Fig. 14.10. When the electrostatic potential energy eV_s just exceeds the maximum kinetic energy, the photoelectric current I will be reduced to zero. Thus:

$$hf = W + eV_s$$

Often W is written as $e\phi$, where ϕ is the work function specified in volts.

e   If a range of frequencies f is used it is possible to determine both h and ϕ, but unless a number of well defined spectral lines are used this is not a very accurate method. If a series of filters with broad bands of wavelength transmission are used, the photoelectric cut-off potential is ill-defined and the value of h is correspondingly subject to a large uncertainty.

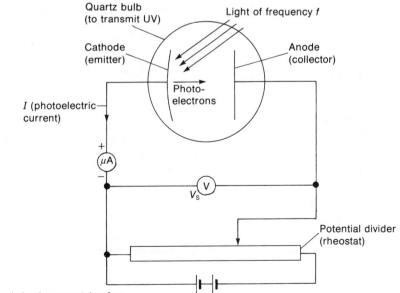

Fig. 14.10   Photoelectric emission from a metal surface.

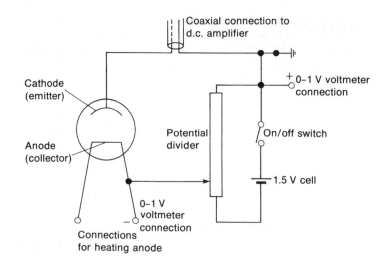

Fig. 14.11 Circuit diagram for the Unilab photoelectric unit.

MEASUREMENT OF THE VARIATION OF V_s WITH f

f Since the photoelectric current is very small (less than 1 nA), it is necessary to use a d.c. amplifier (see section 14.1). An input resistance of 10^{11} Ω should give an output current of about 1 mA. However, for a more precise determination of the point at which $I = 0$ when a stopping potential V_s is applied to the photocell, a centre reading galvanometer with a full scale deflection of 100 μA should be used. Alternatively a normal 100 μA meter may be used with its pointer set somewhere near to the centre of the scale (see (j)).

g The procedure described is the same whether you use a mercury lamp and the appropriate filters for the mercury spectrum, or white light and filters with a fairly wide band of wavelength transmission. The latter give a less well defined cut-off for V_s.

h Connect up the photocell as shown in Fig. 14.11 with the screw cap covering the photocell from external light. Switch the unit on. Check that the battery of the photocell will go up to at least $V_s = 1$ V by turning the potentiometer dial fully clockwise.

i Sometimes after prolonged use the anode becomes coated with the cathode material. This will cause photoemission from the anode and it will be impossible to reduce the photoelectric current to zero. This material on the anode can be vaporised by connecting a 2 V a.c. or d.c. supply across the anode for 1–2 seconds only. The potentiometer should be set fully clockwise.

j The d.c. amplifier should be connected to the photoelectric unit using the coaxial cable. Turn on the d.c. amplifier and check the battery voltage (see section 14.1.1). The switch on the amplifier should be set to 'rest'. Adjust the 'set zero' potentiometer so as to obtain a mid-scale reading on the microammeter. When you switch to the 'R' position there should be no alteration in the microammeter reading. Return the switch to the 'rest' position.

k Remove the cap from the photocell and place the filter holder on the tube. Align the mercury lamp with the centre of the holder (see Fig. 14.12). Place the lamp quite close to the filter holder (about 2 cm), but not so near as to cause excessive heating of the filters. Follow the instructions on the power supply for switching the mercury lamp on. A similar set-up is used for a white light source but, depending on its intensity, this source must be placed at least 10 cm from the filters to avoid damaging them by overheating.

l You should not touch the connections to the photocell unit or to the d.c. amplifier; this could cause false readings since the photoelectric current is very small.

m Starting with the shortest wavelength filter in the slide holder (see Table 14.2), adjust V_s using the potentiometer on the photocell unit, so that when the switch on the d.c. amplifier is moved from 'rest' to 'R' there is no change in the microammeter reading. The photoelectric current is then zero.

Table 14.2 Wavelengths and filters

Mercury vapour lamp

Filter	λ/nm
Chance-Pilkington OV1 + OY10	404.7
Ilford 806 mercury violet	435.8
Ilford 807 mercury green	546.0
Ilford 808 mercury yellow	577.0

White light

Filter	λ/nm
Ilford 601 violet	380–450
Ilford 602 blue	440–490
Ilford 603 blue–green	470–520
Ilford 605 yellow–green	530–570
Ilford 607 orange	575–610

Note how sensitive the balance point is to variations in V_s.

n Repeat the measurements of V_s for the filters provided. Whilst the filter is being changed you should shield the photocell from the lamp. Tabulate λ and V_s. Leave a further column for analysis. For white light tabulate the two extreme values of λ for each filter. Note the variations in V_s for each filter. You may not obtain a value for V_s for the longest wavelength filter and white light since it is very near to the cut-off frequency f_0.

o When you have made all your measurements switch off both the photocell and the d.c. amplifier (to preserve the internal batteries if included).

SINGLE WAVELENGTH FILTERS

p From the theory of the photoelectric effect:

$$hf = eV_s + e\phi$$

or, using wavelengths:

$$\frac{hc}{\lambda} = eV_s + e\phi$$

so that:

$$V_s = \left(\frac{hc}{e}\right)\frac{1}{\lambda} - \phi.$$

Hence plot a suitable graph to obtain a straight line between the two variables V_s and λ. From its slope determine a value for h (remember that λ is in nm, or 10^{-9} m). Take the values for c and e to be $c = 3.00 \times 10^8$ m s^{-1} and $e = 1.60 \times 10^{-19}$ C.

q To obtain a value for ϕ the simplest method would be to extrapolate your graph and obtain a negative intercept on the V_s axis. However, this would normally be outside the scale chosen for your V_s axis. Therefore you should use the intercept on the other axis to calculate ϕ.

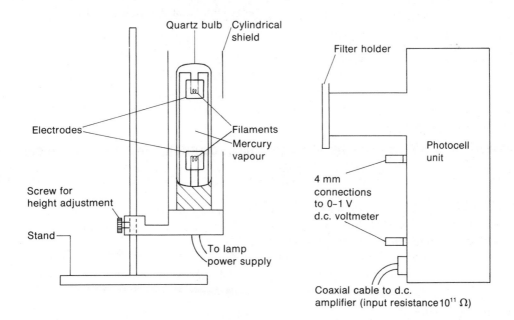

Fig. 14.12 Measurement of the photoelectric emission caused by a mercury light source.

r From the variations you found in V_s for $I = 0$ estimate the uncertainties in h and ϕ. Compare your value of h and ϕ with the accepted values.

WAVELENGTH BAND FILTERS

s The analysis is the same as given in (p), but now you should plot the two extreme values of $1/\lambda$ for each value of V_s. Draw bars joining the pairs of extreme values of $1/\lambda$.

t You should decide which way to complete your graph. You could produce a straight line passing through the centres of the $1/\lambda$ bars. Try this and determine a value for h. Alternatively it could be reasoned that the maximum value of V_s measured for each filter corresponds to the maximum value of f or the minimum value of λ. Draw this straight line and determine a value for h.

u Obtain two values of ϕ from the two plots in (t) using the method given in (p).

v Estimate the uncertainties in h and ϕ using the two values you obtained. Compare your values of h and ϕ with the accepted values.

NOTES

w Your account should include the principles of measurement of the photoelectric effect. It is not necessary to draw the circuit diagrams for the photoelectric unit and the d.c. amplifier. You should include your analysis leading to values of h and ϕ, together with an estimate of their uncertainties.

x Not only does this experiment confirm the dual nature of light, but the phenomenon can be used in practical situations:

i) The current in an electric circuit can be controlled remotely by altering the light intensity incident on a photocell. Provided that the photon energy exceeds the work function, the current in the circuit is proportional to the light intensity.

ii) The soundtrack on a film is produced by using a strip of varying optical density along the edge of the film to represent the sound levels and frequencies. A photocell placed behind the film would detect the variations in intensity of the transmitted light. The varying photoelectric current could then be amplified and converted into sound.

iii) A photocell can be used as part of a burglar alarm system, so that when the light beam is cut off by an intruder an alarm is triggered.

FURTHER WORK

y You may like to confirm that no photoemission occurs for red light using a bright white light source and a red filter (Ilford 608). For this you will need to reverse the direction of V_s by reversing the battery in the photocell unit so that any photoelectrons emitted are attracted to the anode (collector) of the photocell. You will also need to reverse the connections to the voltmeter. If no photoelectric current is obtained you have confirmed that no photoemission occurs unless hf is greater than the work function W (or $e\phi$) no matter what the intensity of the light source is.

14B Bohr Theory
Investigation of the spectrum of atomic hydrogen and its confirmation of the Bohr model of the atom

This experiment must be carried out in a room that can be blacked out. The light from a hydrogen discharge tube is far less intense than that from a mercury or sodium lamp.

APPARATUS REQUIRED

• diffraction grating spectrometer
• calibrated grating (nominally 300 lines per mm)

• sodium or a mercury lamp with its power supply (for the alignment of the spectrometer)

• hydrogen discharge tube and stand

• high voltage d.c. supply for the discharge tube (about 2.5 kV)

• 2 connecting wires with 4 mm terminals

PRINCIPLES INVOLVED

a The light emitted from a hot gas consists of a whole series of wavelengths. Experimentally it is found that the visible spectrum of atomic hydrogen gas consists of lines of wavelength λ satisfying the empirical relationship:

$$\frac{1}{\lambda} = R_H\left(\frac{1}{2^2} - \frac{1}{n^2}\right)$$

where R_H = the Rydberg constant and n is an integer with a value of 3, 4, 5, . . . according to the line observed.

b The theoretical explanation of the line spectrum was given by Bohr: he proposed that the electron in the hydrogen atom could only occupy specific orbits about the nucleus. Corresponding to each of these orbits the electron had a precise energy. Electromagnetic radiation of frequency f is emitted by an excited atom when an electron makes the transition from the energy level E_n to E_m. The energy of the photon emitted is given by:

$$hf = E_n - E_m$$

The Bohr theory gives as the equation for $\lambda = c/f$:

$$\frac{1}{\lambda} = R_H\left(\frac{1}{m^2} - \frac{1}{n^2}\right)$$

The transition from the energy level n to the second energy level $m = 2$, gives the visible spectrum of atomic hydrogen (see Fig. 14.13). The theoretical value for R_H obtained from the Bohr theory was in excellent agreement with the experimental value.

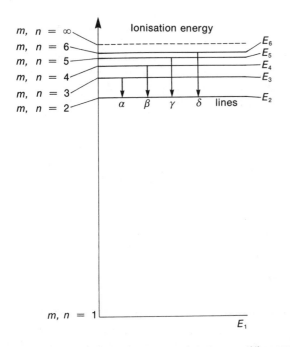

Fig. 14.13 The energy level diagram for atomic hydrogen and the energy transitions producing lines in the visible spectrum.

Note that the transitions to the $m = 1$ level give electromagnetic radiation in the ultra-violet region and transitions to the $m = 3$ level give lines in the infra-red region of the electromagnetic spectrum.

c Although the correspondence between the electron orbits and the energy levels is no longer a valid model, the quantum theory of emission of radiation based on the concept of energy levels is still valid.

d In this experiment you will examine the validity of the Bohr model and determine a value for R_H. You will also be able to check that the values of λ measured using a diffraction grating spectrometer give values of hf consistent with the electron energy levels of atomic hydrogen. There is one slight problem: the hydrogen discharge tube you will use contains molecular hydrogen. So, in addition to the atomic line spectrum, you will also see a band spectrum characteristic of molecular hydrogen. This should not cause too many difficulties since the line spectrum is generally more intense than the band spectrum.

MEASUREMENT OF THE WAVELENGTHS OF THE ATOMIC HYDROGEN SPECTRUM

WARNING. DO NOT TOUCH THE TERMINALS OF THE HIGH VOLTAGE SUPPLY ON THE DISCHARGE TUBE.

e The diffraction grating spectrometer should be adjusted using the standard alignment procedure (see section 8.3 and experiment 8F). Using a sodium or mercury lamp, the telescope is adjusted to receive parallel light, the collimator set to give parallel light, the table levelled and the diffraction grating set normal to the light from the collimator.

f If not calibrated already you should determine the line spacing d for the diffraction grating using a standard wavelength, e.g. sodium orange 589.0 nm and 589.6 nm (mean value 589.3 nm if both are not resolved); mercury–violet 404.7 nm, blue 435.8 nm, blue–green 486.1 nm, yellow 577.0 and 579.0 nm, red 656.3 nm. The nominal value of d from the number of lines/mm marked on the grating is not usually accurate enough.

g Carefully align the narrow stem of the discharge tube with the slit of the collimator of the spectrometer. This setting is critical if you are to see the lines in the blue/violet region of the spectrum.

h Connect the tube to the high voltage supply (Fig. 14.14) and turn the voltage up to 2.5 kV. Spend some time seeing if you can identify the four lines of the hydrogen spectrum. The red line stands out clearly

195

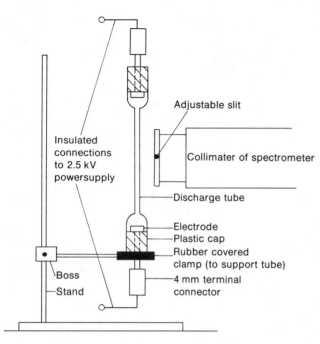

Fig. 14.14 The alignment of the hydrogen discharge tube and its electrical connections.

at the high angle end of the spectrum. You should also be able to identify the green and the blue lines but the violet line is very difficult to identify at the other end of the band spectrum (nearest the zero order). One of the reasons for this problem is the poor transmission of glass in the near ultraviolet.

i Starting at the red end of the spectrum, record the angles θ_1 on the vernier of the spectrometer for each of the four lines in the first order spectrum. Rotate the telescope to the other side of the zero order and measure the angular positions θ_2 for the four lines. Hence determine $2\theta =$ twice the diffraction angle for each wavelength (Fig. 14.15).

j Measuring 2θ avoids the problem of measuring two sets of angles and also virtually eliminates any error resulting from the diffraction grating not being exactly normal to the incident light from the collimator.

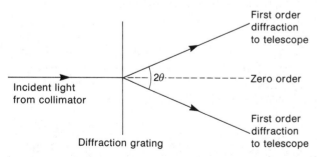

Fig. 14.15 Measurement of the first order diffraction spectrum for a hydrogen discharge tube using a diffraction grating spectrometer.

k Tabulate your values for θ_1, θ_2, 2θ, θ and $\lambda = d \sin \theta$; leave a further column for analysis.

CALCULATION OF R_H AND E_n

l Assuming a relationship predicted by the Bohr theory:

$$\frac{1}{\lambda} = R_H \left(\frac{1}{2^2} - \frac{1}{n^2} \right)$$

plot a suitable graph to confirm this relationship. Obtain two values of R_H. Hence estimate the uncertainty in R_H.

m Now calculate the electron energy levels for the hydrogen atom that your results would predict. Take the value of $E_2 = -3.40$ eV or -0.545×10^{-18} J. First calculate the values of $hf = hc/\lambda$ using $h = 6.626 \times 10^{-34}$ J s and $c = 2.998 \times 10^8$ m s^{-1}. Since $hf = E_n - E_2$ you can now calculate the values for E_n for $n = 3$ (red), $n = 4$ (blue–green), $n = 5$ (blue) and $n = 6$ (violet). If you wish to work in electronvolts take 1 eV $= 1.602 \times 10^{-19}$ J. Draw up a new table with n, hf, E_n and a fourth column left for theoretical values calculated from the Bohr theory.

n The theoretical result for E_n is:

$$E_n = \frac{-m_e e^4}{8\varepsilon_0^2 n^2 h^2}$$

with $m_e = 9.110 \times 10^{-31}$ kg, $e = 1.602 \times 10^{-19}$ C and $\varepsilon_0 = 8.854 \times 10^{-12}$ F m^{-1}. For calculation it is necessary to rearrange the equation to avoid an error or a zero coming up on normal calculators:

$$E_n = \frac{-1}{n^2} \left[\frac{m_e}{8} \left(\frac{e^2}{\varepsilon_0 h} \right)^2 \right]$$

This result is in joules.

NOTES

o Your account should include the description of the measurement of the wavelengths of the spectral lines, the analysis leading to a value for the Rydberg constant, and the calculation of the electron energy levels of the hydrogen atom.

14C Radioactivity
Investigation of the absorption of β- and γ-radiations by metals

APPARATUS REQUIRED

- Geiger–Müller tube and scaler with power supply up to about 500 V
- stand for the Geiger–Müller counter or stand, boss and clamp if used vertically; alternatively semiconductor detector with its power supply (usually 10–100 V) may be used with scaler
- β-, γ- source $^{226}_{88}$Ra (the α-radiation can be stopped easily)
- holder for the radioactive source
- tweezers or forceps to handle the source
- stopwatch or stopclock
- lead sheets, thickness range 1.5–6 mm, to make up a maximum thickness of about 10 mm
- aluminium sheets, thickness range 0.1–3 mm, to make up a maximum thickness of about 6 mm
- holder or stand for supporting the absorbing sheets, or frame, boss and clamp if used vertically
- micrometer screw gauge (if metal sheet thicknesses are not marked)

PRINCIPLES INVOLVED

a   In this experiment you will investigate the absorption of β- and γ- radiation emitted by a radioactive source in various thicknesses of aluminium and lead. γ-rays emitted by the nucleus following α- or β-emission have a well-defined energy and the intensity I of the γ-radiation after traversing a thickness x of material is given by an exponential relationship:

$$I = I_0 \exp(-\mu x)$$

where μ is an absorption coefficient which depends on the material and on the energy of the γ-radiation. To make the absorption coefficient less dependent on the material, it is preferable to use the mass thickness, ρx, instead of x, where ρ is the density of the material. Thus the equation above is rewritten as:

$$I = I_0 \exp(-\mu_m \rho x)$$

where μ_m is the mass absorption coefficient for γ-radiation in the material.

b   Theoretically it is possible to define a mass thickness $(\rho x)_{\frac{1}{2}}$ of absorber for which the intensity I decreases to half of the incident intensity I_0:

$$(\rho x)_{\frac{1}{2}} = \frac{\log_e 2}{\mu_m}$$

or, in terms of the actual thickness of the absorber $x_{\frac{1}{2}}$:

$$x_{\frac{1}{2}} = \frac{\log_e 2}{\rho \mu_m}$$

Values for both μ_m and $x_{\frac{1}{2}}$ are tabulated for lead in appendix 3, Table A3.20 (page 314).

c β-radiation has a much smaller range in absorbers than γ-radiation. Also, β-particles do not have a single energy and it is not expected that they will have a well-defined range as do α-particles.

d   You will investigate whether β-radiation obeys an exponential relationship of the same form as for γ-rays. Irrespective of whether or not such a relationship is valid, it is still possible to determine a value for $(\rho x)_{\frac{1}{2}}$ or $x_{\frac{1}{2}}$ of the absorber for which the number of β-particles is reduced to half its initial value. The values are tabulated for aluminium in appendix 3, Table A3.20 (page 314).

MEASUREMENT OF THE ABSORPTION OF β- AND γ- RADIATIONS IN ALUMINIUM AND LEAD

WARNING – ALWAYS HANDLE RADIOACTIVE SOURCES WITH TWEEZERS OR FORCEPS. CHECK THAT THE EHT SETTING OF THE SCALER IS TURNED TO ITS MINIMUM SETTING BEFORE CONNECTING THE GEIGER–MÜLLER TUBE.

e   Set up the apparatus as shown in Fig. 14.16. If a suitable stand is not available, the absorbing foils may be placed carefully leaning on the Geiger–Müller tube. A thin sheet of paper may be placed over the radioactive source to absorb any α-particles emitted; this is optional since for most absorber thicknesses, the contribution from the α-particles is not likely to be significant. If you do not have a horizontal stand like the one shown in Fig. 14.16 (overleaf), you may rest the radioactive source in its holder on the bench and use the Geiger–Müller tube in a vertical position using a stand, clamp and boss. Clamp the metal collar on the Geiger–Müller tube and not the tube itself, which can easily be damaged. The absorbers can then be supported by a metal frame held in position by a second clamp and boss.

f   Switch on the scaler and increase the EHT value to about 400 V (or the value recommended for your particular Geiger–Müller tube to operate in the Geiger region). Before commencing any counting, ensure that the display is reset to zero (see section 14.3.2).

197

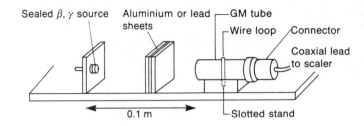

Fig. 14.16 Measurement of the absorption of β- and γ-radiation by sheets of aluminium or lead using a Geiger–Müller counter.

g First determine the background count rate in the absence of the radioactive source (which should be sealed in its lead container well away from the Geiger–Müller tube). Determine the number of counts N_b in one minute (see section 14.4.2).

h Work out a table of metal sheet combinations so that you obtain a set of 10 aluminium absorbers from thickness $x = 0.1$ mm to about 6 mm and a set of 5 lead absorbers from thickness $x = 1.5$ mm to about 10 mm. For each thickness work out the mass thickness ρx (units kg m^{-2}) using $\rho_{Al} = 2710$ kg m^{-3} and $\rho_{Pb} = 11\,340$ kg m^{-3}. Sometimes the sheets are marked with their mass thicknesses, but usually in non-SI units such as mg cm^{-2} or g cm^{-2}; the factors for conversion to kg m^{-2} are 10^{-2} and 10^{1} respectively. If in doubt measure the thicknesses of the absorbers with a micrometer screw gauge; remember that lead is a very soft metal so the micrometer should be closed very carefully using its rachet mechanism.

Your final table of ρx should range from 0.3 kg m^{-2} for aluminium up to about 110 kg m^{-2} for lead. Leave three further columns in your table.

i Measure the count rate N_0 in the absence of any absorbers. Now measure the count rate for each of the sheets or combinations of sheets with the radioactive source in place. A count time of one minute is usually used, although for the thicker sheets of lead you should count for longer to reduce the statistical error (see section 14.4.1). Record in your table the counts N_u made in one minute (uncorrected for background radiation). Do not forget to reset your display to zero before each count is commenced.

j Calculate the corrected count rate $N = (N_u - N_b)$ in counts min^{-1} and enter these values in your table. In the final column calculate $\log_e N$.

k The results for the contributions to the count rate for both β- and γ-radiations range over several orders of magnitude. This cannot easily be displayed on a normal linear graph, and so a log–linear graph is used. Therefore plot a graph of $\log_e N$ (ordinate) against

ρx (abscissa). Because of the range of ρx used it may be more convenient to use the graph paper sideways on.

ANALYSIS OF γ- AND β-ABSORPTION CURVES

l It is known that the range of γ-radiation is much greater than β-particles in matter. Your graph should assist you to discriminate between the two contributions to the count rate (see Fig. 14.17).

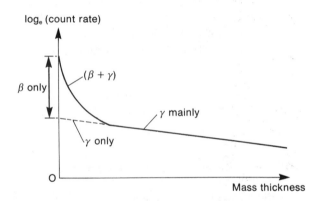

Fig. 14.17 Subtraction of the γ-radiation contribution from the total absorption curve.

m Use this discrimination to determine the γ-' absorption curve. Since the count rate N is proportional to the intensity I of the γ-radiation it is expected that N will follow the relationship:

$$N = N_0 \exp(-\mu_m \rho x)$$

where N_0 is the theoretical γ-count rate for $\rho x = 0$. Thus the graph of $\log_e N$ against ρx should be a straight line for γ-radiation.

n Use the graph produced in (m) to determine a value for μ_m and hence $x_{\frac{1}{2}}$. From these values estimate the energy of the γ-radiation using Table A3.20 in appendix 3 (page 314). The energies of the γ-radiation emitted by the $^{226}_{88}$Ra series range from 0.2–2.4 MeV with the most prominent γ-energy of 0.6 MeV.

o To investigate the absorption of β-particles you will use only the results for the aluminium sheets. Produce another table of ρx for the aluminium sheets and the corrected count rate N. Leave 3 further columns in the table. Now N includes contributions from β- and γ-radiations. The contribution from the γ-radiation can be determined by extrapolating the γ-curve (hopefully a straight line!) on your log–linear graph back to $\rho x = 0$. For each value of ρx read from your graph the value for $\log_e N_\gamma$ and convert it to N_γ. Add these values to your table and calculate $N_\beta = (N - N_\gamma)$, the count rate for the β-radiation only.

p Tabulate values of $\log_e N_\beta$. Plot a graph of $\log_e N_\beta$ against ρx for aluminium. Comment on whether the graph confirms an exponential relationship between N_β and ρx for β-particles.

q Even if the graph in (p) does not confirm an exponential relationship you can still estimate a value of $(\rho x)_{\frac{1}{2}}$ for which N_β decreases by a factor of two from its initial value at $\rho x = 0$. The value of N_β for $\rho x = 0$ can be calculated by subtracting N_γ at $\rho x = 0$ from N_0 determined in (i). You can then estimate

$(\rho x)_{\frac{1}{2}}$ from your table or from your graph by finding the value of ρx for which N_β is half of the value of $(N_0 - N_\gamma)$ at $\rho x = 0$. Calculate $x_{\frac{1}{2}} = (\rho x)_{\frac{1}{2}}/\rho$.

r Using your value for $x_{\frac{1}{2}}$ and Table A3.20 (page 314) determine a value for the maximum β-particle energy emitted by the radioactive source. The maximum β-particle energy emitted by the $^{226}_{88}$Ra series is 3.3 MeV.

NOTES

s Your account should include a diagram of the apparatus, tables of measurements, the graphical analysis leading to a value of μ_m and of $x_{\frac{1}{2}}$ for γ-radiation, and a value of $x_{\frac{1}{2}}$ for β-radiation.

t The discrimination between β- and γ-radiations is not as effective as it could be. The detection efficiency of a Geiger–Müller counter for γ-radiation is only about 1%, since most γ-rays pass through the detector without causing any primary ionisation. It is nearly 100% efficient for β-radiation. For γ-radiation measurements it would therefore be preferable to use a different form of detector, such as a scintillation counter.

14D Radioactive Decay
Use of a d.c. amplifier to measure the half-life of thoron gas

APPARATUS REQUIRED

- plastic bottle of thorium hydroxide which is the source of the radioactive gas thoron $^{220}_{86}$Rn
- d.c. amplifier with an input resistance value of 10^{11} Ω
- ionisation chamber to fit d.c. amplifier
- d.c. power supply of about 9–20 V (need not be stabilised)
- 0–1 mA d.c. ammeter
- stopwatch

PRINCIPLES INVOLVED

a A single radioactive species decays according to the exponential law shown in Fig. 14.18. In principle the half-life $T_{\frac{1}{2}}$ can be measured by determining the decay curve in Fig. 14.18 and recording the values of time t for which the original number of nuclei decreases from the initial number N_0 at $t = 0$ to $N_0/2$, $N_0/4$, $N_0/8$, etc. This would not be a practical method in a school laboratory for a radioactive species with a half-life of several hours or longer.

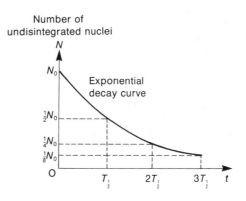

Fig. 14.18 The decay curve for a single radioactive species of half-life $T_{\frac{1}{2}}$.

b Measuring the decay curve for a short-lived species such as $^{220}_{86}$Rn (thoron) by this method is possible but not very accurate unless a large number of determinations are made. Since the radioactive decay is a random process, there are irregularities in the decay curve and measuring the exact time at which $N = N_0/2$ is quite difficult. It is much easier and more accurate to use the theoretical equation for the decay curve:

$$N = N_0 \exp(-\lambda t)$$

where N is the number of nuclei present at time t and λ is the decay constant. λ is related to the half-life of the species by:

$$T_{\frac{1}{2}} = \frac{\log_e 2}{\lambda} = \frac{0.693}{\lambda}$$

A suitable linear graph relating N and t can be plotted to give an average value for λ and hence $T_{\frac{1}{2}}$.

c In practice, the number of nuclei present at time t cannot be measured. What can be measured is the number of disintegrations per second or the activity of the source $A = -dN/dt$. The only change required in the exponential equation is the replacement of N and N_0 by the activities A and A_0 at times t and $t = 0$:

$$A = A_0 \exp(-\lambda t).$$

d The first problem encountered in measuring the half-life of a single radioactive substance is that most radioactive sources consist of a series of species in radioactive equilibrium. Any measurements on the activity of such a source will include contributions from all species present. It is then impossible to determine the half-life of one of the species by simple techniques. One way to avoid the problem is to isolate one of the species from the series. In thorium one of the species in radioactive equilibrium is the gas thoron. Because of its very short half-life compared with the other species, it is present in very small quantities. However, since thoron as a gas can be separated from the other species in the series, its radioactive decay can be measured. There is one slight problem: that thoron itself decays to produce a radioactive series:

$$^{220}_{86}\text{Rn} \xrightarrow{\alpha} ^{216}_{84}\text{Po} \xrightarrow{\alpha} ^{212}_{82}\text{Pb} \xrightarrow{\beta} ^{212}_{83}\text{Bi, etc.}$$
thoron gas $\qquad T_{\frac{1}{2}} = 0.16\text{ s} \quad T_{\frac{1}{2}} = 10.6\text{ h}$

You will need to think later about why these further species hardly affect the shape of the activity decay curve for thoron.

PROCEDURE

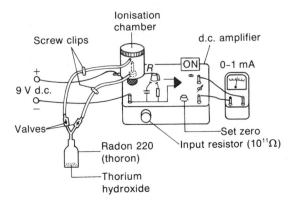

Fig. 14.19 Measurement of the radioactive half-life of radon gas using an ionisation chamber and a d.c. amplifier.

e Connect up the apparatus as shown in Fig. 14.19.

f The bottle of thorium hydroxide (or other thorium salt) provides a source of α-emitting thoron gas. The screw clips should be closed initially. The ionisation chamber should have its centre disc removed (if present) and be fitted with its solid cover to ensure that no thoron gas escapes.

g The 9–20 V d.c. supply, connected across the ionisation chamber, enables the positively charged ions and electrons produced by the α-particles to be collected (see section 14.2.1). The ionisation current is amplified by the d.c. amplifier and displayed on the milliammeter as a current I. This current is proportional to the activity of the source A.

h The d.c. amplifier should be set initially with the control R at the 'rest' position. Check that the 10^{11} Ω input resistor has been connected to the amplifier. Switch on the d.c. amplifier. Using a voltmeter check that the battery voltage is correct (see section 14.1.1). If it is significantly below the specified value for the amplifier, this experiment will not produce satisfactory results.

i It is very important from now on that you do not touch the ionisation chamber, because you will produce a larger effect on the milliammeter than that produced by the ionisation processes in the chamber (ionisation currents are only about 10 pA).

j   Adjust the 'set zero' control on the d.c. amplifier so as to give a zero reading on the milliammeter. Switch 'R' to the R position and record the milliammeter reading I_b. This corresponds to the background activity from cosmic rays and the laboratory. This current must be subtracted from all subsequent readings of I (see section 14.4.2).

k   Open the screw clips on the tubing and squeeze the plastic bottle once; there is a time delay before the milliammeter indicates an ionisation current. If the reading is negative, reverse the connections to the milliammeter. Close the clips firmly. Wait until the needle falls to 1 mA and commence timing. Determine an approximate value for the half-life $T_{\frac{1}{2}}$ of thoron by measuring the time for the current to decrease to half of its initial value I_0. Notice how the readings fluctuate as a result of the random nature of radioactive decay.

l   From the approximate value of $T_{\frac{1}{2}}$ obtained in (k) you should be able to decide on what time intervals you should use to obtain a well-defined activity curve $I\ (\propto A)$ against time t.

m   Wait for the reading of the milliammeter to decrease to the background value I_b. Now refill the ionisation chamber as in (k). Record readings of I at the time intervals chosen in (l) until the value of I decreases to about $\frac{1}{10}$ of the reading at $t = 0$, I_0. The process is quite rapid so you will need to take the readings down roughly at first. Do not worry about fluctuations in the readings.

n   Tabulate your results for t, I in μA and $(I - I_b)$ in μA. Leave a further column for analysis of the data.

o   Plot a graph of $(I - I_b)$ against time t and hence measure three values of $T_{\frac{1}{2}}$ from the time taken for I to decrease to $I_0/2$, $I_0/4$ and $I_0/8$ (see Fig. 14.18). Calculate the average value of $T_{\frac{1}{2}}$.

p   Alternatively, you may determine a value for λ, and hence $T_{\frac{1}{2}}$, by using the exponential relationship $I = I_0 \exp(-\lambda t)$. Plot a suitable graph to determine λ. Calculate $T_{\frac{1}{2}}$ from $\log_e 2/\lambda$. Estimate the uncertainty in λ and $T_{\frac{1}{2}}$ from your graph.

q   Compare the results for $T_{\frac{1}{2}}$ obtained in (o) and (p) with the accepted value for $^{220}_{86}\mathrm{Rn}$. Which method do you consider to produce a more accurate result? Which method is more generally applicable to the measurement of the half-life of a radioactive source?

r   Explain why you can ignore the fact that $^{220}_{86}\mathrm{Rn}$ produces other radioactive species $^{216}_{84}\mathrm{Po}$ ($T_{\frac{1}{2}} = 0.16$ s) and $^{212}_{82}\mathrm{Pb}$ ($T_{\frac{1}{2}} = 10.6$ h) emitting α- and β-particles.

NOTES

s   Your account should include a description of the experimental procedure, the analysis leading to two values of $T_{\frac{1}{2}}$ together with the estimates of the uncertainties in $T_{\frac{1}{2}}$.

15 ANALOGUE ELECTRONICS

15.1 THE OPERATIONAL AMPLIFIER: AN INTRODUCTION

15.1.1 Analogue electronics

All the experiments in this chapter are concerned in one way or another with an *operational amplifier,* or op-amp as it is usually called. Op-amps were designed originally for use in analogue computers, in which continuously variable voltages are used to represent physical quantities. (In the more familiar digital computers information is represented by only two states; normal numbers are converted to their binary equivalents before processing.) The adjective 'operational' refers to the use of these amplifiers in performing simple mathematical operations like addition and subtraction, and even more complicated ones like differentiation and integration. Analogue computers have now been largely succeeded by powerful digital computers, but op-amps have survived; their versatility has led to many useful applications, some of which are included in the experiments in this chapter.

15.1.2 The op-amp IC

All operational amplifiers in use these days are assembled in integrated circuit (IC) form. An example is the 741 op-amp, which is suitable for all of the experiments in this section. The circuit for the 741 includes 20 transistors, which are formed with other components on to a small silicon chip less than 3 mm square. Connections are made to the chip before it is sealed into a black plastic rectangular block, and these connections are terminated at the eight connecting pins that protrude below the block. The circuit formed on the chip is the concern of the manufacturer only. Designers of electronic equipment, the users of op-amps and other ICs, require building blocks from which complex circuits can be made, and for each type of building block they need to know *what* it does, not *how* it does it. This *black box* approach will also be ours.

IC technology improves at a rate that renders some devices obsolete very quickly. The 741 is cheap and has been widely available for several years. Though op-amps have been developed more recently that have better characteristics than the 741 and are no more expensive, the 741 is so well established in industry and elsewhere as the standard op-amp that its use seems likely to con-

tinue. Most of the modern alternative op-amps have pin connections that are compatible with the 741, and it is therefore a simple matter to remove the 741 from your circuit and plug in one of the alternatives. All of the circuits suggested in this section work perfectly well with virtually any op-amp and require no modification if an alternative to the 741 is used.

15.1.3 Voltage amplification

Currents in analogue devices are kept as low as possible to reduce power dissipation, which is wasteful and leads to overheating; for this reason, voltages rather than currents are used to represent physical quantities. The op-amp is therefore designed to be a *voltage amplifier,* i.e. it produces an output voltage A_0 times the voltage input, where A_0 is the *voltage gain.* It will become apparent as you work through the experiments that the op-amp is very often used with a feedback loop, which allows a proportion of the output voltage to be fed back into the input. A_0 is a useful quantity that applies to the performance of the op-amp without feedback, and it is therefore called the *open-loop voltage gain* to distinguish it from the *closed-loop voltage gain A,* which applies to the complete amplifier circuit consisting of the op-amp and its associated feedback network.

15.2 CONNECTIONS TO THE OP-AMP

15.2.1 Power supplies

Although currents are not as important as voltages in the study of the op-amp's behaviour, its output current is generally larger than its input current, which means that the op-amp amplifies current as well as voltage (though not necessarily by the same amount). Electrical power $P = VI,$ and since both V and I are increased, it would seem that the op-amp is delivering more power from output than it receives at its input. This apparent contravention of the law of conservation of energy is explained when we realise that a *power supply,* such as a battery, must always be connected; extra power is drawn from the power supply as required. The power supply connections to electronic circuits, including those containing op-amps, are so often taken for granted that they are usually omitted from circuit diagrams.

The op-amp requires a twin power supply. Although no common or earth connection is made to the op-amp itself, it is convenient to measure all voltages relative to a common rail, whose voltage level we call zero. If, for example, a potential difference of 11 V exists between a particular point P in a circuit and the common rail, with P at the lower potential, the voltage of P is said to be -11 V. Using this convention we call the voltages of the two power supply connections $+V_s$ and $-V_s$, and, since each one is measured relative to the common rail, the p.d. between them is $2V_s$. Usually $V_s = 15$ V, for which a source with e.m.f. of 30 V is required, but most op-amps work satisfactorily over a range of V_s from 4 V to 18 V. Note that access is required to the centre of the source to provide the common rail connection. For example, if V_s is to be 9 V, two 9 V radio batteries might be used in series (a combined e.m.f. of 18 V) with the common rail connected between them (Fig. 15.1). A pair of batteries makes a satisfactory power supply for an op-amp circuit, but mains powered supplies are more convenient and economical for use in the laboratory. For $V_s = 15$ V, the three terminals of such a supply are at voltages of $+15$ V, 0 V (ground) and -15 V.

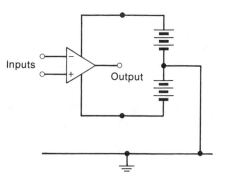

Fig. 15.1   Conventional power supply arrangements for the op-amp.

The common rail does not have to be earthed, but in practice it is difficult to avoid connecting it to earth at some point. In the experiments that follow, input voltages are supplied from a signal generator, and voltages are displayed on a CRO. Both these essential pieces of equipment usually have one of their connecting terminals earthed internally, which is the one to which the common rail of the op-amp circuit should be connected. In this chapter, the common rail is indicated on circuit diagrams by the conventional earth symbol and referred to in the text as *ground*.

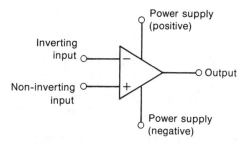

Fig. 15.2   The five principal op-amp connections: two for the power supply, two inputs and one output.

15.2.2 Inputs and output

The op-amp has one output and two separate inputs, as shown in Fig. 15.2. A voltage V_- at the *inverting input* (marked with a minus sign on the op-amp symbol) produces an output voltage $V_o = -A_o V_-$; i.e. V_- and V_o have opposite signs. A voltage V_+ at the *non-inverting input* (marked with a plus sign) produces an output voltage $V_o = A_o V_+$; V_+ and V_o have the same sign. Remember that all voltages are measured relative to ground. Note that the plus and minus signs used to label the inputs on the standard op-amp symbol are *not* indications of voltage polarity. In this chapter we use them also as subscripts to label the two voltage inputs, each of which may normally have any value between $-V_s$ and $+V_s$.

If voltages are now applied to the inputs simultaneously, we have:

$$V_o = A_o V_+ - A_o V_-$$
so
$$V_o = A_o(V_+ - V_-) \qquad [15.1]$$

from which we see that V_o is A_o times the *difference* between the two input voltages V_+ and V_-, and for this reason the op-amp is referred to sometimes as a *differential amplifier*. Inputs should never be left unconnected, or *open*; if only one of the two inputs is required, the other must be grounded (connected to the common rail). For example, in a simple inverting amplifier the non-inverting input would be grounded $(V_+ = 0)$.

It is important to realise that the op-amp's output voltage V_0 can never exceed $+V_s$, nor fall below $-V_s$; thus the range of output voltage swing is limited to $2V_s$. If the input voltage and the gain of the amplifier demand a value of V_0 outside this range, the output waveform will be *clipped* at around $+V_s$ and $-V_s$, as shown in Fig. 15.3 (overleaf). Clipping is generally to be avoided in linear circuits, in which it is responsible for one form of *distortion*. However, in some of these experiments the op-amp is used intentionally in a *saturated* condition: V_o is driven up to $+V_s$ and down to $-V_s$. In practice the output voltage range is about 3 V less than $2V_s$, because the op-amp reaches a state of saturation when V_o is a volt or so lower than $+V_s$ (or higher than $-V_s$). For $V_s = 15$ V, V_o has limiting values $\pm V_s$ of about ± 13 V.

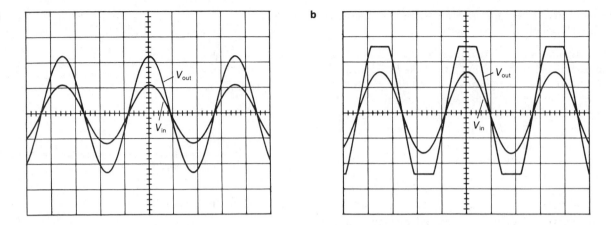

Fig. 15.3 Waveforms of input and output voltages displayed on the CRO from an amplifying circuit with a nominal voltage gain of 2. The Y-sensitivities of both channels are set at 5 V/div.
a When the amplitude of V_{in} is just less than the 6 V the amplitude of V_{out} is 11 V, as expected.
b When the amplitude of V_{in} is increased to 8 V the op-amp is driven into saturation that causes clipping of the output waveform. Note that the clipping here is asymmetric: V_{out} is clipped at +13 V when high, but at −12 V when low.

In this chapter we use the symbols V_+ and V_- to indicate the voltages at the two inputs of the op-amp, while input or signal voltages to the complete amplifier circuit are indicated by V_{in}, V_1, V_2, etc. A signal might be applied directly to one of the op-amp inputs (putting $V_+ = V_2$, for example), but usually a network of other components is assembled around the op-amp, and input signals are applied via resistors or capacitors. Table 15.1 lists the symbols used to represent the various voltages that may be encountered in this chapter.

Table 15.1

Symbol	Voltage
$+V_s, -V_s$	Supply voltages (usually 15 V)
$+V'_s, -V'_s$	Op-amp output saturation voltages ($V'_s < V_s$)
V_+	Voltage at non-inverting input of op-amp
V_-	Voltage at inverting input of op-amp
V_o	Voltage obtained at output of op-amp
V_{in}	Signal or input voltage (usually alternating) applied to amplifier circuit
V_1, V_2, etc.	Other input voltages, e.g. d.c.
V_{out}	Output voltage obtained from amplifier circuit
A_o	Open-loop voltage gain of op amp $\left(= \dfrac{V_o}{(V_+ - V_-)} \right)$
A	Closed-loop voltage gain of circuit $\left(= \dfrac{V_{out}}{V_{in}} \right)$

Note also that:
a) all voltages are measured relative to ground.
b) in nearly all circuits the output voltage V_{out} is obtained at the output of the op-amp, i.e. $V_{out} = V_o$.
c) where more than one op-amp is used in a circuit, outputs are labelled V_{o1}, V_{o2}, etc.

15.2.3 Offset null

So far five of the eight connections to the op-amp IC have been identified: two inputs, one output and two for the power supply. A sixth connecting pin is not used at all. We now consider the remaining two. Since the output voltage V_o is determined by the difference $(V_+ - V_-)$ between the two input voltages, we might expect V_o to be zero when $V_+ = V_-$. However, there are several reasons why this may not be so. The input stage of the op-amp consists of two matched circuits. Any imbalance between these circuits, which arises inevitably during manufacture, produces an *input offset voltage* (typically 1 mV for the 741). Differences between the circuit components before the inputs of the op-amp can also produce an offset voltage: although average input currents are very small (typically 80 nA for the 741), p.d.s of several millivolts are established across the large resistors through which these currents flow. If the equivalent resistances between each input and ground are not roughly equal, a difference exists between these p.d.s that appears as an offset voltage between the inputs. Even if these two resistances are equal, any difference between the input currents, known as the input offset current (perhaps 20 nA for the 741), produces its own offset voltage.

All these offset voltages are amplified by the op-amp, so the likelihood of V_o being zero when we expect V_+ and V_- to be equal is remote. The problem actually worsens when we realise that these offset currents and voltages are affected by temperature fluctuations within the IC (caused by power dissipation), over which we have little control. Surprisingly perhaps, in most applications of the op-amp, problems that might be caused by offset voltages are resolved by the use of feedback, which has already been mentioned in connection with voltage gain, and no compensation is necessary. However, some circuits do require means of compensation, and two connections on the op-amp are provided for this. For the 741, a 10 kΩ potential divider is connected between them with its wiper connected to $-V_s$. This is known as an *offset null* control. Some other op-amps require slightly different means of compensation. Further details are given in the text where such compensation is necessary; for all other circuits it may be assumed that offset null is not required, and the two connections should be left open.

15.3 OP-AMP PERFORMANCE: IDEAL AND REAL

15.3.1 Voltage gain

We now consider some of the functions of an operational amplifier. A description of the ideal op-amp emerges with consideration of some of the parameters that determine its performance. Essentially, the op-amp is required to perform a variety of amplification tasks in analogue circuits. One very obvious requirement is a voltage gain over which we have control: either of some chosen fixed value, or variable (such as a volume control), or even controlled electronically by some property of the signal (such as the tone controls of an audio amplifier; when the bass control is turned up, for example, signals of low frequency are amplified by a greater amount than those of middle and higher frequencies, i.e. the gain of the amplifier is partly determined by the frequency of the incoming signal).

The op-amp is a sealed unit to which no internal adjustments can be made. The only means by which we can control the overall gain of an amplifier circuit is through the other components that we connect around the op-amp to form the complete circuit. The application of negative feedback, in which part of the output is fed back to the inverting input, forms the basis of many such circuits, whose closed-loop voltage gain is determined by the values of resistances in the feedback network. The ideal op-amp therefore has an infinite open-loop voltage gain, or at least one that is much larger than we would ever require. We can then use it with suitable feedback components to assemble an amplifier having any reasonable gain, fixed or variable, whose value does not depend on any property of the op-amp itself.

There are other advantages of designing the amplifier this way. No two op-amps of the same type are likely to be identical since their complexity and small size prevent the achievement of close manufacturing tolerances. Furthermore, the performance of the op-amp itself is affected by temperature variations, and therefore, even if op-amps having the required nominal gain were available, it would not be possible to rely on either the precision or the stability of this gain. Resistors, on the other hand, are available with close resistance tolerances, high stabilities and low temperature coefficients; their resistances are

much more reliable than any property of the op-amp. Instead of having many different types of op-amp, each with its own gain, it is better to have just one, with a very high gain, which can then be combined with resistive feedback components to provide the gain that is required.

15.3.2 Impedances

The ideal op-amp would have an infinite input impedance and a zero output impedance. Like resistance, *impedance* is a voltage/current ratio (and therefore measured in ohms), but it applies where currents and voltages might be changing or alternating, and its magnitude generally depends on their frequency of alternation. For the op-amp, neither input nor output impedance varies much with frequency, so the terms input and output resistance are sometimes used instead.

The impedance between the two inputs of the op-amp is called the *input impedance* and determines the size of the input current, which ideally should be zero. When no feedback network is connected, this current is drawn from the source and could affect the signal voltage, particularly if either the current or the source impedance (or both) is appreciable. Just as an ideal voltmeter has an infinite resistance (such that it draws no current from, and has no effect on, the circuit to which it is connected) so the ideal op-amp, which is a voltage operated device, has an infinite input impedance. When a feedback loop is connected the effective impedance of the amplifier depends upon the values of feedback components, and most of the current drawn from the source flows around the feedback loop, and not into the op-amp.

For similar reasons, the *output impedance* of the op-amp is ideally zero. The output side may be regarded as a source of e.m.f. whose internal resistance is equivalent to output impedance. Any current drawn from the op-amp produces a p.d. across the output impedance, and the output voltage V_o consequently falls.

15.3.3 Frequency effects

The ideal op-amp would cover a very wide range of signal frequencies, from d.c. ($f = 0$) upwards, over which the open-loop voltage gain A_o is constant. Normally we would want all signals, of whatever frequency, to be amplified by the same amount. Such an amplifier is said to have a large *bandwidth*. The real op-amp falls a long way short of meeting this requirement. For the 741, $A_o \approx 10^5$ at very low frequencies (including d.c.), but falls to unity at about 1 MHz. However, we have already seen how the op-amp is nearly always used with negative feedback to provide a stable closed-loop gain A that is independent of A_o. The application of feedback reduces the gain but it greatly increases the bandwidth over which the gain is constant. There is in fact a direct relationship between closed-loop gain and bandwidth: one can be sacrificed for the other.

One other op-amp parameter that must be considered here is the maximum rate at which the output voltage can change. This is called the *slew rate* and is measured in V s^{-1} or, more appropriately, V μs^{-1}. When a high frequency signal is applied to one of the inputs, the amplified output voltage V_o has to alternate rapidly between its minimum and maximum values. Above a particular frequency, whose value depends on the amplitude, V_o would have to change at a rate faster than the slew rate to maintain the amplified waveform, but, as this is not possible, the output waveform becomes distorted.

Summary

Table 15.2 lists some of the parameters we have considered and gives their ideal values. For comparison, corresponding values for the 741 and also for the 081, one of the better alternative op-amps, are given.

Table 15.2

	Ideal	741	081
Open-loop voltage gain A_o (d.c.)	∞	2×10^5	2×10^5
Input impedance	∞	2 MΩ	10^{12} Ω
Input bias current	0	80 nA	30 pA
Output impedance	0	150 Ω	20 Ω
Slew rate	∞	0.5 V μs^{-1}	13 V μs^{-1}

15.4 PRACTICAL CIRCUITS

15.4.1 Circuit assembly

There are many different ways of connecting up the circuits required for this chapter. It would be inappropriate (and impossible) to describe them all here in the sort of detail that you might need to proceed without additional guidance from your teacher. Indeed, the diversity of commercially manufactured systems alone rules out such description, and in many schools and colleges other systems have been designed and made whose variety is clearly boundless. It is therefore assumed that the system in use in your laboratory, especially the means of interconnecting pieces of equipment, is either demonstrated or otherwise explained (e.g. in a manual), so that you are able to assemble circuits from the simple conventional circuit diagrams that are used in the text. Broadly speaking, each circuit consists of a few components assembled around one or more op-amps. Many of the circuits require input signals or voltages and produce an output voltage that must be monitored. Some general guidance and advice follows that may help you to interpret the diagrams. Most importantly, remember that:

a) Power supply connections are omitted from circuit diagrams.

b) The power supply should be switched off or disconnected before changing components or making other alterations.

15.4.2 Op-amp ICs

Single op-amps are commonly available in an 8-pin dual-in-line (DIL) IC *package*. Some types of op-amp, including the 741, are also available with two or four op-amps in one package, usually 14-pin DIL; these are useful where space is limited. Two methods by which the pins of any IC can be identified are adopted by manufacturers: either pin 1 is indicated by a dimple, or a slot indicates the end between the first and highest-numbered pins. Pin connections for the single 8-pin package are shown in Fig. 15.4. Note that pin 8 has no internal connections and is therefore not used at all (nor, in nearly all of the circuits, are pins 1 and 5).

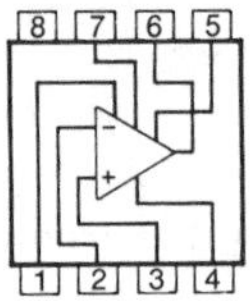

Fig. 15.4 Pin connections for the op-amp IC in its normal 8-pin DIL package:

2 inverting input V_-

3 non-inverting input V_+

6 output V_o

4 power supply (negative) $-V_s$

7 power supply (positive) $+V_s$

1 & 5 offset null

8 not used

15.4.3 Input voltages

Variable input voltages or signals of two types, d.c. (steady) and a.c. (varying continuously, usually sinusoidally) are required. Most d.c. voltage inputs may be obtained from a potential divider connected between the two power supply rails. This arrangement provides input voltages V_1, V_2, etc. that can be varied between $-V_s$ and $+V_s$. Where greater sensitivity is required, a second, fixed potential divider is used.

Alternating voltage inputs are obtained from a signal generator, on which the high impedance output terminals should always be used. Connect the earthed terminal to the common rail (ground) of your circuit, and the other, 'live' one to the point where V_{in} is to be applied. When small alternating voltages are required the amplitude control of the signal generator may be too insensitive, so use the voltage attenuation switch. This usually allows reductions of the output voltage amplitude by factors of 10 or 100. (These may be labelled −20 dB and −40 dB, which refer to corresponding reductions of power.) The small currents drawn by the inputs of the op-amp have already been mentioned in connection with offset null adjustments. These currents have a d.c. component that is required to *bias* the transistors in the input stages of the op-amp, and it is essential that a d.c. path to each input is provided through which these currents can flow. Most signal generator outputs provide a path, but some are intentionally capacitor-coupled to block d.c. components of the signals they produce, and a large resistance to compensate for this should then be connected between the op-amp input and ground.

15.4.4 Voltage monitoring and measurement

All signal levels and other voltages are conveniently measured with a CRO, though in some experiments other means are used. One dual trace CRO is more useful than two single trace ones; observations and direct comparisons of amplitude, phase and waveform can then be made between two different voltages, for example those at the input and output stages of an amplifier. Detailed instructions on the use of the CRO are not given in the text of individual experiments, except where necessary. However, the following points should be considered carefully in addition to the information contained in appendix 1 (page 290).

a) If triggering is fixed on one channel, this should generally be the one on which the output waveform is displayed, labelled channel 2 on circuit diagrams. Select a time base setting that produces a display of about two or three complete cycles for a.c. voltage waveforms.

b) Use both channels on their d.c. settings. Normally it is convenient to place the ground (zero voltage) levels of both channel traces exactly half-way up the screen, but before taking voltage measurements from the screen check that these ground levels have not shifted. This precaution is not necessary when a waveform's amplitude is being measured; it is then usually more convenient to shift the waveform until its top or bottom lies over a graticule on the screen.

c) Adjust the Y-sensitivities of the two channels independently to give displays that almost fill the screen. In many experiments V_{out} varies over its maximum range, between $-V'_s$ and $+V'_s$, so if $V_s = 15$ V, a suitable setting for channel 2 is 5 V/div. The Y-sensitivity of the other channel, on which a much smaller input voltage might be displayed, may need to be up to 1000 times greater.

d) In some of the circuits the op-amp is used in a state of saturation at all times, such that V_{out} switches, or is switched, between its two extreme values of $-V'_s$ and $+V'_s$. The op-amp is then functioning as a two-state device (like the digital ICs considered in section 16), and it is useful to have an alternative means of monitoring V_{out} so that the two channels of the CRO are available for monitoring other parts of the circuit and investigating the switching action. Some form of indicator system, based on twin light emitting diodes (LEDs) or a lamp that is either on or off, is ideal, but a second CRO (single beam) would be adequate.

15.4.5 Resistors

Resistors are identified by their coloured bands; see appendix 3 (page 314). All the resistance values that are used in the experiments of this chapter are listed in Table 15.3 with their alternative code labelling and the corresponding colours of the first three bands. (The fourth band indicates tolerance, typically 5% for which a gold band is used.)

Table 15.3

Resistance	Code	Colours of first three bands
100 Ω	100R	Brown, black, brown
1.0 kΩ	1K0	Brown, black, red
2.7 kΩ	2K7	Red, violet, red
10 kΩ	10K	Brown, black, orange
22 kΩ	22K	Red, red, orange
39 kΩ	39K	Orange, white, orange
47 kΩ	47K	Yellow, violet, orange
100 kΩ	100K	Brown, black, yellow
1.0 MΩ	1M0	Brown, black, green

15.4.6 Experimental precision

All component values have a manufacturing tolerance indicating the range in which their true value lies, above or below the nominal value. Resistance tolerances (typically 5% or 10%) are usually lower than those of capacitances. The tolerances of components combined in these circuits can lead to significant differences between results predicted from theoretical analysis and those obtained from measurements. A good knowledge of many op-amp applications and features can be gained from these experiments without wasting time on precise measurements. For this reason, to investigate the effect of changing parameters on the circuit, component values are changed typically by a factor of about 10 (e.g. from 10 kΩ to 100 kΩ) and frequencies of input signals by a factor of about 3 (e.g. from 1 kHz to 3 kHz).

15A Voltage Comparison

Investigation of the use of the op-amp in a state of either positive or negative saturation in switching applications

APPARATUS REQUIRED

- circuit assembly board or system
- twin op-amp power supply, $V_s = 15$ V
- signal generator
- dual trace CRO
- two state indicator (or voltmeter reading up to 10 V d.c.)
- 0–10 V d.c. voltmeter
- 741 op-amp (or equivalent)
- ORP 12 light dependent resistor
- TH-3 thermistor
- 2 10 kΩ variable resistors (potentiometers)
- resistors: 1.0 kΩ, 2.7 kΩ
- connecting wires

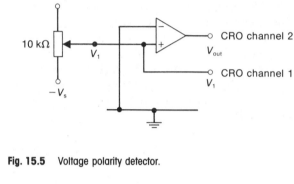

Fig. 15.5   Voltage polarity detector.

PRINCIPLES INVOLVED

a   Equation [15.1] shows how the output voltage V_o of an op-amp is A_o times the difference between the two input voltages. The open-loop gain A_o is so high, however, that the op-amp saturates (i.e. V_o reaches either $+V_s'$ or $-V_s'$) when the differential voltage input $|V_+ - V_-|$ is well under a millivolt. Nearly all op-amp circuits, including those used in the other experiments of this chapter, incorporate some form of negative feedback network that reduces the overall gain. However, in this experiment you will investigate applications of the op-amp in which no feedback network is used; input voltages are applied directly to the op-amp inputs.

VOLTAGE POLARITY DETECTOR

b   Connect up the circuit of Fig. 15.5, in which the potential divider is used to apply a variable voltage V_1 directly to the non-inverting input; the inverting input is grounded. Display V_1 ($= V_+$) and V_{out} ($= V_0$) on the CRO. Vary V_1 over the full range between the power supply voltages $-V_s$ and $+V_s$, and observe how V_{out} always has one of only two values: $-V_s'$ or $+V_s'$. (If both channels on the CRO are set to the same sensitivity, the difference between the power supply voltages $\pm V_s$ and the limits of the op-amp's output range $\pm V_s'$ will be evident.) The changeover occurs when V_1 passes through zero, so concentrate on this region and try to 'capture' the trace representing V_{out} somewhere between its two extreme positions on the screen.

c   The difficulty of this last task gives you some idea of how large A_o is. It is simply not possible to maintain V_1 at a value close enough to zero for V_o to lie somewhere between $-V_s'$ and $+V_s'$. Note that since $V_- = 0$, $V_o = A_o V_+$; i.e. V_{out} and V_1 always have the same sign.

d   Now interchange the connections to the two inputs so that V_1 is applied to the inverting input, and the non-inverting input is grounded. Repeat section (b). Note and explain the difference between these circuits, and their behaviour.

VOLTAGE COMPARATOR

e   The value of V_1 at which V_{out} changes from one stable value to the other can be set to a value other than zero by applying a voltage V_2 to the input that was grounded in section (b). This leads to the idea of voltage comparison (hence the name of the circuit): V_{out} can have one of only two values, depending on whether $V_1 > V_2$ or $V_1 < V_2$. The op-amp is behaving as a digital device, with 'high' and 'low' digital levels represented by the op-amp's two output states.

f   Investigate this by connecting up the circuit shown in Fig. 15.6, in which a second potential divider is used to apply a voltage V_2 directly to the inverting input. Display V_1 and V_2 on the CRO and monitor V_{out} with the two-state indicator. (Alternatively, monitor V_2 with the voltmeter and display V_{out} on the CRO.) Set V_2 at $+5$ V, vary V_1 as before, and note how V_{out} now changes when $V_1 = +5$ V.

LIGHT-SENSITIVE CIRCUIT

g A simple light-operated switching circuit can be made by incorporating a light-dependent resistor (LDR) into one of the potential dividers of Fig. 15.6. The resistance of the ORP 12, which is made from cadmium sulphide, decreases as the incident light increases. Typical resistance values are:

direct sunlight	$20\ \Omega$
a sunny room	$1\ \mathrm{k}\Omega$
good artificial illumination	$5\ \mathrm{k}\Omega$
well covered (e.g. by hand)	$100\ \mathrm{k}\Omega$
complete darkness	$10\ \mathrm{M}\Omega$

Note that the great sensitivity of the ORP 12 to changes of light intensity means that these values should only be used as a guide. In the circuit shown in Fig. 15.7 the voltage V_2 is obtained from a normal potential divider, as before, but the voltage V_1 depends on the relative values of the resistances R_L and R_1, which together form the second potential divider. (The $1\ \mathrm{k}\Omega$ fixed resistor in R_1 limits the current that could flow between the two power supply rails.)

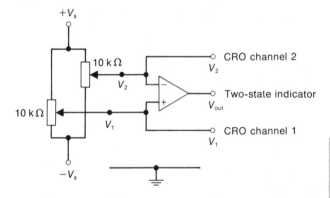

Fig. 15.6 Voltage comparator.

h Connect up the circuit of Fig. 15.7, displaying or otherwise monitoring V_1, V_2 and V_{out} as in section (f). Turn R_1 up to its maximum value and place the LDR in a well-lit position. Cover the LDR and notice how V_1 rises. Set V_2 at a suitable value such that $V_1 < V_2$ when the LDR is exposed and $V_1 > V_2$ when it is covered. Observe the switching action and notice that, no matter how slowly you cover or uncover the LDR, V_{out} switches instantly between its two values. Use the variable resistance R_1 (as adjustment for ambient light intensity) and the setting of V_2 (as adjustment for the light intensity at which you want switching to occur) to make your circuit react to various changes of illumination. Try some of the following actions: closing a curtain on the far side of the room, moving the splayed fingers of your hand across the LDR, placing light and dark articles of clothing in front of the LDR, switching off the ceiling light.

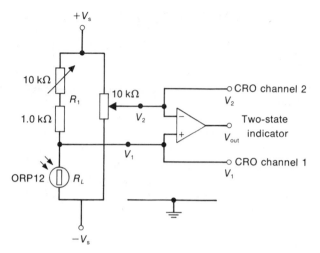

Fig. 15.7 Light-sensitive circuit.

i Think of two ways in which the circuit of Fig. 15.7 could be altered to reverse the action of the circuit; i.e. to switch V_{out} from high $(+V'_s)$ to low $(-V'_s)$ when the LDR is covered. Test your ideas experimentally.

TEMPERATURE-SENSITIVE CIRCUIT

j A similar circuit that is temperature operated uses a thermistor in place of the LDR. The resistance of the TH-3 thermistor is about $600\ \Omega$ at room temperature, but falls to half that value when warmed gently. It does not cover such a wide resistance range as the LDR, but it is used in the same way.

k Connect up the circuit of Fig. 15.8. Observe the fairly high level of V_1. Adjust the variable resistor to increase V_2 until V_{out} switches from $+V'_s$ to $-V'_s$; set V_2 just above V_1. Now hold the thermistor tightly and notice that V_1 rises as the thermistor becomes warmer. Confirm that switching occurs when $V_1 = V_2$. Release the thermistor and allow it to cool (a very slow process). Notice that V_{out} switches back as V_1 falls below V_2.

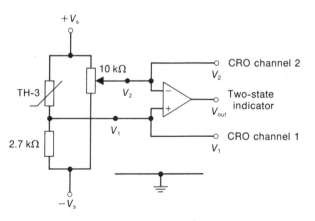

Fig. 15.8 Temperature-sensitive circuit.

SINE WAVE TO SQUARE WAVE CONVERTER

l Investigate the effect of applying a sinusoidal input voltage V_{in} to the simple voltage comparator. Connect up the circuit of Fig. 15.9 and set the frequency f of the signal generator that supplies V_{in} at about 500 Hz. Adjust the CRO time base to display both V_{in} and V_{out} waveforms. Notice how V_{out} switches between $-V'_s$ and $+V'_s$ as V_{in} passes through zero, to produce a square wave. However, because the rate at which V_{out} is able to change is limited (to the *slew rate* – see section 15.3.3), the *rise* and *fall times* are significant, i.e. the sides of the square wave lean a bit. Vary the amplitude of V_{in}: is there any effect on V_{out}?

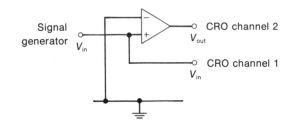

Fig. 15.9 Sine wave to square wave converter.

m To investigate the limiting effect of the slew rate further, increase f by a factor of 10 to about 5 kHz, suitably adjusting the CRO time base, and notice how the sides of the square wave now appear to lean even more, though in fact this is due only to the increased time base frequency that you have set. It should also be obvious that the two waveforms are no longer in phase. To identify the cause of this, switch the waveform of V_{in} from sinusoidal to square on the signal generator. Observe the waveforms of V_{in} and V_{out} and notice how the changeover of V_{out} *starts* each time as V_{in} passes through zero (which it does very rapidly,

since it is a square wave), but how the finite time that the changeover takes is a significant proportion of the duration of each half cycle (Fig. 15.10). Vary f slightly to confirm this point. Increase the time base frequency to expand the waveforms on the screen and use the CRO calibrations to measure the slew rate of the op-amp ($= \Delta V_{out}/\Delta t$).

n Connect up the circuit of Fig. 15.11, a combination of the circuits of Figs. 15.6 and 15.9. Set f at 500 Hz and vary both V_2 and the amplitude of V_{in} to show that $V_{out} = +V'_s$ when $V_{in} > V_2$, and $V_{out} = -V'_s$ when $V_{in} < V_2$.

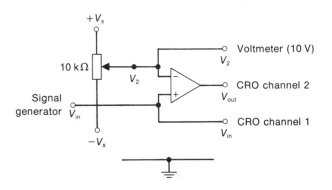

Fig. 15.11 Sine wave to square wave converter with variable mark-space ratio.

o Now set the amplitude of V_{in} at about 5 V, vary V_2 and notice how the *mark-space* ratio of the V_{out} waveform, defined as the ratio of the durations of the two parts of the cycle, can be controlled. The mark-space ratio of the waveform shown in Fig. 15.12 is about 1:3.

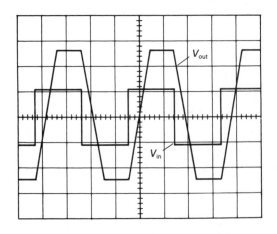

Fig. 15.10 Waveforms of V_{in} and V_{out} displayed on the CRO from the circuit of Fig. 15.9, when a square wave of frequency about 5 kHz is applied.

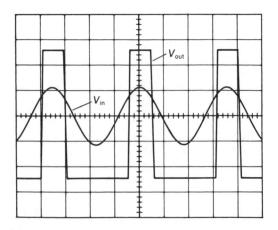

Fig. 15.12 Waveforms of V_{in} and V_{out} displayed on the CRO from the circuit of Fig. 15.11.

p   Your record should include labelled circuit diagrams, where appropriate.

q   The voltage comparator is used in analogue-to-digital (A to D) converters. An analogue signal that varies continuously is converted into a digital signal, consisting of pulses in which only two voltage levels are allowed. In your experiments these levels have been $\pm V_s'$, but specially designed comparator op-amps with fast slew rates and output levels compatible with digital systems such as TTL are available (e.g. the 710). The frequency of the digital pulses is the same as that of the analogue signal, but the duration of the pulses depends on the mark-space ratio.

FURTHER WORK

r   Replace the 741 by one of the better alternative op-amps, such as the 081. Repeat (l) and (m) and compare the slew rates of the two op-amps.

15B Linear Amplification
Investigation of the use of negative feedback in simple non-inverting and inverting amplifying circuits

APPARATUS REQUIRED

- circuit assembly board or system
- twin op-amp power supply, $V_s = 15$ V
- signal generator
- dual trace CRO
- 741 op-amp (or equivalent)
- 100 Ω, 1.0 kΩ, and 2 10 kΩ resistors
- connecting wires

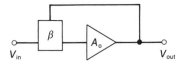

Fig. 15.13   Amplifier with simple feedback loop.

PRINCIPLES INVOLVED

a   The high open-loop voltage gain of the op-amp is of little direct practical use in amplifier circuits, especially as it decreases with frequency. In this experiment you will construct and test amplifier circuits with much lower, specified gains that can be chosen and controlled.

b   Fig. 15.13 shows a simple amplifier system in which a feedback loop is connected between the output and input of an amplifier. A fraction β of the output voltage V_{out} is fed back to the input such that, although V_{in} is the input voltage for the complete system, the voltage that appears at the input of the actual amplifier is $(V_{in} + \beta V_{out})$. If A_o is the voltage gain of the amplifier, then:

$$V_{out} = A_o(V_{in} + \beta V_{out})$$

Re-arranging, we have:

$$V_{out}(1 - \beta A_o) = A_o V_{in}$$

which leads to an expression for the net gain A of the complete system:

$$A = \frac{V_{out}}{V_{in}} = \frac{A_o}{(1 - \beta A_o)} \qquad [15.2]$$

c   Feedback can be either positive ($\beta > 0$) or negative ($\beta < 0$), depending on whether the feedback voltage is applied in phase or in antiphase with V_{in}. Positive feedback has some practical applications, but in amplifying circuits it produces instability. Negative feedback is far more useful despite the fact that it reduces the net gain: if $\beta < 0$, $A < A_o$. However, if β is chosen such that $\beta < 0$ *and* $|\beta A_o| \gg 1$, then:

$$A \approx \frac{A_o}{-\beta A_o} = \frac{1}{-\beta} \qquad [15.3]$$

from which we see that the net (or closed-loop) voltage gain A is independent of the open-loop gain of the amplifier and depends only on β, which is determined by values of components in the feedback loop, usually resistances.

NON-INVERTING AMPLIFIER

d   A signal voltage V_{in} applied to the non-inverting input of the op-amp produces an output voltage V_o that is in phase with V_{in}. This provides the basis for a non-inverting amplifier. Negative feedback is obtained by applying a fraction of V_o to the inverting input. The feedback network consists of two resistances R_a and R_f as shown in Fig. 15.14. If the input impedance of the op-amp is very high compared with both R_a and R_f, the current flowing into the inverting input is negligible compared with the currents I_a and I_f. Applying Kirchhoff's first law to the junction at P we therefore have:

$$I_a \approx I_f$$

Hence the sum of the voltages across R_a and R_f is given by:

$$V_a + V_f = I_a R_a + I_f R_f \approx I_a(R_a + R_f)$$

The voltage across R_a is given by:

$$V_a = I_a R_a$$

Since the open-loop gain of the op-amp is high, the differential input $(V_+ - V_-)$ must always be very small if V_{out} $(= V_o)$ is to remain below $+V_s'$ and above $-V_s'$. But $V_+ = V_{in}$, so V_- must be close to V_{in}. If, therefore, we assume that $V_- \approx V_{in}$, then:

$$V_a = (V_- - 0) \approx V_{in}$$

Since $(V_a + V_f) = V_{out}$, it follows that the closed-loop voltage gain A is given by:

$$A = \frac{V_{out}}{V_{in}} = \frac{V_a + V_f}{V_a} = \frac{I_a(R_a + R_f)}{I_a R_a}$$

Hence:

$$A = \frac{R_a + R_f}{R_a} \qquad [15.4]$$

Alternatively, we can derive the same expression for A from equation [15.3] by considering R_a and R_f as a potential divider connected between V_{out} and ground. The voltage V_a at the point P is given by:

$$V_a = \left(\frac{R_a}{R_a + R_f}\right) V_{out}$$

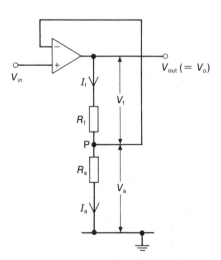

Fig. 15.14 Voltages and currents in the non-inverting amplifier.

But V_a is the voltage that is fed back to the input of the op-amp, so the value of β (the fraction of V_{out} that is fed back) that applies to this circuit is given by:

$$\beta = -\left(\frac{R_a}{R_a + R_f}\right)$$

in which the minus sign arises because V_a is applied to the inverting input of the op-amp. Equation [15.3] then leads to equation [15.4].

e Connect up the circuit shown in Fig. 15.15 (which you should confirm is essentially the same as the circuit of Fig. 15.14) putting $R_a = R_f = 10$ kΩ. Note that equation [15.4] predicts that the gain of this non-inverting amplifying circuit is 2. Set the signal generator to produce a small sinusoidal voltage V_{in} at a frequency of about 200 Hz. Display V_{in} and V_{out} on the CRO and adjust the output of the signal generator until the amplitude of V_{in} is 50 mV (or any other convenient small value, but no greater than 100 mV). Maintain V_{in} at this level throughout the experiment. By comparing the amplitudes of the displayed voltage waveforms, measure the closed-loop voltage gain A $(= V_{out}/V_{in})$ over the frequency range 10 Hz to 100 kHz. Increase the frequency f by a factor of about 3 between measurements; suitable values would therefore be f/Hz = 10, 32, 100, 320, 1000, 3200, 10 000, 32 000, 100 000. Tabulate your values of f and A, but there is no need to record values of V_{in} and V_{out}.

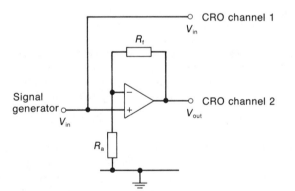

Fig. 15.15 Non-inverting amplifier. Values for the resistances R_a and R_f may be found in the text: see (e), (f) and (g).

f Put $R_a = 1.0$ kΩ and repeat (e), ensuring that the amplitude of V_{in} is again maintained at 50 mV (or whatever value was selected before). Is A constant and are V_{in} and V_{out} in phase over the entire frequency range, as predicted by equation [15.5]? If not, note the frequency (or frequencies) at which these predictions cease to apply. See Fig. 15.16.

g Put $R_a = 100 \ \Omega$ and repeat (f).

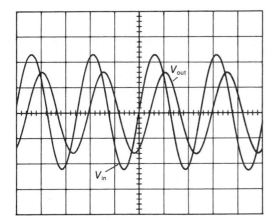

Fig. 15.16 Waveforms of V_{in} and V_{out} displayed on the CRO from a non-inverting amplifier with a nominal gain of 11, showing phase-shift and gain reduction, which occur at high frequencies. CRO Y-sensitivities: channel 1 (V_{in}) – 20 mV/div; channel 2 (V_{out}) – 0.2 V/div. (The gain is therefore about 7.)

h Draw up one set of axes on which to plot A (ordinate) against f (abscissa); both scales should be logarithmic. Allow for values of A up to 100 000. Use equation [15.4] to calculate the theoretical gain of each circuit that you have investigated and draw a straight line parallel to the f-axis to represent each one. Plot your experimental results. Note how gain and *band-width* are interdependent: either can be increased or decreased at the expense of the other. See section 15.3.3.

i The envelope of the closed-loop gain/frequency graphs that you have plotted is the line showing how the open-loop gain A_o of the op-amp varies with frequency (Fig. 15.17). Only the central part of this line is straight: A_o is fairly constant at frequencies below 10 Hz and falls rapidly to zero above 1 MHz.

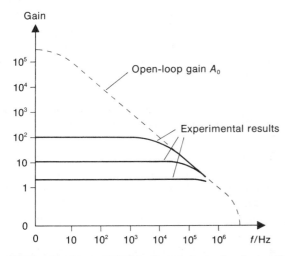

Fig. 15.17 Closed-loop gain/frequency graphs for non-inverting amplifier circuits. The variation with frequency of the open-loop gain A_0 of the op-amp can be estimated by extending the line that envelopes the graphs. Note that the scales along both axes are logarithmic.

j Use your set of graphs to plot the central, straight part of this envelope and hence estimate (i) the value of A_o when $f = 10$ Hz; (ii) the value of f when $A_o = 1$.

INVERTING AMPLIFIER

k A signal voltage V_{in} applied to the inverting input of the op-amp produces an output voltage V_o that is in antiphase with V_{in}. This provides the basis for an inverting amplifier. Negative feedback is obtained by applying a fraction of V_o to the inverting input as before. The feedback network consists of two resistances R_a and R_f as shown in Fig. 15.18. If the input impedance of the op-amp is very high compared with both R_a and R_f, the current flowing into the inverting input is negligible compared with the currents I_a and I_f. Applying Kirchhoff's first law to the junction at the inverting input we therefore have:

$$I_a \approx I_f$$

The voltages across R_a and R_f are therefore approximately proportional to their resistances:

$$\frac{V_f}{V_a} = \frac{I_f R_f}{I_a R_a} \approx \frac{R_f}{R_a}$$

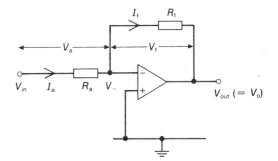

Fig. 15.18 Voltages and currents in the inverting amplifier.

Since the open-loop gain of the op-amp is high, the differential input $(V_+ - V_-)$ must always be very small if V_{out} $(= V_o)$ is to remain below $+V_s'$ and above $-V_s'$. But $V_+ = 0$, so V_- must be close to ground potential. The inverting input is then referred to as a *virtual earth*. If, therefore, we assume that $V_- \approx 0$, then:

$$V_a = (V_{in} - V_-) \approx V_{in}$$

and:

$$V_f = (V_- - V_{out}) \approx -V_{out}$$

213

The closed-loop voltage gain A is therefore given by:

$$A = \frac{V_{out}}{V_{in}} = \frac{-V_f}{V_a}$$

Hence:

$$A = -\left(\frac{R_f}{R_a}\right) \qquad [15.5]$$

The minus sign arises because the current that flows through R_a *towards* the junction at the inverting input (as shown in Fig. 15.18) flows through R_f *away* from the junction; i.e. if $V_{in} > V_-$ then $V_{out} < V_-$. This indicates that the amplifying circuit inverts: V_{out} and V_{in} are in antiphase. Note that equation [15.5] is not so easily derived from equation [15.3] (as was equation [15.4] at the end of (d)), but A here is also independent of A_o and depends only on values of resistances in the feedback loop.

l   Connect up the circuit shown in Fig. 15.19 putting $R_a = R_f = 10\ k\Omega$. Note that equation [15.5] predicts that the gain of this inverting amplifying circuit is 1. By following the procedure in (e), measure the closed-loop voltage gain A over the frequency range 10 Hz to 100 kHz.

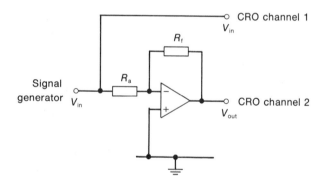

Fig. 15.19   Inverting amplifier. Values for the resistances R_a and R_f may be found in the text: see (l) and (m).

m   Repeat for two more values of R_a: 1.0 kΩ and 100 Ω, as in (f) and (g).

n   Prepare a second set of axes on which to plot A against f. Use equation [15.5] to calculate the theoretical gain of each circuit, and plot your theoretical and experimental results as in (h).

o   Repeat (j) using this set of graphs.

214

NOTES

p   Your record should include labelled circuit diagrams, where appropriate, and derivations of the expression for the closed-loop voltage gain of each type of amplifying circuit.

q   Although equations [15.4] and [15.5] predict that both closed-loop voltage gains depend only on resistance *ratios*, there are some restrictions on the values of R_a and R_f that can be used. In general R_f should be greater than the output impedance of the op-amp but smaller than the input impedance. Putting $R_f = 10\ k\Omega$ satisfies these conditions, and R_a is then chosen to give the gain required.

r   In deriving equations [15.4] and [15.5] in (d) and (k) two simplifying conditions were assumed. Both are important and will be recalled later. Bear in mind that they are approximations and that they apply to the op-amp only when in a non-saturated condition, used with feedback components. They are repeated here for easy reference:

(i) Input currents are negligible.

(ii) There must always be a negligible voltage between the two inputs; if one is grounded, the other becomes a virtual earth.

FURTHER WORK

s   Your investigations have probably not revealed the distorting effect of the op-amp's slew rate on the output waveform, which becomes apparent only when f and V_{out} are *both* high. V_{out} is greatest when the gain is large, but for such an amplifier V_{out} decreases as f increases. To see the effects of the op-amp's slew rate we require an amplifying circuit with a very low gain (e.g. $A = 2$, as in (e)) that does not appear to vary with frequency, but the amplifier must be used with a high level of V_{in} so that V_{out} is also high.

t   Repeat (e) but with the amplitude of V_{in} set and maintained at 10 V, which is 200 times greater than the value suggested in (e). What happens at high frequencies?

u   Replace the 741 by one of the better alternative op-amps, such as the 081. Repeat (t) to observe its vastly superior high-frequency performance.

v   Repeat (e), (f), (g) and (h) using the alternative op-amp to determine the variation of its open-loop voltage gain with frequency, as in (j). Compare your results with those you obtained for the 741.

15C Further Amplification
Investigation of amplifying circuits that perform particular functions

APPARATUS REQUIRED

- circuit assembly board or system
- twin op-amp power supply, $V_s = 15$ V
- signal generator
- dual trace CRO
- 741 op-amp (or equivalent)
- 1N4001 diode
- 3.3 nF (0.0033 µF), 33 nF (0.033 µF), 68 nF (0.068 µF) and 680 nF (0.68 µF) capacitors
- 1.0 kΩ, 10 kΩ and 2 100 kΩ resistors
- connecting wires

c This unity-gain, non-inverting amplifier is called a *voltage-follower* or *buffer*. The usefulness of such an amplifier, whose output is identical in every respect to its input, may not be obvious. But in fact the voltage follower has many applications for impedance matching: it is an amplifier with a very high input impedance (that of the op-amp) and a low output impedance. It is used to isolate a source of e.m.f. from a load in situations where the current drawn by the load might reduce the e.m.f. For example, a p.d. can be applied via a voltage follower to a conventional moving-coil voltmeter to produce effectively a voltmeter of very high resistance – several megohms, compared with perhaps only several kilohms if the meter is used alone.

VOLTAGE FOLLOWER

a Consider the non-inverting amplifier circuit shown in Fig. 15.20, in which no resistors are used at all. The resistance between the output and ground is infinite, while the resistance between the output and the inverting input of the op-amp is zero. In terms of equation [15.4], which applies to the circuit of Fig. 15.14, we therefore have $R_a = \infty$ and $R_f = 0$, and the voltage gain of the amplifier is given by:

$$\frac{V_{out}}{V_{in}} = \frac{R_f + R_a}{R_a} \approx 1$$

b Connect up the circuit shown in Fig. 15.20. Use the signal generator to apply a small sinusoidal voltage V_{in}, and display V_{in} and V_{out} on the CRO. Measure the closed-loop voltage gain of the circuit over the frequency range 10 Hz to 100 kHz as in experiment 15B (e). Is the gain unity, and are V_{in} and V_{out} in phase over the entire frequency range, as predicted above?

PERFECT RECTIFIER

d A silicon diode normally conducts in one direction only (the forward direction), but even in this direction no conduction occurs unless the p.d. applied across the diode exceeds a threshold value V_t of about 0.6 V. (You may have already investigated this in experiment 10A.) This means that rectification of alternating p.d.s cannot be achieved below this value using silicon diodes. The rectification of an alternating p.d. of, say, 12 V is hardly affected by this problem, since $V > V_t$ for most of the half-cycle, whereas a small p.d. of a few hundred millivolts cannot be rectified at all.

e Connect up the simple half-wave rectifier circuit shown in Fig. 15.21, in which the signal generator is used to apply an alternating p.d. V_{in} across a diode in series with a load resistance R. Display V_{in} and the p.d. V_{out} across R on the CRO. Set the frequency of V_{in} at about 500 Hz and its amplitude at 4.0 V. Notice the relationship between V_{in} and V_{out}. Reduce V_{in} by a factor of 10 and observe how rectification is now poor. Sketch both waveforms.

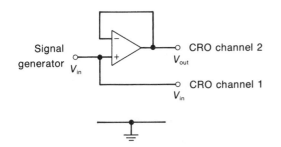

Fig. 15.20 Voltage follower.

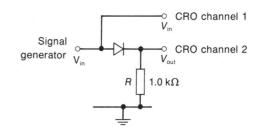

Fig. 15.21 Simple half-wave rectifier.

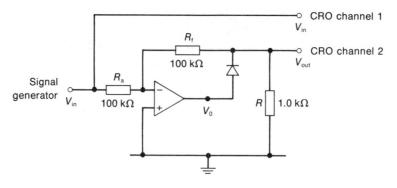

Fig. 15.22 Perfect half-wave rectifier.

f Now connect the same diode and load resistance in the inverting amplifier circuit shown in Fig. 15.22 and note again the relationship between V_{in} and V_{out} when the amplitude of V_{in} is first 4.0 V and then 400 mV. Reduce V_{in} by another factor of 10, to 40 mV. Does the circuit produce perfect rectification for even this low input voltage level? Note that the circuit inverts the half-waves that it admits.

g To explain the operation of this perfect half-wave rectifying circuit we consider the diode to be part of the feedback network in a unity-gain inverting amplifier (see experiment 15B (k)). During positive half-cycles, when $V_{in} > 0$, V_o is negative, so the diode is reverse biased and its resistance $R_d \approx \infty$. The gain of the amplifier $(= -(R_f + R_d)/R_a)$ is very large, but since $R_d \gg R_f$, V_{out} equals the voltage V_- at the inverting input, which is a virtual earth; i.e. $V_{out} = 0$. During negative half-cycles, when $V_{in} < 0$, V_o is positive, and the diode is forward biased provided that $V_o > V_t$. R_d is then effectively zero and the amplifier acts as a normal unity-gain inverting amplifier. However, when $V_o < V_t$, R_d is very large, and the gain of the amplifier increases to the point where $V_o > V_t$. The diode then conducts again, $R_d \approx 0$, and the gain falls back to unity.

from which it can be seen that X_C decreases as frequency f increases. Thus a capacitance connected in series with a resistance has little effect at high frequencies, but at low frequencies the impedance of the CR combination rises as f decreases. Such a combination can be used in bass controls. Conversely, a capacitance connected in parallel with a resistance has little effect at low frequencies, but at high frequencies the impedance of this CR combination falls as f increases, and such a combination is used in treble controls.

i Connect up the inverting amplifying circuit shown in Fig. 15.23. You have probably already investigated this circuit in experiment 15B (m) and found it to have a closed-loop voltage gain of about 10 (as predicted by equation [15.5]) up to a frequency of about 10 kHz. Measure this gain at two or three frequencies between 100 Hz and 10 kHz, and check that it is constant. Draw up a set of axes on which to plot A (ordinate) against f (abscissa), using logarithmic scales for both. Allow for values of A between 2 and 50 and for values of f between 100 Hz and 10 kHz. Draw a straight line parallel to the f-axis to represent the gain of your circuit.

TONE CONTROLS

h Tone controls are used in amplifiers to increase (*boost*) or reduce (*cut*) signals of a particular range of frequencies. A treble control is used to boost or cut high frequency signals, and a bass control is used for low frequency signals. For each function the gain of the amplifier has to be frequency dependent. To achieve this we include in the feedback network a *reactive* component, i.e. one whose impedance varies with frequency. The reactive impedance X_C of a capacitance C is given by:

$$X_C = \frac{1}{2\pi f C}$$

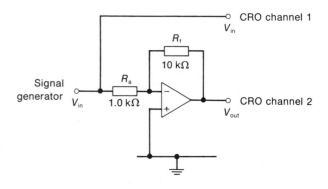

Fig. 15.23 Inverting amplifier with closed-loop gain of 10.

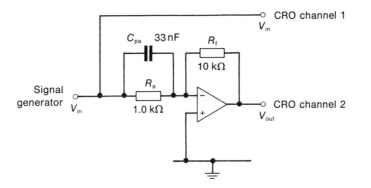

Fig. 15.24   The inverting amplifier of Fig. 15.23 modified to give treble boost.

j   Construct an inverting amplifier with treble boost by connecting a capacitance $C_{pa} = 33$ nF (0.033 µF) in parallel with R_a, as shown in Fig. 15.24. Measure A over the frequency range covered by your graph, noting the phase relationship between V_{out} and V_{in} when $f = 10$ kHz. Suitable values for f would be $f/Hz = 100, 200, 450, 1000, 2000, 4500$ and $10\,000$. Plot your results on the graph.

k   Construct an inverting amplifier with treble cut by connecting a capacitance $C_{pf} = 3.3$ nF (0.0033 µF) in parallel with R_f, as shown in Fig. 15.25. Measure A as in (j) over the same frequency range, noting the phase relationship between V_{out} and V_{in} when $f = 10$ kHz, and plot your results on the graph.

l   Construct an inverting amplifier with bass cut by connecting a capacitance $C_{sa} = 680$ nF (0.68 µF) in series with R_a, as shown in Fig. 15.26. Measure A as in (j) over the same frequency range, noting the phase relationship between V_{out} and V_{in} when $f = 100$ Hz. Plot your results on the graph.

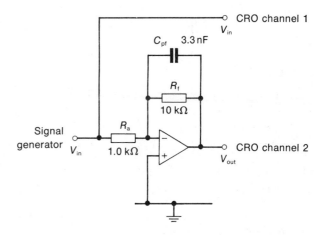

Fig. 15.25   The inverting amplifier of Fig. 15.23 modified to give treble cut.

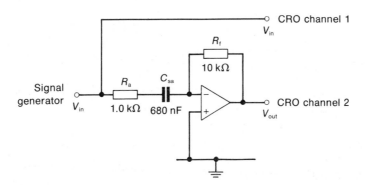

Fig. 15.26   The inverting amplifier of Fig. 15.23 modified to give bass cut.

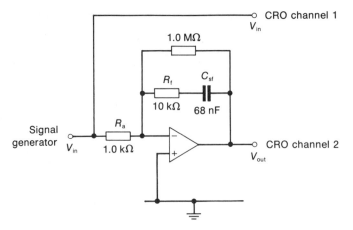

Fig. 15.27 The inverting amplifier of Fig. 15.23 modified to give bass boost.

m Construct an inverting amplifier with bass boost by connecting a capacitance $C_{sf} = 68$ nF (0.068 μF) in series with R_f, as shown in Fig. 15.27. Include the large resistance in parallel with R_f and C_{sf}, which provides a d.c. path between the output and the inverting input of the op-amp; without it V_{out} may have a large and varying d.c. component. Measure A as in (j) over the same frequency range, noting the phase relationship between V_{out} and V_{in} when $f = 100$ Hz. Plot your results on the graph.

n Examine your four frequency response curves and compare the effects of the four tone controls. Note how these effects are all minimal at a frequency near the middle of the range – at around 1 kHz.

NOTES

o Your record should include labelled circuit diagrams, where appropriate.

15D Addition and Subtraction
Investigation of circuits that combine signals arithmetically

APPARATUS REQUIRED

- circuit assembly board or system
- twin op-amp power supply, $V_s = 15$ V
- dual trace CRO
- 0–10 V d.c. voltmeter
- 741 op-amp (or equivalent)
- 2 10 kΩ variable resistors (potentiometers)
- 2 2.7 kΩ, 22 kΩ, 2 39 kΩ, 47 kΩ and 4 100 kΩ resistors
- connecting wires

INTRODUCTION

a The circuits that you will investigate here perform the simple arithmetical processes of addition and subtraction on applied input voltages. Circuits that amplify the sum of, or difference between, applied voltages are included. Of the two kinds of amplifier circuit investigated in experiment 15B, the inverting amplifier is the more straightforward to use (since its closed-loop gain is given

by the simple ratio of two resistances) and it is therefore used here as the basis from which most of the circuits that follow are developed.

ADDERS

b Consider the inverting amplifier circuit shown in Fig. 15.28, in which two input voltages V_1 and V_2 are applied via separate input resistances R_{a1} and R_{a2}. Equation [15.4] predicts that the voltage V_1 produces an output voltage $V_{out}\ (=V_o) = -(R_f/R_{a1})V_1$ and V_2 produces an output voltage $V_{out} = -(R_f/R_{a2})V_2$. If both input voltages are applied simultaneously we have:

$$V_{out} = -R_f\left(\frac{V_1}{R_{a1}} + \frac{V_2}{R_{a2}}\right) \qquad [15.6]$$

c In a simple inverting adder circuit R_{a1} and R_{a2} are both put equal to R_f, and equation [15.6] then becomes:

$$V_{out} = -(V_1 + V_2) \qquad [15.7]$$

In an inverting summing amplifier circuit R_{a1} and R_{a2} are

218

put equal, but to some value R_a that is less than R_f. Equation [15.6] then becomes:

$$V_{out} = -\left(\frac{R_f}{R_a}\right)(V_1 + V_2) \qquad [15.8]$$

The sum of the two voltages is amplified.

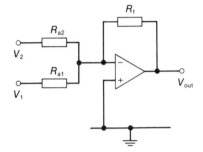

Fig. 15.28 Simplified adder: inverting amplifier with two inputs.

d Connect up the simple adder shown in Fig. 15.29, putting $R_{a1} = R_{a2} = 100$ kΩ. Two potential dividers are used to apply the input voltages V_1 and V_2; display these on the CRO (for which a suitable setting of both Y-sensitivities is 2 V/div) and set them initially close to zero. Monitor V_{out} on the voltmeter. Vary V_1 and V_2 and confirm that, within the range covered by the voltmeter, V_{out} equals minus the sum of V_1 and V_2 as predicted by equation [15.7].

e Modify the circuit of Fig. 15.29 to construct a summing amplifier with a gain of about 2.5 by putting $R_{a1} = R_{a2} = 39$ kΩ. The range over which V_1 and V_2 can now be varied to test the circuit is much smaller, so increase the Y-sensitivities on the CRO as appropriate. Vary V_1 and V_2 and confirm that V_{out} can be predicted by equation [15.8].

D TO A CONVERTER

f If R_{a1} and R_{a2} in the circuit of Fig. 15.28 are not equal, one input voltage will be amplified more than the other. The circuit shown in Fig. 15.30 has three different input resistances R_{a1}, R_{a2} and R_{a3}, whose values in

relation to the feedback resistance R_f are R_f, $R_f/2$ and $R_f/4$. The same voltage V_1 applied in turn to the points A, B and C therefore produces output voltages of V_1, $2V_1$ and $4V_1$. This circuit forms the basis of a digital-to-analogue (D to A) converter. Digital numbers and the binary code are explained fully in chapter 16. Each of the points A, B and C is an input for a binary digit (bit). Three-bit numbers up to 111 (7) may be applied: the least significant bit (either 0 or 1) to A and the most significant bit (representing either 0 or 4) to C.

g Connect up the circuit of Fig. 15.30 (overleaf) (use 47 kΩ and 2.7 kΩ resistors in series for R_{a2}, and 22 kΩ and 2.7 kΩ resistors in series for R_{a3}). Set V_1 to precisely −1.0 V and use the flying lead to apply V_1 to the input points A, B and C in turn. Ensure that V_1 is maintained at −1.0 V: it may fall slightly when applied to the inputs, particularly C. Record the voltmeter readings and confirm that the binary number 1 (represented by −1 V) produces the decimal numbers 1, 2 and 4 (represented by 1 V, 2 V and 4 V), depending upon which input it is applied to.

h Now apply V_1 (still maintained at −1.0 V) simultaneously to any number of the three input points to represent some binary number between 000 and 111. Confirm that the output of the circuit is the number's decimal equivalent. Test the circuit using several input combinations.

SUBTRACTORS

i Consider the circuit shown in Fig. 15.31 (overleaf), in which voltages V_1 and V_2 are applied through identical resistances $(=R_a)$ to the non-inverting and inverting inputs of the op-amp, and in which one of two other identical resistances $(=R_f)$ is connected between each input and the ground and output respectively. A full analysis, similar to those applied in experiment 15B (d) and (k), leads to an expression for V_{out} in terms of V_1 and V_2. Alternatively, it is rather more simple to consider each series combination of R_a and R_f as a potential divider.

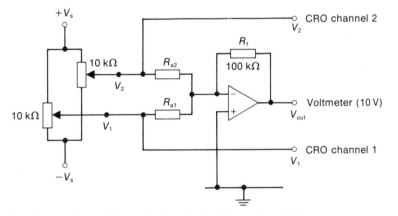

Fig. 15.29 Adder. Values for the resistances R_{a1} and R_{a2} may be found in the text: see (d) and (e).

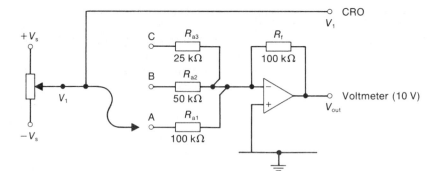

Fig. 15.30 Digital-to-analogue converter.

The p.d. across R_{a1} and R_{f1} is $(V_1 - 0)$ and the voltage V_+ is therefore given by:

$$V_+ = 0 + (V_1 - 0)\frac{R_f}{(R_a + R_f)}$$

The p.d. across R_{a2} and R_{f2} is $(V_2 - V_{out})$ and the voltage V_- is therefore given by:

$$V_- = V_{out} + (V_2 - V_{out})\frac{R_f}{(R_a + R_f)}$$

Note that these two expressions are valid only if the first of the two simplifying conditions of experiment 15B (r) is assumed. The second condition gives $V_- = V_+$.

Thus:
$$V_{out} + \frac{R_f(V_2 - V_{out})}{(R_a + R_f)} = \frac{R_f V_1}{(R_a + R_f)}$$

$$(R_a + R_f)V_{out} - R_f V_{out} = R_f V_1 - R_f V_2$$

and:
$$V_{out} = \frac{R_f}{R_a}(V_1 - V_2) \qquad [15.9]$$

j In a simple subtractor circuit all four resistances are equal (i.e. $R_a = R_f$) and equation [15.9] becomes:

$$V_{out} = (V_1 - V_2) \qquad [15.10]$$

In a differential amplifier circuit R_a is less than R_f and the difference between the two voltages is amplified according to equation [15.9].

k Connect up a simple subtractor circuit with $R_a = R_f = 100 \text{ k}\Omega$ and follow the procedure in (d) to confirm that V_{out} equals the difference between V_2 and V_1 as predicted by equation [15.10].

l Modify your circuit to construct a differential amplifier with a gain of about 2.5 by putting $R_a = 39 \text{ k}\Omega$. Follow the procedure in (e) to confirm that V_{out} can be predicted from equation [15.9].

NOTES

m Your record should include labelled circuit diagrams, where appropriate, and derivations of the expression for V_{out} in terms of V_1 and V_2 for each type of amplifier.

n One application of the summing amplifier is a mixer circuit, in which several input signals are combined or mixed to give one output. The resistance R_a connected between each input and the op-amp's inverting input effectively isolates it from the others, so that varying the strength of one signal has no effect on the others. In the laboratory, a mixer circuit is useful for combining the outputs of two signal generators to show superposition effects.

o The differential amplifier has applications in servo-mechanisms, in which, for example, the predetermined position of a mechanical component is chosen and represented by the voltage V_1. The actual position is represented by V_2, so that the voltage difference $(V_1 - V_2)$ represents the displacement error: the difference between where we want the component to be and where it actually is. This voltage error is fed to the component's drive system, which therefore ceases to move the component when $V_2 = V_1$, i.e. when the component has reached the predetermined position.

FURTHER WORK

p Equation [15.9] applies to the differential amplifier circuit of Fig. 15.31 only under the special conditions that $R_{a1} = R_{a2} (= R_a)$ and $R_{f1} = R_{f2} (= R_f)$. Derive an expression for V_{out} in terms of V_1 and V_2 that applies to the more general condition: that $R_{a1} \neq R_{a2}$ and $R_{f1} \neq R_{f2}$.

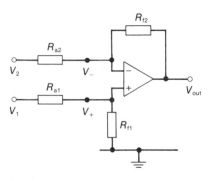

Fig. 15.31 Simplified subtractor.

15E Memory and Timing
Investigation of the use of positive feedback in bistable, monostable and astable multivibrator circuits

APPARATUS REQUIRED

- circuit assembly board or system
- twin op-amp power supply, $V_s = 15$ V
- dual trace CRO
- 741 op-amp (or equivalent)
- 2 1N4001 diodes
- 10 nF (0.01 µF), 100 nF (0.1 µF) and 1.0 µF capacitors
- 10 kΩ variable resistor (potentiometer)
- 1.0 kΩ, 10 kΩ, 39 kΩ, 100 kΩ and 1.0 MΩ resistors
- connecting wires

PRINCIPLES INVOLVED

a Multivibrators are circuits in which the output has only two permitted states represented by different voltage levels. There are three types of multivibrator:

(i) In the *bistable* multivibrator both output states are stable; either may be maintained indefinitely. Some external triggering signal or action is required to change the output from one state to the other. This action is 'remembered' by the circuit. Bistables are used as memory elements to store bits of information.

(ii) In the *monostable* multivibrator one state is stable and the other is unstable. An external triggering action is required to change the output from the former to the latter, but after a finite time determined by circuit component values, the output reverts to its stable state. Monostables are used for timing.

(iii) In the *astable* multivibrator neither output state is stable. The output alternates between the two states at a rate determined by circuit component values, and the circuit therefore generates a series of square waves.

b Examples of analogous devices in everyday use may help you to distinguish between the three types:

(i) Bistable: a simple electric light has two states, on and off, that are both stable.

(ii) Monostable: an electric toaster is pressed down into its unstable state, but after a minute or two it returns to its stable state by popping up.

(iii) Astable: the direction indicators of a car have two states, on and off, but flash between them alternately at a predetermined rate.

c In multivibrator circuits based on the op-amp the two voltage levels that the output $V_{out} (= V_o)$ is allowed

to have are $+V'_s$ and $-V'_s$. The op-amp is always in one of its two saturated conditions, and its output state is determined by the sign of the differential voltage input:

$$\text{If } V_+ < V_-, \quad V_{out} = +V'_s$$
$$\text{If } V_+ > V_-, \quad V_{out} = -V'_s$$

In these circuits, therefore, the op-amp is used as a voltage comparator (see experiment 15A). Positive feedback, where some part of V_{out} is fed back to the non-inverting input of the op-amp, ensures that after each changeover the new output state is maintained, until internal or external factors bring about the next changeover, as intended.

d All these circuits include a capacitor–resistor (CR) network, and the exponential charging and discharging of the capacitor through the resistor are important processes in their operation. In particular, CR component values determine the astable's switching rate and the time that the monostable remains in its unstable state.

BISTABLE MULTIVIBRATOR

e Connect up the circuit shown in Fig. 15.32, in which the CR network is joined to the inverting input of the op-amp. The potential divider is used to apply a proportion $+kV_{out}$ of the output voltage to the non-inverting input, where $0 < k < 1$; this is the positive feedback. Display $V_+ (= kV_{out})$ and V_{out} on the CRO. Use a flying lead as the switch S to connect plate A of the capacitor alternately to ground and to $+V_s$ (the positive power supply rail) and note the behaviour of V_{out}. In particular, notice how once the state of V_{out} has been set by connecting plate A to one of the two terminals, a change back to the other state occurs not when plate A is disconnected from the terminal, but only when a definite connection is made to the other terminal.

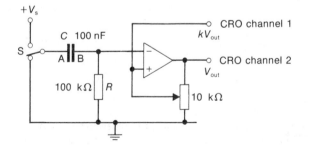

Fig. 15.32 Bistable multivibrator.

f   In this way the circuit is acting as a *latch*. Contact for switching can therefore be of any duration, and no change occurs to the output if contact is lost, as, for example, when switch contacts bounce apart.

g   Change the setting of the potential divider to vary k and investigate whether or not the value of k has any effect on the bistable's operation. k can be interpreted from the CRO screen as the ratio of the displacements of the two traces: $k = (V_+/V_{out})$.

h   The bistable's operation can be explained by examining the sequence of events as follows. (A clearer understanding of the operation of the bistable, and also that of the monostable, may develop after you have investigated the astable, in which voltages change continuously and may therefore be displayed on the CRO for examination.)

1. Let us assume that plate A of the capacitor C has been grounded for some time. Thus $V_{out} = +V_s'$, $V_+ = +kV_s'$, and $V_- = 0$ (connected to ground through R); since $V_+ > V_-$, the output state is perfectly stable.

2. When plate A is disconnected from ground, no p.d. can develop across C because it holds no charge. V_- remains at zero, and the output state is maintained.

3. Plate A is now connected to $+V_s$. V_- must also rise instantaneously to $+V_s$ because C is initially uncharged and there can be no p.d. across it. V_- is now greater than V_+ so V_{out} changes from $+V_s'$ to $-V_s'$, and V_+ is therefore changed to $-kV_s'$; this is the positive feedback.

4. As C charges exponentially through R, V_- falls towards zero, at which level it still exceeds the new value of V_+ so the output state is quite stable. The p.d. across C eventually reaches $+V_s$.

5. When plate A is disconnected from $+V_s$ there is no change: the p.d. across C remains and $V_- = 0$.

6. When plate A is reconnected to ground, the p.d. across C, which cannot change until discharging commences, drops the voltage of plate B (and therefore V_-) instantaneously to $-V_s$. V_- is now less than V_+ so V_{out} changes from $-V_s'$ to $+V_s'$, changing V_+ to $+kV_s'$.

7. C discharges exponentially through R and V_- rises to zero, at which level it is still less than V_+. This output state is therefore stable and our starting point in the sequence has been reached again.

The variations with time of V_- and V_{out} throughout this sequence are shown in Fig. 15.33. The times t_1, t_2, etc. marked along the t-axis are those at which the events 1, 2, etc. listed above occur.

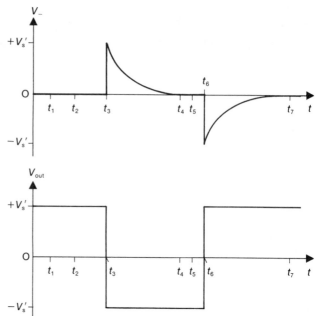

Fig. 15.33   Voltage-time variations in the bistable multivibrator.

MONOSTABLE MULTIVIBRATOR

i   Connect up the circuit shown in Fig. 15.34, in which the CR network is now joined to the non-inverting input of the op-amp to provide the necessary positive feedback. The potential divider, consisting of one variable and two fixed resistors, is used to apply a voltage $+kV_s$ to the inverting input. Trigger the circuit by briefly setting V_- at $-V_s$: use a flying lead (as the switch S) from the negative power supply rail. Observe that V_{out} changes, but changes back again after a second or so. The output is a single pulse whose duration depends on circuit parameters.

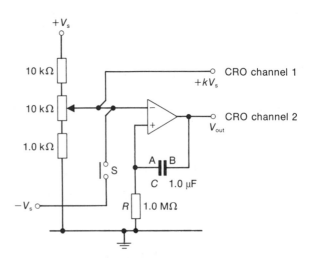

Fig. 15.34   Monostable multivibrator.

j Vary the setting of the variable resistor and note the effect on the pulse duration. Measure the shortest and longest durations obtainable from your circuit. (Note that it would be possible to increase the difference between these times by removing the two fixed resistors from the potential divider; they have been included only to eliminate the risk of connecting the negative power supply rail directly to either the positive one or ground.)

k Investigate the effect on the pulse duration of leaving the switch closed for a longer time than the normal pulse duration, instead of closing it for only a short time.

l The monostable's operational sequence runs as follows.

1. The switch has been open for some time: $V_- = +kV_s$ and $V_+ = 0$ (connected to ground through R). Since $V_+ < V_-$, $V_{out} = -V_s'$, which is a perfectly stable state. There exists across C a p.d. of $+V_s'$.

2. The switch is closed briefly and V_- drops instantaneously to $-V_s$. V_+ is now greater than V_- so the pulse begins as V_{out} changes from $-V_s'$ to $+V_s'$, a rise of $2V_s'$, taking the voltage of plate B of the capacitor with it. To maintain the p.d. across C, initially at least, the voltage of plate A must also rise by this amount, to $+2V_s'$, which keeps V_+ above V_-.

3. The switch is reopened and V_- reverts to $+kV_s$. However, V_{out} remains at $+V_s'$ because the positive feedback has ensured that V_+ is well above V_-, at least for the time being: as C discharges through R, V_+ decreases exponentially towards zero.

4. The pulse ends when V_+ eventually falls through the level of V_- ($= +kV_s$). V_{out} then returns to its stable state of $-V_s'$.

The variations with time of V_+, V_- and V_{out} during this sequence are shown in Fig. 15.35. Note how V_+ drops at the end of the pulse and rises exponentially back to zero. This gives the circuit a 'dead time' during which it is not ready to produce the next pulse. The duration of the monostable's pulse depends on the value of the proportional constant k and on the time constant CR.

m Use Fig. 15.35 to explain the results of your investigations in (j) and (k). Remember that the potential divider is used to set the proportional constant k.

ASTABLE MULTIVIBRATOR

n Connect up the circuit shown in Fig. 15.36 (overleaf), in which the CR network is joined to the inverting input of the op-amp while a proportion kV_{out} of the op-amp's output voltage is obtained from the

potential divider and fed back to the non-inverting input. Put $C = 1.0\ \mu\text{F}$ and $R = 1.0\ \text{M}\Omega$. Note that there is no switch in this circuit. Observe how V_{out} alternates between $+V_s'$ and $-V_s'$ at a frequency that depends on the proportional constant k: change the setting of the potential divider to vary k.

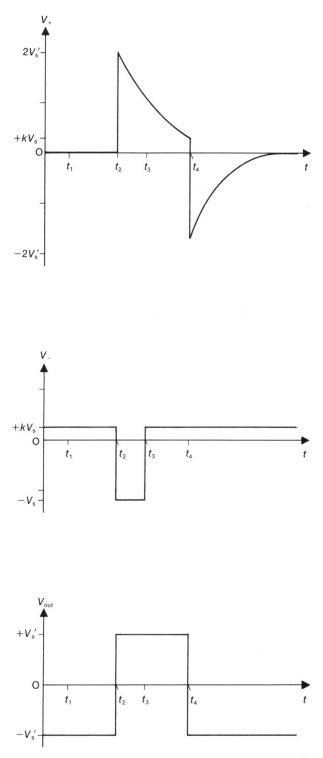

Fig. 15.35 Voltage–time variations in the monostable multivibrator.

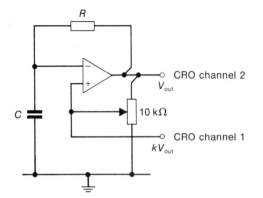

Fig. 15.36 Astable multivibrator. Values for the capacitance C and for the resistance R may be found in the text: see (n) and (p).

o The sequence of events that produces these alternations runs as follows.

1. Let us assume that V_{out} has just changed to $+V'_s$, so V_+ will have just changed to $+kV'_s$. V_{out} remains high because V_+ is more than V_-, but V_- is rising exponentially towards $+V'_s$ as the capacitor C charges through R.

2. When V_- rises through the level of V_+ ($= +kV'_s$), V_{out} changes to $-V'_s$, changing V_+ to $-kV'_s$. This positive feedback ensures that V_+ drops well below the level to which V_- has risen, thereby maintaining V_{out} at $-V'_s$.

3. V_- is now falling exponentially towards $-V'_s$ as C discharges through R.

4. When V_- falls through the level of V_+ ($= kV'_s$) V_{out} changes back again. V_+ is changed back to $+kV'_s$ and V_- will start to rise towards $+V'_s$ to continue the process.

The time T' that V_- takes to rise exponentially from $-kV'_s$ to $+kV'_s$, between stages 2 and 4, is given by:

$$T' = CR \log_e \left(\frac{1+k}{1-k} \right) \qquad [15.11]$$

This is the interval between two successive alternations of V_{out}, i.e. the duration of half of the astable's cycle. The period T of the astable is therefore given by:

$$T = 2CR \log_e \left(\frac{1+k}{1-k} \right) \qquad [15.12]$$

p Increase the frequency of the astable by putting $C = 10$ nF (0.01 μF) and $R = 100$ kΩ, so that the traces of V_+ and V_{out} may now be displayed on the CRO as waveforms. Use the potential divider to vary k

(interpreted as the ratio of the two waveform amplitudes) and observe how the astable's period depends on k. Set $k = 0.5$ and use the CRO's time base calibration to measure the period of the astable. Compare your result with the theoretical value obtained by substituting appropriate values of C, R and k into equation [15.12].

q Now display V_+ and V_- simultaneously on the CRO. Observe how V_- rises and falls exponentially between $-kV'_s$ and $+kV'_s$, and that each half-cycle ends when V_- rises up, or falls down, to the level of V_+. Increase k and notice that the period increases as each exponential process continues for longer. Sketch graphs to show the simultaneous variations with time of V_+, V_- and V_{out}.

r There is no reason why the two parts of the astable cycle must be equal. The rate of exponential growth and decay of V_- depends on the time constant CR. Fig. 15.37 shows how the single resistance R can be replaced by two resistances R_1 and R_2 connected in parallel. The opposing diodes, one in series with each resistance, ensure that C charges up through R_1 but discharges through R_2. R_1 and R_2 are chosen to give a required mark-space ratio T'_1/T'_2 where T'_1 and T'_2 are the durations of the two parts of the complete cycle (see experiment 15A (o)).

s Connect up the circuit shown in Fig. 15.37 putting $R_1 > R_2$ as indicated. Set $k = 0.5$ and measure T'_1 and T'_2. Compare your results with the theoretical values obtained by substituting appropriate values of C, R and k into equation [15.11] for each part of the cycle.

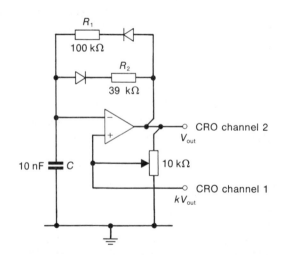

Fig. 15.37 Astable multivibrator with unequal half-cycles.

† Display V_+ and V_- simultaneously on the CRO and observe how the two different values of T' are caused by unequal rates of exponential growth and decay of V_-.

NOTES

u Your record should include labelled circuit diagrams, where appropriate.

v All three types of multivibrator can be constructed in many ways; around individual transistors or logic gates, instead of op-amps, for example. They have many useful functions and you may come across them under their more familiar names: *flip-flop* (bistable), *one-shot* (monostable) and *free-running* (astable). The astable is a type of *relaxation oscillator,* a term which refers to the way its period depends on the time taken for a capacitor to charge up and then discharge ('relax') through a resistor.

FURTHER WORK

w If the effect of the op-amp's slew rate on the output waveform was evident in (p) (i.e. if the sides of the astable's square-wave output were not vertical), use the CRO's calibrations to measure the slew rate. Compare your answer with any value that you obtained in experiment 15A (m).

15F Integration and Differentiation
Investigation of circuits that integrate and differentiate signals with respect to time

APPARATUS REQUIRED

- circuit assembly board or system
- twin op-amp power supply, $V_s = 15$ V
- signal generator
- dual trace CRO
- 741 op-amp (or equivalent)
- 6 V battery
- 1.0 nF (0.001 µF), 100 nF (0.1 µF) and 1.0 µF capacitors
- 2 10 kΩ variable resistors (potentiometers)
- 1.0 kΩ, 10 kΩ and 100 kΩ resistors
- single-pole switch
- connecting wires
- stopwatch

PRINCIPLES INVOLVED

a Integration and differentiation are both mathematical processes that are required in analogue computing. The op-amp can be adapted quite easily to produce an operational integrator; i.e. a circuit that integrates (sums) the input voltage with respect to time. The output of such a circuit is given by:

$$V_{out} \propto \int V_{in}\, dt$$

The output of a differentiator, which correspondingly differentiates the input voltage with respect to time, is given by:

$$V_{out} \propto \frac{dV_{in}}{dt}$$

b Most of this experiment is based on the integrator, though you will also briefly investigate the differentiator. In practical circuits, operational differentiators are not often used because they are too susceptible to high frequency input 'noise'. However, differentiation can be treated as a process that is the reverse of integration. This will become evident if you attempt some of the analogue computing tasks in experiment 15G.

INTEGRATOR

c A simple operational integrator is shown in Fig. 15.38. The voltages across R and C in this circuit are given by:

$$V_R = (V_{in} - V_-) = I_R R$$

and:

$$V_C = (V_- - V_{out}) = \frac{Q}{C}$$

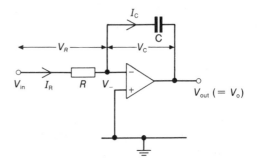

Fig. 15.38 Voltages and currents in the integrator.

where Q is the charge on the plates of the capacitor. If the op-amp is always used in an unsaturated state, the two simplifying conditions of experiment 15B (r) apply, and we may assume that $I_R = I_C$. Furthermore, since $V_+ = 0$, the inverting input is a virtual earth, i.e. $V_- = 0$.

Therefore:
$$I_C = \frac{V_{in}}{R}$$

and:
$$-V_{out} = \frac{Q}{C}$$

But:
$$I_C = \frac{dQ}{dt}$$

so:
$$Q = \int I_C\, dt$$

$$= \int \frac{V_{in}}{R}\, dt$$

and:
$$V_{out} = -\left(\frac{1}{CR}\right)\int V_{in}\, dt \qquad [15.13]$$

V_{out} is therefore proportional to the negative integral of V_{in}.

d   The practical integrator circuit to be used during the first part of the experiment is shown in Fig. 15.39. The arrangement of two potential dividers, one variable and one fixed, is used to provide a steady input voltage V_1 that can be sensitively varied over a range limited to only one or two volts on either side of zero. The switch S is used to start the integrating process: while S is closed, there can be no p.d. across C, and V_{out} must remain at zero; but when S is opened, C charges up, and V_{out} rises (or falls). The switching action of S should be definite: neither a flying lead nor a plug key is suitable.

e   Connect up the circuit of Fig. 15.39. Close S and set $V_1 = -0.1$ V as precisely as possible, using an appropriate setting for the Y-sensitivity of channel 1

of the CRO, on which V_1 is displayed. Open S and observe how V_{out} increases steadily until it reaches $+V_s'$. Close S to reset V_{out} at zero and repeat the process, measuring the time t it takes V_{out} to reach $+13$ V.

f   Equation [15.13] can be applied to the integration process in (e). V_{in} is a constant $(= V_1)$, so equation [15.13] becomes:
$$V_{out} = -\left(\frac{V_1}{CR}\right)\int_0^t dt$$

which, on integrating, gives:
$$V_{out} = \left(\frac{-V_1}{CR}\right)t + V' \qquad [15.14]$$

where V' is the constant of integration, representing any initial (preset) value of V_{out}.

g   Substitute appropriate values of V_1, C and R in equation [15.14] to find the value of the constant $(-V_1/CR)$, and calculate the time that V_{out} takes to reach $+13$ V from zero (i.e. $V' = 0$). Compare this result with the time that you measured in (e).

h   Initial conditions other than $V_{out} = 0$ are set by applying an appropriate p.d. V' across C. When S is opened V_{out} changes as before, but from an initial value V'.

i   Modify your circuit by including the 6 V battery in series with S, as shown in Fig. 15.40. Note the polarity of the battery, and check that when S is closed V_{out} drops to -6 V or thereabouts. Open S to start the integration process, and observe how V_{out} changes. Make the necessary measurements and calculations to compare the theoretical and experimental values of the time that V_{out} takes to reach $+13$ V from an initial value $V' = -6$ V.

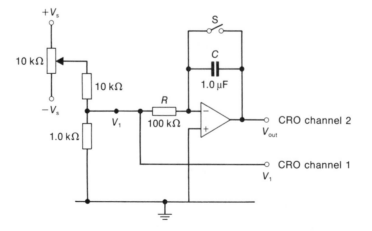

Fig. 15.39 Integrator with constant input.

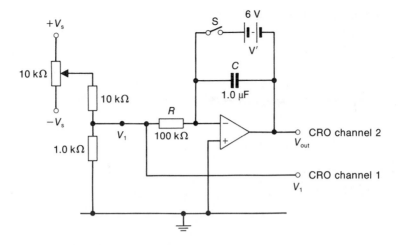

Fig. 15.40 Integrator with constant input, but with preset initial output.

j It is useful to be able to display the variation of V_{out} on the CRO as a steady waveform, and this can be done by applying a square wave to the input of the integrator, as shown in the circuit of Fig. 15.41a. V_{in} alternates between two 'constant' values of $-V_1$ and $+V_1$, where V_1 is the amplitude of the square wave, and the process of integrating a constant is repeated continuously. The problem of offset voltage may arise here (see section 15.2.3), and it is therefore advisable to include the offset-null network shown in Fig. 15.41b, which can be used to provide some compensation.

k Equation [15.14] can be rearranged to give:

$$\frac{V_{out} - V'}{t} = \frac{-V_1}{CR}$$

The expression on the right-hand side of this equation is a constant, and therefore the rate of change of V_{out} with time (dV_{out}/dt) is constant too. The output waveform should therefore be triangular, with a slope:

$$\frac{dV_{out}}{dt} = \frac{-V_1}{CR} \qquad [15.15]$$

l Connect up the circuit of Fig. 15.41, including the offset-null network of Fig. 15.41b. Set the frequency f of V_{in} at 500 Hz and its amplitude V_1 at precisely 0.1 V (i.e. the 'step' height should be 0.2 V). Use the offset-null adjustment as necessary to obtain an unclipped triangular waveform for V_{out}. (You may need to use the Y-shift control on the CRO to keep this waveform on the screen; alternatively, switch the channel 2 input to its a.c. setting.) Measure $\Delta V_{out}/\Delta t$ on the CRO screen and compare your result with the theoretical value calculated by substituting appropriate values of V_1, C and R into equation [15.15].

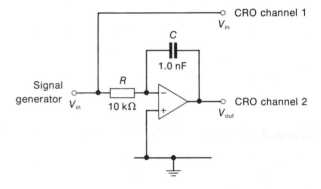

a Integrator with square-wave input.

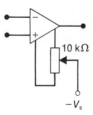

b Offset-null compensation network. The potential divider is connected between pins 1 and 5 of the 741 op-amp.

Fig. 15.41

m If a sinusoidally varying voltage of the form:

$$V_{in} = V_1 \sin \omega t$$

is applied to the input of the integrator, equation [15.13] predicts that:

$$V_{out} = -\left(\frac{1}{CR}\right)\int V_1 \sin \omega t \, dt$$

227

which, on performing the integration, becomes:

$$V_{out} = \left(\frac{-V_1}{CR}\right)\frac{-\cos \omega t}{\omega}$$

so:

$$V_{out} = \left(\frac{V_1}{\omega CR}\right)\cos \omega t \qquad [15.16]$$

where V_1 is the amplitude and $\omega\,(=2\pi f)$ is the angular frequency of V_{in}. Equation [15.16] predicts that V_{out} also varies sinusoidally, with the same frequency as V_{in}, but V_{out} leads V_{in} by $\pi/2$ (one quarter of a cycle) and its amplitude is $(V_1/\omega CR)$.

n Switch the waveform of V_{in} from square to sinusoidal on the signal generator and adjust the output until the amplitude V_1 is 0.1 V, with $f = 500$ Hz as in (l). Observe the waveform of V_{out} and the phase relationship between V_{in} and V_{out}. Do your observations confirm the predictions in (m)? Measure the amplitude of V_{out} and compare your result with the theoretical result predicted by equation [15.16].

DIFFERENTIATOR

o Consider the circuit shown in Fig. 15.42 and compare it with the integrator of Fig. 15.38. Notice that C and R are interchanged. The voltages across C and R here are gven by:

$$V_C = (V_{in} - V_-) = \frac{Q}{C}$$

and:

$$V_R = (V_- - V_{out}) = I_R R$$

If the same assumptions made in (c) are made here, then:

$$V_{in} = \frac{Q}{C}$$

and:

$$-V_{out} = I_C R$$

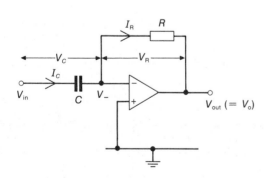

Fig. 15.42 Voltages and currents in the differentiator.

228

But:

$$I_C = \frac{dQ}{dt}$$

$$= C\frac{dV_{in}}{dt}$$

so:

$$V_{out} = -CR\frac{dV_{in}}{dt} \qquad [15.17]$$

V_{out} is therefore proportional to the negative differential of V_{in}, i.e. to the rate of change of V_{in} with time.

p If a sinusoidally varying voltage of the form:

$$V_{in} = V_1 \sin \omega t$$

is applied to the input of the differentiator, equation [15.17] predicts that:

$$V_{out} = -CR\frac{d}{dt}(V_1 \sin \omega t)$$

which, after performing the differentiation, becomes:

$$V_{out} = -\omega CRV_1 \cos \omega t \qquad [15.18]$$

from which we see that V_{out} also varies sinusoidally, with the same frequency as V_{in}, but V_{out} lags behind V_{in} by $\pi/2$ and its amplitude is (ωCRV_1).

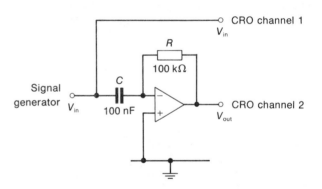

Fig. 15.43 Differentiator with sinusoidal input.

q Connect up the differentiator circuit shown in Fig. 15.43 and use the signal generator to apply a sine wave of amplitude $V_1 = 0.2$ V and frequency $f = 500$ Hz. Observe the waveform of V_{out} and the phase relationship between V_{in} and V_{out}. Do your observations confirm the predictions in (p)? Measure the amplitude of V_{out} and compare your result with the theoretical result predicted by equation [15.18].

NOTES

r Your record should include labelled circuit diagrams, where appropriate.

15G Analogue Computing
The use of integrators to perform simple analogue computing tasks

APPARATUS REQUIRED

- circuit assembly board or system
- twin op-amp power supply, $V_s = 15$ V
- signal generator
- dual trace CRO
- 3 741 op-amps (or equivalent)
- 2 3 V batteries
- 2 1.0 μF capacitors
- 2 10 kΩ variable resistors (potentiometers)
- 4 100 kΩ and 2 1.0 MΩ resistors
- double-pole switch
- connecting wires
- stopwatch

PRINCIPLES INVOLVED

a In this experiment you will solve problems using simple analogue computers. Although it is the process of differentiation that has to be performed in all of the examples that follow, the differentiator circuit will not be used, and its function performed instead by the integrator (see experiment 15F (b)). Some of the circuits require two integrators linked together such that the output of the first is applied directly to the input of the second.

b For the simple integrator of Fig. 15.38 in experiment 15F (c) we derived equation [15.13]:

$$V_{out} = -\left(\frac{1}{CR}\right) \int V_{in} \, dt$$

When both sides are differentiated:

$$\frac{dV_{out}}{dt} = -\left(\frac{1}{CR}\right) V_{in}$$

so:

$$V_{in} = -CR \frac{dV_{out}}{dt} \qquad [15.19]$$

from which we see that the input of an integrator is proportional to the negative differential of the output. Used this way an integrator can perform the differentiating tasks required to solve differential equations.

c Six examples of equations encountered during the investigation of mechanical systems are considered. For each one a differential equation describing the variation of the displacement s (of some part of the system) with time t is stated. A circuit that represents this variation of s with t can then be designed, constructed and tested. In all the circuit diagrams that follow, the voltage of a point in a circuit appears below the point, while the quantity that it represents appears in a rectangle above the point. All six examples are simple enough to be solved by normal mathematical means, and it is therefore possible to check any experimental results that you obtain. For this purpose it is convenient to choose values of C and R in the integrators such that their product (the time constant CR) equals 1.0 s. Real analogue computers are used to solve very complex problems, for which, of course, conventional mathematical computation may not be possible.

CONSTANT VELOCITY

d Motion at constant velocity v is described by the differential equation:

$$\frac{ds}{dt} = v \qquad [15.20]$$

Fig. 15.44 shows how a single integrator can be used to simulate this equation. If equation [15.19] is applied to this circuit, $V_{in} = V_1$ (a constant voltage obtained from the potential divider) and V_{out} is used to represent s, so V_1 represents $-CR(ds/dt) = -CRv$. But since $CR = 1.0$ s, V_1 effectively represents $-v$.

e The general solution of equation [15.20] is:

$$s = s_0 + vt \qquad [15.21]$$

where s_0 is any initial displacement (i.e. the value of s when $t = 0$). If required, s_0 can be represented in the circuit of Fig. 15.44 by the e.m.f. of a battery connected in series with the switch S, as shown; the battery presets V_{out}.

f Connect up the circuit of Fig. 15.44 (overleaf), omitting the battery at first (i.e. $s_0 = 0$). Close the switch S and adjust the potential divider until V_1 is set at -1.0 V to represent a constant velocity $v = +1.0$ m s^{-1}. Open S and observe how V_{out} steadily increases. Repeat and measure the time that it takes V_{out} to rise to 10 V (representing $s = 10$ m) from zero. Compare your result with a theoretical value calculated from equation [15.21].

g Now include the 3 V battery in series with S to represent an initial displacement $s_0 = +3$ m. Repeat your observations and measure again the time it takes s to reach 10 m. Reverse the connections to the battery ($s_0 = -3$ m) and repeat the measurement. Compare your results with theoretical values calculated from equation [15.21].

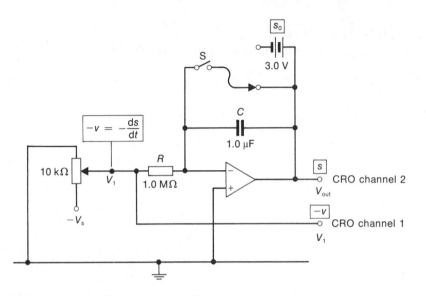

Fig. 15.44   Integrating circuit that simulates motion at constant velocity.

CONSTANT ACCELERATION

h   Motion at constant acceleration a is described by the differential equation:

$$\frac{\mathrm{d}^2 s}{\mathrm{d}t^2} = \frac{\mathrm{d}v}{\mathrm{d}t} = a \qquad [15.22]$$

Fig. 15.45 shows the integrating circuit required to simulate this equation. Two integrators are used: the output V_{o1} of the first is applied to the input of the second. If equation [15.19] is applied to each integrator, we have:

$$V_1 = -CR\frac{\mathrm{d}V_{o1}}{\mathrm{d}t}$$

and:

$$V_{o1} = -CR\frac{\mathrm{d}V_{out}}{\mathrm{d}t}$$

If V_{out} represents s, V_{o1} represents $-CR(\mathrm{d}s/\mathrm{d}t) = -CRv$. Similarly, V_1 represents $(-CR)^2(\mathrm{d}v/\mathrm{d}t) = (CR)^2 a$. Since $CR = 1.0$ s, $-v$ is represented by V_{o1}, and a by V_1.

i   The general solution of equation [15.22] is:

$$s = s_0 + v_0 t + \tfrac{1}{2}at^2 \qquad [15.23]$$

where s_0 and v_0 are initial values of displacement and velocity (when $t = 0$), and are represented in the circuit of Fig. 15.45, if required, by the e.m.f.s of batteries, as shown. Note carefully the polarities of these two batteries: the output V_{o1} of the first integrator represents $-v$, while the output V_{out} of the second represents $+s$. Batteries with the polarities indicated therefore set *positive* values of v_0 and s_0.

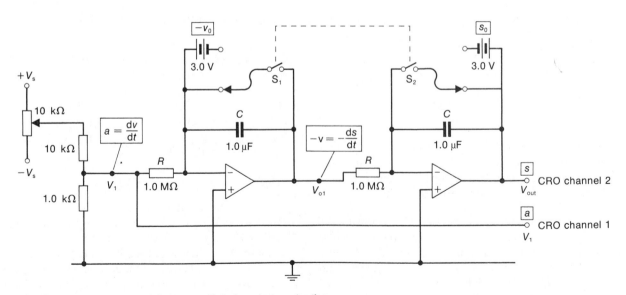

Fig. 15.45   Integrating circuit that simulates motion at constant acceleration.

j Connect up the circuit of Fig. 15.45 omitting both batteries at first. The two switches S_1 and S_2 should be ganged together (use the double-pole switch) so that they may be opened simultaneously. Close the switches and adjust the potential divider until V_1 is set at $+0.5$ V, to represent a constant acceleration $a = 0.5$ m s^{-2}. Open the switches and observe how V_{out} 'accelerates' up the screen. Repeat as necessary and measure the time that it takes V_{out} to rise to 10 V (representing $s = 10$ m) from zero. Compare your result with a theoretical value calculated from equation [15.23].

k Now connect the two 3 V batteries as shown to represent an initial displacement $s_0 = +3$ m and an initial velocity $v_0 = +3$ m s^{-1}. Only the presetting of s_0 will be evident on the CRO. Use the potential divider to put $V_1 = -0.5$ V as precisely as possible, to represent $a = -0.5$ m s^{-2}. Open the switches and observe how the trace of V_{out} moves: your computer is simulating the motion of an object thrown upwards with a velocity of 3 m s^{-1} from a height of 3 m, but on a planet where g is only 0.5 m s^{-2}. Use your computer to measure   (i) the maximum height reached (where $v = 0$) and   (ii) the time taken by the object to fall back to datum level (where $s = 0$). Compare your results with theoretical values calculated from equation [15.23] and from one of the familiar equations of linear motion under constant acceleration:

$$v^2 = u^2 + 2as$$

which, expressed in a form more appropriate for use here, becomes:

$$v^2 = v_0^2 + 2a(s - s_0)$$

EXPONENTIAL DECAY

l The exponential decay of a quantity s is described by the differential equation:

$$\frac{ds}{dt} = -\lambda s \qquad [15.24]$$

in which λ is the decay constant. Fig. 15.46 shows the integrator required to simulate this equation. The potential divider is used to feed a proportion k of V_{out} back to the input, where $0 \leqslant k \leqslant 1$. If equation [15.19] is applied, V_{out} represents s and V_{in} represents $-CR(ds/dt)$. Since $CR = 1.0$ s, V_{in} represents $-(ds/dt)$, but the feedback loop ensures that $V_{in} = kV_{out}$, and therefore V_{in} also represents λs, where $\lambda = k/CR$; i.e. λ is represented by k.

m The general solution of equation [15.24] is:

$$s = s_0 \exp(-\lambda t) \qquad [15.25]$$

where s_0 is the initial value from which s decays to zero, and is represented in the circuit of Fig. 15.46 by the e.m.f. of the battery, which is not an optional extra in this circuit.

n Connect up the circuit of Fig. 15.46 using the 3 V battery as shown to represent an initial displacement $s_0 = +3$ m. Close the switch S, then vary the setting of the potential divider and observe how k can be varied between 0 and 1, indicated by the relative positions of the CRO traces of V_{in} and V_{out}. Set $k = 1$ ($\lambda = 1$ s^{-1}), for which the two traces should coincide if the Y-sensitivities of the two CRO channels are equal; open S, and observe the rapid fall of V_{out} (and V_{in}). Now set $k = 0.1$ ($\lambda = 0.1$ s^{-1}) and repeat your observations. Measure the half-life of the decay process, i.e. the time V_{out} takes to decay to half its initial value, representing the decay of s from s_0 to $s_0/2$. Compare your result with a theoretical value calculated from equation [15.25].

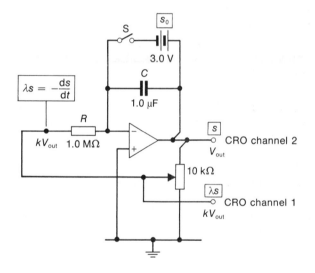

Fig. 15.46   Integrating circuit that simulates exponential decay.

EXPONENTIAL GROWTH

o Exponential growth is described by the differential equation:

$$\frac{ds}{dt} = +\lambda s \qquad [15.26]$$

in which λ is a constant. Fig. 15.47 shows the integrating circuit required to simulate this equation. To the circuit of Fig. 15.46 has been added an inverting amplifier (of unity gain) such that the feedback component kV_{out} is inverted before being applied to the integrator, whose input therefore represents both $-\lambda s$ and $-(ds/dt)$.

231

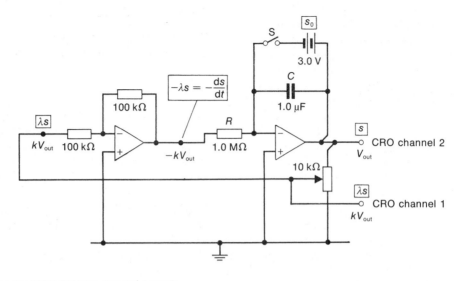

Fig. 15.47   Integrating circuit that simulates exponential growth.

p   The general solution of equation [15.26] is:

$$s = s_0 \exp(\lambda t) \qquad [15.27]$$

where s_0 is the initial value from which s grows exponentially towards infinity, and is represented by the e.m.f. of the battery, as before.

q   Connect up the circuit of Fig. 15.47 using the 3 V battery to represent an initial displacement $s_0 = +3$ m. Set $k = 1$ ($\lambda = 1$ s^{-1}), as in (n), and observe the rapid rise of V_{out}. Now set $k = 0.1$ ($\lambda = 0.1$ s^{-1}) and measure the time V_{out} takes to grow to twice its initial value, representing the growth of s from s_0 to $2s_0$. Compare your result with a theoretical value calculated from equation [15.27].

SIMPLE HARMONIC MOTION

r   Undamped s.h.m. is described by the differential equation:

$$\frac{d^2 s}{dt^2} = -\omega^2 s \qquad [15.28]$$

in which ω is a constant related to the period T of the oscillations. Fig. 15.48 shows the integrating circuit required to simulate this equation. Two integrators are preceded by an inverting amplifier (of unity gain), whose output is applied to the input of the first integrator. The potential divider is used to feed a proportion k of V_{out} back to the input of the inverting amplifier. If equation [15.19] is applied to each integrator, we have:

$$-kV_{out} = -CR\frac{dV_{o1}}{dt}$$

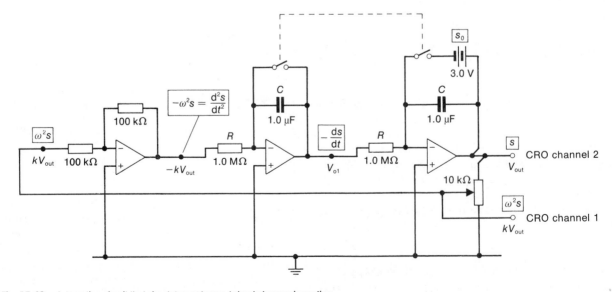

Fig. 15.48   Integrating circuit that simulates undamped simple harmonic motion.

and:

$$V_{o1} = -CR\frac{dV_{out}}{dt}$$

$$-kV_{out} = (-CR)\frac{d^2V_{out}}{dt^2}$$

If V_{out} represents s, V_{o1} represents $-(ds/dt)$ and the input of the first integrator represents (d^2s/dt^2). This is where the inverted feedback component $-kV_{out}$, which represents $-\omega^2s$, is applied. $\omega^2 = k/(CR)$, but since $CR = 1.0$ s, ω^2 is represented by k.

S A solution of equation [15.28] is:

$$s = s_0 \cos \omega t$$

where s_0 is the initial displacement and amplitude of the oscillations; it is represented by the e.m.f. of the battery in Fig. 15.48. This leads to the familiar relationship between T and ω:

$$T = \frac{2\pi}{\omega} \qquad [15.29]$$

† Connect up the circuit of Fig. 15.48 using the 3 V battery to represent an initial displacement $s_0 = 3$ m. Close the ganged switches, and use the potential divider to set $k = 1$ ($\omega = 1$ rad s^{-1}), as in (n). Open the switches and observe the oscillations of the CRO trace of V_{out}. Measure the period of oscillation. Now set $k = 0.5$ ($\omega = \sqrt{0.5}$ rad s^{-1}) and measure the period again. Compare your results with theoretical values calculated from equation [15.29]. If time permits, allow the oscillations to continue undisturbed for about ten minutes. What happens to the amplitude?

DAMPED SIMPLE HARMONIC MOTION

U Equation [15.28] can be modified to describe damped s.h.m. by introducing a velocity component:

$$\frac{d^2s}{dt^2} = -\omega^2s - \lambda\frac{ds}{dt} \qquad [15.30]$$

in which λ is a damping coefficient. Fig. 15.49 shows the integrating circuit required to simulate this equation. To the circuit of Fig. 15.48 has been added a second potential divider that is used to feed back a proportion j of V_{o1}. The inverting amplifier in Fig. 15.48 is replaced by a subtractor, whose output $(jV_{o1} - kV_{out})$ is applied to the input of the first integrator. If V_{out} represents s, it follows that V_{o1} represents $-(ds/dt)$, so the input of the first integrator is made to represent both (d^2s/dt^2) and $-(\omega^2s + \lambda ds/dt)$. $\omega^2 = k/(CR)^2$, as before and $\lambda = j/CR$, and since $CR = 1.0$ s, ω^2 is represented by k, and λ by j.

V Connect up the circuit of Fig. 15.49. Set $k = 1$, and $j = 1$, and observe the rapidly decaying oscillations of the CRO trace of V_{out}. Reduce j so that the decay rate is less, and display jV_{o1} on channel 1 of the CRO instead of kV_{out}. Notice the phase relationship between V_{out} (representing displacement) and jV_{o1} (representing negative velocity) as you repeat the process.

NOTES

W Your record should include labelled circuit diagrams, where appropriate.

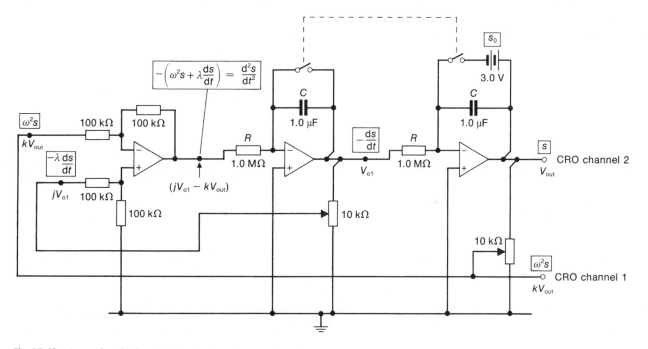

Fig. 15.49 Integrating circuit that simulates damped harmonic motion.

X Analogue computers are not now as common as they used to be, largely because digital computing techniques have advanced, and continue to advance, so rapidly. Once programmed, analogue computers do have the advantages of simultaneous and instantaneous display of variable quantities, and easy variation of parameters that affect the system under investigation. However, not only do the speed and power of modern digital computers enable them to offset these advantages, but it is now quite easy to present information to them, and retrieve it from them, in analogue (i.e. direct) form.

16 DIGITAL ELECTRONICS

16.1 DIGITAL LOGIC

16.1.1 Digital electronics

In the circuits that you will investigate in this section, information is represented by electric signals that have only two permitted voltage levels. These digital circuits consist mainly of transistors, and the two voltage levels are related to the two stable states in which a transistor can be operated – fully on and fully off. This gives digital circuits the advantage of great accuracy over their analogue counterparts, in which information is represented by continuously variable voltages. The accuracy of processes carried out in digital circuits is not limited by the tolerance and stability of circuit parameters, which greatly affect the performance of analogue circuits.

16.1.2 Binary numbers

Since only two voltage levels are permitted, only two different numbers can be represented. It follows that the *binary* number system is used with digital circuits and systems, and all quantities must be expressed in binary form before processing. The numbers we use in everyday life belong to the *decimal* (or *denary*) system, in which ten different digits are used. (It's a fair assumption that our ancestors originally adopted the decimal system because they found counting easy using their ten fingers.)

Table 16.1 lists the first sixteen numbers in decimal and binary form. Notice that in the binary system the numbers two, four, eight and sixteen have the significance that ten, one hundred, one thousand, etc. have in the decimal system: each one requires the first use of an extra digit. Arithmetic operations and processes like addition, subtraction and multiplication on binary numbers are essentially the same as those on decimal numbers. In the experiments that follow only numbers below sixteen will be encountered. Up to four binary digits, or *bits* (= *bi*nary dig*its*) as they are called, will therefore be required to represent each number. However, *all* binary numbers will be expressed here as four-bit numbers, including those below eight, which will therefore start with zeros that might be considered unnecessary.

Table 16.1 Decimal and binary equivalents of numbers up to sixteen.

Decimal	Binary	Pure binary code (four-bit)
0	0	0 0 0 0
1	1	0 0 0 1
2	10	0 0 1 0
3	11	0 0 1 1
4	100	0 1 0 0
5	101	0 1 0 1
6	110	0 1 1 0
7	111	0 1 1 1
8	1000	1 0 0 0
9	1001	1 0 0 1
10	1010	1 0 1 0
11	1011	1 0 1 1
12	1100	1 1 0 0
13	1101	1 1 0 1
14	1110	1 1 1 0
15	1111	1 1 1 1
16	10000	—

This simple system of coding binary numbers for processing in digital circuits is called the *pure binary code*. The binary coded forms of numbers below sixteen are listed in the third column of Table 16.1. (Clearly sixteen cannot be expressed in a four-bit code.) Reading each coded number from the left, successive bits represent in decimal either zero or 8 ($= 2^3$), 4 ($= 2^2$), 2 ($= 2^1$) and 1 ($= 2^0$). Notice that, as in the decimal system, the *most significant bit* (m.s.b.) is written on the left of each number, and the *least significant bit* (l.s.b.) is written on the right. There are other systems of coding for digital processing, but in every one only the binary digits 0 and 1 are allowed. One obvious alternative to the pure binary code is a code in which the sequence of bits is reversed, such that the m.s.b. of a binary number is written on the right. In another coding system, called 'binary coded decimal' (BCD) a number is kept in its decimal form, but each decimal digit is expressed in pure binary code. Thus the decimal number 13 would be expressed in BCD as 0 0 0 1 0 0 1 1.

16.1.3 Logic levels

The two binary numbers, 0 and 1, are represented by the two permitted levels. Provided the difference between these two levels is sufficiently large, and can be avoided, there is a range of voltages around each nominal level within which any voltage can be accepted as representing the appropriate number. This accommodating property of digital circuits gives them their inherent accuracy. The voltage ranges are usually only referred to as *low* and *high*, since their precise values depend on the type of digital circuitry being used and its power supply voltage. With the convention known as positive logic the low voltage level, which lies near 0 V, represents the binary number 0, and the high level, which lies just below the positive power supply voltage V_s, represents the binary number 1. (With negative logic, now used less frequently, the voltage level that represents 1 is negative and lies *below* the higher voltage, near zero that represents 0.) Positive logic is used here, and we will refer to the high voltage level as *logical 1* and to the low voltage level as *logical 0*.

16.1.4 Logic gates

All digital circuits are assembled as combinations of logic *gates*. Modern electronic gates are based on transistors. Gates can be constructed from individual components, but it is more convenient to deal with them in integrated circuit (IC) form. A simple digital IC might contain only four logic gates, while more complex ICs, like those used in computers, contain many thousands in pre-arranged combinations. Each type of logic gate performs a particular logic *function,* the study of which forms the main purpose of the first experiments in this section. None of the logic gates that you will encounter here has more than two inputs and one output, though other types are quite common. Each output is, of course, only allowed to be at either logical 0 or logical 1. Fig. 16.1 shows the conventional symbols for five basic logic gates.

In *combinational logic* the state of the output of a gate depends only on the present combination of input voltages, each of which like the output, can only be at either logical 0 or logical 1. In *sequential logic* the state of the output depends somehow on the sequence in which input voltages have been applied. Sequential logic circuits, which might consist of several basic gates, form the basis of memory systems.

16.1.5 Truth tables

The behaviour of a logic gate, or a circuit made from gates, is most conveniently recorded for recall and analysis in a *truth table,* in which all possible input combinations are listed, and against each one is written the corresponding state of the output. An example is Table 16.2, which is the truth table for one particular logic gate. As the gate has two inputs, four different input combinations are possible.

Table 16.2   Truth table for logic gate

Inputs		Output
0	0	0
0	1	0
1	0	0
1	1	1

There are several ways of summarising the information contained in the table. For example, the truth table shows that:

(i) If either (or both) of the inputs is at logical 0, the output is at logical 0.

(ii) The output of the gate is at logical 0 except when both inputs are at logical 1.

(iii) The output is at logical 1 only when both inputs are at logical 1.

All three statements, of course, amount to the same thing. By convention we normally describe the function of a gate by referring to the conditions under which the output is at logical 1, so the third of these summaries becomes the most appropriate. This convention leads to the allocation of a name for each type of gate. Table 16.2 is the truth table of an AND gate, for which the output is at logical 1 only when one input *AND* the other are *both* at logical 1. Truth tables are so called because the two states represented by logical 1 and logical 0 are associated in some applications with the 'truth' and 'falsehood' of statements. The logic of an AND gate, for example, might therefore be described as 'the output statement is true only if both input statements are true'.

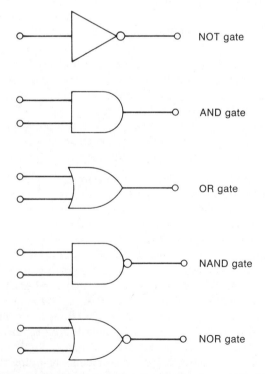

Fig. 16.1   Circuit symbols for basic logic gates. Inputs are on the left of each symbol, with outputs on the right.

16.1.6 Logic families

Logic gates and other digital devices are readily available as dual-in-line (DIL) IC packages, most of which have either 14 or 16 pins. There are several different types or *families* of logic circuitry, and a whole series of digital ICs is available in each. The two principal families in common use are called TTL (transistor–transistor logic) and CMOS (complementary metal oxide semiconductor). Each one has advantages over the other, and it is possible to build circuits containing ICs of both families. But you need to be aware of which family you are using, if only because their pin connections are quite different. TTL ICs are numbered from 7400 onwards and CMOS ICs are numbered from 4001 onwards. Pin connections for the ICs that are used in the experiments in this section will be shown in Fig. 16.6.

Table 16.3 Characteristics of the two principal logic families.

Characteristic	Standard TTL 74 series	CMOS 4000 series
Transistors used in construction	Bipolar	Field effect
Switching time	10 ns	150 ns
Quiescent power consumption	10 mW	1 nW
Power supply voltage V_s	+5.0 V ($\pm$0.25 V)	+3 V to +15 V
Max. source current (logical 1)	500 μA	1 mA
Max. sink current (logical 0)	15 mA	2 mA
Acceptable input voltage ranges		
for logical 0	0–1 V	0–$0.4V_s$
for logical 1	2 V–5 V	$0.6V_s$–V_s
Output voltages		
logical 0	0–0.4 V	≈ 0
logical 1	2.4 V–4.0 V	$\approx V_s$
Fan-out	10	50

Table 16.3 lists some of the important characteristics of the two families. Notice that CMOS gates are rather slower than TTL gates, but they require much less power, which makes them more suitable for battery-powered circuits. CMOS gates operate over a wide range of power supply voltages, while TTL gates demand a well-regulated and fairly precise supply voltage. About half-way down the table, the *source* current is the current that flows from a gate output at logical 1 to the lower power supply rail (0 V), and the *sink* current is the current that flows into a gate output at logical 0 from the higher power supply rail (V_s). The relatively large current that TTL outputs can sink renders them useful for driving the output stages of logic circuits. The switching characteristics of CMOS gates are far better than those of TTL gates: the transition between logical 0 and logical 1 as interpreted at CMOS

inputs is sharp and occurs at about 0.5 V_s, and CMOS output voltage levels lie close to their ideal values of 0 V and V_s. *Fan-out* is the number of gate inputs that can be driven by one output. The relatively high currents required by TTL inputs limits the fan-out of TTL outputs to only about ten.

It would appear that CMOS gates are superior to TTL gates in most respects. However, CMOS ICs are far more vulnerable to accidental misuse. They can be destroyed by static electric charge that accumulates on their pins, and by the omission of their power supply connections. TTL ICs are unlikely to be destroyed unless they are connected to the wrong power supply.

16.2 PRACTICAL CIRCUITS

16.2.1. Circuit systems

It was stated in section 15 that there are many ways of connecting up analogue circuits, including those that make use of purpose-built systems. The same applies to digital circuits. Systems are available in which individual logic gates are mounted with the necessary terminals to make connections to their inputs, output and power supply. Such systems would be cumbersome to use for the more complex digital circuits in this section. It is far more convenient to build circuits from gates on digital ICs.

If you are able to use either TTL or CMOS ICs, you are strongly recommended to assemble your circuits on a piece of solderless breadboard. Such boards have been developed for easy and quick assembly of prototype and other temporary circuits. Most of them contain two sets of rows of five interconnected sprung sockets, into which all components are simply pushed, and two long rows of interconnected sockets for use as power supply rails. Single strand wire is used to connect the rows. At the end of every experiment all components and wire connections can be pulled out from the board and kept for further use. A solderless breadboard of convenient size is shown in Fig. 16.2 (overleaf). Note that the IC around which the circuit is formed is placed on the board such that it straddles the gap between the two sets of rows. Each pin of the IC is inserted into one socket of a row so that up to four more connections can be made to it.

16.2.2 Inputs and outputs

In each experiment digital signals will be applied to various inputs of a circuit, and the behaviour of the circuit is then investigated by monitoring the states of outputs. Input signals consist of logical 0 or logical 1, or continuous alternations between them (i.e. pulses). The simplest

Fig. 16.2 A simple digital circuit assembled on a piece of solderless breadboard. This board has two sets of 47 rows of interconnected sockets across the middle with continuous contact rows at the top and the bottom for use as power supply rails.

means of obtaining logical 0 and logical 1 is to make direct connections to the appropriate power supply rail, preferably through a resistance of a few hundred ohms to protect the gate from voltage fluctuations in the power supply. If a switch is available, the system shown in Fig. 16.3 is rather more convenient. Unconnected TTL inputs 'float' to logical 1 (i.e. they behave as if a logical 1 signal were applied there), but CMOS inputs are far less predictable and should never be left unconnected.

The simplest way of monitoring one of the outputs of a logic circuit is to use a light-emitting diode (LED). As its name suggests, an LED is a diode that emits light, and it does so when a current flows through it in the forward direction. The cathode connecting pin of an LED is the one nearer the slightly flattened part of an otherwise round rim. LEDs are available in three colours – red, green and yellow. It would seem sensible to use an LED as a logic indicator such that it emits light for logical 1 and no light for logical 0. Fig. 16.4 shows how this could be done. Note the use of a series resistance, which limits the current that can flow through the LED. Unfortunately, in this simple system, when the gate output is at logical 1 it has to act as a current *source*. Neither TTL nor CMOS outputs are good at sourcing currents, but TTL outputs at logical 0 can *sink* relatively large currents – certainly enough to light an LED. Fig. 16.5 shows a much better indicator system in which the LED and its current-limiting resistance R_1 are connected between the higher power supply rail (V_s) and the output of a TTL logic inverter. When the monitored gate output is at logical 1, the output of the inverter is at logical 0, and it sinks enough current to flow through the LED to light it. When the gate output is at logical 0, the inverter's output is at logical 1, and the p.d. across the LED is not sufficient to drive a current through it. The resistance R_2 'pulls down' the inverter's input to logical 0 when no gate output is connected for monitoring. Without R_2 the inverter's input would float to logical 1 and the LED would be lit. Though this indicator includes a TTL inverter, it will satisfactorily monitor the outputs of

CMOS gates run from a 5 V power supply. For other voltages a CMOS inverter must be used with appropriate values of R_1 and R_2.

Up to four output indicators will be required. These, together with a couple of switched logic inputs, need to be readily available for all the experiments in this section. If they are to be permanently installed, the switched inputs should be combined with logic indicators to reveal their state. Also required in some experiments will be a push-button operated 'de-bounced' switched input, i.e. one in which the effects of contact bounce are eliminated, and a slow logic pulse generator.

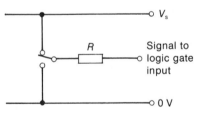

Fig. 16.3 Simple switched logic input; R should be a few hundred ohms.

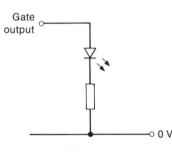

Fig. 16.4 Simple LED logic indicator in which the monitored gate output acts as a current source.

238

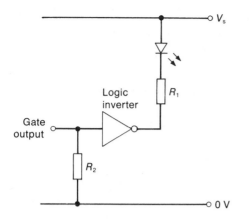

Fig. 16.5 Improved LED logic indicator.

16.2.3 Circuit assembly

Some of the circuits in this section are quite complex, and to reduce the risk of incorrectly connecting components you will need to assemble each circuit methodically. Insert the ICs first, make the necessary power supply connections to them, and then work through the circuit diagram from left to right. For each gate, make connections to the inputs before you make them from the output. If possible, use wires of different colours to identify the various connections within the circuit. Connections to the two power supply rails, inputs, outputs and connections within each part of the circuit can then be distinguished. The following points are most important:

(i) Power supply connections to gates are omitted from circuit diagrams.

(ii) The power supply should be switched off or otherwise disconnected before changing connections or making any other alterations to the circuit.

(iii) ICs should be inserted into the board and removed from it with care; the pins will snap off if they are bent or twisted too much.

(iv) No gate input should ever have more than one connection made to it; each output can feed several inputs (fan-out), but each input must only be fed by one output.

(v) CMOS inputs must never be left open; connect each one to an appropriate power supply rail.

(vi) Open TTL inputs float to logical 1.

16.2.4 Digital ICs

You will require only seven different ICs to complete all the experiments in this section. For easy reference, the pin connection diagrams of them all are shown in Fig. 16.6, and again in the text where they are first mentioned. TTL and CMOS equivalents are both shown, but in general you should use ICs of one family or the other and avoid circuits containing a mixture. The first five ICs (in both family lists) each contain four or six basic gates, isolated from each other but with a common pair of power supply connecting pins. The other two are more complex. In the text TTL IC numbers are given first, with their CMOS equivalents following and in parentheses.

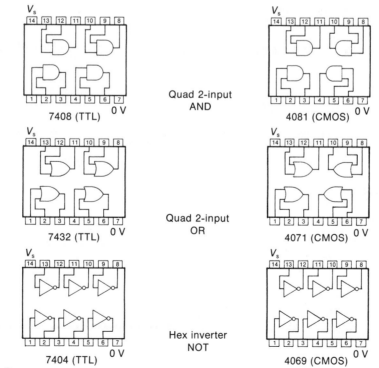

Fig. 16.6 (continues overleaf)

239

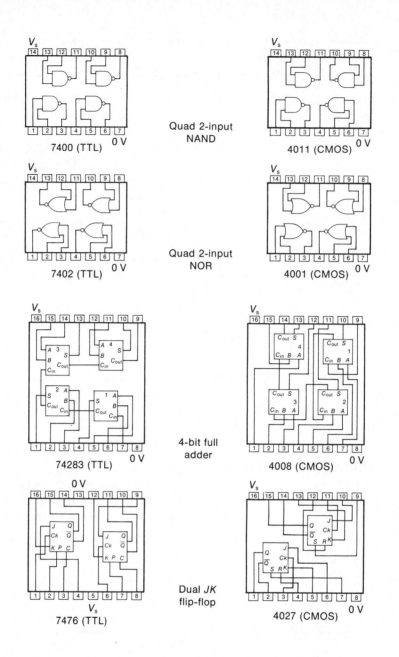

Quad 2-input NAND — 7400 (TTL), 4011 (CMOS)

Quad 2-input NOR — 7402 (TTL), 4001 (CMOS)

4-bit full adder — 74283 (TTL), 4008 (CMOS)

Dual JK flip-flop — 7476 (TTL), 4027 (CMOS)

Fig. 16.6. Pin connections for the ICs required for experiments in this section. Pin 1 on each IC is identified either by a dimple beside it, or by a slot between it and the highest numbered pin. The pins are shown as the IC is viewed from above.

16A Basic Logic Gates
Investigation of the behaviour of five basic logic gates: AND, OR, NOT, NAND and NOR

APPARATUS REQUIRED

- circuit assembly board or system
- TTL power supply, $V_s = 5$ V (or CMOS equivalent)
- output indicator
- 7400, 7402, 7404, 7408 and 7432 TTL ICs (or 4011, 4001, 4069, 4081 and 4071 CMOS ICs)
- connecting wires

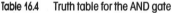

AND GATE

a The truth table for the AND gate is shown in Table 16.4. The two inputs A and B have four possible combinations of logic levels. These are listed in the truth table against the corresponding levels of the output Q. The logic of this gate can be described by the statement 'Q is 1 only if both A and B are 1'. Note that the word *and* does not refer here to any kind of addition process. Fig. 16.7a shows the conventional symbol for the AND gate.

Table 16.4   Truth table for the AND gate

Inputs		Output
A	B	Q
0	0	0
0	1	0
1	0	0
1	1	1

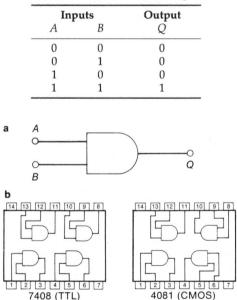

Fig. 16.7 AND gate: **a** conventional circuit symbol, and **b** pin connections for quad 2-input AND gate ICs.

b Check the truth table in Table 16.4 experimentally by applying in turn all four input combinations to one of the four AND gates on the 7408 (or 4081) IC. Note carefully the pin connections shown in Fig. 16.7b, and don't forget to make the connections to the power supply rails.

OR GATE

c Now investigate the logic of the OR gate. Use one of the four gates on the 7432 (or 4071) IC (see Fig. 16.8). Use your observations to draw up a truth table for the OR gate in the format of Table 16.4. Confirm that the logic of this gate may be described by the statement 'Q is 1 if either A or B is 1', to which should be added 'or both' to distinguish an OR gate from a sixth type of gate that will be considered in experiment 16D.

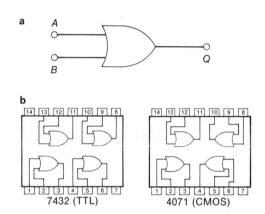

Fig. 16.8 OR gate: **a** conventional circuit symbol, and **b** pin connections for quad 2-input OR gate ICs.

NOT GATE (INVERTER)

d Repeat this procedure using one of the six NOT gates on the 7404 (or 4069) IC (see Fig. 16.9). Notice that the NOT gate has one input, so its truth table has only two rows. Confirm that the level of Q is the opposite of the level of the single input A, i.e. 'Q is *not* A'.

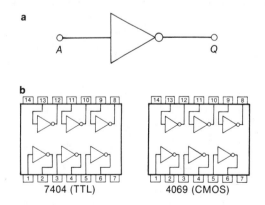

Fig. 16.9 NOT gate (inverter): **a** conventional circuit symbol, and **b** pin connections for hex inverter ICs; TTL and CMOS alternatives have the same pin connections.

241

NAND GATE

e Repeat this procedure using one of the four NAND gates on the 7400 (or 4011) IC (see Fig. 16.10). Compare the truth table of the NAND gate with that of the AND gate. Confirm that the logic of the NAND gate may be described by 'Q is *not* 1 (i.e. Q is 0) only if both A *and* B are 1'.

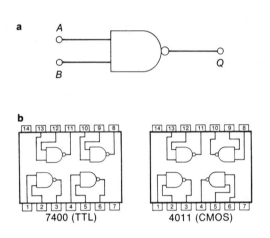

Fig. 16.10 NAND gate: **a** conventional circuit symbol, and **b** pin connections for quad 2-input NAND gate ICs.

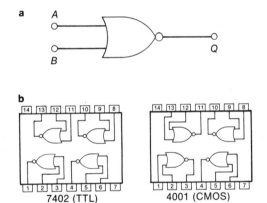

Fig. 16.11 NOR gate: **a** conventional circuit symbol, and **b** pin connections for quad 2-input NOR gate ICs; note that the gates on the 7402 IC are orientated from right to left – the opposite way to the gates on the other TTL ICs.

NOR GATE

f Repeat this procedure using one of the four NOR gates on the 7402 (or 4001) IC (see Fig. 16.11). Compare the truth table of the NOR gate with that of the OR gate. Confirm that the logic of the NOR gate may be described by 'Q is *not* 1 (i.e. Q *is* 0) if A *or* B (or both) is 1'.

UNCONNECTED INPUTS (TTL ONLY)

g Return to the 7408 IC and connect the output from one of its four AND gates to an output indicator, but leave its two inputs unconnected. Note the level of the output. Refer to the truth table of the AND gate in Table 16.4. What is the only input combination that produces this output?

h This simple test illustrates an important feature of all TTL ICs: unconnected (open) inputs 'float' to logical 1. In later experiments we will make good use of this. Where we require inputs to be permanently at logical 1 we can save time (and wire) by leaving them alone. Should you be tempted to test one of these unconnected inputs directly, by connecting it to an indicator, you will probably find that it drops to logical 0, and that the output of the AND gate will therefore also have dropped to logical 0. The LED connection effectively shorts the input to the 0 V rail, and prevents it from floating to logical 1.

NOTES

i Your record should include the symbols and truth tables for all five gates.

j You should check that for all four of the two-input gates you have used both inputs are identical: the two input combinations of $A = 1$, $B = 0$ and $A = 0$, $B = 1$ produce the same output.

k The symbols for logic gates used in these diagrams and throughout this chapter are those in common use in Britain and elsewhere, but they are actually American. Standard British symbols (to BS 3939) are shown in Fig. 16.12 for reference only. They have never gained significant acceptance. Note how in both systems a small circle drawn on the right-hand side of a symbol signifies inversion.

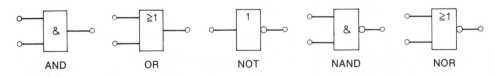

Fig. 16.12 British logic gate symbols (BS 3939).

16B Simple Gate Combinations

Obtaining the five basic logic functions from combinations of either NAND gates only or NOR gates only

APPARATUS REQUIRED

- circuit assembly board or system
- TTL power supply, $V_s = 5$ V (or CMOS alternative)
- output indicator
- 7400, 7402 and 7404 TTL ICs (or 4011, 4001 and 4069 CMOS ICs)
- connecting wires

NAND GATE COMBINATIONS

a   Since the logical function of the NAND gate is a combination of AND and NOT functions, we might expect a NAND gate to act as an AND gate if its two inputs are inverted, i.e. if we connect NOT gates to both inputs as shown in Fig. 16.13.

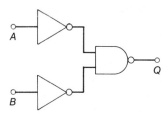

Fig. 16.13   NAND gate with inverted inputs.

b   Connect up the circuit shown in Fig. 16.13 using gates on the 7404 and 7400 (or 4069 and 4011) ICs. Investigate the logic of the circuit by applying all four input combinations. Draw up a truth table to show how Q depends upon A and B. Compare this truth table with those you obtained in experiment 16A and confirm that this circuit behaves in fact as an OR gate.

c   Now find out what happens when the output of the NAND gate is inverted. Connect up the circuit shown in Fig. 16.14, investigate its logic, and confirm that it behaves as an AND gate. Add a second NOT gate to invert the output twice. What is the effect of this double inversion?

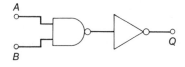

Fig. 16.14   NAND gate with inverted output.

d   Investigate the logic of the simple arrangement shown in Fig. 16.15, in which the inputs of a single NAND gate are joined together. Note that there is only one input to this circuit. Draw up a truth table to show how Q depends on A and confirm that the arrangement behaves as a NOT gate.

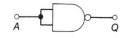

Fig. 16.15   NAND gate with connected inputs.

Table 16.5   Truth table for the NAND gate

Inputs		Output
A	B	Q
0	0	1
0	1	1
1	0	1
1	1	0

e   Examine the truth table of the NAND gate (Table 16.5), and see if you can devise another means of obtaining the NOT function from a single NAND gate. Assume that A is to be the NOT gate's input: which *constant* logic level would B have to be at to maintain Q as the complement of A? Check your idea experimentally, by connecting B to the appropriate logic level.

f   Since NAND gates with connected inputs could be used as the NOT gates in the circuits of Figs. 16.13 and 16.14, OR and AND functions could be produced by combining respectively three and two NAND gates. You have therefore discovered ways of combining NAND gates to produce only OR, AND and NOT functions, and of course NAND itself. Just as the NAND gate is an AND gate with its output inverted, so inverting the output of the OR gate should create a NOR gate. This remaining logic function may therefore be obtained with NAND gates only by connecting the NOT function arrangement of Fig. 16.15 to the output of the OR function circuit of Fig. 16.13.

g   Assemble such a circuit using all four NAND gates on the 7400 (or 4011) IC. Investigate its logic, draw up a truth table and confirm that it does indeed behave as a NOR gate.

NOR GATE COMBINATIONS

h Devise, assemble and test circuits containing only NOR gates that also provide the five basic logic functions. Follow steps equivalent to those outlined in (a) to (g); there is even a second means of obtaining the NOT function from a single NOR gate, equivalent to that suggested in (e).

NOTES

i Your record should include four labelled circuit diagrams that show NAND gate combinations providing OR, AND, NOT and NOR functions, and four more diagrams that show NOR gate combinations providing AND, OR, NOT and NAND functions.

j Complex logic networks are often constructed from only one type of gate, using the combinations that you have investigated in this experiment. Inevitably, the number of gates that has to be used is then increased, but this disadvantage is outweighed by the simplicity of assembly and modification.

16C Laws of Logic
Representation of logic statements in Boolean algebra and investigation of some of its theorems

APPARATUS REQUIRED

- circuit assembly board or system
- TTL power supply, $V_s = 5$ V (or CMOS alternative)
- 2 output indicators
- 7400, 7404, 7408 and 7432 TTL ICs (or 4011, 4069, 4081 and 4071 CMOS ICs)
- connecting wires

BOOLEAN ALGEBRA

Table 16.6   Boolean expressions for the five basic logic functions

Logic function	Boolean notation
A AND B	$A \cdot B$
A OR B	$A + B$
NOT A	$\overline{A}$
A NAND B, i.e. NOT (A AND B)	$\overline{A \cdot B}$
A NOR B, i.e. NOT (A OR B)	$\overline{A + B}$

a Table 16.6 shows how the five basic logic functions are written in the algebraic notation that we use as a kind of shorthand to write down logic expressions and equations. In this form they are called Boolean expressions.

Note carefully:

(i) A dot is used to represent AND and a plus sign to represent OR. Do not confuse these signs with their arithmetic counterparts representing multiplication and addition. Be particularly careful not to use a plus sign for AND, a mistake that arises from the false association of AND with addition.

(ii) It is common practice to omit the dot in AND and NAND expressions, just as it is with conventional algebraic multiplication, but no such form of abbreviation will be used here. (Rather, we would use the term *AB*, for example, to represent a two-bit binary number that has possible values 00, 01, 10 and 11.)

(iii) A bar over a logic quantity or expression indicates *inversion* (negation). We say that $\overline{A}$ is the *complement* of A.

b The algebra of logic was developed in the nineteenth century by George Boole, but it took the comparatively recent development of digital electronics to reveal its usefulness. The laws of logic expressed in Boolean algebra are known as *theorems*. Table 16.7 contains nineteen theorems, numbered for easy reference in this and later experiments, grouped beside an appropriate generic name to simplify verification. Remember that the logic quantities A, B and C can each have only two values: 0 or 1. Parentheses are used in complex expressions to establish priority, just as in conventional algebra.

Table 16.7 Theorems of Boolean algebra.

Name	No.	Theorem
AND function	1	$A \cdot 0 = 0$
	2	$A \cdot 1 = A$
	3	$A \cdot A = A$
	4	$A \cdot \overline{A} = 0$
OR function	5	$A + 0 = A$
	6	$A + 1 = 1$
	7	$A + A = A$
	8	$A + \overline{A} = 1$
NOT function	9	$\overline{\overline{A}} = A$
Theorems of commutation	10	$A \cdot B = B \cdot A$
	11	$A + B = B + A$
Theorems of association	12	$(A \cdot B) \cdot C = A \cdot (B \cdot C)$
	13	$(A + B) + C = A + (B + C)$
Theorems of distribution	14	$A \cdot (B + C) = (A \cdot B) + (A \cdot C)$
	15	$A + (B \cdot C) = (A + B) \cdot (A + C)$
Theorems of absorption	16	$A \cdot (A + B) = A$
	17	$A + (A \cdot B) = A$
De Morgan's theorems	18	$\overline{A \cdot B} = \overline{A} + \overline{B}$
	19	$\overline{A + B} = \overline{A} \cdot \overline{B}$

c The aim of this experiment is the verification of some of these theorems, which will provide practice at the recognition and use of Boolean expressions, and further experience of the assembly and testing of gate combinations. Do not be daunted by the awesome contents of Table 16.7. They are merely formal expressions of logical identities, more than half of which you have already met (in experiments 16A and 16B, though almost certainly without realising it). Most importantly, do not attempt to learn the theorems.

d Verification of the first eleven theorems is quite straightforward. Theorems 12 to 19 are rather more difficult to verify, and two alternative methods will be considered:

(i) For verification of a theorem by analysis all possible input combinations (four with two variables and eight with three variables) are considered, and for each one the values of the expressions on either side of the theorem equation are calculated and compared.

(ii) For verification by experiment all possible input combinations are applied to a circuit that has two outputs, representing the two expressions of the theorem equation. The identity of the two outputs is then checked.

THEOREMS 1 TO 11

e The first eight theorems can be verified by referring to truth tables for two of the basic logic gates. For example,

the interpretation of theorem 1 is that if one of the inputs to an AND gate is at logical 0, the output must be at logical 0, whatever the level of the other input A. The first and third lines of the appropriate truth table (see Table 16.4) confirm this. Theorem 8, to take another example, indicates that if the two inputs to the OR gate are at different (i.e. complementary) logic levels, the output must be at logical 1.

f Examine the truth tables for AND and OR gates that you obtained in experiment 16A and verify theorems 1 to 8.

g Verifications of theorems 9, 10 and 11 need hardly be demonstrated: theorem 9 states that a second inversion cancels the effect of a first one, and theorems 10 and 11 refer to the interchangeability of the inputs to a two-input gate. See experiment 16A (j).

THEOREMS 12 TO 19

h The truths of the remaining eight theorems are less obvious. It is suggested that you verify only the first of each pair, but that you do so both analytically and experimentally, as outlined in (d).

Table 16.8 Analytical verification of theorem 12.

1 A	2 B	3 C	4 $A \cdot B$	5 $B \cdot C$	6 $(A \cdot B) \cdot C$	7 $A \cdot (B \cdot C)$
0	0	0	0	0	0	0
0	0	1	0	0	0	0
0	1	0	0	0	0	0
0	1	1	0	1	0	0
1	0	0	0	0	0	0
1	0	1	0	0	0	0
1	1	0	1	0	0	0
1	1	1	1	1	1	1

i Table 16.8 shows how theorem 12 can be verified by analysis. All eight possible combinations of the three variables A, B and C are listed in the first three columns. Entries in the other four columns can be confirmed by referring to the truth table of the AND gate. The expressions in columns 6 and 7 represent the two sides of the equation for theorem 12, and the identity of these two columns verifies the theorem (which, incidentally, renders unnecessary the parentheses in both expressions).

j Connect up the circuit of Fig. 16.16 (overleaf) to verify theorem 12 by experiment. Use all four AND gates on one 7408 (or 4081) IC. Connect the two outputs of the circuit, which represent the two sides of the equation for theorem 12, to indicators. Apply in turn all eight input combinations and check that each one generates identical outputs, which according to Table 16.8 are at logical 0 except when A, B and C are all 1.

Table 16.9 Analytical verification of theorem 14. The first of eight lines has been completed.

A	B	C	B + C	A . B	A . C	A . (B + C)	(A . B) + (A . C)
0	0	0	0	0	0	0	0

Table 16.10 Analytical verification of theorem 16. The first of four lines has been completed.

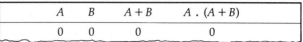

A	B	A + B	A . (A + B)
0	0	0	0

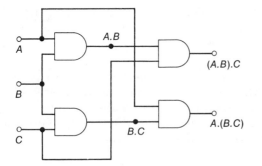

Fig. 16.16 Experimental verification of theorem 12.

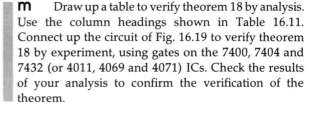

Fig. 16.18 Experimental verification of theorem 16.

k   Draw up your own table to verify theorem 14 by analysis. Use the column headings shown in Table 16.9 above, in which only the first line is entered. Connect up the circuit of Fig. 16.17 to verify theorem 14 by experiment, using gates on the 7408 and 7432 (or 4081 and 4071) ICs. Check the results of your analysis to confirm the verification of the theorem.

m   Draw up a table to verify theorem 18 by analysis. Use the column headings shown in Table 16.11. Connect up the circuit of Fig. 16.19 to verify theorem 18 by experiment, using gates on the 7400, 7404 and 7432 (or 4011, 4069 and 4071) ICs. Check the results of your analysis to confirm the verification of the theorem.

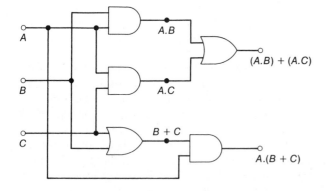

Fig. 16.17 Experimental verification of theorem 14.

Table 16.11 Analytical verification of theorem 18. The first of four lines has been completed.

A	B	$\bar{A}$	$\bar{B}$	$A . B$	$\overline{A} . \overline{B}$	$\overline{A} + \overline{B}$
0	0	1	1	0	1	1

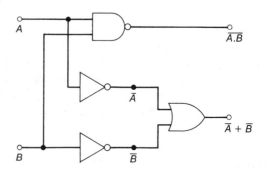

Fig. 16.19 Experimental verification of theorem 18.

l   Draw up a table to verify theorem 16 by analysis. Use the column headings shown in Table 16.10. Connect up the circuit of Fig. 16.18 to verify theorem 16 by experiment, using gates on the 7408 and 7432 (or 4081 and 4071) ICs. Check the results of your analysis to confirm the verification of the theorem.

n Your record should include a list of all the theorems of Boolean algebra, with tables and diagrams of circuits used for verification.

o The theorems of Boolean algebra are used for the simplification of complex logic networks through conversion to equivalent forms. They would have enabled most of the findings of experiment 16B to have been predicted quite easily. For example, if both expressions of theorem 3 are inverted, we have:

$$\overline{A \cdot A} = \overline{A} \quad \text{(i.e. } A \text{ NAND } A = \text{NOT } A\text{)}$$

and if both expressions of theorem 2 are inverted (and using theorem 10), we have:

$$\overline{1 \cdot A} = \overline{A} \quad \text{(i.e. } 1 \text{ NAND } A = \text{NOT } A\text{)}$$

These two statements show how the NOT function can be obtained from a single NAND gate. See experiment 16B (d) and (e), where they were tested experimentally.

p De Morgan's two theorems are particularly useful since they allow conversions between AND- and OR-based expressions. For example, if both expressions of theorem 19 are inverted, we have:

$$\overline{\overline{A + B}} = \overline{\overline{A} \cdot \overline{B}}$$

Theorem 9 can obviously be applied to the left-hand side to give:

$$A + B = \overline{\overline{A} \cdot \overline{B}} \quad \text{(i.e. } A \text{ OR } B = (\text{NOT } A) \text{ NAND } (\text{NOT } B))$$

which confirms the findings of experiment 16B (b): inverting the inputs of a NAND gate produces an OR function.

q De Morgan's two theorems may be summarised in a single statement: *the complement of a logic statement is obtained by inverting each term and exchanging AND with OR and vice versa.* They are often used in their inverted form. Thus:

$$A \cdot B = \overline{\overline{A} + \overline{B}} \quad \text{theorem 18 (inverted)}$$
$$A + B = \overline{\overline{A} \cdot \overline{B}} \quad \text{theorem 19 (inverted)}$$

16D Two More Logic Gates

Obtaining exclusive OR and exclusive NOR functions from convenient combinations of the five basic logic gates

APPARATUS REQUIRED

- circuit assembly board or system
- TTL power supply, $V_s = 5$ V (or CMOS alternative)
- output indicator
- 7400, 2 7402, 7404, 7408 and 7432 TTL ICs (or 4011, 2 4001, 4069, 4081 and 4071 CMOS ICs)
- connecting wires

Table 16.12 Truth table for the EOR gate.

Inputs		Output
A	B	Q
0	0	0
0	1	1
1	0	1
1	1	0

PRINCIPLES INVOLVED

a In experiment 16A the four basic two-input logic gates were investigated. The logic of one of these, the OR gate, is described by 'Q is 1 if A or B or both is 1'. However, in many logic circuits we require a modified form of OR gate: one whose logic is described by 'Q is 1 if either A or B, *but not both*, is 1' (i.e. 'Q is 1 if A and B are complementary'). Such a gate is called an exclusive OR (EOR) gate, and where there might be some confusion the normal OR gate of the type investigated in experiment 16A is referred to as an *inclusive* OR gate. Table 16.12 is the truth table for the EOR gate, and its conventional circuit symbol is shown in Fig. 16.20. In the notation of Boolean algebra the EOR function is represented by a circled plus sign.

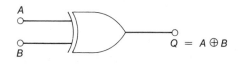

Fig. 16.20 EOR gate: conventional circuit symbol.

b The inverted output of an EOR gate is at logical 1 when the two inputs are equal. Such a gate is called an exclusive NOR, or *parity* gate, whose logic is therefore described by 'Q is 1 if A and B are equal'. Table 16.13 is the truth table for the parity gate, and its circuit symbol is shown in Fig. 16.21 (both overleaf).

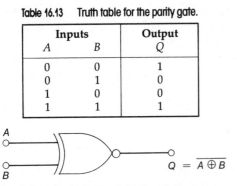

Table 16.13   Truth table for the parity gate.

| Inputs | | Output |
A	B	Q
0	0	1
0	1	0
1	0	0
1	1	1

$$Q = \overline{A \oplus B}$$

Fig. 16.21   Parity gate: conventional circuit symbol.

c   In this experiment you will investigate circuits that provide these two logic functions. Some of the theorems of Boolean algebra listed in Table 16.7 will be applied to simplify them and reduce to a minimum the number of basic gates required.

EOR GATE

d   To construct a circuit that provides the EOR function we must start with a statement that describes its logic. Examine the truth table in Table 16.12 and notice that the output Q is 0 in lines 1 and 4, when the two inputs are equal, and that Q is 1 in lines 2 and 3, when the inputs are complementary. Consider the logic statement:

$$Q = (A \cdot \overline{B}) + (\overline{A} \cdot B)$$

(i) When $A = B$, one and only one variable in each of the two terms on the right-hand side *must* be 0.

Since: $0.1 = 1.0 = 0$

and: $0 + 0 = 0$

then: $Q = 0$

(ii) When A and B are complementary, both variables in one term *must* be 1, and both terms in the other term *must* be 0.

Since: $1.1 = 1$

and: $1 + 0 = 1$

then: $Q = 1$

Hence: $A \oplus B = (A \cdot \overline{B}) + (\overline{A} \cdot B)$ [16.1]

e   Connect up the circuit of Fig. 16.22, which directly represents equation [16.1], using gates on the 7404, 7408 and 7432 (or 4069, 4081 and 4071) ICs. Investigate the logic of the circuit by applying all four input combinations. Draw up a truth table to show how Q depends upon A and B, and confirm that the circuit behaves as an EOR gate.

f   The circuit of Fig. 16.22 contains five gates of three different types. The first stage of simplification is achieved by applying one of De Morgan's two theorems (theorem 19) in its inverted form (see experiment 16C (q)) to equation [16.1]:

$$A \oplus B = \overline{\overline{(A \cdot \overline{B})} \cdot \overline{(\overline{A} \cdot B)}}$$ [16.2]

from which the circuit of Fig. 16.23 is derived. Essentially, the final OR gate of the circuit of Fig. 16.22 is replaced by a NAND gate with inverted inputs, as in experiment 16B (b), to make a slightly more economical circuit: there are still five gates, but now of only two different types.

g   Connect up the circuit of Fig. 16.23 using gates on the 7400 and 7404 (or 4011 and 4069) ICs. Investigate its logic, draw up a truth table and confirm that it behaves as an EOR gate.

h   To continue the process of simplification, other theorems of Boolean algebra can be used as follows. The number of the theorem, as listed in Table 16.7, that applies to each transformation is stated at the beginning of the line. Starting with equation [16.2]:

$$A \oplus B = \overline{\overline{(A \cdot \overline{B})} \cdot \overline{(\overline{A} \cdot B)}}$$

(Theorem 5)

$$= \overline{\overline{(0 + (A \cdot \overline{B}))} \cdot \overline{(0 + (\overline{A} \cdot B))}}$$

(Theorem 4)

$$= \overline{\overline{((A \cdot \overline{A}) + (A \cdot \overline{B}))} \cdot \overline{((\overline{B} \cdot B) + (\overline{A} \cdot B))}}$$

(Theorem 14)

$$= \overline{\overline{(A \cdot (\overline{A} + \overline{B}))} \cdot \overline{(B \cdot (\overline{A} + \overline{B}))}}$$

(Theorem 18)

$$A \oplus B = \overline{\overline{(A \cdot \overline{(A \cdot B)})} \cdot \overline{(B \cdot \overline{(A \cdot B)})}}$$ [16.3]

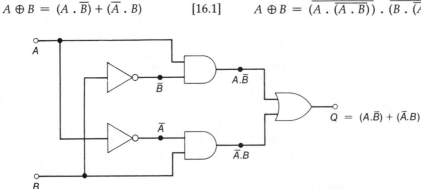

$$Q = (A.\overline{B}) + (\overline{A}.B)$$

Fig. 16.22   Experimental investigation of equation (16.1).

248

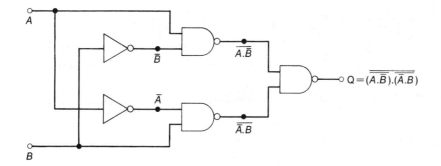

Fig. 16.23 Experimental investigation of equation (16.2).

The circuit that represents equation [16.3] is shown in Fig. 16.24. The number of gates has been reduced to four, but, of more importance, they are all of the same type, so this circuit may be constructed conveniently using only one IC.

i Connect up the circuit of Fig. 16.24 using all four NAND gates on one 7400 (or 4011) IC. Investigate its logic, draw up a truth table and confirm that it too behaves as an EOR gate.

PARITY GATE

j As the parity function is obtained by inverting the output of an EOR gate, we can write down three statements that describe the logic of the parity function simply by inverting equations [16.1], [16.2] and [16.3].

Thus: $\overline{A \oplus B} = \overline{(A \cdot \overline{B}) + (\overline{A} \cdot B)}$ [16.4]

$\overline{A \oplus B} = \overline{(A \cdot \overline{B}) \cdot (\overline{A} \cdot B)}$ [16.5]

$\overline{A \oplus B} = \overline{(A \cdot \overline{(A \cdot B)}) \cdot (B \cdot \overline{(A \cdot B)})}$ [16.6]

Circuits that represent these three equations can be constructed by adding a NOT gate to the output of each of the three circuits in Figs. 16.22, 16.23 and 16.24. Alternatively, the final OR gate of the circuit in Fig. 16.22 can be replaced by a NOR gate, and the final NAND gate in each circuit of Figs. 16.23 and 16.24 can be replaced by an AND gate.

k Connect up circuits that represent equations [16.4], [16.5] and [16.6] using appropriate ICs. Investigate the logic of each one, draw up truth tables, and confirm that they all behave as parity gates.

l All of these circuits contain at least two different types of gate. However, it is possible to construct a parity gate circuit from four gates of the same type, thereby using only one IC. Starting with equation [16.4]:

$$\overline{A \oplus B} = \overline{(A \cdot \overline{B}) + (\overline{A} \cdot B)}$$

(Theorem 18)

$$= \overline{\overline{\overline{(A + B)}} + \overline{(A + \overline{B})}}$$

(Theorem 2)

$$= \overline{(1 \cdot \overline{(A + B)}) + (1 \cdot \overline{(A + \overline{B})})}$$

(Theorem 8)

$$= \overline{(\overline{(\overline{B} + B)} \cdot \overline{(A + B)}) + (\overline{(A + \overline{A})} \cdot \overline{(A + \overline{B})})}$$

(Theorem 15)

$$= \overline{\overline{(B + \overline{(A \cdot \overline{B})})} + \overline{(A + \overline{(A \cdot \overline{B})})}}$$

(Theorem 19)

$$\overline{A \oplus B} = \overline{(B + \overline{(A + B)})} + \overline{(A + \overline{(A + B)})}$$ [16.7]

The circuit that represents equation [16.7] is shown in Fig. 16.25 (overleaf). Note its similarity to the circuit in Fig. 16.24.

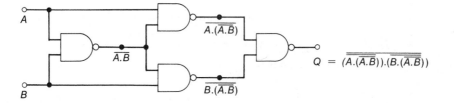

Fig. 16.24 Experimental investigation of equation (16.3).

249

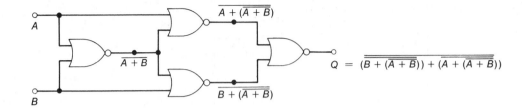

Fig. 16.25 Experimental investigation of equation (16.7).

m   Connect up the circuit in Fig. 16.25 using all four NOR gates on one 7402 (or 4001) IC. Investigate its logic, draw up a truth table and confirm that it behaves as a parity gate.

Set $A_2A_1 = 00$ and test the output Q for each possible value of B_2B_1. Repeat this procedure for $A_2A_1 = 01$, 10 and 11. Record your results in a 16-line truth table and confirm that $Q = 1$ only if $A_2A_1 = B_2B_1$.

n   Parity gates are used mainly to test for the identity of two binary numbers. Two such numbers are identical only if all pairs of corresponding bits are equal. In the circuit of Fig. 16.26 two parity gates test for the identity of two two-bit numbers, A_2A_1 and B_2B_1. The numbers are identical only if both $A_1 = B_1$ *and* $A_2 = B_2$. The parity gates test for these identities, and if both their outputs are at logical 1, the output Q will be at logical 1. Each of the two numbers can represent one of four decimal numbers from zero to three, so there are sixteen possible input combinations.

NOTES

p   Your record should include circuit diagrams of all the circuits you have assembled and tested.

FURTHER WORK

q   It is possible to construct EOR and parity gate circuits from only three gates, though not of the same type. Starting with equation [16.1] use the theorems of Boolean algebra to prove the following two equations:

$$A \oplus B = \overline{(A . B) + \overline{(A + B)}}$$

$$A \oplus B = \overline{(A . B)} . (A + B)$$

Connect up circuits that represent these equations and investigate their logic.

o   Connect up the circuit of Fig. 16.26 using two 7402 (or 4001) ICs to construct the parity gates as in Fig. 16.25, and one 7408 (or 4081) IC. If you have only three switched inputs, connect A_2 to an appropriate power supply rail since its value will be altered least often; on the other hand, B_1 will be altered most often.

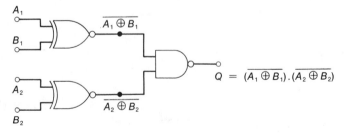

Fig. 16.26 Comparison of two two-bit binary numbers to test for their identity.

250

16E Addition and Subtraction
Investigation of circuits that combine binary digits arithmetically

APPARATUS REQUIRED

- circuit assembly board or system
- TTL power supply, $V_s = 5$ V (or CMOS alternative)
- 4 output indicators
- 7402, 7408 and 74283 TTL ICs (or 4001, 4081 and 4008 CMOS ICs)
- connecting wires

PRINCIPLES INVOLVED

a When two numbers are added, corresponding digits in each number are added to produce a *sum* term, which becomes one digit of the final answer, and a *carry* term, which is incorporated in the addition of the next pair of digits. For example, if 65 is to be added to 37, the least significant digits, 5 and 7, are added first to give a sum term of 2 and a carry term of 1, which must then be added to 6 and 3 to give a second sum term of 0 and a carry term of 1. This last carry term becomes part of the final answer (102), since there are no more pairs of digits to be considered. These principles apply equally to the addition of binary numbers and decimal numbers. The gate or circuit that adds the least significant bits, where there is no carry bit from any previous stage to consider, is called a *half adder*. The gate or circuit that adds all subsequent pairs of bits, where there is a carry bit from a previous stage to be included, is called a *full adder*, and can be constructed from two half adders. Fig. 16.27 shows the block symbols that are used to represent the half adder and full adder in circuit diagrams.

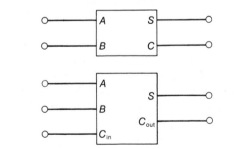

a

b

Fig. 16.27 Adders: conventional circuit symbols for **a** half adder and **b** full adder.

b Similar processes are involved in the subtraction of two numbers. Corresponding digits are subtracted to produce a *difference* term, which becomes one digit of the final answer, and a *borrow* term, which is incorporated in the subtraction of the next pair of digits. Consider again the same two numbers: to subtract 37 from 65, 7 is first

subtracted from 5 to give a difference term of 8 and a borrow term of 1. This borrow term represents the amount that had to be 'borrowed' to allow the first stage of subtraction to take place: in this example the borrowed 1 turned the 5 into 15, and must then be added to the 3 (or subtracted from the 6) to give a second difference term of 2 and a borrow term of 0. The final answer is therefore 028. We shall only consider here the gate or circuit that adds the least significant bits of two binary numbers, where there is no borrow bit from any previous stage to consider. This is called a *half subtractor*, the block symbol for which is shown in Fig. 16.28.

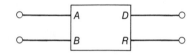

Fig. 16.28 Conventional circuit symbol for the half subtractor.

HALF ADDER

c Table 16.14 lists the sum and carry bits produced when two bits A and B are added. These are the outputs that a half adder is therefore required to generate. Comparison of this table with some of the truth tables of gates that you investigated in experiments 16A and 16D reveals that EOR and AND gates are the ones required to generate S and C, which are given by:

$$S = A \oplus B$$

$$C = A \cdot B$$

Table 16.14 Inputs and outputs of the half adder.

Inputs		Sum	Carry
A	B	S	C
0	0	0	0
0	1	1	0
1	0	1	0
1	1	0	1

d Any of the EOR gate circuits investigated in experiment 16D may be used with an AND gate to construct a half adder. It is not possible to use just four gates of the same type (on one IC), but it is possible to use three gates of two different types. In experiment 16D (q) you were asked to prove that:

$$A \oplus B = \overline{(A \cdot B) + (\overline{A + B})}$$

The circuit that represents this equation contains only three gates. Its output is $A \oplus B$, but it includes an AND gate whose output is $A \cdot B$, and it can therefore provide both the outputs required of a half adder (see Fig. 16.29, overleaf).

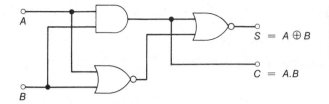

Fig. 16.29 Half adder constructed from only three gates.

$S = A \oplus B$

$C = A.B$

e Connect up the circuit of Fig. 16.29 using gates on the 7402 and 7408 (or 4001 and 4081) ICs. Investigate its logic by testing both outputs for all four input combinations, draw up a truth table and confirm that it behaves as a half adder.

FULL ADDER

Table 16.15 Inputs and outputs of the full adder.

Inputs		Carry in	Sum	Carry out
A	B	C_{in}	S	C_{out}
0	0	0	0	0
0	1	0	1	0
1	0	0	1	0
1	1	0	0	1
0	0	1	1	0
0	1	1	0	1
1	0	1	0	1
1	1	1	1	1

f Table 16.15 lists the sum and carry bits that a full adder must generate to add two bits A and B with a carry bit C_{in} from a previous stage. Essentially, the full adder is required to add three bits. A and B are first applied to a half adder, whose sum bit S_1 is then applied with C_{in} to a second half adder. The complete circuit is shown in Fig. 16.30. The final sum bit S is obtained from the second half adder. Notice that the output carry bit C_{out} is obtained by applying the carry bits from the two half adders to an OR gate: $C_{out} = C_1 . C_2$. There is no need to use a third half adder here: C_1 and C_2 cannot both be 1, since $S_1 = 0$ if $C_1 = 1$, and C_2 must be 0 if either of the two inputs to the second half adder, one of which is S_1, is 0.

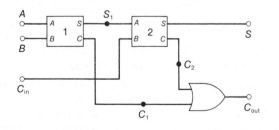

Fig. 16.30 Full adder constructed from two half adders and one OR gate.

g Connect up the circuit of Fig. 16.30 using the circuit of Fig. 16.29 to construct the two half adders and an OR gate on the 7432 (or 4071) IC. Investigate its logic by testing both outputs for all eight input combinations, draw up a truth table and confirm that it behaves as a full adder.

h The addition of two multi-bit numbers requires one full adder for each stage (i.e. for each pair of corresponding bits). Fig. 16.31 shows how three full adders are connected for the addition of two three-bit numbers $A_3 A_2 A_1$ and $B_3 B_2 B_1$. The least significant bits A_1 and B_1 are applied to the first full adder, which is only really used as a half adder, and must therefore have its carry input permanently connected to logical 0. (Remember that unconnected TTL inputs 'float' to logical 1.) The carry output from the third full adder provides the fourth sum bit: the computed sum is the binary number $S_4 S_3 S_2 S_1$.

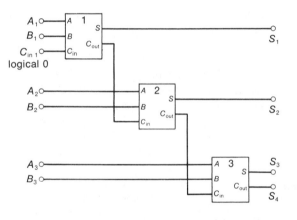

Fig. 16.31 Three-bit adder. The sum of $A_3 A_2 A_1$ and $B_3 B_2 B_1$ is $S_4 S_3 S_2 S_1$.

i To construct this circuit from individual gates, connecting them as in the circuits of Figs. 16.29 and 16.30, would require six AND gates, twelve NOR gates and three OR gates – all contained on no less than six ICs. Instead, we can use just one IC! The 74283 (or 4008) IC contains four full adders, whose arrangement and pin connections are shown in Fig. 16.32. Notice that carry bit connections between one full adder and the next are made internally. Unlike the logic gates on ICs that you have used so far, the full adders on this IC *must* be used in a particular sequence. The IC has therefore only two external carry bit connections: the carry input C_{in1} to the first full adder the carry output C_{out4} from the fourth. All four full adders on the IC must always be considered, even when less than four are needed. The fourth sum bit

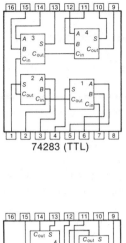

74283 (TTL)

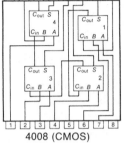

4008 (CMOS)

Fig. 16.32 Pin connections for four-bit full adder ICs.

in the circuit of Fig. 16.31 is obtained not from the third full adder, to whose carry output there is no access, but from the fourth full adder, which accepts the third's carry bit and passes it unchanged to its sum output, but does so only if its own input bits A_4 and B_4 are both 0. Like C_{in1} they must therefore be permanently connected to logical 0. These essential modifications to the circuit of Fig. 16.31 are shown in Fig. 16.33.

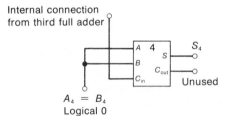

$A_4 = B_4$
Logical 0

Fig. 16.33 Necessary modifications to the circuit of Fig. 16.31 that allow the addition of two three-bit numbers with a four-bit adder IC.

j Connect up the adding circuit of Figs. 16.31 and 16.33 around the 74283 (or 4008) IC and use it to compute the sum of two three-bit numbers as follows. Set the value of $A_3A_2A_1$ at 101 (= 5) by connecting the three A inputs to appropriate power supply rails. Connect the three B inputs to switched inputs, so that the number $B_3B_2B_1$ can be varied easily, and the four sum outputs to indicators, with the least significant bit

(S_1) on the right-hand side. Remember to connect C_{in1}, A_4 and B_4 to logical 0. Vary the number $B_3B_2B_1$ from 000 (= 0) up to 111 (= 7) and record the indicated sums that the circuit computes. Are they all correct?

k Find out what happens if one of the inputs C_{in1}, A_4 or B_4 is at logical 1. Set $B_3B_2B_1$ at 010 (= 2) and check that the computed sum indicated is 0111 (= sum of 101 and 010). Set C_{in1} at logical 1 instead of logical 0 (with the 74283 you can just disconnect it, leaving it to float to logical 1) and note the effect on the indicated sum. Return C_{in1} to logical 0 and repeat the procedure with A_4 and B_4. Account for your observations.

HALF SUBTRACTOR

l Table 16.16 lists the difference and borrow bits that a half subtractor must generate to subtract one bit A from another B. Note that the difference bit D is 1 if either A or B (but not both) is 1 and that the borrow bit R is 1 only if both A and D are 1. (The third row of the table is also the only row in which both $A = 1$ and $B = 0$, and in which both $B = 0$ and $D = 1$.)

Table 16.16 Inputs and outputs of the half subtractor.

Inputs		Difference	Borrow
A	B	D	R
0	0	0	0
0	1	1	0
1	0	1	1
1	1	0	0

m Study Table 16.16 and write down logical expressions for D and R. (For R there are three alternatives, as implied in (l), but choose the first one – express R in terms of A and D.) Hence design, construct and test a half subtractor circuit, i.e. one that generates the two outputs D and R.

NOTES

n Your record should include diagrams of all the circuits you have assembled and tested.

o The circuit in Fig. 16.31, in which all the pairs of bits are applied simultaneously, is known as a *parallel adder*. In a *series adder* both numbers are applied one bit at a time as a series of pulses. For the addition of multibit numbers serial addition is simpler, requiring smaller circuits, but parallel addition is obviously much faster.

p In a digital computer, binary adding circuits form the basis of the arithmetic unit at the heart of the central processing unit (CPU). All arithmetic operations may be reduced to addition processes.

16F Elements of Memory

Investigation of the use of positive feedback to produce bistable multivibrators (flip-flops)

APPARATUS REQUIRED

- circuit assembly board or system
- TTL power supply, $V_s = 5$ V (or CMOS alternative)
- 2 output indicators
- 7400, 7402 and 7404 TTL ICs (or 4011, 4001 and 4069 CMOS ICs)
- 2 1.0 kΩ resistors
- connecting wires

INTRODUCTION

a A circuit whose output has two stable states, either of which can be maintained indefinitely, is called a bistable multivibrator (see experiment 15E). In digital applications, a bistable is often called a *flip-flop*, and the two stable states of the output are, of course, logical 0 and logical 1. The output may be changed from one state to the other by a particular operation that depends on the type of circuit. This operation may only be transitory, but in all types of bistable positive feedback ensures that its effect lasts until the next operation. Bistables are used as memory units in circuits like counters and registers. In this experiment you will investigate some of the simpler types of bistable.

NOT GATE BISTABLE

b A simple bistable consisting of a pair of cross-coupled NOT gates is shown in Fig. 16.34. The circuit has no real inputs, but it has two outputs, labelled here Q_A and Q_B, each of which is the output of one NOT gate and the input of the other. Since the output of a NOT gate is always complementary to its input, it follows that Q_A and Q_B must be complementary. One of them is adopted as the output of the circuit, and its logic level is then regarded as the state of the bistable.

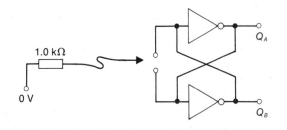

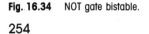

Fig. 16.34 NOT gate bistable.

c Connect up the circuit of Fig. 16.34 using two gates on the 7404 (or 4069) IC. Check that Q_A and Q_B are complementary when you switch on. Change the state of the bistable by briefly connecting whichever input is at logical 1 to logical 0, using the flying lead from the lower power supply rail via the 1.0 kΩ resistor. Repeat this procedure several times and confirm that the outputs are always complementary. Devise and test another means of changing the state of this bistable.

d Even this simple circuit can be regarded as a form of memory unit, though it has no practical applications because it has no inputs. The brief operation of setting one of the inputs at logical 0 is 'remembered' until the next operation. The part played in this circuit by positive feedback should be identified: when the input of one of the NOT gates is put at logical 0 its output must then be at logical 1, and feedback from this output to the input of the other gate changes its output to logical 0. This in turn is fed back to the input of the first gate, where the original logical 0 signal can be removed, leaving the circuit in a perfectly stable state. Note that by connecting the input of one gate to one of the power supply rails, to change the state of the circuit, you are simultaneously connecting the output of the other gate to that power supply rail. The 1.0 kΩ resistor is there to ensure that neither output is ever connected directly to one of the power supply rails.

SIMPLE NAND GATE BISTABLE

e Connect up the circuit of Fig. 16.35 using two gates on the 7400 (or 4011) IC. Note that this bistable has two inputs, A and B. Connect these to switched inputs, set them both at logical 0 and check that Q_A and Q_B are both at logical 1. Investigate the logic of the circuit by working through the two short sequences listed in Table 16.17, changing one input at a time. Copy and complete the table by recording your observations to form a truth table. Confirm that the input combination of $A = B = 1$ (reached in two stages from the starting combination of $A = B = 0$) produces an output combination that depends on the intermediate stage.

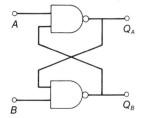

Fig. 16.35 Simple NAND gate bistable ($\overline{SR}$ bistable).

Table 16.17 Two short sequences with which to test the simple NAND gate bistable.

	A	B	Q_A	Q_B
Start	0	0	1	1
	1	0		
	1	1		
Restart	0	0	1	1
	0	1		
	1	1		

Table 16.18 A longer sequence of operations with which to test the simple NAND gate bistable.

	A	B	Q_A	Q_B
Start	0	0	1	1
1	1	0	0	1
2	1	1		
3	0	1		
4	1	1		
5	0	1		
6	1	1		
7	1	0		
8	1	1		
9	1	0		
10	1	1		
11	0	1		
12	1	1		

f This simple test illustrates the principle of *sequential* logic, as opposed to *combinational* logic. In the first five experiments of this chapter the output or outputs of every circuit have been entirely dependent on the existing combination of voltages applied to the circuits' inputs. However, with the circuit of Fig. 16.35 it is the sequence in which the inputs are applied that determines the output levels.

g The logic of the NAND gate can be used to explain the behaviour of the simple NAND gate bistable. When $A = B = 0$ the two NAND gates each have one of their inputs at logical 0, so their outputs must both be at logical 1. All other input combinations produce complementary outputs ($Q_A = \overline{Q}_B$), and it is certainly not possible for Q_A and Q_B to be at logical 0 simultaneously. (If one of the outputs is at logical 0, this is fed back to one of the inputs of the other NAND gate forcing its output to be at logical 1.) Your truth tables should show that when one of the two inputs is first set to logical 1 the output of that NAND gate changes to logical 0, and there is no further change to either output when the other input is switched to logical 1. In other words the circuit *remembers* which input has been most recently at logical 0, and indicates (stores) this by maintaining that gate's output at logical 1. Note that for this particular bistable this *store* state occurs when both inputs are at logical 1.

h Now follow the longer sequence listed in Table 16.18. Start, as before, with $Q_A = Q_B = 0$, and thereafter change one input at a time. Copy the table and complete it as a truth table. Record your observations also on a *timing diagram*, which consists of a series of related logic level–time graphs, though here each unit of time along the common time axis actually represents the interval between two successive operations in the sequence. See Fig. 16.36 (overleaf), which shows the levels of A and B throughout the sequence and the first two levels of Q_A and Q_B. Copy and complete the diagram to show the variations of Q_A and Q_B throughout the sequence.

i Your timing diagram should show more clearly how this bistable behaves. Apart from the initial state, where $A = B = 0$ and $Q_A = Q_B = 1$, the outputs are always complementary. The output state of the bistable can be changed only by switching one particular input from logical 1 to logical 0. The input that must be switched is the one to the NAND gate whose output is at logical 0, but once this has been done, further switching of this input between logical 0 and logical 1 has no effect. For example, the state of the bistable is changed at operation 3 when A is switched from 1 to 0. Further changes of A have no effect, and it is not until operation 7, when B is switched from 1 to 0, that the bistable next changes its state, after which further changes of B have no effect.

j Notice that Q_A and Q_B are complementary throughout the sequence except while $A = B = 0$, for which $Q_A = Q_B = 1$. This is a perfectly stable condition and the output levels it produces are quite predictable. It is referred to as the bistable's *indeterminate state*, since a sudden return from it to the rest or store state ($A = B = 1$) produces an output combination that depends on which of the two inputs is actually switched first; it is impossible, electrically or mechanically, to switch both of them at precisely the same time. If this state can be avoided, one of the bistable's two outputs can be adopted as *the* output

255

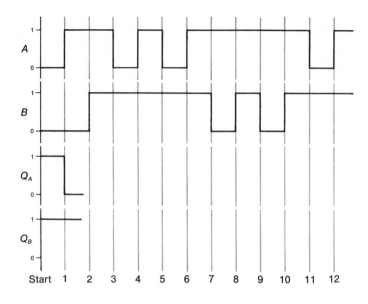

Fig. 16.36 Timing diagram for the sequence listed in Table 16.18.

Q and the other one is then always the output's complement $\overline{Q}$. It is therefore worth taking the trouble to ensure that a bistable is never allowed to be in its indeterminate state, which has no practical use anyway; we can then regard the two outputs as Q and $\overline{Q}$. For example, we might adopt Q_A as Q, and Q_B then becomes $\overline{Q}$.

k It is sometimes appropriate to consider the action of switching A from 1 to 0 (as at operation 3 in the sequence of Table 16.18) as one that *sets* the bistable, because this changes Q ($=Q_A$) from 0 to 1. Switching B from 1 to 0 (as at operation 7) then *resets* (or *clears*) the bistable by changing Q back to 0. The simple NAND gate bistable is therefore a form of *set-reset* (*SR*) bistable, though strictly this name is given to a bistable whose properties differ slightly from those of the simple NAND gate bistable (which is more accurately referred to as an $\overline{S}\,\overline{R}$ bistable – see (s)).

l The circuit forms the basis of a *de-bounced* switch, i.e. one in which the effects of mechanical contact bounce are eliminated. Fig. 16.37 shows the complete arrangement. The two resistors 'pull up' the inputs of A and B to logical 1 unless a direct connection to either is made from logical 0 through the switch S. (The resistors would not be necessary if TTL NAND gates are used as A, and B can be left to float to logical 1.) With the switch in the position shown, $A = 1$, $B = 0$ and $Q = 0$. While the switch is being moved across, $A = B = 1$, the bistable is in its store state, and Q remains at logical 0. When contact is made, $A = 0$ and Q is changed to logical 1, but if contact is lost and remade at A (representing 'bounce'), Q is not affected. Only a definite connection through the switch of B to logical 0 can return Q to logical 0.

m Connect up the circuit of Fig. 16.37 using a flying lead as the switch S. Confirm that Q is changed only when the switch is first moved across to either A or B, and that simulated bounces at these contacts have no effect.

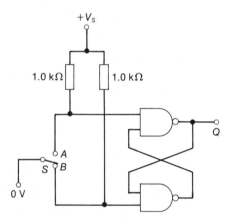

Fig. 16.37 Simple NAND gate bistable used as a de-bounced switch.

SR BISTABLE

Table 16.19 Two short sequences with which to test the *SR* bistable.

	A	B	Q_A	Q_B
Start	1	1		
	1	0		
	0	0		
Restart	1	1		
	0	1		
	0	0		

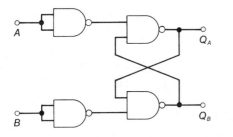

Fig. 16.38 *SR* bistable: cross-coupled NAND gates with inverted inputs.

n Investigate the logic of a NAND gate bistable whose inputs are inverted. Use the remaining two NAND gates on the 7400 (or 4011) IC, as shown in Fig. 16.38, and follow the two short sequences listed in Table 16.19. Copy the table and complete it to form a truth table.

o The circuit of Fig. 16.38 is called an *SR* bistable. When its inputs are both at logical 0 it is in its store state, and when they are both at logical 1 it is in its indeterminate state $(Q_A = Q_B = 1)$. In these two respects it differs from the simple NAND gate bistable of Fig. 16.35: the input conditions that determine these two states are reversed. Provided that the indeterminate state is avoided, Q_A can be adopted as the output Q of the *SR* bistable, which is set by switching A from 0 to 1 and reset by switching B from 0 to 1. The two inputs to the *SR* bistable are therefore normally labelled S and R. Fig. 16.39 shows the block symbol that is used to represent the *SR* bistable in circuit diagrams.

p Connect up the circuit of Fig. 16.40 using two NOR gates on the 7402 (or 4001) IC. Investigate its logic by following again the two short sequences of Table 16.19 and confirm that this circuit is also an *SR* bistable, with Q_B as Q and Q_A as $\overline{Q}$.

q Notice that the two *SR* bistables that you have investigated behave in the same way except when they are in their indeterminate states. This is yet another reason for avoiding this state. The input condition of $A = B = 1$ produces identical outputs in both circuits, but they are at logical 1 in the NAND gate version of Fig. 16.38 and at logical 0 in the NOR gate version of Fig. 16.40.

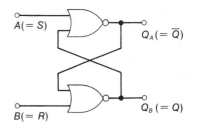

Fig. 16.40 *SR* bistable: cross-coupled NOR gates.

NOTES

r Your record should include diagrams of all the circuits you have assembled and tested.

s If, as has been suggested, the inputs to the circuit of Fig. 16.38 are relabelled S and R, the outputs of the two inverters on the left-hand side of the circuit become $\overline{S}$ and $\overline{R}$. These are applied to the simple NAND gate bistable (like that of Fig. 16.35) on the right-hand side, which is therefore referred to as an $\overline{S}\overline{R}$ bistable (Fig. 16.41). In the $\overline{S}\overline{R}$ bistable the outputs change when one of the inputs is switched low (from logical 1 to logical 0), while in the *SR* bistable the outputs changed when one of the inputs is switched high (from 0 to 1).

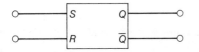

Fig. 16.39 Conventional circuit symbol for the *SR* bistable.

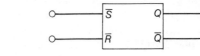
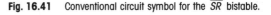

Fig. 16.41 Conventional circuit symbol for the $\overline{SR}$ bistable.

16G Synchronisation
Investigation of bistables controlled by clocking pulses

APPARATUS REQUIRED

- circuit assembly board or system
- TTL power supply, $V_s = 5$ V (or CMOS alternative)
- CRO (single beam adequate)
- 4 output indicators
- 2 7400, 7404 and 7408 TTL ICs (or 2 4011, 4069 and 4081 CMOS ICs)
- de-bounced switched input
- connecting wires

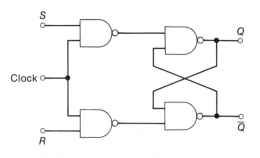

Fig. 16.42 Clocked SR bistable. A de-bounced switch should be used to provide the clock pulses.

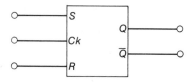

Fig. 16.43 Conventional circuit symbol for the clocked SR bistable.

INTRODUCTION

a When information from two or more sources has to arrive at a point in a large digital system, to interact or be combined in some way, it is essential that it all arrives simultaneously. The progress of the information through the system has to be controlled and must not be allowed to take place freely at a rate determined only by circuit parameters. Digital systems are therefore equipped with a *clock* that generates pulses at a steady rate. These pulses are fed to all component parts of the system, and any digital information that arrives at the inputs of a particular component will not be processed until the next clock pulse arrives, even if such processing involves nothing more than a direct transfer of information from the inputs of the component to its output. In this way operations in the system can be synchronised. Bistables are used to store and move bits of digital information and in this experiment you will investigate the principles of operation of bistables that have a clock input.

CLOCKED SR BISTABLE

b Consider the circuit shown in Fig. 16.42, which is a modified version of the SR bistable of Fig. 16.38. While the clock input is at logical 1 the first two NAND gates act as inverters, and the whole circuit behaves as an SR bistable. While the clock input is at logical 0 the outputs of the first two NAND gates are held at logical 1, irrespective of the levels of the other inputs, S and R; the second pair of NAND gates form a simple NAND gate ($\overline{SR}$) bistable, which is held in its store state (see experiment 16F (e), (g) and (s)). Hence the clock input can be used to control the circuit, which is called a clocked SR bistable. Its block symbol is shown in Fig. 16.43.

c In normal use a series of short clock *pulses* is applied to the clock input of the bistable. Fig. 16.44 shows how these are represented on timing diagrams. At the arrival of a pulse the clock input is raised from logical 0 to logical 1, and at the end of the pulse the clock input is returned to logical 0. The clock input is therefore at logical 1 only for the *duration* of the pulse, which is usually small compared with the time interval between two successive pulses. Signals applied to the S- and R-inputs only affect the outputs of the circuit when a clock pulse is present. The circuit does have an indeterminate state (see experiment 16F (j)), which is to be avoided, and as with the SR bistable it occurs when $S = R = 1$. But it only affects the outputs when the clock input is also at logical 1.

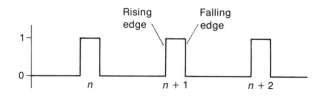

Fig. 16.44 Timing diagram showing part of a sequence of clock pulses. Three pulses are shown: the nth, $(n + 1)$th and $(n + 2)$th.

d If changes to S and R are made during the interval between two clock pulses, they may have no effect. At the arrival of a clock pulse the levels of S and R present at that time determine what happens to the circuit's output

Q. The subscript n is used to refer to a particular pulse. S_n and R_n are the levels of the two inputs at (i.e. just before) the arrival of the nth clock pulse, and Q_n is the level of the output. Q_{n+1} is the level of the output at the end of the clock pulse, which is therefore maintained until the arrival of the next $((n+1)$th$)$ clock pulse. If $Q_{n+1} = Q_n$, it means that Q has not been changed by the arrival or presence of the clock pulse. Note that it is the clock pulse's arrival (its *rising* edge) that causes the change, if any, to occur; this is why the duration of the clock pulse is not important and can be kept to a minimum. Table 16.20 summarises the behaviour of the clocked SR bistable.

Table 16.20 Truth table for the clocked SR bistable. Q_{n+1} is the level of the output at the end of the nth clock pulse. Its value depends on the levels S_n and R_n of the two inputs at the arrival of the nth clock pulse. Note that the indeterminate state $(S_n = R_n = 1)$ has not been included.

S	R	Q_n	Q_{n+1}	Interpretation
0	0	0	0	Q_n No change
		1	1	
0	1	0	0	0 No change if $Q_n = 0$
		1	0	inversion if $Q_n = 1$
1	0	0	1	1 Inversion if $Q_n = 0$
		1	1	no change if $Q_n = 1$

e Connect up the circuit of Fig. 16.42 using all four NAND gates on the 7400 (or 4011) IC, and use a debounced switched input to apply clock pulses manually (see experiment 16F (l)). Confirm that the switching of both S and R between logical 0 and logical 1 has no effect on the output Q unless the clock input is at logical 1. Check the results shown in Table 16.20 by applying all three input combinations while the clock input is at logical 0 and then note the effect on Q when the clock input is switched to logical 1 (simulating the arrival of a clock pulse). Test each input combination when $Q_n = 0$ and again when $Q_n = 1$.

D BISTABLE

f The circuit shown in Fig. 16.45 has only one input, labelled D, which is applied directly to the S-input of a clocked SR bistable, and whose complement is applied to the R-input. Note that this arrangement eliminates the

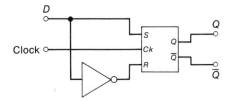

Fig. 16.45 *D* bistable based on clocked *SR* bistable.

indeterminate state of the clocked SR bistable, since S and R cannot both be at logical 1 simultaneously. This circuit is called a D bistable, and its block symbol is shown in Fig. 16.46.

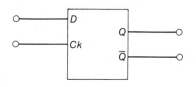

Fig. 16.46 Conventional circuit symbol for the *D* bistable.

g Connect up the circuit in Fig. 16.45 using all four NAND gates on the 7400 (or 4011) IC to construct the clocked SR bistable (as in Fig. 16.42), with a NOT gate on the 7404 (or 4069) IC. Set D at logical 0 and find out what happens to Q on the arrival of the next clock pulse. Do this for $Q_n = 0$ and $Q_n = 1$ and repeat with D set at logical 1. Draw up a two-line truth table to show how Q changes from Q_n to Q_{n+} on the arrival of the nth clock pulse.

h Your truth table should show that $Q = D$ immediately after the arrival of a clock pulse, and that Q retains this level when the clock pulse ends. Thus $Q_{n+1} = D_n$. Q is said to *latch* on to D, and this bistable is referred to as a *data-latch*. It is used to store a *bit* of digital information, in a readout or display for example. We can also think of its function in terms of providing *delay*: a bit applied to the D-input before the arrival of a clock pulse and present at its arrival is retained (as Q) after the clock pulse has ended. Note that the words 'data' and 'delay' both begin with the same letter that gives this bistable its name.

THE IDEAL BISTABLE

i It is worth considering at this stage what we require of a clocked bistable and what we have achieved so far. When a clock pulse arrives there are four possible consequences, any one of which might be required, depending on the application:

1	$Q_{n+1} = Q_n$	(no change)
2	$Q_{n+1} = 0$	
3	$Q_{n+1} = 1$	
4	$Q_{n+1} = \overline{Q}_n$	(inversion)

Each one should occur whichever level Q_n happens to be at – either logical 0 or logical 1. Since there are four possible input combinations that can be applied to a two-input bistable it would seem sensible to arrange for each consequence to result from a particular input combination.

Table 16.20 shows that the first three consequences can be achieved with the clocked *SR* bistable. And in (g) you will have found that effectively the second and third can be achieved with the *D* bistable. There remains the fourth consequence – a guaranteed inversion of the output, known as *toggling* – to be achieved. The one unused input combination $S_n = R_n = 1$ can be assigned for this, but in all the bistables investigated so far this has produced the indeterminate state with outputs that are not complementary.

SIMPLE *JK* BISTABLE

j The circuit shown in Fig. 16.47 has two inputs labelled *J* and *K*. Each one is applied to an AND gate whose other input is connected directly to one of the two outputs of the circuit as shown – another instance of feedback. If we assume that the outputs are complementary, then even when $J = K = 1$ the outputs *S* and *R* of the two AND gates cannot both be at logical 1, since one of them has an input at logical 0. The *SR* bistable part of this circuit can therefore never be in its indeterminate state, so the outputs *are* always complementary, which was the assumption with which we started. Note the rather circular nature of this argument: complementary outputs prevent *S* and *R* both being at logical 1, and if *S* and *R* are never both at logical 1 the outputs are always complementary!

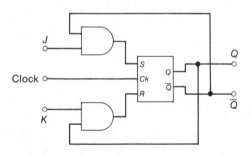

Fig. 16.47 Simple *JK* bistable based on clocked *SR* bistable.

k Connect up the circuit of Fig. 16.47 using all four NAND gates on the 7400 (or 4011) IC to construct the clocked *SR* bistable (as in Fig. 16.42), with two AND gates on the 7408 (or 4081) IC. Monitor both Q and Q̄. Check that the first three consequences in (i) can be achieved by applying the input combinations listed in Table 16.21. Remember to test each one with $Q_n = 0$ and $Q_n = 1$, and remember also that Q changes from Q_n to Q_{n+1} on *arrival* of the *n*th clock pulse.

Table 16.21 Simple *JK* bistable: the first three consequences of ideal bistable behaviour.

J_n	K_n	Q_{n+1}
0	0	Q_n
0	1	0
1	0	1

l To test for the fourth consequence, put $J = K = 1$, apply a long clock pulse and examine the two output indicators. Compare their brightness with another indicator that is fully on. What are the states of Q and Q̄? Display Q on the CRO with the time base set to give the shortest sweep time. Observe that Q is not constant but alternates between the two logic levels. Use the time base calibrations to measure the period of these alternations and hence calculate their frequency. Roughly how far does light travel during one period of alternation?

m The fourth consequence $(Q_{n+1} = \overline{Q}_n)$ *can* be achieved with the simple *JK* bistable, but these alternations arise because the process of inversion continues while the clock input is still at logical 1, i.e. for the duration of the clock pulse. No sooner is Q changed that it is changed back again and so on. The alternations take place at a rate determined by the speed at which electrical signals move around the circuit (along the wires and within the ICs).

n The simple *JK* bistable is of little more practical use than the *SR* bistable: the first three consequences can be achieved, but the fourth one could only be achieved properly if the clock pulses are very short. In some applications it may be possible to ensure that the duration of clock pulses is of the order of nanoseconds, but the ideal bistable should be able to produce the desired inversion of the output with clock pulses of any duration.

JK MASTER-SLAVE BISTABLE

o The circuit shown in Fig. 16.48 consists of an *SR* bistable added on to a simple *JK* bistable. The outputs of the *SR* bistable are fed back to the inputs of the *JK* bistable. The clock pulse is applied directly to the *JK* bistable, but its complement is applied to the *SR* bistable, which therefore receives a *rising* edge (interpreted there as the *start* of a clock pulse) at the *end* of the applied clock pulse. Conversely, at the start of the applied clock pulse the *SR* bistable receives a *falling* edge, interpreted there as

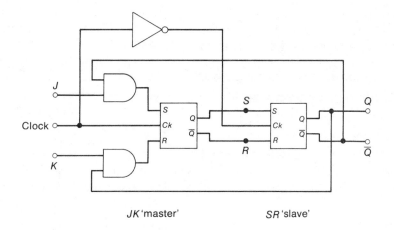

Fig. 16.48 *JK* master–slave bistable based on two clocked *SR* bistables.

the *end* of a clock pulse. When a clock pulse arrives, changes can occur at the outputs of the *JK* bistable (labelled *S* and *R* in Fig. 16.48) that depend on the levels of *J* and *K*. But these changes are not accepted by the *SR* bistable because its clock input is at logical 0. At the end of the applied clock pulse the clock input of the *SR* bistable rises to logical 1, and the new levels of *S* and *R* can now change the outputs Q and $\overline{Q}$. These changes are fed back to the inputs of the *JK* bistable, where they have no immediate effect because the clock input there has returned to logical 0. The alternations generated in the simple *JK* bistable when $J = K = 1$ do not occur here because Q and $\overline{Q}$ cannot change during the presence of an applied clock pulse, which is the only time that *S* and *R* *can* change. The *JK* bistable in this circuit is referred to as the *master* and the *SR* bistable then becomes the *slave*. The whole circuit is called a *JK* master–slave bistable, and its block symbol is shown in Fig. 16.49.

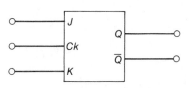

Fig. 16.49 Conventional circuit symbol for the *JK* master–slave bistable.

p Connect up the circuit of Fig. 16.48 using eight NAND gates on two 7400 (or 4011) ICs to construct the two clocked *SR* bistables (as in Fig. 16.42), with two AND gates on the 7408 (or 4081) IC and a NOT

gate on the 7404 (or 4069) IC. Monitor *S*, *R*, Q and $\overline{Q}$. Check that all four consequences in (i) can be achieved, by applying the input combinations listed in Table 16.22. Test each one with both levels of Q_n. Note that *S* and *R* change at the beginning of each clock pulse, but Q and $\overline{Q}$ change at the end.

Table 16.22 *JK* master–slave bistable: ideal bistable behaviour.

J_n	K_n	Q_{n+1}
0	0	Q_n
0	1	0
1	0	1
1	1	$\overline{Q}_n$

NOTES

q Your record should include diagrams of all the circuits you have assembled and tested.

r The *JK* master–slave bistable has all the properties of the ideal bistable, listed in (i). It differs in one respect from all the other clocked bistables investigated in this experiment in that the outputs change on the *falling* edge of the clock pulse. It can be regarded as the universal bistable to be used in many ways; as a *D* bistable, for example, with *J* as the *D*-input and a NOT gate used to put $K = \overline{J}$. All of the counting circuits in the next experiment are constructed from *JK* master–slave bistables. The words 'master–slave' are usually omitted so that it is commonly referred to as the *JK* bistable. (The simple *JK* bistable of Fig. 16.47 has no practical use except as part of the *JK* master–slave bistable.)

16H Counting
Investigation of the use of clocked bistables in counters

APPARATUS REQUIRED

- circuit assembly board or system
- TTL power supply, $V_s = 5$ V (or CMOS alternative)
- 4 output indicators
- 7400, 7402, 7408 and 2 7476 TTL ICs (or 4081, 4001, 4069 and 2 4027 CMOS ICs)
- de-bounced switched input
- pulse generator
- connecting wires

INTRODUCTION

a Of the four consequences considered in experiment 16G (i) for the ideal bistable, the last one, in which the output is inverted after the arrival of a clock pulse, is the one required in counting circuits. This inverting action is known as *toggling*. The *JK* master–slave bistable (referred to from now on simply as the *JK* bistable) is the only bistable of those investigated in experiment 16G in which toggling can be achieved, so it will be used in all the circuits of this experiment. ICs are available on which complete *JK* bistable circuits are formed and these are convenient to use. Unfortunately, however, the TTL and CMOS equivalents have quite different properties.

b The TTL 7476 IC contains two *JK* bistables. Its pin connections are shown in Fig. 16.50. Each bistable has two over-ride facilities called *preset* and *clear* that allow the output to be 'preset' to logical 1 or 'cleared' to logical 0, whatever its existing state and whether or not a clock pulse is present. Since unconnected TTL inputs float to logical 1 these two facilities are brought into operation by the application of logical 0 at the appropriate input, and if they are not required they can therefore be left unconnected. As with the *JK* bistable that you assembled from individual gates and tested in experiment 16G (p), changes to the outputs of the *JK* bistables on the 7476 IC occur at the *end* of a clock pulse; they are said to be triggered by *falling edges*. See Fig. 16.44.

c The CMOS equivalent to the 7476 IC is the 4027 IC. Its pin connections are also shown in Fig. 16.50. Its equivalent facilities to preset and clear are called *set* and *reset*, which are both brought into operation by the application of logical 1 to the appropriate input, which must otherwise be connected to logical 0. (Remember that CMOS inputs should never be left unconnected.) Changes to the outputs of the two *JK* bistables on the 4027 occur at the beginning of a clock pulse; they are triggered by *rising edges*.

T BISTABLE

d The circuit shown in Fig. 16.51 has only one input, labelled *T*, which is applied simultaneously to both *J*- and *K*-inputs of a *JK* bistable. This arrangement is called a *T* bistable, and its block symbol is shown in Fig. 16.52. Compare it with the *D* bistable of experiment 16G (f), in which *R* is put equal to $\bar{S}$ such that only the second and third consequences of the ideal bistable are possible. With the *T* bistable only the first and fourth consequences are possible, though in normal use the *T* bistable has its one input connected to logical 1 so that toggling action (output inversion) occurs, and this gives the bistable its name. (Toggling is sometimes called *triggering*, but both words begin with the same letter; a similar coincidence was noted at the end of experiment 16G (h).) Two versions of the circuit are shown to allow for the differences between TTL and CMOS ICs. Both circuits are falling edge triggered. In Fig. 16.51b the clock pulses applied to the *JK* bistable on the CMOS 4027 IC, which is rising edge triggered, are inverted, to make this effectively falling edge triggered.

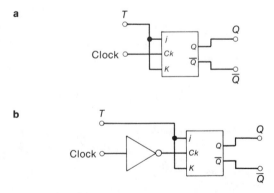

a

b

Fig. 16.51 *T* bistable based on *JK* bistable; both versions here are triggered by falling edges. **a** Arrangement suitable for TTL 7476 IC. **b** Arrangement suitable for CMOS 4027 IC; clock pulses are inverted by the NOT gate.

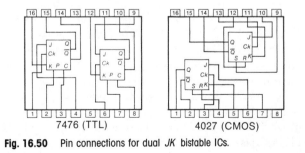

7476 (TTL)   4027 (CMOS)

Fig. 16.50 Pin connections for dual *JK* bistable ICs.

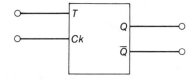

Fig. 16.52 Conventional circuit symbol for the *T* bistable (which could be triggered by either rising or falling edges). This symbol will be used in all subsequent circuit diagrams where it is intended that *J*- and *K*-inputs are joined, as in Fig. 16.51a or b.

e Connect up the arrangement in Fig. 16.51a using one *JK* bistable on the 7476 IC (or 4027 IC, with clock pulses applied via a NOT gate on the 4069 IC as in Fig. 16.51b). Connect the *T*-input to logical 1, apply a series of de-bounced clock pulses and note how the output *Q* changes at the end of every clock pulse.

f Fig. 16.53 shows the relationship between *Q* and the clock input. One complete output pulse is produced for every two input clock pulses. The *T* bistable therefore divides the number of clock pulses by two, and by doing so it provides the basis of a binary counter.

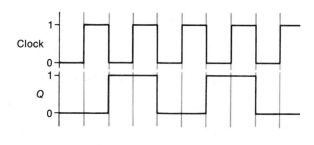

Fig. 16.53 Timing diagram for the *T* bistable (*T* = 1).

BINARY COUNTERS

g Fig. 16.54 shows how two *T* bistables are connected together to form a 2-bit binary up-counter, in which the output Q_1 of the first bistable is the least significant bit and is applied (inverted in Fig. 16.54b) to the clock input of the second bistable. Q_1 changes once for every clock pulse and therefore undergoes a complete cycle for every two clock pulses, while Q_2 changes once for every complete cycle of Q_1 and therefore undergoes a complete cycle for every two cycles of Q_1. Table 16.23 shows how the outputs change with successive clock pulse ends. Only four output combinations are possible, representing the decimal numbers 0, 1, 2 and 3, and this little sequence is repeated continuously while clock pulses are applied.

Table 16.23 Outputs of a 2-binary up-counter.

Clock pulse	Q_2	Q_1
Start	0	0
1	0	1
2	1	0
3	1	1
4	0	0
5	0	1
6	1	0
7	1	1
8	0	0
9	0	1

h The circuit of Fig. 16.54a is suitable only if falling edge triggered bistables, such as those on the TTL 7476 IC, are used. The *JK* bistables on the CMOS 4027 IC are triggered by rising edges, and if they are to be used to construct an up-counter two modifications are necessary. In addition to clock pulse inversion, which wasn't essential in Fig. 16.51b but is here, the clock input of the second bistable must be connected to $\overline{Q}_1$ and not to Q_1. These differences are shown in Fig. 16.54b.

i Connect up the circuit of Fig. 16.54a using the two *JK* bistables on the 7476 IC (or the 4027 IC with a NOT gate on the 4069 IC as in Fig. 16.54b). Connect the two outputs to indicators with the least significant bit (Q_1) on the right-hand side. Apply a series of de-bounced clock pulses and check that the outputs follow the correct sequence. Draw a timing diagram to show the relationship between Q_1, Q_2 and the clock pulses. Investigate the effect of not using a de-bounced switch to supply clock pulses.

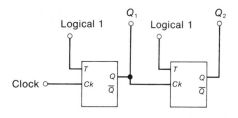

a Arrangement suitable for falling edge triggered *JK* bistables like those on the TTL 7476 IC; remember that unconnected TTL inputs float to logical 1, so the *J*- and *K*-inputs can be left open.

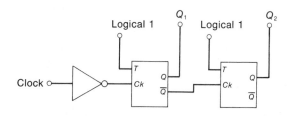

b Arrangement suitable for rising edge triggered *JK* bistables like those on the CMOS 4027 IC.

Fig. 16.54 Binary up-counter constructed from two *T* bistables.

263

j   Modify your circuit to count down instead of up. (Hint: consider the variation of the two inverted outputs $\overline{Q}_2$ and $\overline{Q}_1$ in the circuit you already have.)

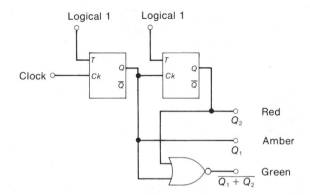

Fig. 16.55   Simple traffic light sequence generator based on 2-bit binary up-counter. This arrangement is suitable if falling edge triggered *JK* bistables, like those on the TTL 7476 IC, are used; remember also that unconnected TTL inputs float to logical 1, so the *J*- and *K*-inputs can be left open. Modify the circuit according to Fig. 16.54b if *JK* bistables triggered by leading edges, like those on the CMOS 4027 IC, are to be used.

SEQUENCE GENERATORS

k   Binary counters can be used to operate repeated sequences, of which perhaps the most familiar example is the standard traffic light sequence. This has four stages and uses lights of three different colours. If a light on is represented by logical 1, the sequence can be tabulated as in Table 16.24. Several deductions can be made: amber changes at every stage; red is on for two successive stages and off for the other two; green is on only when the other two are off.

Table 16.24   Traffic light sequence.

Stage	Red	Amber	Green
1	1	0	0
2	1	1	0
3	0	0	1
4	0	1	0

l   The four output stages of the 2-bit binary up-counter of Fig. 16.54 can be matched to this sequence (see Table 16.23). Q_1 changes at every stage and is therefore an obvious candidate to represent amber. Similarly, Q_2 ought to represent red. These two colours can therefore be allocated as shown in Table 16.25. Three combinations are produced in the correct order, so the first line of the table must be allocated to the remaining stage – green only. A NOR gate can be used to provide a logical 1 only when Q_2 and Q_1 are both at logical 0. The complete circuit is shown in Fig. 16.55.

Table 16.25   Allocation of two colours to the outputs of the 2-bit binary up-counter.

Q_2	Q_1	Colours
0	0	
0	1	Amber
1	0	Red
1	1	Red and amber

m   Connect up the circuit of Fig. 16.55 using two *JK* bistables on the 7476 IC and a NOR gate on the 7402 IC (or use the 4027, 4069 and 4001 ICs after referring to Fig. 16.54b). Connect the three outputs to indicators (suitably coloured and positioned, if possible). Apply a series of de-bounced clock pulses and check that the correct sequence is followed.

n   If clock pulses were to be applied to this circuit from a continuous source, such as a pulse generator, all four stages of the sequence would have the same duration. In the real traffic light sequence the two stages in which amber is on are much shorter than the other two. To make a more realistic sequence, we therefore require a generator with more than four output conditions, which can then be allocated unevenly.

o   Connect three *T* bistables together to form a 3-bit binary up-counter; use two 7476 (or two 4027 and one 4069) ICs. Draw up a table to show how the three outputs change with successive clock pulses and check your predictions experimentally. Adapt your circuit to generate the traffic light sequence, allocating the eight stages of the counting sequence such that red and green are each on alone for three-eighths of the time.

DECADE COUNTER

p   Connect four *T* bistables together to form a 4-bit binary up-counter; use two 7476 (or two 4027 and one 4069) ICs. Connect the four outputs to indicators with the least significant bit (Q_1) on the right-hand side and the most significant bit (Q_4) on the left. Draw up a table to show how the four outputs Q_4, Q_3, Q_2 and Q_1 change with successive clock pulses and check your predictions experimentally.

q   The 4-bit binary up-counter counts up to and including the number 15 ($= 1111$ in binary) before automatically restarting. But a decimal counter is required to count only up to and including the number 9 ($= 1001$). As soon as the number 10 ($= 1010$) is reached the outputs must all be returned to logical 0 to restart the count. This is achieved by applying logical 0 to the clear inputs of the *JK* bistables on the 7476 ICs (or logical 1 to the reset inputs of the *JK* bistables on the 4027 ICs). The binary number 1010 is the first in the sequence that has a 1 as both its first (most significant) and third bits. A suitable gate is therefore used to detect when both Q_4 and Q_2 are at logical 1, and its output is applied to the clear (or reset) inputs of the second, third and fourth bistables. Fig. 16.56 shows the complete circuit. Note that Q_3 is already at logical 0 but it would be changed to logical 1 by the resetting of Q_2 were the clear signal not applied to its bistable as well. Q_1 is not affected by any earlier bistable, so the clear signal does not have to be applied to the first bistable.

r Adapt your 4-bit binary counter to become a decade counter by adding a NAND gate on the 7400 IC (or an AND gate on the 4081 IC) as shown in Fig. 16.56. Apply clock pulses continuously (from a pulse generator) and check the performance of the circuit. Find out what happens if the clear (or reset) signal is not applied to the third bistable.

s Modify your circuit to become a duodecimal counter, i.e. to count up to and including the number 11 (= 1011) in the system of numbers based on 12 (= 1100).

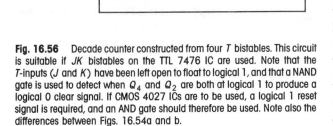

Fig. 16.56 Decade counter constructed from four *T* bistables. This circuit is suitable if *JK* bistables on the TTL 7476 IC are used. Note that the *T*-inputs (*J* and *K*) have been left open to float to logical 1, and that a NAND gate is used to detect when Q_4 and Q_2 are both at logical 1 to produce a logical 0 clear signal. If CMOS 4027 ICs are to be used, a logical 1 reset signal is required, and an AND gate should therefore be used. Note also the differences between Figs. 16.54a and b.

NOTES

t Your record should include diagrams of all the circuits you have assembled and tested.

u All the counting circuits you have investigated in this experiment are called *asynchronous* systems, because the bistables in them do not all change 'synchronously', i.e. under the influence of a single supply of clock pulses. They are sometimes also called *ripple* counters, since a change to the least significant bit can cause a change to 'ripple through' some or all of the subsequent outputs. For example, in the 4-bit binary up-counter, when the number 1111 has been reached, the next clock pulse causes all the outputs to change – they may appear to do so simultaneously, but of course they really change one by one; the change of Q_1 causes Q_2 to change, which then causes Q_3 to change, which then causes Q_4 to change.

16I Storing
Investigation of the use of clocked bistables in shift registers

APPARATUS REQUIRED

- circuit assembly board or system
- TTL power supply, $V_s = 5$ V (or CMOS alternative)
- 4 output indicators
- 7404, 7432 and 2 7476 TTL ICs (or 4069, 4071 and 2 4027 CMOS ICs)
- de-bounced switched input
- connecting wires

INTRODUCTION

a One of the clocked bistables investigated in experiment 16G was the *D* bistable, with which the second and third consequences of the ideal bistable can be achieved; remember that the *D* bistable has only one input. In this experiment you will construct chains of *D* bistables to form *shift registers*, circuits that are used to store a series of bits.

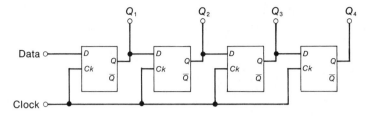

Fig. 16.57 Shift register constructed from four D bistables.

SHIFT REGISTER

b Consider the chain of D bistables shown in Fig. 16.57. The output of each bistable is applied to the D-input of the next one in the chain, and the same supply of clock pulses is applied to all four. After one clock pulse the bit at the circuit's data input will have been transferred to the output Q_1 of the first bistable. (Whether this transfer occurs at the beginning or end of the clock pulse depends on the type of bistable being used.) The second clock pulse transfers the bit to Q_2, and after the fourth clock pulse it will have reached Q_4. Meanwhile, other bits will have been 'shifted' along behind it. This circuit is called a shift register.

c Although special ICs containing D bistables are available, it is a simple matter to construct D bistables from one of several other types of bistable, including the SR bistable (as in experiment 16G (f)) and the JK bistable, which will be used here. Refer to experiment 16H (b), where details of TTL and CMOS ICs that each contain two JK bistables are given. Fig. 16.58 shows how the shift register can be constructed from four JK bistables. The output Q of each bistable is applied to the J-input of the next one, but instead of using an inverter to apply $\overline{Q}$ to the K-input, each K-input is fed from the previous $\overline{Q}$-output, though an inverter must be used before the first bistable, as shown. Note also that the clear inputs of the four bistables are joined together to a common clear input, to which is applied an appropriate signal whenever the register needs to be cleared.

> **d** Connect up the circuit in Fig. 16.58 using four JK bistables on two 7476 ICs and a NOT gate on the 7404 IC (or use two 4027 and one 4069 ICs). Connect switched logic inputs to the data input of the circuit and to the clear input, and monitor all four outputs. Clear the register and apply logical 1 to the data input. Apply one de-bounced clock pulse and note how the bit is transferred to Q_1. Switch the data input back to logical 0, apply three more pulses and note how the bit is shifted along one stage by each clock pulse. Try shifting other bit combinations, e.g. a single logical 0 amongst a train of logical 1 bits.

RING COUNTER

e If the output Q_4 is connected to the data input, each bit, once it reaches the end, will start going through the register again – an arrangement known as a *ring counter*. To allow bits from both the data input and Q_4 to enter the first bistable, they are applied to an OR gate, whose output is then connected to the first bistable, as shown in Fig. 16.59. (Otherwise it becomes necessary to leave Q_4 open, enter the four bits, disconnect the data input and reconnect Q_4 every time a new combination of four bits has to be entered.)

> **f** Adapt your shift register to become a ring counter by adding an OR gate on the 7432 (or 4071) IC as shown in Fig. 16.59. Test the circuit by entering various 4-bit combinations (at the end of which the data input must be switched to logical 0) and note how they circulate continuously as clock pulses are applied.

NOTES

g Your record should include diagrams of both of the circuits you have assembled and tested.

h Shift registers are called *synchronous* systems, because all the bistables that form the chain are fed from the same supply of clock pulses, and therefore all react simultaneously.

i The type of shift register that you have assembled is called *series in parallel out* because the bits are entered one after the other (in a series) but can be read or extracted together (in parallel) by a parallel adder, for example; see experiment 16E (o). Other types of shift register exist. One application of this type that you may have come across is in the display of a calculator: with most modern calculators digits appear at one end of the display when first entered, but are shifted along as succeeding digits are entered.

j Ring counters are used in advertising displays to produce moving slogans.

266

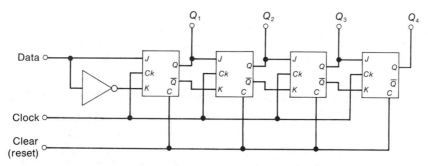

Fig. 16.58 Shift register constructed from four *JK* bistables, connected as a chain of *D* bistables. This circuit is suitable if *JK* bistables on either TTL 7476 ICs or CMOS 4027 ICs are used. Note, however, that on the 7476 the bistables are cleared by the application of logical 0 to their common clear input (which should otherwise be left switched to logical 1), but on the 4027 the bistables are cleared by the application of logical 1 to their common reset input (which should otherwise be left switched to logical 0).

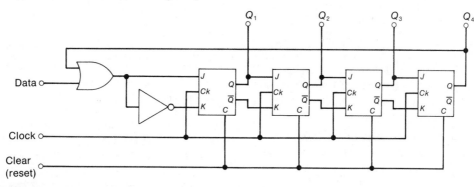

Fig. 16.59 Shift register adapted as a ring counter.

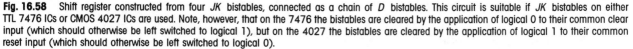

16J Timing
Investigation of the use of positive feedback in monostable and astable multivibrators

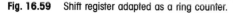

APPARATUS REQUIRED

- circuit assembly board or system
- TTL power supply, $V_s = 5$ V (or CMOS alternative)
- 2 output indicators
- dual trace CRO
- 2 7400 TTL ICs (or 2 4011 CMOS ICs)
- 2 1.0 µF, 2 470 µF and 2 4700 µF capacitors
- 2 1.0 kΩ resistors
- connecting wires

INTRODUCTION

a   Multivibrators are circuits in which the output has two permitted states. There are three types, and an explanation of each is given in experiment 15E. The digital version of the bistable multivibrator was introduced in experiment 16F and used extensively in various forms in the experiments that followed. Here we are concerned with digital versions of the other two: the *monostable*, which has one stable and one unstable state, and the *astable*, in which neither state is stable. Each type includes a capacitor–resistor (CR) network; see experiment 15E (d). The monostable produces a single pulse, and can be used for timing processes. The astable produces a series of pulses, and can therefore be used as a pulse generator.

MONOSTABLE MULTIVIBRATOR

b   Connect up the circuit shown in Fig. 16.60 (overleaf) using two NAND gates, labelled X and Y, on the 7400 (or 4011) IC. Connect the trigger input to the upper power supply rail ($+V_s$) via the 1.0 kΩ resistor as shown (or, if you are using the TTL 7400 IC you can leave this input unconnected to float to logical 1). Observe that the circuit's output Q is at logical 0. Trigger the circuit by briefly connecting the flying lead from the lower power supply rail (0 V) to the trigger input, and observe how this causes Q to change to logical 1. What happens after a few seconds?

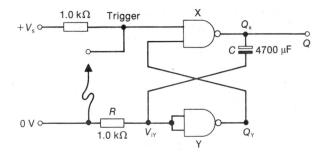

Fig. 16.60 Monostable multivibrator.

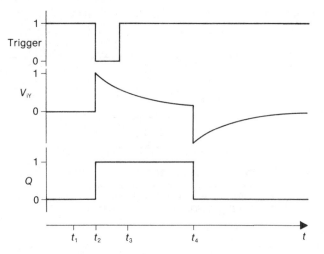

Fig. 16.61 Voltage–time variations in the monostable multivibrator.

c   The output of the monostable is a single pulse whose duration depends on various circuit parameters. The operational sequence runs as follows.

1. Normally Q $(=Q_X) = 0$ and the input of gate Y is also at logical 0, to which it is connected through the resistor R. Gate Y is an inverter so its output $Q_Y = 1$. Both inputs to gate X are at logical 1 so Q remains at logical 0. This condition is perfectly stable and there exists across the capacitor C no p.d.

2. The trigger input is set briefly to logical 0. This forces Q to rise instantly to logical 1 (since the output of a NAND gate can only be at logical 0 if both of its inputs are at logical 1). To maintain the zero p.d. across C, initially at least, the voltage V_{iY} of plate B of the capacitor must also rise to logical 1, which causes Q_Y to fall to logical 0.

3. At the end of the trigger pulse the trigger input reverts to logical 1. However, Q remains at logical 1 because logical 0 has been fed back from the output of gate Y to the other input of gate X. Meanwhile, as C discharges through R, V_{iY} decays exponentially.

4. The monostable pulse ends when V_{iY} (i.e. the input of the inverter, gate Y) decays to the threshold switching level of gate Y. Q_Y is then changed to logical 1, and as both inputs to gate X are now once more at logical 1, Q returns to its stable state of logical 0.

The variations with time of the trigger input, V_{iY}, and Q during this sequence are shown in Fig. 16.61. The times t_1, t_2, etc. marked along the t-axis are those at which the events 1, 2, etc. listed above occur. Note how V_{iY} drops at the end of the pulse, to maintain the p.d. across C, before rising exponentially back to logical 0. This gives the circuit a 'dead time'. The duration of the pulse depends mainly on the time constant CR.

d   Investigate the effect on the pulse of the following, in turn: (i) increase C by connecting another 4700 μF capacitor in parallel with the one shown;   (ii) decrease R by connecting another 1.0 kΩ resistor in parallel with the one shown;   (iii) apply a long trigger pulse, i.e. one that lasts longer than the normal duration of a pulse;   (iv) apply a second trigger pulse very shortly after the output pulse has ended. Use Fig. 16.61 to explain your observations.

ASTABLE MULTIVIBRATOR

e   Connect up the circuit shown in Fig. 16.62 using two NAND gates, labelled X and Y, on the 7400 (or 4011 IC). Put $C_X = C_Y = 470$ μF and monitor both Q_X and Q_Y. Observe that they both alternate but are always complementary.

f   The sequence of events that produces these alternations runs as follows.

1. Let us start at the instant that Q_X changes to logical 1. This voltage rise is transferred through the capacitor C_X, across which there can be no p.d. while it is unchanged. Both NAND gates act as inverters, so Q_Y drops to logical 0, and this voltage drop is transferred through C_Y to the input of gate X, whose output is therefore maintained at logical 1.

2. As C_X discharges through the resistor R_X, across which a p.d. has been established, the voltage V_{iY} of the input to gate Y decays exponentially.

3. When this voltage decays to the threshold switching level of gate Y, Q_Y suddenly changes to logical 1. This voltage rise is transferred across the uncharged C_Y to the input of gate X, whose output then drops to logical 0.

4. C_Y discharges through R_Y, and the voltage V_{iX} of the input to gate X decays exponentially to continue the process.

g   Increase the frequency of the astable by putting $C_X = C_Y = 1.0$ μF, and simultaneously display Q_X on the cro with first V_{iX}, then Q_Y, and then V_{iY}. Remember to connect the CRO ground to the lower power supply rail. Observe how V_{iX} and V_{iY} rise and fall exponentially. Sketch graphs to show the simultaneous variations with the time of V_{iX}, Q_X, V_{iY} and Q_Y. Mark along the t-axis times t_1, t_2, etc. at which the events 1, 2, etc. listed in (f) occur.

NOTES

h Your record should include labelled circuit diagrams.

i Monostable and astable multivibrators based on CMOS ICs are both more versatile than their TTL equivalents, because much longer periods may be obtained. The relatively low input impedance of TTL gates effectively limits the resistance (in the CR network) that can be used with them to about 1.0 kΩ. Much higher resistances can be used with CMOS gates.

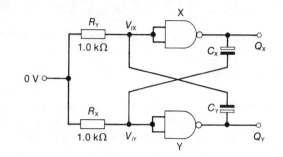

Fig. 16.62 Astable multivibrator. Values for the capacitances C_X and C_Y may be found in the text: see (e) and (g).

17 PROBLEM EXPERIMENTS

INTRODUCTION

This section provides a selection of problem experiments taken from recent A-level practical examination papers. The questions are taken from the following Examining Boards:

The Associated Examining Board (AEB)
Joint Matriculation Board (JMB)
Oxford and Cambridge Schools Examination Board (O & C)
University of Cambridge Local Examinations Syndicate (C)
University of London School Examinations Board (L)
University of Oxford Delegacy of Local Examinations (OLE)

The experiments are designed to take approximately 90 minutes to complete with the exception of the AEB practicals, which are of 45 minutes duration. The experiments are divided into the following categories:

measurement (2 experiments)
mechanical properties of matter (4 experiments)
oscillations and waves (6 experiments)
geometrical and physical optics (8 experiments)
thermal properties of matter (3 experiments)
current electricity (4 experiments)
capacitance (1 experiment)
semiconductor devices (2 experiments)

These problem experiments will either be set as class exercises as you complete each group of topics, or as part of your revision program for the practical examination. Unlike all the other practicals in this book, no hints are provided other than those given in the questions.

Measurement

17A MEASUREMENT OF THE RADIUS OF CURVATURE OF A CONCAVE SURFACE

You are to estimate the radius of curvature of the concave surface of each of two watch glasses by three methods.

a) Take the larger glass and set it level, concave upwards, supported on the bench by a ring of Plasticine. Measure and record the period T of the motion of the ball-bearing (i) when released from rest to oscillate along the diameter of the glass, and (ii) when released with a tangential velocity so as to move in a circle.

Calculate the radius of curvature R of the inner glass surface, using the relation:

$$T = 2\pi \sqrt{\frac{7(R-r)}{5g}}$$

where T is the average period for motions (i) and (ii). Measure the radius r of the ball-bearing with a micrometer screw guage. Take g to be 9.8 m s^{-2}.

Repeat your experiment for the smaller glass.

Suggest which is the largest contribution to the error in your results for R and give an estimate of the total error.

b)

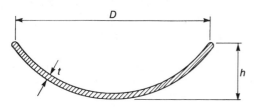

Fig. 17.1

Measure for each glass the dimensions D, h, and t.

Calculate the radius of curvature R, using the relation:

$$4(h-t)(2R-h+t) = D^2$$

Suggest which is the largest contribution to the error in your results for R and give an estimate for the total error.

c) Find the self-conjugate point (where image and object coincide) for each glass operating as a concave mirror. Use the tip of the pin provided as the object. The radius of curvature R is the distance between the self-conjugate point and the centre of the mirror (glass) reflecting surface. (You may find that placing a dark surface behind the glass makes the reflected image more visible.)

Suggest which is the largest contribution to the error in your results for R and give an estimate of the total error.

(O & C 1980)

17B FLOW OF LIQUID THROUGH A BURETTE

Join the end of the burette to the capillary tube using the small piece of tubing. Clamp the burette vertically and the capillary tube horizontally. The capillary tube should be high enough for a beaker to be placed underneath to collect water. Tie a short piece of thread round the tube about 5 mm from the end and let the end of the thread hang into the beaker so that water drips into the beaker as it leaves the tube. With the burette tap closed fill the burette to above the 0 ml mark. Open the tap fully and determine the time t, in seconds, taken for the level of the water to fall from the 0 ml to the 5 ml mark. **Without altering the tap** fill the burette up again and repeat, finding the time for the level to fall from the 0 ml to **six** other marks. Measure the vertical height in cm, h, from the bench top to the 5 ml mark and to each subsequent mark used. Measure the vertical height in cm, h_0, from the bench top to the centre of the bore of the capillary tube.

Plot a graph having $\log_e (h - h_0)$ as ordinate and t as abscissa.

Find the gradient G of the graph and evaluate $\log_e 2/G$.

Explain

a) how you ensured that the burette was vertical and that the capillary tube was horizontal,

b) any precautions you took to reduce errors in the measurement of t.

(JMB 1979)

Mechanical Properties of Matter

17C BENDING OF A LOADED METRE RULE

You are required to investigate the bending of a metre rule loaded at its end.

Use the G-clamp and blocks of wood to clamp the metre rule along the top of the bench so that 90.0 cm of the rule projects over the end of the bench. Hang a mass m ($=100$ g) from the hook at the end of the rule and determine the vertical depression y_{90} of the end of the rule due to this load. Record the value of y_{90} for a total of **five** different values of m. Repeat the experiment but this time determine the vertical depression y_{80} with 80.0 cm of the rule projecting over the end of the bench, again using a total of **five** different values of m.

Using a single set of axes having y as ordinate and m as abscissa, plot a graph of each set of readings.

Determine the gradients G_{90} and G_{80} of the two graphs. (If your graphs depart from linearity, then find the gradients of the initial linear sections.)

Evaluate $\dfrac{G_{90}}{G_{80}}$.

Draw and label a diagram of your experimental arrangement.

Explain how you used the wire (or pin) and plane mirror.

(JMB 1983)

17D OSCILLATIONS OF A HACKSAW BLADE

In this experiment, you are asked to make measurements of a vibrating system, and use the results to determine the value of the Young modulus of the material of a strip (hacksaw blade).

The vibrating system consists of a horizontal hacksaw blade with a mass M fixed to one end and the other end clamped so that the face of the blade is vertical, as shown in Fig. 17.2. When the mass is displaced through a small horizontal distance at right angles to the length of the blade and released, the system performs oscillations of period T. The relationship between T, M, and the Young modulus E of the material of the hacksaw blade is:

$$T^2 = \left(\frac{16\pi^2 M}{bd^3 E}\right) x^3$$

where b is the breadth, d is the thickness and x is the vibrating length (distance between clamped end and centre of mass of M) of the blade.

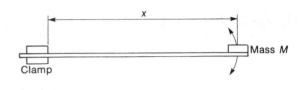

Fig. 17.2 (Plan view)

a) Measure the breadth b and the thickness d of the blade, at a number of positions along the blade, and obtain the average values.

b) i) Set up the vibrating system, and for a series of values of x from 0.15 m up to 0.30 m (that is, up to the highest practical value for x), measure the period T.

ii) Plot a graph of T^2 against x^3.

iii) Determine the gradient of the graph, and use it to obtain a value for E. What is the accuracy of your result?

(The value of the mass M is given to you.)

c) Set up the blade, as best you can, so that the unloaded blade would have its face horizontal, as illustrated in Fig. 17.3, with x_0 about 0.25 m. Measure the period of the oscillations which occur when the mass is given a small vertical displacement and released.

d) Compare the value of the period observed in (c) with that obtained for the same value of x using the results of (b) (i). How is the difference, if any, accounted for?

e) List the experimental precautions taken in your measurements, and describe the difficulties, if any, encountered and how you overcame them.

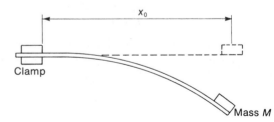

Fig. 17.3 (Side View)

(OLE 1983)

17E EXTENSION OF A SPRING

1. Count the number of turns, N, on the spring provided.

2. With the turns of the spring in close contact, measure the length, l, of the spring. Hence deduce the radius, r, of the wire.

3. The radius, R, of the spring is written on a piece of card. Record its value.

4. Attach the scale pan or weight hanger to the spring and suspend the spring vertically so that the extension, x, produced by an additional mass, M, can be measured.

5. Measure x for various values of M, without exceeding an extension $x = 4l$.

6. Plot a graph of x as ordinate against M as abscissa.

7. Determine the slope of the linear part of the graph. Hence write down the rate of change, S, of x with M.

8. Calculate $\dfrac{4NR^3g}{Sr^4}$, where $g = 9.8$ m s^{-2}.

9. Remove the spring and stretch it plastically until, on release, its length is more than $10l$. Measure its new length, L.

10. Using the spring of length l, repeat steps (4) and (5) to obtain a new set of extensions x'. (x' should not exceed $4l$.)

11. Using the same axes as in (6) plot a graph of x' as ordinate against M as abscissa.

12. Comment on the physical significance of your graphs.

(L 1980)

17F VARIATION OF THE FLOW OF WATER THROUGH A CAPILLARY TUBE WITH TEMPERATURE

Set up the apparatus shown in Fig. 17.4, with the distance h (which should be measured and recorded) between the reference mark on the beaker and the lower end of the siphon approximately 20 cm.

a) For a number of temperatures θ ranging from close to 0 °C up to about 60 °C, measure the time t for 50 cm^3 of water to be siphoned out and collected. Start each *timing* with the water-level in the beaker at the reference mark; it will of course have to be refilled well above this level beforehand. The pressure conditions are then approximately the same in each case.

b) Under these conditions, for each value of θ the time should be very directly proportional to the viscosity η of the water at that temperature.

i) Plot a graph of t against θ.

ii) Taking the value of η at 20 °C to be 1.00×10^{-3} Pa s, use your graph to find the values of η at 0 °C and 60 °C.

c) More accurately, at each temperature the time t is proportional to η/ρ, where ρ is the density of the water. Values of ρ to three significant figures are:

Temperature in °C	0	20	60
Density ρ in kg m^{-3}	1000	998	983

Calculate the percentage error in your value of η for 0 °C and 60 °C due to the assumption that ρ does not vary with temperature. Discuss whether this is worth taking into account, bearing in mind the other sources of error in this experiment.

(The supervisor will explain to you how to fill and operate the siphon.)

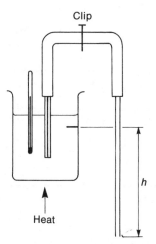

Fig. 17.4

(OLE 1980)

Oscillations and Waves

17G OSCILLATIONS OF A BIFILAR PENDULUM

Investigate the variation in period of angular oscillations of a bifilar pendulum as the spacing and length of the supporting strings is varied.

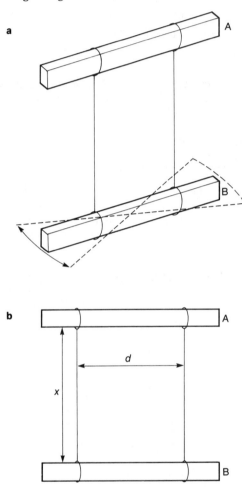

Fig. 17.5

The pendulum consists of a half-metre rule B suspended from another half-metre rule A clamped in a horizontal position. B is set in oscillation as a bifilar pendulum, in a horizontal plane about a vertical axis through its centre (Fig. 17.5a).

Arrange the strings on A and B symmetrically, using slip knots or Sellotape, so that the positions and lengths of the strings may be varied. At rest B should hang horizontal, vertically below A.

Theory indicates that the period of oscillation T of B is related to the dimensions shown in Fig. 17.5b by the equation:

$$T^2 = (16\pi^2 k^2 x)/(gd^2)$$

where k^2 is a constant and g is the acceleration due to gravity (9.8 m s^{-2}).

Carry out experiments to check the predictions of this formula by varying **(a)** d for constant x, and **(b)** x for constant d.

Plot suitable graphs to display your results and deduce a value of the constant k^2. The constant k^2 has the dimensions of (length)^2 and should equal $L^2/12$ where L is the length of ruler B.

Comment on the agreement or otherwise between your results and the predictions of theory.

(O & C 1982)

17H OSCILLATIONS OF A PENDULUM AGAINST A KNIFE EDGE

Construct a simple pendulum of length about 75 cm from the thread and mass provided. The pendulum should be supported about 60 cm above the bench by clamping together the two pieces of metal or wood in a vertical plane with the thread passing between them. The pendulum should hang over the edge of the bench. Measure the period T_0 of oscillation of the pendulum.

Mount the knife edge horizontally in the second retort stand and position it at a distance of approximately 30 cm below the point of support of the pendulum and **just touching** the thread of the pendulum when the pendulum hangs vertically at rest. The knife edge should be at a right angle to the edge of the bench. Measure the height h between the knife edge and the point of support of the pendulum. Displace the pendulum in a plane at 90° to the knife edge and release it from rest. Measure the new period of oscillation T_1.

Repeat for **four** other values of the distance h.

Plot a graph with $T_1(T_0 - T_1)$ as ordinate and h as abscissa. Determine the gradient G of the graph.

Evaluate:

$$\frac{\pi^2}{G}$$

Describe:

a) where you placed the fiducial mark and why you made this choice;

b) how you measured the periods of oscillation and why you adopted this procedure.

274

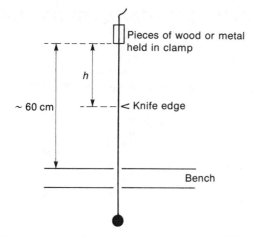

Fig. 17.6 (JMB 1981)

17I OSCILLATIONS OF A SPRING SYSTEM

You are provided with a system of springs attached to two stands. A load carrier of mass 0.1 kg has been attached to the centre of the spring system. The position of the stands and the points at which the springs have been fixed to the stands must not be changed during the experiment.

a) i) Measure the distance d from the bench to a convenient point at the bottom of the load. Increase the mass of the load to 0.5 kg in steps of 0.1 kg. For each load measure the corresponding value of d.

ii) Draw up a table showing corresponding values of total load m, distance d, and the change in d for each 0.1 kg increase in load.

b) i) Reduce the mass of the load to the original 0.1 kg. Set the mass into a vertical oscillation of small amplitude, and measure the time period T of the oscillations.

ii) Repeat the measurement of time period for various values of load m, up to a maximum of 0.5 kg.

iii) Plot a graph of T^2 (y-axis) against m (x-axis).

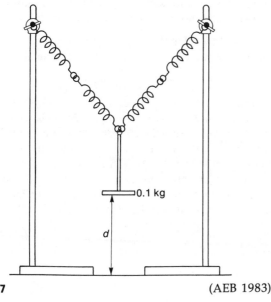

Fig. 17.7 (AEB 1983)

17J OSCILLATIONS OF A LOADED TEST TUBE

In this experiment you will investigate the behaviour of a loaded test tube floating in water. From your results you will calculate the average mass of the shot used to load the tube and also g, the acceleration of free fall.

PROCEDURE

a) Place just enough lead shot in the test tube provided to enable it to float stably and in an upright position in water. Measure h, the height of the rim of the test tube above the surface of the water.

b) Displace the tube vertically in the water and release. The tube will oscillate about its equilibrium position. Time a number of these oscillations and hence obtain a value for the period T of the oscillations.

c) Add a number of shot to the tube so as to decrease h. Measure the new h and the new period. Record N (the number of shot added), h and T.

d) Repeat your measurements for a set of values of h and tabulate N, h, T and T^2.

e) Measure D, the average outside diameter of the test tube.

f) Plot a graph of h against N', where N' is the *total* number of shot added to the tube since the initial timing in (b). (Note that N' will be zero for the measurements in (b).) Measure the slope S_1 (where $S_1 = -\Delta h/\Delta N'$) of this graph.

g) Plot also a graph of h against T^2. Measure the slope S_2 (where $S_2 = -\Delta h/\Delta T^2$) of this graph.

h) Calculate M, the average mass of a single lead shot, given that:

$$M = \pi D^2 S_1 \rho_w/4$$

where ρ_w, the density of water, is equal to 1.0×10^3 kg m^{-3}.

i) Calculate g, given that:

$$g = 4\pi^2 S_2$$

(C 1979)

17K DAMPED OSCILLATIONS OF A HALF-METRE RULE

When a compound pendulum (half-metre rule) is made to oscillate freely in air about one end, the damping of the oscillations is small.

If a wire fixed to the free end of the rule moves in water (as shown in Fig. 17.8, overleaf) the damping of the oscillations is much increased, due to the viscous resistance of the water. In this case the amplitude a_n after n oscillations is given by:

$$a_n = a_0 \exp (-\lambda n)$$

where a_0 is the initial amplitude and λ is the damping factor.

a) Measure the diameter d of the separate length of wire, and estimate the accuracy.

b) Measure the period T of the pendulum for small oscillations **in air**, and estimate the accuracy. (Ensure that the rule oscillates with its broad face parallel to the plane of oscillation.)

c) Set up the apparatus so that the wire is dipping in the water to a depth l_1 of about 20 mm, and record the value of l_1.

   i) Starting with an initial amplitude a_0 of 30 mm, measure the amplitude a_n after n full oscillations. Repeat for various values of n, each time starting with $a_0 = 30$ mm. (Ensure that the same plane of oscillation is maintained as in (b).)

   ii) Plot a graph of $\log_e (a_0/a_n)$ on the y-axis against n.

   iii) Find the slope of the graph, and hence obtain a value for the damping factor $\lambda_1 (= \log_e(a_0/a_n)/n)$, and estimate its accuracy.

d) Repeat the procedures of (c) for a new depth l_2 of about 50 mm, plotting the graph of $\log_e (a_0/a_n)$ against n on the same sheet, and obtaining a value for the new damping factor λ_2.

e) The viscosity η of the water is given by the relationship:

$$\eta = \frac{1}{\pi T \rho}\left(\frac{M(\lambda_2 - \lambda_1)}{9\pi d\,(l_1 - l_2)}\right)^2$$

where M is the mass of the rule and ρ is the density of water, the values of which are given to you.

Calculate a value for η.

f) List the experimental precautions taken in your measurements, and describe the difficulties, if any, encountered and how you overcame them.

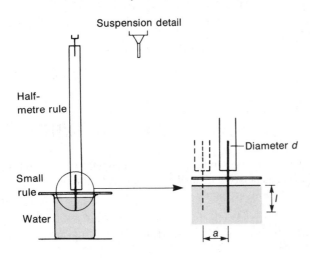

Suspension detail

Half-metre rule

Small rule

Water

Diameter d

Fig. 17.8

(OLE 1984)

17L VIBRATIONS OF A VERTICAL WIRE UNDER TENSION

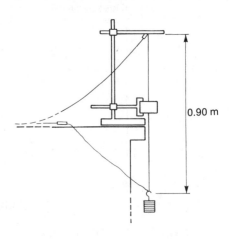

0.90 m

Fig. 17.9

You are to investigate the resonant vibrations of a wire under tension.

Clamp a retort stand to the edge of the bench and arrange a boss and clamp so that the copper wire hangs vertically to a point below the bench top with about a 0.5 m length above bench level. Hang a mass, initially about 0.9 kg, at a wire length of 0.90 m from the support. The remainder of the wire should then pass loosely back onto the bench. Connect the low voltage alternating supply with a current-limiting resistor in series to the ends of the wire with the crocodile clips.

Place the horseshoe magnet so that the midpoint of the wire passes between the pole pieces, perpendicular to the magnetic field. Adjust the weight hanging from the wire until the wire oscillates with maximum amplitude in its fundamental mode of vibration (a single antinode).

Theory shows that the length of the wire at resonance is related to the tension in the wire T by the equation:

$$T = 4mf^2l^2$$

where f is the driving frequency of 50 Hz, m is the mass per unit length of the wire, and l is the distance between adjacent nodes. Find the tension in the wire for maximum amplitude with two and three antinodes on the wire by varying the mass hanging from the wire. Repeat the experiment to find the tension for one, two and three antinodes on a wire of length 0.80 m and then for a single antinode only on wire lengths 0.70 m and 0.50 m.

Plot a suitable graph of your results to test the formula given. Hence find the mass per unit length of the copper wire.

(O & C 1982)

Geometrical and Physical Optics

17M MEASUREMENT OF THE REFRACTIVE INDEX OF A LIQUID

Investigate the refraction of light by a cylindrical lens, using the following method.

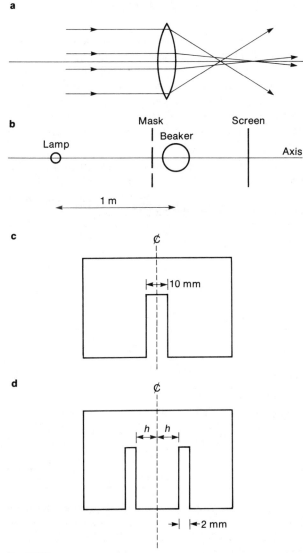

Fig. 17.10

When light is refracted through a lens, rays of light passing through different parts of the lens are brought to a focus at different points on the axis of the lens (Fig. 17.10a). In this experiment the lens is a beaker of liquid which forms an image of a lamp bulb filament.

Place 100 cm³ of water in the beaker. Set up the lamp with its filament vertical, 1 m from the centre of the beaker, so that the light passes horizontally through the liquid in the beaker. Locate an image of the filament on the screen (Fig. 17.10b).

Prepare a set of six different masks from the card provided. The first mask should have a single slit 10 mm wide on the centre line (Fig. 17.10c). The other masks should each contain two slits, each 2 mm wide, symmetrically disposed about the centre line and at distances h between 10 and 25 mm from it (Fig. 17.10d). The length of all slits should roughly equal the depth of water in the beaker. The masks are to be mounted between the lamp and the beaker so that the centre line of the mask lies on the axis of the beaker.

Place the mask containing the single slit in front of the beaker and locate a sharp image of the lamp filament on the screen. Record the position of the image, x_0. Use each other mask in turn to produce a pair of rays of light, at equal distances from the axis, incident on the lens. Locate where these rays intersect on the axis after refraction by the lens. For each mask measure the displacement d of the point of intersection from the position x_0.

Theory shows that d is related to the distance h at which the ray strikes the beaker, by the equation:

$$d = \alpha h^2$$

where α is a constant. Plot a suitable graph to find a value of α from your readings.

Repeat your measurements using 100 cm³ of liquid X in place of water. On the same graph plot your results for liquid X and find a value of α for liquid X.

For lenses of the same shape and dimensions, theory shows that the value of α is proportional to $1/(n-1)$ where n is the refractive index of the material of the lens. Given that $n = 1.33$ for water, use your data to find the refractive index of liquid X.

(O & C 1982)

17N REFRACTION BY A CYLINDRICAL LENS

A ray of light AB is incident at an angle i on a cylinder of liquid of radius R and refractive index n, as shown in Fig. 17.11. It is refracted at B and undergoes a further refraction at C to emerge along the path CD. The initial path AB is at a distance h from the parallel line XY through the centre O of the cylinder; the emergent path CD is at an angle δ to XY. It can be shown that:

$$h = nR \sin (i - \tfrac{1}{2}\delta)$$

and that

$$i = \sin^{-1}(h/R)$$

277

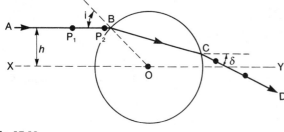

Fig. 17.11

a) Measure the diameter $2R$ of the beaker.

b) (Note that the squared paper used is to be submitted as part of your answer to this question.) Draw a circle of radius R on a sheet of squared paper and a suitable line XY through its centre O. Pour liquid L into the beaker to a depth of about 40 mm, and place the beaker inside the circle on the squared paper.

   i) Place two vertical pins (P_1 and P_2) along a line parallel to XY at a distance $h(= 5\text{ mm})$ with P_2 adjacent to the beaker and P_1 at a distance of about 30 mm from it. Locate the ray CD using two more pins, and measure the angle δ. Repeat the observations for further values of h (10 mm, 15 mm, 20 mm, etc.).

   ii) Draw up a table of values of h, δ, i ($= \sin^{-1}(h/R)$), $i - \frac{1}{2}\delta$, and $\sin(i - \frac{1}{2}\delta)$.

   iii) Plot a graph of h on the y-axis against $\sin(i - \frac{1}{2}\delta)$.

   iv) Determine the slope of the best straight line of the graph, and use this to obtain a value for the refractive index n of the liquid. What is the accuracy of the value?

c) For rays close to the axis (h small), the cylinder behaves as a cylindrical lens. Place a vertical mirror behind the beaker and mask the front to restrict the aperture, as illustrated in Fig. 17.12.

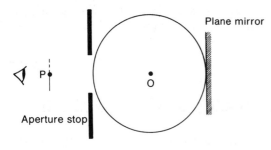

Fig. 17.12

   i) Move a pin (mounted horizontally) backwards and forwards in front of the cylinder until the position P of no-parallax between the object pin and its image seen in the mirror is found. Measure the distance OP. Repeat the observation and obtain an average value for OP.

   ii) Calculate another value for the refractive index of the liquid using the relationship:

278

$$OP = \frac{nR}{2(n-1)}$$

What is the accuracy of the value?

d) List the experimental precautions taken in your measurements, and describe the difficulties, if any, encountered and how you overcame them.

(OLE 1984)

170 USE OF DISPLACED IMAGES TO DETERMINE THE REFRACTIVE INDEX OF A BLOCK

In this experiment the object is a small lamp and a real image of it is formed on a screen by a converging lens as shown in Fig. 17.13a. The object and image distances (both reckoned positive for the purpose of this question) are labelled u and v respectively. When the image is sharply focused you should be able to see details of the filament clearly, especially after a red filter is placed close to the lens.

The effect of inserting a block of material between the lamp and the lens is shown in Fig. 17.13b. The image distance is increased by an amount y, to $(v + y)$. This is because refraction by the block has caused an apparent displacement x of the object, towards the lens. The value of x is the same whatever the values of u and v.

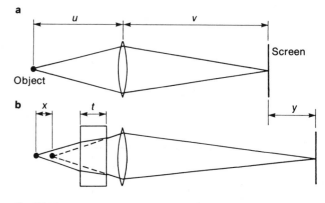

Fig. 17.13

a) In order to find the focal length f of the lens from readings of u and v it is most accurate to work in the region where the values of u and v are fairly close to one another (each about $2f$). Take several sets of values of u and v and for each set calculate f using the formula $f = uv/(u + v)$. State the average value of f.

b) In order to find the object displacement x, it is best to work with large values of v since these result in large values of y to be measured. Before taking any readings, satisfy yourself that you can observe the displacement y for values of v in the range 100 cm–130 cm. For each value of v, observe the displacement of the image when the block is inserted (so that its large faces are at right angles to the axis) between the lamp and the lens. Calculate the value of x using the formula:

$$x = \frac{yf^2}{(v-f)(v+y-f)}$$

and find the average value of x.

c) Measure the thickness t of the block, and calculate the refractive index n of the material of the block using the formula $n = t/(t-x)$.

(OLE 1979)

17P MEASUREMENT OF THE FOCAL LENGTH OF A CONVERGING LENS USING CONJUGATE IMAGES

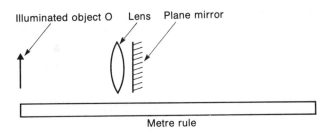

Illuminated object O   Lens   Plane mirror

Metre rule

Fig. 17.14

a) Set up the apparatus as shown in Fig. 17.14 so that the centres of the components are on the same straight line.

Adjust the position of the lens until a sharply focused image of the cross wires is obtained alongside the object. Make sure that the image has been formed by reflection at the mirror. Record f the distance between the object and the centre of the lens.

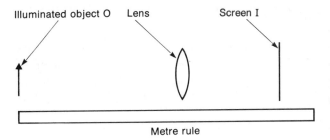

Illuminated object O   Lens   Screen I

Metre rule

Fig. 17.15

b) Remove the plane mirror and place the screen I as shown in Fig. 17.15 so that the distance between the object O and the screen I is about $5f$.

Record p, the distance between the object and the screen.

Adjust the position of the lens until a sharply focused image of the object is produced on the screen.

For the image, record l_1, the distance between the inner edges of the vertical lines at the place where the fine horizontal line crosses them.

Without changing the positions of O and I move the lens until a second sharp image is obtained. Record l_2, the new value of the distance between the inner edges of the vertical lines.

c) Move I to a new position and repeat the procedure until you have 5 sets of values of p, l_1 and l_2 for values of p not less than $4f$.

d) Plot a graph of p (y-axis) against $(l_1 + l_2)$ (x-axis).

e) Determine the slope of the graph.

(AEB 1985)

17Q MEASUREMENT OF THE FOCAL LENGTH OF AN INACCESSIBLE LENS

You are to find the position of an inaccessible converging lens and measure its focal length.

a) To measure d, the distance of the lens from the end A of the tube.

Construct a rectangular aperture of horizontal width 1.0 cm and mount it in front of an illuminated ground glass to act as a luminous object O. Choose 5 values of L, the distance between the object and a screen, in the range 50 to 90 cm. For each value of L, determine the two distances x_1 and x_2 of the end A of the tube from O which give a sharp image of O on the screen. Keep the end A of the tube pointing towards O throughout this section of the experiment.

Theory shows:

$$L = x_1 + x_2 + 2d$$

where d is the distance of the lens from the end A of the tube. Evaluate d and estimate the error in your result.

b) To measure f, the focal length of the lens.
Place a piece of 1 mm graph paper to cover the screen.

Choose 5 values of x, the distance of the nearer end of the tube from O, in the range 10–25 cm. For each value of x, position the screen to observe a focused image of O and deduce the magnification produced by the lens:

i) with the end A of the tube closer to O: m_1,

ii) with the tube reversed, but x unchanged: m_2.

Theory shows:

$$\frac{1}{m_2} - \frac{1}{m_1} = \frac{t - 2d}{f}$$

where t is the length of the tube and f is the focal length of the lens. Evaluate f and estimate the error in your result.

(O & C 1980)

17R MEASUREMENT OF THE ABSORPTION OF LIGHT IN GLASS USING AN LDR

The resistance of a light-dependent resistor (LDR) depends upon the intensity of light incident on it. In the LDR circuit shown in Fig. 17.16 the LDR current I is directly proportional to the light intensity.

The set-up provided (see Fig. 17.16) is to be used to measure the proportion of the light transmitted by a number of glass plates (microscope slides). It may be shown that the ratio of the transmitted/incident light which is equal to the ratio (I/I_0) of the LDR currents is given by:

$$\frac{I}{I_0} = \left(\frac{4n}{(n+1)^2}\right)^x$$

where I_0 is the LDR current with no glass plate interposed, I the LDR current with x plates interposed, and n the refractive index of the glass.

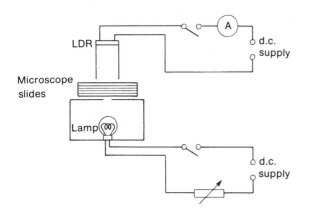

Fig. 17.16

Switch on the power supplies to the lamp circuit and the LDR circuit. Adjust the position of the LDR (leaving enough space to interpose the 12 microscope slides) and the supply to the lamp so that the ammeter registers a value near to full-scale (say, 90%). When this has been done, **do not adjust further the power supply to the lamp or the position of the LDR tube.**

a) Switch off the lamp and check that the LDR current is very small, adjusting the dark cloth provided to ensure that no light is reaching the LDR. Record the value of the LDR dark current.

b) Switch on the lamp and measure the LDR current I_0 with no glass plate interposed. This should not change significantly throughout the experiment.

c) Insert one glass plate between the lamp and the LDR and measure the LDR current I. In turn, insert further glass plates and measure the current each time until all

twelve plates are between the lamp and the LDR. Repeat the measurements in the reverse sequence, removing glass plates one at a time until none is left.

d) Plot a graph of log (I/I_0) on the y-axis against the number x of glass plates.

e) Determine the slope $(= \log(4n/(n+1)^2))$ of the graph. What is its accuracy?

f) A typical value of the refractive index n for glass of the type from which the microscope slides are made is 1.50. By substituting this and other suitable values for n into the expression given in (e) for the slope, find the value for n given by this experiment and its accuracy. Show your working clearly.

g) List the experimental precautions taken in your measurements, and describe the difficulties, if any, encountered and how you overcame them.

(OLE 1984)

17S MEASUREMENT OF THE WAVELENGTH OF LIGHT USING A DIFFRACTION GRATING

The object of this experiment is to estimate the ranges of visible wavelengths λ emitted by a given light source and transmitted by two colour filters, using a diffraction grating.

a) Place the sodium light source and slit S at the centre of one of the longer sides of the drawing board, and the diffraction grating G at the centre of the opposite side. One of the sighting pins P should be fixed into the board very close to G, as shown in Fig. 17.17. Draw the line SP.

b) A second pin P' should be placed in line with P and the first order diffraction spectrum seen through G. Measure the angle θ between SP and PP'. (A third pin could be used if desired.) Given that the wavelength of sodium light is 589 nm, determine the grating spacing d from the grating formula $d \sin \theta = \lambda$.

c) Repeat the experiment with the white light source in place of the sodium source and determine the wavelengths λ_v and λ_r of the violet and red edges of the first order spectrum.

d) Carry out further experiments to determine the wavelengths transmitted by the filters A and B separately and when superposed. Comment on your results obtained with the filters.

e) Carry out repeat experiments with the angle θ on the other side of the normal and hence estimate the errors in all your measurements.

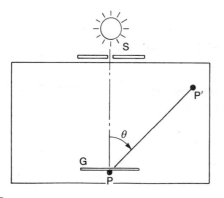

Fig. 17.17

(O & C 1981)

17T MEASUREMENT OF THE OPTICAL ROTATION OF POLARISED LIGHT

The passage of plane-polarised light through a solution of certain substances results in a rotation of the plane of polarisation. The angular rotation θ is given by:

$$\theta = Rch$$

where h is the length of the path in the solution, c is the concentration of the solution, and R is a constant for the solution which depends on the wavelength of the light used.

The experimental arrangement supplied for you to investigate this relationship is illustrated in Fig. 17.18a. A filament lamp and a fixed Polaroid provides plane-polarised light. Selection of the wavelength of light is achieved by colour filters. The solution is placed in a sample tube and the rotation is measured using a second rotatable Polaroid.

The procedure for determining the angular rotation θ is illustrated in Fig. 17.18b. Place the second rotatable Polaroid on the upper glass plate which is half covered with a piece of white card (fixed, but easily removed). With the sample tube empty, find the position of the rotatable Polaroid for minimum light transmission and mark the line $\theta = 0°$ for a conveniently chosen edge of the Polaroid mount. Check that this gives a minimum with both green and red filters in place. Then, fill the sample tube to a height h of 100 mm with the solution concerned. Re-adjust the rotatable Polaroid for minimum transmission (for green light and red light) and mark the two lines on the card of the same edge of the Polaroid mount. Label the line for green light G and that for red light R. Measure the angles between the lines and the line $\theta = 0°$. (Note that in this experiment θ will always be less than 90°.)

a) i) Measure the angular rotations for each of the solutions X, Y and Z of given concentrations for (A) green light and (B) red light. Use a new piece of card for each solution and label these X, Y, Z, as appropriate. The pieces

of card must be stuck on script paper and submitted as part of your answer.

ii) On the same graph paper, plot graphs of the angular rotation against concentration c for (A) green light and (B) red light.

iii) Determine the slope of each graph and hence the values of R for (A) green light and (B) red light.

b) Measure the angular rotations for the same height of the solution S of unknown concentration for green light and red light. Obtain values for the concentration in each case, using the graphs of (a) (ii). What is the accuracy of your answers?

c) List the experimental precautions in your measurements, and describe the difficulties, if any, encountered and how you overcame them.

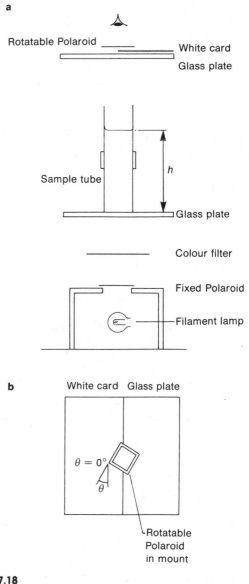

Fig. 17.18

(OLE 1983)

281

Thermal Properties of Matter

17U MEASUREMENTS ON THE COOLING OF BORAX SOLUTIONS

In this experiment you will investigate the cooling of a solution.

PROCEDURE

You are provided with a hot solution of borax contained in two tubes of different diameters. Perform the first half of the experiment with the wider tube containing the thermometer. Meanwhile, the other tube should be kept as hot as possible in the water bath until you are ready to do the second half of the experiment.

a) Remove the wider tube from the water bath and dry the outside. Support the tube in a clamp (within the draught shield, if provided). Take observations of the temperature θ and time t as the solution cools. Keep the solution well stirred during the cooling and continue taking observations until θ is below 50 °C. Record θ_0, the value of room temperature near your apparatus. Tabulate θ, t, $(\theta - \theta_0)$, and $\log_{10}[(\theta - \theta_0)/°C]$.

b) Measure and record h, the height of the meniscus of the solution above the bottom of the tube.

c) Plot a graph of $\log_{10}[(\theta - \theta_0)/°C]$ against t.

d) Repeat (a) and (b) with the second tube. It is advisable to wipe the thermometer clean and then to insert it into the second tube a minute or so before removing the tube from the bath. Tabulate your observations and plot a graph of $\log_{10}[(\theta - \theta_0)/°C]$ against t for the second tube on the same paper and axes as for the first tube.

e) Find the slopes S_1 and S_2 (decrease in logarithm ÷ increase in time) of the graphs at the points corresponding to $\theta = 65$ °C.

f) Calculate k, the power lost by unit area of the tube surface below the meniscus per unit excess temperature for each tube, given that:

$$k = 0.58 \, CdS$$

where C, the heat capacity of unit volume of the solution is taken as 4.0×10^6 J K^{-1} m^{-3}, d is the diameter of the tube and S is the corresponding slope.

(C 1979)

17V MEASUREMENT OF THE THERMAL CONDUCTIVITY OF GLASS

In this experiment, you will measure the thermal conductivity λ of glass.

PROCEDURE

Measure the temperature θ_1 of the iced water in the large vessel provided. Record your result.

Clamp the empty test tube so that most of its length is immersed in the iced water. Pour warm water into the test tube until the level inside the tube is about 1 cm below the level of the iced water.

Insert the stirrer, thermometer and cork as shown in Fig. 17.19 and note the temperature of the contents.

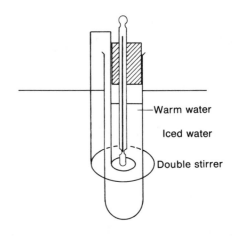

Fig. 17.19

When the temperature reaches about 20 °C, start reading temperature and time, keeping the liquids well stirred throughout. Continue taking readings until the temperature falls to about 3 °C. Record your results.

Repeat the experiment, timing from the same initial temperature.

The equation relating temperature and time t is:

$$\log_{10}\left(\frac{\theta_0}{\theta}\right) = \frac{\lambda t}{Brx}$$

where θ and θ_0 are respectively the temperature at time t and the starting temperature in °C, λ is the thermal conductivity of the glass, r is the inner radius of the tube, x is the thickness of the glass and B is a constant equal to 4.64×10^6 J m^{-3} K^{-1}.

Tabulate your values of θ and t and also the corresponding values of $\log_{10}(\theta_0/\theta)$.

Plot a graph of $\lg(\theta_0/\theta)$ against t. Measure the slope $S(= \Delta(\log_{10}(\theta_0/\theta))/\Delta t)$ of this graph and hence determine the value of λ, given that:

$$\lambda = SBrx$$

You will need to measure the inner and outer diameters of the test tube to find r and x.

(C 1981)

17W MEASUREMENTS ON A VAPOUR IN AN ENCLOSED SPACE

In this experiment you will measure the atmospheric pressure by observing the behaviour of the vapour of a volatile liquid in an enclosed space.

PROCEDURE

a) The given capillary tube contains a bead of mercury some 100 mm long, trapping a short length of the volatile liquid and an air space saturated with the vapour of the liquid. Fasten the tube to the half-metre rule and arrange

the whole so that   (i) it may be supported at different angles to the vertical,   (ii) measurements may be made of the following quantities: θ, the angle to the vertical; h, the length of the bead of mercury; a, the length of the saturated air space; l, the length of the column of the liquid. See Fig. 17.20.

Measure t, the air temperature.

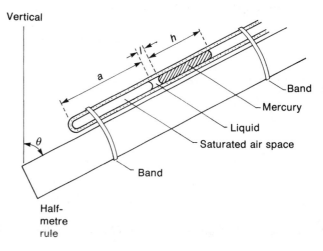

Fig. 17.20

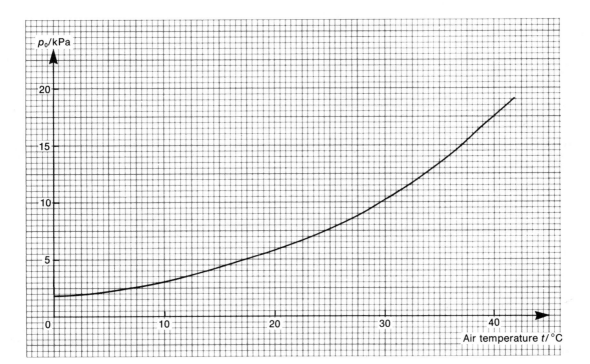

Fig. 17.21

b) Starting with the tube vertical $(\theta = 0°)$ and the open end uppermost, measure sets of values of the angle θ, and the lengths h, l, and a, in that order, for values of θ from 0° to 180°. Record your readings.

c) From your readings, tabulate a^{-1} and $\cos \theta$. (N.B. $\cos (180° - \theta) = -\cos \theta$.)

Plot a graph of a^{-1} against $\cos \theta$. From it, deduce a value of m, the gradient of the line, and read off c, the intercept on the a^{-1} axis. Record these values.

d) Calculate $\langle h \rangle$, the average value of h.

Hence calculate a value of p_1, given that $p_1 = c\langle h \rangle \rho g/m$,

where the product ρg has the value in this experiment of 0.133 kPa mm^{-1} and $\langle h \rangle$ is expressed in mm.

e) From the graph in Fig. 17.21, read off the value of p_v, the saturated vapour pressure of the liquid at the temperature t of your experiment.

Calculate a value of the atmospheric pressure, p_0, given that:

$$p_0 = p_1 + p_v$$

(C 1984)

Current Electricity

17X MEASUREMENTS ON THE ELECTRICAL CHARACTERISTICS OF A COMPONENT

You are provided with a power supply E of fixed value (about 3 V), a variable resistor R, a switch S, a milliammeter A, a voltmeter M and a component X whose electrical characteristics are to be investigated. Do **not** attempt to open the container in which X is sealed.

Setting the variable resistor at the centre of its range, assemble a circuit in which E, R, S, A and X are in series. The current should enter X at terminal P and leave at terminal Q. The variable resistor is to be used to control the current. **Do not allow the current through X to exceed 100 mA**. Connect meter M to measure the potential difference V across X.

Draw and label a diagram of the circuit.

a) Record the values of the potential difference V for **five** different values of the current I through X, taking these values of V and I as positive.

b) Rearrange the connections to X so that current enters at Q and leaves at P. Record the values of V for **five** different values of I, taking these values of V and I as negative.

Plot **all** your readings on a single set of axes with V as ordinate and I as abscissa.

Find the gradient of the linear part of the graph.

Component X is made up according to one of the diagrams given in Fig. 17.22. Use your readings to decide which diagram, **a**, **b** or **c** is appropriate and give the reasons for your choice.

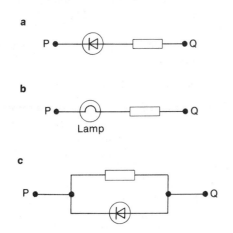

Fig. 17.22

(JMB 1982)

17Y MEASUREMENT OF THE e.m.f. AND INTERNAL RESISTANCE OF A SOURCE

In this experiment you will determine the e.m.f. and internal resistance of a source.

PROCEDURE

As opportunity arises, measure the average diameter d of the resistance wire provided. Record your results.

Connect up the bridge circuit shown in Fig. 17.23.

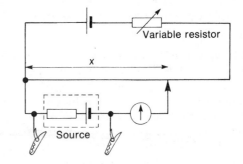

Fig. 17.23

a) For the first part of the experiment the crocodile clips should be unconnected.

Set the resistance of the variable resistor to its maximum value. With the jockey touching the slide wire near its extreme right-hand end, try to obtain a balance. You will probably find that the balance point is off the end of the wire. Reduce the resistance of the variable resistor until you obtain a balance at about 90 cm. Keep this setting of the variable resistor *constant* during the rest of the experiment.

Measure x_0, the balance length, and also V, the potential difference across the ends of the slide wire. The supervisor will supply a voltmeter for this purpose. Record your results.

Calculate the e.m.f. $\mathcal{E}$ of the small cell, given that:

$$\mathcal{E} = \frac{Vx_0}{L}$$

where L is the overall length of the slide wire.

b) By means of the crocodile clips, connect a length l of the resistance wire in parallel with the source. Measure x, the new balance length of the bridge. Repeat this procedure for different values of l. Record your values of l and x, together with the corresponding values of z, where $z = x/(x_0 - x)$.

Plot a graph of l against z.

Calculate the slope s $(= \Delta l/\Delta z)$ of this graph.

Calculate R, the internal resistance of the source, given that:

$$R = \frac{4\rho s}{\pi d^2}$$

The value of ρ, the resistivity of the wire, will be given to you by the supervisor.

(C 1982)

17Z MEASUREMENT OF THE RESISTANCE OF A GALVANOMETER USING A METRE BRIDGE

Set up the metre-bridge circuit shown in Fig. 17.24 and use it to determine the resistance R_G of the galvanometer G and the e.m.f. V of the cell E.

R and R are two resistance boxes which should be set initially to 100 Ω each. Find the balance point of the bridge circuit, and record the shift x from the balance point required for a current of 1 mA to flow through the galvanometer. Keeping the resistors R and R equal to each other, for a range of values of their resistance R between 100 Ω and 1000 Ω, find the displacement x from the balance point, for each value of R, for a current of 1 mA to flow in the galvanometer.

Assuming that the internal resistance of cell E and the resistance of the slide wire are both small compared with R, theory shows that the current through the galvanometer I_G is given by:

$$I_G = \frac{x}{l} \cdot \frac{V}{(R_G + R/2)}$$

where l is the total length of the slide wire.

Use this relationship to:

a) Plot a linear graph relating the resistance R to the displacement x of the slider;

b) Determine the resistance R_G of the galvanometer;

c) Determine the e.m.f. V of the cell E.

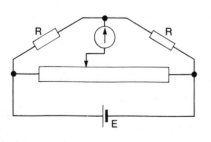

Fig. 17.24

(O & C 1980)

17AA MEASUREMENTS ON THE CHARACTERISTICS OF A LAMP USING A METRE BRIDGE

In this experiment, you will investigate how the resistance of the filament of a small lamp varies with the power dissipated in it.

Connect the circuit shown in Fig. 17.25.

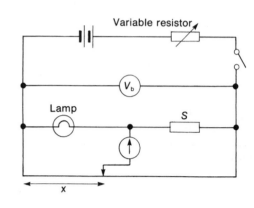

Fig. 17.25

PROCEDURE

a) Set the variable resistor to give the lowest current through the bridge which gives a measurable balance point on the bridge wire. Note the balance length x and the potential difference V_b across the bridge as given by the reading of the voltmeter. Take a series of readings of x and V_b for various settings of the variable resistor up to the maximum value of V_b available.

b) Tabulate your values of x and V_b together with the calculated values of:

   i) The resistance R of the filament,

   ii) The potential difference V across the lamp, at each setting and also the corresponding values of the power P $(= V^2/R)$ dissipated in the lamp. The value of the standard resistor S will be given to you by the supervisor.

c) Plot a graph of $\log_{10} (P/\text{W})$ against $\log_{10} (R/\Omega)$.

d) Calculate the slope of this graph in the region corresponding to the lamp being brightly lit and record your result. Record the total length of the bridge wire.

(C 1981)

Capacitance

17AB DISCHARGE OF A CAPACITOR THROUGH A RESISTOR

For a capacitor C connected in series with a resistor R and charged from a d.c. supply of e.m.f. $\mathcal{E}$, the current I in the circuit at a time t after the start of charging is given by:

$$I = I_0 \exp(-t/\tau)$$

where the time-constant $\tau = RC$ and I_0 is the initial current.

Set up the circuit as shown in Fig. 17.26, taking care that the connections to the capacitor are of the correct polarity (the invigilator will check this). You will be given the value of R. (The ammeter should be kept on the same range throughout the experiment.)

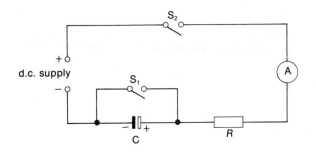

Fig. 17.26

a) Close switches S_1 and S_2 and record the current I. Use this value to find the e.m.f. $\mathcal{E}$ ($= IR$) of the supply. The resistances of the supply and the ammeter are negligible. What is the accuracy of $\mathcal{E}$?

b)   i) Starting with switches S_1 and S_2 open, close S_2 and at the same time start the stopwatch and take the initial ammeter reading I_0. After that, record the ammeter reading I every 20 s for a period of 500 s, by which time the current will have reduced to a small value. Repeat the observations after discharging the capacitor by closing S_1.

ii) Plot a graph of I against t.

iii) Find the initial value of the p.d. V_0 ($= I_0R$) across the resistor, which is equal to the p.d. across the fully charged capacitor. What is its accuracy?

iv) Determine, by counting squares, the area between the curve and the t-axis from $t = 0$ to $t = 500$ s. This area represents the total charge Q on the fully charged capacitor. Find the value of this charge.

v) Determine a value for the capacitor C ($= Q/V_0$). What is the accuracy of this value?

c) Compare the value of V_0 with that of the e.m.f. $\mathcal{E}$ of the supply found in (a) and comment on any difference.

d) The value of τ ($= RC$) may also be found from the $I - t$ graph, by using the result that $I = I_0/e$ ($= 0.368I_0$), when $t = \tau$.

i) Obtain a value for τ using this relationship.

ii) Use this to obtain another value for C. What is its accuracy?

iii) Compare the values of C obtained by the two methods and comment on any difference.

e) List the experimental precautions taken in your measurements, and describe the difficulties, if any, encountered and how you overcame them.

(OLE 1984)

Semiconductor Devices

17AC MEASUREMENTS ON THE CHARACTERISTICS OF AN LED

A light-emitting diode (LED) emits light when it is carrying a current and is forward biased so that the voltage across it exceeds a threshold value V_t.

The network provided (see Fig. 17.27a) contains a red LED, a yellow LED, and an unknown resistor R, connected in parallel. When a voltage is applied across the terminals A and B with A positive, the red LED only will pass current and emit light, whereas the yellow LED will pass no current. If the voltage is reversed so that B is positive, the yellow LED will pass current and emit light.

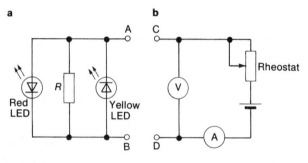

Fig. 17.27

a) i) Connect up the circuit of Fig 17.27b and set the rheostat at its maximum value. Connect terminal A to C and B to D. Gradually reduce the rheostat resistance and record corresponding values of voltage V and current I up to $I = 100$ mA. Note the threshold voltage V_{tr} at which the red LED first emits light.

ii) Reconnect the circuit with terminal A connected to D and B to C. Repeat the procedure and measurements of (a) (i). Again, note the threshold voltage V_{ty} at which the yellow LED emits light.

iii) On the same graph paper, plot graphs of voltage V against current I for the red LED and the yellow LED. Mark the threshold voltages V_{tr} and V_{ty}.

b) At small voltages, the LEDs have a high resistance, and therefore the effective resistance of the network is equal to that of R. Draw a tangent to the V–I graphs near the origin, and obtain a value for R. What is the accuracy of your result?

c) Since the resistor R is connected in parallel with the LEDs, the voltage across each component is the same, and the current I_d through an LED is given by $I_d = I - (V/R)$.

i) Use the value of R determined in (b) and the results of (a) (i) to calculate a set of values of voltage V and current I_d for the red LED.

ii) Plot a graph of V against I_d for the red LED.

d) The threshold voltages V_{tr} and V_{ty} are related to the wavelengths λ of the light emitted by the relationship $V = k/\lambda$, where k is a constant of value 1.23×10^{-6} V m. Calculate the wavelengths of the light emitted by the red LED and the yellow LED.

e) List the experimental precautions taken in your measurements, and describe the difficulties, if any, encountered and how you overcame them.

(OLE 1983)

17AD MEASUREMENTS ON AN LED AND AN LDR

A light-emitting diode (LED) emits light when the forward biasing voltage across it exceeds a threshold value. The amount of light which is emitted in unit time (luminous flux) is directly proportional to the diode current I_d.

a) Set up the circuit shown in Fig. 17.28 so that the LED is forward biased. The polarity required for this is clearly indicated on the LED.

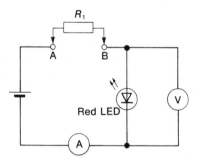

Fig. 17.28

i) Insert the resistors (labelled R_1, R_2, R_3, R_4, R_5 and R_6) in turn between the terminals A and B. Record the corresponding values of diode voltage V_d and current I_d.

ii) Plot a graph of V_d against I_d.

The resistance R_l of a light-dependent resistor (LDR) changes with the intensity of illumination E according to the relationship:

$$E = \text{constant} \times (R_l)^x$$

where x is a constant exponent.

b) Disconnect the first circuit and set up the circuits shown in Fig. 17.29. Place the LED as close as possible to the LDR so that its light-emitting face points directly at the sensitive face of the LDR. Use the light screen (cloth) provided to exclude external light.

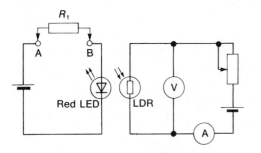

Fig. 17.29

i) Record the voltage V_l and the current I_l for the LDR circuit when the resistors (labelled R_1, R_2, R_3, R_4, R_5 and R_6) are inserted in turn in the diode circuit. The diode current I_d can be taken as that given by your results of (a) (i). Calculate the resistance R_l ($= V_l/I_l$) of the LDR for each value of I_d.

(Note that the rheostat may be adjusted to give maximum readings of I_l and V_l as the resistors in the LED circuit are changed.)

ii) Plot a graph of $\log I_d$ against $\log R_l$.

iii) Determine the gradient of this graph and hence a value for the exponent x. How accurate is your value?

c) List the experimental precautions taken in your measurements, and describe the difficulties, if any, encountered and how you overcame them.

(OLE 1983)

APPENDIX 1 THE CATHODE RAY OSCILLOSCOPE

1 INTRODUCTION

The CRO is perhaps the most versatile instrument in the school physics laboratory. Its use is required in many of the experiments in this book. It is not possible to provide here a comprehensive guide to all makes and models: the functions of controls and switches, their arrangements on front panels, and the names with which they are labelled, vary enormously. You should therefore familiarise yourself with the controls on the CRO that you will be using, referring to the manufacturer's manual if necessary. Information in the paragraphs that follow can provide only general guidance. Names in italicised capitals are those used by some manufacturers on their front panels (probably in abbreviated form) and may therefore enable some controls to be identified.

The functions of *POWER ON/OFF*, *INTENSITY* and *FOCUS* controls are obvious. If stray magnetic fields incline traces to the horizontal lines on the screen *graticule*, a *TRACE ROTATION* control can be used to re-align them.

2 THE DUAL TRACE CRO

In a dual trace CRO two separate traces are produced from one electron beam, either by a process known as *chopping*, in which the beam is switched between the two traces at a predetermined rate, or by alternate sweeping, where the beam *sweeps* out complete traces alternately. If you are able to select either *MODE* use *CHOP* at low frequencies and *ALTERNATE* at high frequencies. Other modes that may be provided include *CHANNEL 1* only, *CHANNEL 2* only and *ADD*, which produces a single trace that represents the algebraic sum of the signals from the two channels.

If the display is to be stable the traces must be swept out repeatedly over the same part of the screen. The *time base* circuit, connected to the horizontal deflection system, ensures this by *triggering* the sweep every time at precisely the same instant in the signal's cycle: the instant at which the signal reaches a particular *LEVEL*. It is usually convenient to set this level at zero, but it can be varied; in addition, it may be possible to choose whether triggering occurs as the signal rises or falls through the level (+ or − *SLOPE*). The time base circuit synchronises the sweep with the signal.

The signal that provides the triggering pulse may be the one applied to either *CHANNEL 1* or *CHANNEL 2*. On some models one particular channel is used permanently as the trigger channel, while on other models either may be chosen. If the frequencies of the two signals are identical, as they usually are, it probably won't matter which channel is used. Other signals may also be chosen to provide the triggering pulse: an *EXTERNAL* signal that is applied to a third, separate input socket, a *LINE* signal obtained from the mains supply, *TV* and video signals that require special synchronisation.

3 SIGNAL FREQUENCIES

To measure signal frequencies (or, more specifically, their *periods*, from which frequencies may be easily calculated) it is necessary to know the *sweep speed* of the beam as it traces out waveforms across the screen. The sweep speed control has fixed settings labelled with the time (in s, ms or μs) that the beam takes to sweep across one horizontal division of the graticule on the screen; i.e. *TIME/DIVISION*. Note that one horizontal division is the distance between two adjacent vertical lines. Intermediate settings may be obtained by using a separate, continuously variable, control, but this must be switched off if the *CALIBRATIONS* of the main control are to be used for time measurements.

4 X-Y MODE

At one particular setting of the main sweep speed control the time base circuit is switched off. This setting usually also connects the signal applied to the input of one of the two channels to the horizontal deflection system. The channel is then used for the X signal and the other one for the Y signal when the CRO is to be used in its X–Y *MODE* for the display of Lissajous' figures.

Signals applied to the two inputs are normally connected via amplifiers to the vertical deflection system. The Y sensitivity control of each channel has fixed settings labelled with the p.d. (in V or mV) represented by a vertical deflection of 1 division of the graticule on the screen; i.e. *VOLTS/DIVISION*. If, in addition, continuously variable controls are incorporated, ensure that they are switched off before you use the *CALIBRATIONS* of the main controls to measure voltages. The calibrations of the channel used for the X signal are usually still valid when the CRO is being used in its X–Y mode.

5 X AND Y POSITION

X and Y *POSITION* controls allow the traces to be moved horizontally and vertically over the screen. It is possible to move traces right off the screen, so if nothing appears when the CRO is switched on, check that these controls are set at their mid positions. If still no traces appear, turn down the Y sensitivities and adjust the triggering level.

6 DC AND AC COUPLING

Each channel input has a switch that allows either *direct coupling* (DC) of the signal to the deflection system or *AC coupling*, where any steady (d.c.) component of the signal is eliminated. It is natural to assume that the a.c. setting must always be used for the display of alternating voltages, but this is quite wrong, and the d.c. setting can be used for most applications. A third setting of this switch connects the input direct to *GROUND* and is used to set, and occasionally check, the zero voltage level of each channel on the screen.

7 A DISPLAYED WAVEFORM

Fig. A1 shows how the waveform of a sinusoidally varying voltage should be displayed. The Y sensitivity and sweep speed controls have been set to produce a trace that fills most of the screen and includes about three complete cycles.

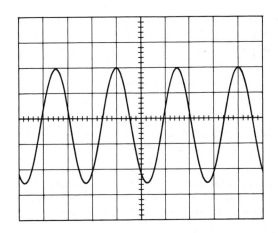

Fig. A1 Typical CRO trace. If the Y sensitivity is set at 0.5 V/DIV and the sweep speed is set at 0.1 ms/DIV confirm that the display represents a sinusoidally varying signal of amplitude 1.1 V and frequency 4.0 kHz.

APPENDIX 2   LEAST SQUARES FITTING OF EXPERIMENTAL DATA

1 THE PRINCIPLE OF LEAST SQUARES FITTING

An objective measure of how well a set of data follows a linear relationship can be obtained from a *least squares fit*. In this procedure the sum of the squares of the differences between the experimental data, y_{exp}, and the fitted values, $y_{fit} = mx + c$, is minimised. In mathematical notation:

$$S = \chi^2 = \sum_{i=1}^{i=N} [(y_{exp})_i - (y_{fit})_i]^2 = \text{minimum}$$

for N experimental points.

Using simple differential calculus this condition is satisfied if the differentials of the sum S with respect to m and c are both zero. The mathematical analysis is outside the A-level syllabus, and so only the results are given:

$$\text{slope } m = \frac{NS_{xy} - S_x S_y}{NS_{x^2} - S_x S_x}$$

and the intercept on the y-axis:

$$c = \frac{S_x S_{xy} - S_y S_{x^2}}{S_x S_x - NS_{x^2}}$$

S_x, S_y, S_{x^2} and S_{xy} denote the summations:

$$S_x = \sum_{i=1}^{i=N} x_i, \quad S_y = \sum_{i=1}^{i=N} y_i,$$

$$S_{x^2} = \sum_{i=1}^{i=N} (x_i)^2, \quad S_{xy} = \sum_{i=1}^{i=N} x_i y_i$$

x_i and y_i denote the pairs of experimental points.

The uncertainties in m and c, Δm and Δc, are calculated from the following equations:

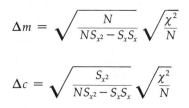

$$\Delta m = \sqrt{\frac{N}{NS_{x^2} - S_x S_x}} \sqrt{\frac{\chi^2}{N}}$$

$$\Delta c = \sqrt{\frac{S_{x^2}}{NS_{x^2} - S_x S_x}} \sqrt{\frac{\chi^2}{N}}$$

The value of $\Delta m/m$ will give an indication of the reliability of the fit of the experimental data by a linear relationship. The value of Δc will also give an indication of deviations from an exact theoretical relationship; for example, if it is expected that a line should pass through the origin of coordinates, then $(c \pm \Delta c)$ will show whether proportionality has been confirmed within experimental error. A systematic error may also be indicated by an intercept.

2 A LEAST SQUARES FITTING PROGRAM FOR LINEAR RELATIONSHIPS (BBC BASIC)

The program listing for the least squares fitting procedure is included in this appendix together with some examples of its use on experimental data. The program is written in BBC BASIC; the main changes required for other forms of Basic are in the input and output statements. Some of the function statements such as logarithms to the base 10 and to the base e are not available in some forms of BASIC; if only $\log_e$ is available then the $\log_{10}$ statements will have to be replaced by $\log_e x/\log_e (10)$.

The following options are available:

Option 2
Fitting a known power law relationship $y^r = mx^n + c$ for arbitrary values of r and n; the simplest option would be $y = mx + c$ with $r = 1$ and $n = 1$ (see Example 1, page 297). For the relationship of the form $y = x^2$, $r = 1$ and $n = 2$ (see Example 2, page 299). For the inverse relationship $y = m/x + c$, $r = 1$ and $n = -1$ (see Example 3, page 300).

Option 3
Determining n in the power law relationship $y = kx^n$ using $\log_{10}(y) = n \log_{10}(x) + \log_{10}(k)$ (see Example 4, page 301).

Option 4
Fitting an exponential relationship $y = a \exp(kx)$ using $\log_e(y) = kx + \log_e(a)$ (see Example 5, page 302).

Option 5
Fitting an exponential relationship of the form $y = a \exp(k/x)$ using $\log_e(y) = k/x + \log_e(a)$ (see Example 6, page 304).

The normal input and output from the program is to a visual display unit (VDU); some alterations are required for the output to a line printer so as to avoid wasting paper on paging.

Details of data input and output

Although the uncertainties in the slope and intercept will indicate how well your data follows a linear relationship, this is no substitute for actually plotting the fitted straight line and the data points. It is assumed in the fitting procedure that the errors in 'y' are random; thus the points from your experiment should be equally distributed either side of the fitted straight line. Points systematically above or below the fitted line indicate either a systematic error or quite simply that your data does not follow a linear relationship. In testing whether your data conforms to a certain relationship using options 2, 3, 4 or 5 the uncertainties in m and c alone cannot be used to distinguish between models.

an exponent E, indicating the power of 10:

$$2.75E\text{-}3 = 0.00275$$
$$1.20E\text{-}2 = 0.0120$$
$$9.63E\text{-}1 = 0.963$$
$$1.45E0 = 1.45$$
$$5.65E1 = 56.5$$
$$3.73E2 = 373$$

This format has the advantages of giving the same number of significant figures irrespective of the size of the number and ensuring the alignment of data in tables. This is not an ideal format for integers, but you can always alter the format according to your own experimental data.

3 A NOTE ON THE OUTPUT OF THE DATA

Because of the wide range of data values and of the fitted constants that may arise the floating point format has been chosen for the output. Thus a number is followed by

4 SIGNIFICANT FIGURES

Very rarely does experimental data obtained in a school laboratory justify more than three significant figures.

Even so you must decide whether even three figures are justified: generally the number of significant figures should not be greater than the number in your least accurate piece of data. Also, the error in m or c determines the number of significant figures you use in m or c: $m = 0.473 \pm 0.0185$) should be written as (0.47 ± 0.02) since the third decimal place cannot be significant with an error in the second decimal place; sometimes it is more difficult to decide whether or not to retain a decimal place, for example (2.39 ± 0.04) should not be reduced to (2.4 ± 0.1) unless your experimental data shows only two significant figures.

LISTING OF THE LEAST SQUARES FITTING PROGRAM IN BBC BASIC

```
10 MODE3
20 @%=&1030D
30 CLEAR
40 FLAG%=0
50 REM ------------------------------------------------------------------
60 REM                STRAIGHT LINE FITTING PROGRAM
70 REM ------------------------------------------------------------------
80 PRINT CHR$(12)
90 REM
100 REM              OPTIONS
110 REM
120 PRINT "CHOOSE AN OPTION"
130 PRINT
140 PRINT "ENTER NEW SET OF DATA                               1"
150 PRINT
160 PRINT "FIT Y TO ANY POWER AGAINST X TO ANY POWER (INC ONE)  2"
170 PRINT "FIT LOG(10)Y AGAINST LOG(10)X                        3"
180 PRINT "FIT LOG(E)Y AGAINST X                                4"
190 PRINT "FIT LOG(E)Y AGAINST 1/X                              5"
200 PRINT
210 PRINT "EXIT FROM PROGRAM                                    6"
220 INPUT A%
230 IF A%<1 OR A%>6 THEN GOTO 90
240 ON A% GOSUB 270,680,870,990,1100,1210
250 CLEAR
260 END
270 REM
280 REM              DATA INPUT
290 REM
300 PRINT CHR$(12)
310 IF FLAG%=1 THEN CLEAR
320 PRINT"WHAT TITLE DO YOU WANT TO GIVE THIS EXPERIMENT (MAX  75 CHARACTERS)"
330 INPUT AA$
340 INPUT "HOW MANY DATA POINTS DO YOU HAVE ",N%
350 DIM X(N%),Y(N%),U(N%),V(N%),VFIT(N%),YFIT(N%)
360 PRINT:PRINT"WHAT UNIT IS X MEASURED IN"
370 INPUT "(NOT MORE THAN 10 CHARACTERS) ",B$
380 IF LEN(B$)>10 THEN GOTO 360
390 PRINT:PRINT"WHAT UNIT IS Y MEASURED IN"
400 INPUT "(NOT MORE THAN 10 CHARACTERS ) ",C$
410 IF LEN(C$)>10 THEN GOTO 390
420 PRINT
430 PRINT "PLEASE ENTER DATA"
440 PRINT"X VALUE FIRST,THEN Y VALUE SEPARATED BY A COMMA"
450 FOR I%=1 TO N%
460 INPUT "X,Y ",X(I%),Y(I%)
470 NEXT I%
480 I%=1
490 REM
```

```
500 REM              CHECK THAT DATA IS ENTERED CORRECTLY
510 REM
520 PRINT"DATA PT.";TAB(12);"X VALUE";TAB(28);"Y VALUE"
530 FOR I%=1 TO N%
540 PRINT;I%;TAB(11);X(I%);TAB(27);Y(I%)
550 NEXT I%
560 I%=1
570 PRINT
580 INPUT "IS DATA NOW CORRECT ",A$
590 IF LEFT$(A$,1)="Y" THEN FLAG%=1:GOTO 70
600 INPUT "WHICH NUMBER DATA POINT IS WRONG ",J%
610 IF J%>N% OR J%<1 THEN PRINT"PARDON?":GOTO 600
620 PRINT "O.K. WHAT SHOULD POINT "J%" BE ?"
630 INPUT "X,Y ",X(J%),Y(J%)
640 GOTO 490
650 RETURN
660 REM
670 REM              CHANGE OF VARIABLES
680 REM
690 REM              2 Y^R AGAINST X^N
700 REM
710 PRINT "X IS IN "B$
720 INPUT "WHAT POWER OF X DO YOU WANT TO FIT ",N
730 PRINT
740 PRINT "Y IS IN "C$
750 INPUT "WHAT POWER OF Y DO YOU WANT TO FIT ",R
760 FOR I%=1 TO N%
770 IF X(I%)<=0 THEN U=N*LN(0.000001):GOTO 790
780 U=N*LN(X(I%))
790 U(I%)= EXP(U)
800 IF Y(I%)<=0 THEN V=R*LN(0.000001):GOTO 820
810 V=R*LN(Y(I%))
820 V(I%)=EXP(V)
830 NEXT I%
840 I%=1
850 GOTO 1290
860 RETURN
870 REM
880 REM              3 LOG(10)Y AGAINST LOG(10)X
890 REM
900 FOR I%=1TO N%
910 IF X(I%)<=0 THEN U(I%)=LOG(0.000001):GOTO 930
920 U(I%)=LOG(X(I%))
930 IF Y(I%)<=0 THEN V(I%)=LOG(0.000001):GOTO 950
940 V(I%)=LOG(Y(I%))
950 NEXT I%
960 I%=1
970 GOTO 1290
980 RETURN
990 REM
1000 REM              4 LOG(E)Y AGAINST X
1010 REM
1020 FOR I%=1TO N%
1030 U(I%)=X(I%)
1040 IF Y(I%)<=0 THEN V(I%)=LN(0.000001): GOTO 1060
1050 V(I%)=LN(Y(I%))
1060 NEXT I%
1070 I%=1
1080 GOTO 1290
1090 RETURN
1100 REM
1110 REM              5 LOG(E)Y AGAINST 1/X
1120 REM
1130 FOR I%=1 TO N%
1140 U(I%)=1/X(I%)
```

```
1150 IF Y(I%)<=0 THEN V(I%)=LN(0.000001): GOTO 1170
1160 V(I%)=LN(Y(I%))
1170 NEXT I%
1180 I%=1
1190 GOTO 1290
1200 RETURN
1210 REM
1220 REM                  EXIT FROM PROGRAM
1230 REM
1240 PRINT "WARNING - TO EXIT WILL ERASE ALL DATA"
1250 INPUT "DO YOU WANT TO EXIT (YES/NO) ",D$
1260 IF LEFT$(D$,1)="Y" THEN CLEAR:CLS:END
1270 GOTO 70
1280 RETURN
1290 REM
1300 REM              CALCULATE SUMS AND PRODUCTS
1310 REM
1320 SIGU=0:SIGV=0:SIGU2=0:SIGV2=0:SIGUV=0:CHISQ=0
1330 FOR I%=1 TO N%
1340 SIGU=SIGU+U(I%)
1350 SIGV=SIGV+V(I%)
1360 SIGU2=SIGU2+U(I%)^2
1370 SIGV2=SIGV2+V(I%)^2
1380 SIGUV=SIGUV+U(I%)*V(I%)
1390 NEXT I%
1400 I%=1
1410 REM
1420 REM                  CURVE FITTING
1430 REM
1440 M=(N%*SIGUV-SIGU*SIGV)/(N%*SIGU2-SIGU^2)
1450 C=(SIGU*SIGUV-SIGV*SIGU2)/(SIGU^2-N%*SIGU2)
1460 REM
1470 REM          CALCULATE FITTED VALUES AND CHI-SQUARED
1480 REM
1490 FOR I%=1 TO N%
1500 VFIT(I%)=M*U(I%)+C
1510 CHISQ=CHISQ+(V(I%)-VFIT(I%))^2
1520 NEXT I%
1530 CHI=SQR(CHISQ/N%)
1540 I%=1
1550 REM
1560 REM              ERRORS IN M AND C
1570 REM
1580 DEL=(N%*SIGU2)-(SIGU^2)
1590 DELM=N%/DEL
1600 IF DELM<0 THEN DELM=0.000001
1610 DELTAM=CHI*SQR(DELM)
1620 DELC=SIGU2/DEL
1630 IF DELC<0 THEN DELC=0.000001
1640 DELTAC=CHI*SQR(DELC)
1650 REM
1660 REM              DISPLAY RESULTS
1670 REM
1680 ON (A%-1) GOSUB 1790,1890,1980,2060
1690 FOR I%=1 TO N%
1700 PRINT X(I%) Y(I%) U(I%) V(I%) VFIT(I%) YFIT(I%)
1710 NEXT I%
1720 I%=1
1730 PRINT
1740 PRINT "THE FITTED STRAIGHT LINE HAS "
1750 PRINT "SLOPE    = ";M " PLUS OR MINUS ";DELTAM
1760 PRINT "INTERCEPT= ";C " PLUS OR MINUS ";DELTAC
1770 INPUT E$
1780 GOTO 70
1790 PRINT CHR$(12) AA$
```

```
1800 PRINT "X";TAB(14);"Y";TAB(27);"X^";N; TAB(40);"Y^";R; TAB(53);
     "FITTED VALUE";TAB(66);"FITTED VALUE"
1810 PRINT B$; TAB(14); C$; TAB(53);"Y^";R;TAB(66);"OF Y"
1820 FOR I%=1 TO N%
1830 IF VFIT(I%) <=0 THEN VFIT(I%)=0.000001
1840 Y=(1/R)*LN(VFIT(I%))
1850 YFIT(I%)=EXP(Y)
1860 NEXT I%
1870 I%=1
1880 RETURN
1890 PRINT CHR$(12) AA$
1900 PRINT "X";TAB(14);"Y";TAB(27);"LOG(10)X";TAB(40);"LOG(10)Y";TAB(53);
     "FITTED VALUE";TAB(66);"FITTED VALUE"
1910 PRINT B$;TAB(14);C$;TAB(53);"LOG(10)Y";TAB(66);"OF Y"
1920 FOR I%=1 TO N%
1930 Y=VFIT(I%)
1940 YFIT(I%)=10^Y
1950 NEXT I%
1960 I%=1
1970 RETURN
1980 PRINT CHR$(12) AA$
1990 PRINT "X";TAB(14);"Y";TAB(27);"X";TAB(40);"LOG(E)Y";TAB(53);
     "FITTED VALUE";TAB(66);"FITTED VALUE"
2000 PRINT B$;TAB(14);C$;TAB(53);"LOG(E)Y";TAB(66);"OF Y"
2010 FOR I%=1 TO N%
2020 YFIT(I%)=EXP(VFIT(I%))
2030 NEXT I%
2040 I%=1
2050 RETURN
2060 PRINT CHR$(12) AA$
2070 PRINT "X";TAB(14);"Y";TAB(27);"1/X";TAB(40);"LOG(E)Y";TAB(53);
     "FITTED VALUE";TAB(66);"FITTED VALUE"
2080 PRINT B$;TAB(14);C$;TAB(53);"LOG(E)Y";TAB(66);"OF Y"
2090 FOR I%=1 TO N%
2100 YFIT(I%)=EXP(VFIT(I%))
2110 NEXT I%
2120 I%=1
2130 RETURN
```

EXAMPLES OF THE OPTIONS AVAILABLE IN THE PROGRAM

Example 1

Option 2   The determination of the internal resistance, r, and e.m.f., $\mathcal{E}$, of a cell using the equation $V = \mathcal{E} - Ir$. A graph of V against I should be a straight line of slope $-r$ and the intercept on the V axis is $\mathcal{E}$.

```
CHOOSE AN OPTION

ENTER NEW SET OF DATA                                   1

FIT Y TO ANY POWER AGAINST X TO ANY POWER (INC ONE)     2
FIT LOG(10)Y AGAINST LOG(10)X                           3
FIT LOG(E)Y AGAINST X                                   4
FIT LOG(E)Y AGAINST 1/X                                 5

EXIT FROM PROGRAM                                       6
?1
```

```
WHAT TITLE DO YOU WANT TO GIVE THIS EXPERIMENT (MAX  75 CHARACTERS)
?INTERNAL RESISTANCE OF A   CELL
HOW MANY DATA POINTS DO YOU HAVE ?9

WHAT UNIT IS X MEASURED IN
(NOT MORE THAN 10 CHARACTERS) ?AMPS

WHAT UNIT IS Y MEASURED IN
(NOT MORE THAN 10 CHARACTERS ) ?VOLTS

PLEASE ENTER DATA
X VALUE FIRST,THEN Y VALUE SEPARATED BY A COMMA
X,Y ?0.02,1.5
X,Y ?0.03,1.4
X,Y ?0.04,1.3
X,Y ?0.05,1.2
X,Y ?0.06,1.1
X,Y ?0.07,1.0
X,Y ?0.08,0.85
X,Y ?0.09,0.75
X,Y ?0.10,0.65
DATA PT.     X VALUE           Y VALUE
1.00E0       2.00E-2           1.50E0
2.00E0       3.00E-2           1.40E0
3.00E0       4.00E-2           1.30E0
4.00E0       5.00E-2           1.20E0
5.00E0       6.00E-2           1.10E0
6.00E0       7.00E-2           1.00E0
7.00E0       8.00E-2           8.50E-1
8.00E0       9.00E-2           7.50E-1
9.00E0       1.00E-1           6.50E-1

IS DATA NOW CORRECT ?Y




CHOOSE AN OPTION

ENTER NEW SET OF DATA                                    1

FIT Y TO ANY POWER AGAINST X TO ANY POWER (INC ONE)      2
FIT LOG(10)Y AGAINST LOG(10)X                            3
FIT LOG(E)Y AGAINST X                                    4
FIT LOG(E)Y AGAINST 1/X                                  5

EXIT FROM PROGRAM                                        6
?2
X IS IN AMPS
WHAT POWER OF X DO YOU WANT TO FIT ?1

Y IS IN VOLTS
WHAT POWER OF Y DO YOU WANT TO FIT ?1
```

INTERNAL RESISTANCE OF A	CELL				
X	Y	X^1.00E0	Y^1.00E0	FITTED VALUE	FITTED VALUE
AMPS	VOLTS			Y^1.00E0	OF Y
2.00E-2	1.50E0	2.00E-2	1.50E0	1.51E0	1.51E0
3.00E-2	1.40E0	3.00E-2	1.40E0	1.41E0	1.41E0
4.00E-2	1.30E0	4.00E-2	1.30E0	1.30E0	1.30E0
5.00E-2	1.20E0	5.00E-2	1.20E0	1.19E0	1.19E0
6.00E-2	1.10E0	6.00E-2	1.10E0	1.08E0	1.08E0
7.00E-2	1.00E0	7.00E-2	1.00E0	9.76E-1	9.76E-1

```
    8.00E-2       8.50E-1       8.00E-2       8.50E-1       8.68E-1       8.68E-1
    9.00E-2       7.50E-1       9.00E-2       7.50E-1       7.61E-1       7.61E-1
    1.00E-1       6.50E-1       1.00E-1       6.50E-1       6.53E-1       6.53E-1

THE FITTED STRAIGHT LINE HAS
SLOPE    = -1.07E1    PLUS OR MINUS 1.73E-1
INTERCEPT= 1.73E0    PLUS OR MINUS 1.13E-2
?
```

$r = (10.7 \pm 0.2)\ \Omega,$

$\mathcal{E} = (1.73 \pm 0.01)\ \text{V}.$

Example 2

Option 2   The determination of e/m_e using a fine beam tube. The relationship between the accelerating voltage, V_A, and the radius of the circular orbit, r, is $V_A = (eB^2/2m_e)r^2$. A graph of V_A against r^2 should be a straight line with a slope of $(eB^2/2m_e)$ and the intercept should be zero.

```
WHAT TITLE DO YOU WANT TO GIVE THIS EXPERIMENT (MAX   75 CHARACTERS)
?FINE BEAM TUBE: e/m
HOW MANY DATA POINTS DO YOU HAVE ?5

WHAT UNIT IS X MEASURED IN
(NOT MORE THAN 10 CHARACTERS) ?METRES

WHAT UNIT IS Y MEASURED IN
(NOT MORE THAN 10 CHARACTERS ) ?VOLTS

PLEASE ENTER DATA
X VALUE FIRST,THEN Y VALUE SEPARATED BY A COMMA
X,Y ?0.025,80
X,Y ?0.03,110
X,Y ?0.034,140
X,Y ?0.036,170
X,Y ?0.04,200
DATA PT.      X VALUE         Y VALUE
1.00E0        2.50E-2         8.00E1
2.00E0        3.00E-2         1.10E2
3.00E0        3.40E-2         1.40E2
4.00E0        3.60E-2         1.70E2
5.00E0        4.00E-2         2.00E2

IS DATA NOW CORRECT ?YES


CHOOSE AN OPTION

ENTER NEW SET OF DATA                                   1

FIT Y TO ANY POWER AGAINST X TO ANY POWER (INC ONE)     2
FIT LOG(10)Y AGAINST LOG(10)X                           3
FIT LOG(E)Y AGAINST X                                   4
FIT LOG(E)Y AGAINST 1/X                                 5

EXIT FROM PROGRAM                                       6
?2
X IS IN METRES
WHAT POWER OF X DO YOU WANT TO FIT ?2

Y IS IN VOLTS
WHAT POWER OF Y DO YOU WANT TO FIT ?1
```

```
FINE BEAM TUBE: e/m
X                Y                    X^2.00E0        Y^1.00E0        FITTED VALUE  FITTED VALUE
METRES           VOLTS                                                Y^1.00E0      OF Y
      2.50E-2         8.00E1              6.25E-4         8.00E1         7.79E1        7.79E1
      3.00E-2         1.10E2              9.00E-4         1.10E2         1.13E2        1.13E2
      3.40E-2         1.40E2              1.16E-3         1.40E2         1.45E2        1.45E2
      3.60E-2         1.70E2              1.30E-3         1.70E2         1.63E2        1.63E2
      4.00E-2         2.00E2              1.60E-3         2.00E2         2.01E2        2.01E2

THE FITTED STRAIGHT LINE HAS
SLOPE    = 1.27E5    PLUS OR MINUS 5.72E3
INTERCEPT= -1.19E0    PLUS OR MINUS 6.66E0
?
```

$(eB^2/2m_e) = (1.27 \pm 0.06) \times 10^5$ V m^{-2}.

Since $B = 1.23 \times 10^{-3}$ T, $e/m_e = (1.68 \pm 0.08) \times 10^{11}$ C kg^{-1}.

The intercept on the V_A axis is (-1 ± 7) V (zero within the experimental error).

Example 3

Option 2   The resonance tube. The length, l, of the vibrating air column and the frequency of the fundamental, f, are related by $l = c/4f - e$. A graph of l against $1/f$ should be a straight line with slope $c/4$ and the intercept on the l axis $= -e$.

```
WHAT TITLE DO YOU WANT TO GIVE THIS EXPERIMENT (MAX   75 CHARACTERS)
?THE RESONANCE TUBE
HOW MANY DATA POINTS DO YOU HAVE ?8

WHAT UNIT IS X MEASURED IN
(NOT MORE THAN 10 CHARACTERS) ?HERTZ

WHAT UNIT IS Y MEASURED IN
(NOT MORE THAN 10 CHARACTERS ) ?METRES

PLEASE ENTER DATA
X VALUE FIRST,THEN Y VALUE SEPARATED BY A COMMA
X,Y ?256,0.32
X,Y ?288,0.29
X,Y ?320,0.26
X,Y ?341,0.24
X,Y ?384,0.215
X,Y ?426.6,0.19
X,Y ?480,0.17
X,Y ?512,0.155
DATA PT.    X VALUE          Y VALUE
1.00E0       2.56E2          3.20E-1
2.00E0       2.88E2          2.90E-1
3.00E0       3.20E2          2.60E-1
4.00E0       3.41E2          2.40E-1
5.00E0       3.84E2          2.15E-1
6.00E0       4.27E2          1.90E-1
7.00E0       4.80E2          1.70E-1
8.00E0       5.12E2          1.55E-1

IS DATA NOW CORRECT ?Y

CHOOSE AN OPTION

ENTER NEW SET OF DATA                                   1

FIT Y TO ANY POWER AGAINST X TO ANY POWER (INC ONE)     2
```

```
FIT LOG(10)Y AGAINST LOG(10)X                                    3
FIT LOG(E)Y AGAINST X                                            4
FIT LOG(E)Y AGAINST 1/X                                         5

EXIT FROM PROGRAM                                               6
?2
X IS IN HERTZ
WHAT POWER OF X DO YOU WANT TO FIT ?-1

Y IS IN METRES
WHAT POWER OF Y DO YOU WANT TO FIT ?1
```

```
THE RESONANCE TUBE
X             Y             X^-1.00E0    Y^1.00E0    FITTED VALUE FITTED VALUE
HERTZ         METRES                                 Y^1.00E0     OF Y
    2.56E2        3.20E-1       3.91E-3      3.20E-1      3.24E-1      3.24E-1
    2.88E2        2.90E-1       3.47E-3      2.90E-1      2.87E-1      2.87E-1
    3.20E2        2.60E-1       3.13E-3      2.60E-1      2.57E-1      2.57E-1
    3.41E2        2.40E-1       2.93E-3      2.40E-1      2.41E-1      2.41E-1
    3.84E2        2.15E-1       2.60E-3      2.15E-1      2.13E-1      2.13E-1
    4.27E2        1.90E-1       2.34E-3      1.90E-1      1.91E-1      1.91E-1
    4.80E2        1.70E-1       2.08E-3      1.70E-1      1.69E-1      1.69E-1
    5.12E2        1.55E-1       1.95E-3      1.55E-1      1.58E-1      1.58E-1
```

```
THE FITTED STRAIGHT LINE HAS
SLOPE    = 8.51E1    PLUS OR MINUS 1.32E0
INTERCEPT= -8.41E-3   PLUS OR MINUS 3.79E-3
?
```

The speed of sound in air at 295 K $= c = (340 \pm 5)$ m s^{-1}. The end correction $= e = (8 \pm 4)$ mm.

Example 4

Options 2 and 3   The power, P, dissipated by a lamp. $P = cT^4$, assuming $T \gg T_0$ (room temperature in K). A graph of P against T^4 should be a straight line through the origin (option 2). A graph of $\log_{10}(P)$ against $\log_{10}(T)$ should be a straight line of slope 4; the intercept is of no interest (Option 3).

(Data input omitted.)

```
CHOOSE AN OPTION

ENTER NEW SET OF DATA                                           1

FIT Y TO ANY POWER AGAINST X TO ANY POWER (INC ONE)   2
FIT LOG(10)Y AGAINST LOG(10)X                                    3
FIT LOG(E)Y AGAINST X                                            4
FIT LOG(E)Y AGAINST 1/X                                         5

EXIT FROM PROGRAM                                               6
?2
X IS IN KELVIN
WHAT POWER OF X DO YOU WANT TO FIT ?4

Y IS IN WATTS
WHAT POWER OF Y DO YOU WANT TO FIT ?1
```

```
STEFAN'S LAW***POWER DISSIPATED BY A LAMP
X              Y              X^4.00E0     Y^1.00E0     FITTED VALUE FITTED VALUE
KELVIN         WATTS                                    Y^1.00E0     OF Y
     7.46E2         1.44E0         3.10E11      1.44E0         1.34E0       1.34E0
     1.06E3         3.30E0         1.25E12      3.30E0         3.84E0       3.84E0
     1.12E3         5.04E0         1.55E12      5.04E0         4.65E0       4.65E0
     1.31E3         8.12E0         2.91E12      8.12E0         8.27E0       8.27E0
     1.45E3         1.18E1         4.43E12      1.18E1         1.23E1       1.23E1
     1.53E3         1.64E1         5.45E12      1.64E1         1.50E1       1.50E1
     1.64E3         1.90E1         7.18E12      1.90E1         1.96E1       1.96E1

THE FITTED STRAIGHT LINE HAS
SLOPE    = 2.66E-12 PLUS OR MINUS 1.08E-13
INTERCEPT= 5.14E-1  PLUS OR MINUS 4.33E-1
?
```

Intercept on the P-axis $=$ (0.5 ± 0.4) W.

```
CHOOSE AN OPTION

ENTER NEW SET OF DATA                                      1

FIT Y TO ANY POWER AGAINST X TO ANY POWER (INC ONE)   2
FIT LOG(10)Y AGAINST LOG(10)X                         3
FIT LOG(E)Y AGAINST X                                 4
FIT LOG(E)Y AGAINST 1/X                               5

EXIT FROM PROGRAM                                     6
?3

STEFAN'S LAW***POWER DISSIPATED BY A LAMP
X              Y              LOG(10)X     LOG(10)Y     FITTED VALUE FITTED VALUE
KELVIN         WATTS                                    LOG(10)Y     OF Y
     7.46E2         1.44E0         2.87E0       1.58E-1        1.03E-1      1.27E0
     1.06E3         3.30E0         3.02E0       5.19E-1        6.17E-1      4.14E0
     1.12E3         5.04E0         3.05E0       7.02E-1        6.97E-1      4.98E0
     1.31E3         8.12E0         3.12E0       9.10E-1        9.29E-1      8.50E0
     1.45E3         1.18E1         3.16E0       1.07E0         1.08E0       1.21E1
     1.53E3         1.64E1         3.18E0       1.21E0         1.16E0       1.45E1
     1.64E3         1.90E1         3.21E0       1.28E0         1.26E0       1.83E1

THE FITTED STRAIGHT LINE HAS
SLOPE    = 3.40E0    PLUS OR MINUS 1.68E-1
INTERCEPT= -9.65E0   PLUS OR MINUS 5.20E-1
?
```

Slope $= 3.4 \pm 0.2$.

Example 5

Option 4   The measurement of the half-life, $T_{\frac{1}{2}}$, of a radioactive source. The rate of decay, $I(t)$, with time t is $I_0 \exp(-\lambda t)$; λ is the decay constant. A graph of $\log_e(I)$ against t should be a straight line of slope $-\lambda$.

```
CHOOSE AN OPTION

ENTER NEW SET OF DATA                                      1

FIT Y TO ANY POWER AGAINST X TO ANY POWER (INC ONE)   2
FIT LOG(10)Y AGAINST LOG(10)X                         3
FIT LOG(E)Y AGAINST X                                 4
FIT LOG(E)Y AGAINST 1/X                               5
```

```
EXIT FROM PROGRAM                                    6
?1


WHAT TITLE DO YOU WANT TO GIVE THIS EXPERIMENT (MAX  75 CHARACTERS)
?RADIOACTIVE HALF-LIFE OF 220/86 Rn
HOW MANY DATA POINTS DO YOU HAVE ?11

WHAT UNIT IS X MEASURED IN
(NOT MORE THAN 10 CHARACTERS) ?SECONDS

WHAT UNIT IS Y MEASURED IN
(NOT MORE THAN 10 CHARACTERS ) ?MILLIAMPS

PLEASE ENTER DATA
X VALUE FIRST,THEN Y VALUE SEPARATED BY A COMMA
X,Y ?0,.86
X,Y ?10,.78
X,Y ?20,.7
X,Y ?300,.65
X,Y ?40,.55
X,Y ?50,.49
X,Y ?60,.42
X,Y ?70,.37
X,Y ?80,.35
X,Y ?90,.32
X,Y ?100,.28


DATA PT.     X VALUE           Y VALUE
1.00E0      0.00E0            8.60E-1
2.00E0      1.00E1            7.80E-1
3.00E0      2.00E1            7.00E-1
4.00E0      3.00E2            6.50E-1
5.00E0      4.00E1            5.50E-1
6.00E0      5.00E1            4.90E-1
7.00E0      6.00E1            4.20E-1
8.00E0      7.00E1            3.70E-1
9.00E0      8.00E1            3.50E-1
1.00E1      9.00E1            3.20E-1
1.10E1      1.00E2            2.80E-1

IS DATA NOW CORRECT ?NO
WHICH NUMBER DATA POINT IS WRONG ?4
O.K. WHAT SHOULD POINT        4.00E0     BE ?
X,Y ?30,0.65
DATA PT.     X VALUE           Y VALUE
1.00E0      0.00E0            8.60E-1
2.00E0      1.00E1            7.80E-1
3.00E0      2.00E1            7.00E-1
4.00E0      3.00E1            6.50E-1
5.00E0      4.00E1            5.50E-1
6.00E0      5.00E1            4.90E-1
7.00E0      6.00E1            4.20E-1
8.00E0      7.00E1            3.70E-1
9.00E0      8.00E1            3.50E-1
1.00E1      9.00E1            3.20E-1
1.10E1      1.00E2            2.80E-1

IS DATA NOW CORRECT ?Y

CHOOSE AN OPTION

ENTER NEW SET OF DATA                                1

FIT Y TO ANY POWER AGAINST X TO ANY POWER (INC ONE)  2
```

```
FIT LOG(10)Y AGAINST LOG(10)X                           3
FIT LOG(E)Y AGAINST X                                   4
FIT LOG(E)Y AGAINST 1/X                                 5

EXIT FROM PROGRAM                                       6
?4
```

```
RADIOACTIVE HALF-LIFE OF 220/86 Rn
X               Y              X           LOG(E)Y      FITTED VALUE FITTED VALUE
SECONDS         MILLIAMPS                               LOG(E)Y      OF  Y
      0.00E0    8.60E-1        0.00E0      -1.51E-1      -1.36E-1     8.73E-1
      1.00E1    7.80E-1        1.00E1      -2.48E-1      -2.51E-1     7.78E-1
      2.00E1    7.00E-1        2.00E1      -3.57E-1      -3.66E-1     6.93E-1
      3.00E1    6.50E-1        3.00E1      -4.31E-1      -4.81E-1     6.18E-1
      4.00E1    5.50E-1        4.00E1      -5.98E-1      -5.96E-1     5.51E-1
      5.00E1    4.90E-1        5.00E1      -7.13E-1      -7.11E-1     4.91E-1
      6.00E1    4.20E-1        6.00E1      -8.68E-1      -8.26E-1     4.38E-1
      7.00E1    3.70E-1        7.00E1      -9.94E-1      -9.41E-1     3.90E-1
      8.00E1    3.50E-1        8.00E1      -1.05E0       -1.06E0      3.48E-1
      9.00E1    3.20E-1        9.00E1      -1.14E0       -1.17E0      3.10E-1
      1.00E2    2.80E-1        1.00E2      -1.27E0       -1.29E0      2.76E-1
```

```
THE FITTED STRAIGHT LINE HAS
SLOPE    = -1.15E-2   PLUS OR MINUS 2.67E-4
INTERCEPT= -1.36E-1   PLUS OR MINUS 1.58E-2
?
```

$\lambda = (0.0115 \pm 0.0003)$ s^{-1}.

$T_{\frac{1}{2}} = \log_e 2/\lambda = (60 \pm 2)$ s.

The intercept on the $(\log_e I)$-axis $= \log_e I_0 = (-0.136 \pm 0.016)$. (The extra decimal place is retained for the calculation of I_0). $I_0 = (0.87 \pm 0.01)$ mA (measured value of $I_0 = 0.86$ mA).

Example 6

Option 5   The variation of the resistance R of a semiconductor with temperature T (in kelvin) is theoretically expected to be of the form $R = A \exp (\alpha/T)$. A graph of $\log_e (R)$ against $1/T$ should be a straight line, slope α.

```
WHAT TITLE DO YOU WANT TO GIVE THIS EXPERIMENT (MAX  75 CHARACTERS)
?VARIATION OF THE RESISTANCE OF A SEMICONDUCTOR WITH TEMPERATURE
HOW MANY DATA POINTS DO YOU HAVE ?11

WHAT UNIT IS X MEASURED IN
(NOT MORE THAN 10 CHARACTERS) ?KELVIN

WHAT UNIT IS Y MEASURED IN
(NOT MORE THAN 10 CHARACTERS ) ?OHMS

PLEASE ENTER DATA
X VALUE FIRST,THEN Y VALUE SEPARATED BY A COMMA
X,Y ?273,92
X,Y ?283,41
X,Y ?293,27
X,Y ?303,19
X,Y ?313,13.4
X,Y ?323,10.2
X,Y ?333,8.1
X,Y ?3423,6.9
X,Y ?353,5.4
```

```
X,Y ?363,5.1
X,Y ?373,4.1
DATA PT.        X VALUE          Y VALUE
1.00E0          2.73E2           9.20E1
2.00E0          2.83E2           4.10E1
3.00E0          2.93E2           2.70E1
4.00E0          3.03E2           1.90E1
5.00E0          3.13E2           1.34E1
6.00E0          3.23E2           1.02E1
7.00E0          3.33E2           8.10E0
8.00E0          3.43E2           6.90E0
9.00E0          3.53E2           5.40E0
1.00E1          3.63E2           5.10E0
1.10E1          3.73E2           4.10E0


IS DATA NOW CORRECT ?YES

CHOOSE AN OPTION

ENTER NEW SET OF DATA                                      1

FIT Y TO ANY POWER AGAINST X TO ANY POWER (INC ONE)        2
FIT LOG(10)Y AGAINST LOG(10)X                              3
FIT LOG(E)Y AGAINST X                                      4
FIT LOG(E)Y AGAINST 1/X                                    5

EXIT FROM PROGRAM                                          6
?5

VARIATION OF THE RESISTANCE OF A SEMICONDUCTOR WITH TEMPERATURE
```

X	Y	1/X	LOG(E)Y	FITTED VALUE	FITTED VALUE
KELVIN	OHMS			LOG(E)Y	OF Y
2.73E2	9.20E1	3.66E-3	4.52E0	4.14E0	6.31E1
2.83E2	4.10E1	3.53E-3	3.71E0	3.76E0	4.30E1
2.93E2	2.70E1	3.41E-3	3.30E0	3.41E0	3.01E1
3.03E2	1.90E1	3.30E-3	2.94E0	3.07E0	2.16E1
3.13E2	1.34E1	3.19E-3	2.60E0	2.76E0	1.58E1
3.23E2	1.02E1	3.10E-3	2.32E0	2.47E0	1.18E1
3.33E2	8.10E0	3.00E-3	2.09E0	2.19E0	8.98E0
3.43E2	6.90E0	2.92E-3	1.93E0	1.94E0	6.93E0
3.53E2	5.40E0	2.83E-3	1.69E0	1.69E0	5.43E0
3.63E2	5.10E0	2.75E-3	1.63E0	1.46E0	4.31E0
3.73E2	4.10E0	2.68E-3	1.41E0	1.24E0	3.47E0

```
THE FITTED STRAIGHT LINE HAS
SLOPE     = 2.95E3    PLUS OR MINUS 1.58E2
INTERCEPT= -6.68E0    PLUS OR MINUS 4.96E-1
?
```

Slope $= \alpha = (2954 \pm 158)$ K. (The fourth significant figure is retained only for calculation.)

Theoretically, $\alpha = E_g/k$, where $E_g =$ energy gap in the semiconductor and k is the Boltzmann constant $= 1.38 \times 10^{-23}$ J K^{-1}.

Thus $E_g = (4.1 \pm 0.2) \times 10^{-20}$ J or (0.26 ± 0.02) eV.

The intercept is of no interest in this experiment.

APPENDIX 3   A SELECTION OF PHYSICAL CONSTANTS

TABLE A3.1   PHYSICAL AND MATHEMATICAL CONSTANTS

$e = 2.718$ $\log_e 10 = 2.303$ $\log_e 2 = 0.693$ $\pi = 3.142$
1 radian $= 57.30°$ $1° = 0.0175$ radians

Speed of light in free space	c	2.998×10^8 m s^{-1}
Permeability of free space	μ_0	$4\pi \times 10^{-7}$ H m^{-1}
Permittivity of free space	ε_0	8.854×10^{-12} F m^{-1}
Mass of the electron	m_e	9.109×10^{-31} kg
Charge on the electron	$-e$	1.602×10^{-19} C
Specific charge for an electron	e/m_e	1.759×10^{11} C kg^{-1}
Boltzmann constant	k	1.381×10^{-23} J K^{-1}
Planck constant	h	6.626×10^{-34} J s
Ratio h/e	h/e	4.136×10^{-15} J s C^{-1}
Rydberg constant for hydrogen	R_H	1.097×10^7 m^{-1}
The first Bohr radius	a_0	5.29×10^{-11} m
Avogadro constant	N_A	6.023×10^{23} mol^{-1} or 6.023×10^{26} kg mol^{-1}
The Electronvolt	eV	1.602×10^{-19} J

TABLE A3.2   VARIATIONS OF THE ACCELERATION OF FREE FALL DUE TO GRAVITY

The standard value of $g = 9.81$ m s^{-2}(N kg^{-1}).

g varies with the latitude λ according to $g/$m s$^{-2} = 9.8062 - 0.0259 \cos 2\lambda$.

Latitude/degrees	0	10	20	30	40	50	60	70	80	90
$g/$m s^{-2}	9.780	9.782	9.786	9.793	9.802	9.811	9.819	9.826	9.831	9.832

The variation of g with altitude can be considered to be negligible for experiments on the surface of the earth.

TABLE A3.3   DENSITY AND MASS PER UNIT LENGTH FOR SELECTED MATERIALS

Density (kg m^{-3}) **at 293 K**

Aluminium	2710	Brass (70Cu/30Zn)	8800	Copper	8930
Iron (pure)	7870	Lead	11340	Mercury	13550 (13590 at 273 K)
Steel (mild)	7860	Stainless steel (18Cr/8Ni)	7930	Steel (piano wire)	7800
Cotton	1500	Wood (spruce)	400–600	Wood (oak)	700

Water   999.8 (273 K)   999.7 (283 K)   998.2 (293 K)   995.7 (303 K); maximum density 1000 at 277 K
Air   1.3 (varies slightly)

Mass per unit length $(10^{-3}\ \text{kg m}^{-1}$ or $\text{g m}^{-1})$

SWG stands for standard wire gauge; although replaced by metric sizes many schools have large stocks of wire in SWG.

SWG	Diameter/mm	Copper	Iron	Steel (piano wire)
24	0.559	2.19	1.93	1.91
26	0.457	1.46	1.29	1.28
28	0.376	0.99	0.87	0.87
30	0.315	0.70	0.61	0.61
32	0.274	0.53	0.46	0.46
34	0.234	0.38	0.34	0.34
36	0.193	0.26	0.23	0.23
38	0.152	0.16	0.14	0.14
Metric	0.500	1.75	1.54	1.53
	0.400	1.12	0.99	0.98
	0.315	0.70	0.61	0.61
	0.250	0.44	0.38	0.38
	0.200	0.28	0.25	0.25
	0.160	0.18	0.16	0.16

TABLE A3.4 MECHANICAL PROPERTIES OF MATERIALS (at 293 K)

σ_T = tensile strength (stress to cause fracture/breaking)
σ_Y = yield strength for metals only
E = the Young modulus = tensile stress/tensile strain
ε = percentage elongation at fracture/breaking

Material		σ_T/MPa	σ_Y/MPa	ε/%	E/GPa
Copper	cast	150	75	45	117
	wire	280–310	140–160	5–10	117
Iron	cast	300	165	45	206
	wire	460	250	5–10	206
Steel (mild)	cast	460	300	35	210
	wire	1100	600	5–10	210
Steel (piano wire)		1860–2330	600	—	210
Nylon		60–80	—	60–300	0.8–3.1
Polythene[a]		15–29	—	600–350	0.15–1.0
Rubber[b]		17–35	—	450–850	0.001 (ε = 25%), 0.01 (ε = 500%)
Wood (parallel to the grain)[c]		18–21	—	—	12–16

Notes on the above table

a The first figure in the range corresponds to low density polythene and the second figure corresponds to high density polythene.

b E for natural (not cross-linked) rubber increases markedly once all the polymer chains have been stretched. Artificial rubber (polyisoprene) has the lower value for σ_T but its value of E can be as high as 0.02 GPa.

c Laminated woods have much higher values for σ_T and E. E perpendicular to the wood grain is only 1 GPa.

The mechanical strength of wires (at 293 K)

SWG refers to standard wire gauge. F/N refers to the tensile force required to produce yielding in the wire.

SWG	Diameter/mm	F/N		
		Copper	Iron	Steel (piano wire)
24	0.559	37	61	147
26	0.457	25	41	98
28	0.376	17	27	67
30	0.315	12	19	47
32	0.274	8.9	15	36
34	0.234	6.3	11	26
36	0.193	4.4	7.2	18
38	0.152	2.7	4.5	11
Metric	0.500	29	49	118
	0.400	19	31	75
	0.315	12	19	47
	0.250	7.4	12	30
	0.200	4.7	7.8	19
	0.160	3.0	5.0	12

TABLE A3.5   THE VISCOSITY OF SELECTED LIQUIDS

Temperature = 293 K

	Density/ kg m^{-3}	Viscosity/ N s m^{-2}
Water	998	0.0010
Glycerol (propane-1,2,3-triol)	1262	1.49
Paraffin oil	800	1.0

Variation of the viscosity (η/N s m^{-2}) of liquids with temperature

T/K	273	283	288	293	298	303
Water	0.0018	0.0013	0.0011	0.0010	0.00089	0.00080
Glycerol	10.6	3.44	2.41	1.49	0.94	0.66

Variation of the viscosity (η/N s m^{-2}) of glycerol with the percentage water content

Glycerol (%)	Relative density	288 K	293 K	298 K	303 K
100	1.262	2.41	1.49	0.94	0.66
99	1.259	1.98	1.19	0.77	0.51
98	1.257	1.52	0.97	0.63	0.42
97	1.254	1.25	0.80	0.52	0.35
96	1.252	1.02	0.66	0.43	0.30
95	1.249	0.84	0.54	0.36	0.25

The viscosity of air

η varies with temperature (it is proportional to the square root of the temperature in kelvin). For air the values are: $\eta/10^{-6}$ N s m^{-2} is 17.3 at 273 K; 18.2 at 293 K.

TABLE A3.6 THE SPEED OF SOUND WAVES

In dry air at 273 K $c = 331.5$ m s^{-1}; c is proportional to the square root of the temperature in kelvin.

c also varies with the humidity of the air: it decreases to a minimum value of 0.9995 c_0 for 14% relative humidity; for a relative humidity greater then 30%, c increases linearly to 1.0034 c_0 at 100% relative humidity. Note that from the simple theory $c = \sqrt{\gamma RT/M_m}$ for a gas of molar mass M_m, you may expect c to increase uniformly with the water vapour content.

TABLE A3.7 REFRACTIVE INDEX FOR SELECTED SOLIDS AND LIQUIDS
(against air for $\lambda = 587.6$ nm and at 293 K)

Glasses

Crown	1.48–1.61	Light barium crown	1.54	Dense barium crown	1.61
Flint	1.53–1.96	Light flint	1.58	Dense flint	1.62

Liquids

Ethanol (ethyl alcohol)	1.36
Glycerol (propane-1,2,3-triol)	1.47
Liquid paraffin	1.48
Water	1.33

The refractive index n also varies with wavelength (dispersion): for water the values are 1.343 at 405 nm, 1.333 at 588 nm and 1.331 at 671 nm. The variation in n is about 0.01 for the wavelength range 400–650 nm.

TABLE A3.8 WAVELENGTHS OF SPECTRAL LINES FROM SELECTED SOURCES (in nm)

Cadmium (standard wavelengths)

Blue 467.8	Blue 480.0	Green 508.6	Red 643.8

Mercury

Violet 404.7   Blue 435.8   Green 546.1   Yellow 577.0 and 579.0

Hydrogen (atomic spectrum, Balmer series)

δ violet 410.2 γ blue 434.0 β blue–green 486.1 α red 656.3

Sodium (obsolete standard)

Orange (D2) 589.0   Orange (D1) 589.6

TABLE A3.9 OPTICAL FILTERS

The wavelength bands given correspond to greater than 10% transmission of the maximum transmission of the filter (usually in the centre of the range).

Wavelength range/nm	Ilford filter	Kodak Wratten filter
380–450	I601	W76 (400–470 nm)
440–490	I602	W50 (mercury monochromat 430–480 nm)
470–520	I603	W75
500–540	I604	W74 (mercury monochromat 520–560 nm)
530–570	I605	
560–610	I606	W73
575–610	I607	W72B (590–630 nm)
620–700	I608	
660–700	I609	W70

Two other useful filters are W44 (complementary cyan 440–550 nm) and W12 (complementary yellow 520–700 nm).

Recommended filters for the mercury spectrum

Violet	404.7 nm Chance-Pilkington OV1+OY10 or Leybold 46833
Blue	435.8 nm W50 or Ilford 806
Green	546.1 nm W74 or Ilford 807
Yellow	577/579 nm Chance-Pilkington OY1 or Ilford 808

Filter set

The standard filter set consists of the following Ilford filters:

Blue 602	Blue–green 603	Yellow–green 605	Orange 607	Red 608

TABLE A3.10   SELECTED THERMAL PROPERTIES OF MATERIALS

$\theta/\,^\circ\mathrm{C} = T/\mathrm{K} - 273.15$

Melting points/K (at standard atmospheric pressure)

Ice 273	Paraffin wax 330	Napthalene 353

Boiling points/K (at standard atmospheric pressure)

Ethanol (ethyl alcohol) 352	Methanol (methyl alcohol) 337	Water 373	Glycerol (propane-1,2,3-triol) 563

Specific heat capacity/J kg^{-1} K^{-1} (at 293 K)
Metals

Aluminium 878	Copper 381	Iron (pure) 106	Iron (wrought) 480	Brass (70Cu/30Zn) 370

Non-metals

Ice 2100	Napthalene 1310	Paraffin wax 2900

Liquids

Ethanol (ethyl alcohol) 2500	glycerol(propane-1,2,3-triol) 2400	Water 4182

Variation of specific heat capacity with temperature

There is a small variation of the specific heat capacity with temperature:

Aluminium	796 J kg^{-1} K^{-1} at 200 K and 952 J kg^{-1} K^{-1} at 400 K
Copper	357 J kg^{-1} K^{-1} at 200 K and 395 J kg^{-1} K^{-1} at 400 K

This variation is given in detail for water:

T/K	273	278	283	288	293	298	303	308	313	318	323	333	353	373
$c/\mathrm{J\ kg^{-1}\ K^{-1}}$	4217	4202	4192	4186	4182	4179	4178	4178	4178	4179	4180	4184	4196	4216

Specific latent heat of fusion

Ice 334×10^3 J kg^{-1}	Napthalene 149×10^3 J kg^{-1}

Specific latent heat of vaporisation

Ethanol (ethyl alcohol) 0.84×10^6 J kg^{-1}	Water 2.26×10^6 J kg^{-1}	Glycerol(propane-1,2,3-triol) 0.83×10^6 J kg^{-1}
Methanol(methyl alcohol) 1.12×10^6 J kg^{-1}		

Thermal conductivity/W m^{-1} K^{-1} (at 293 K)

Metals

Aluminium 236	Copper 385	Iron (pure) 80	Iron (wrought) 60	Brass (70Cu/30Zn) 110

Non-metals

Cardboard 0.21	Cork 0.04–0.05	Glass (flint-crown) 0.8–1.1	Perspex 0.2	Wood 0.14–0.17

Liquids and gases

Water 0.59   Glycerol(propane-1,2,3-triol) 0.29
Air 0.024 at 273 K increasing to 0.032 at 373 K

Variation of thermal conductivity with temperature

There is a small variation of thermal conductivity with temperature for solids:

Copper   400 W m^{-1} K^{-1} at 273 K and 380 W m^{-1} K^{-1} at 373 K
Iron   82 W m^{-1} K^{-1} at 273 K and 69 W m^{-1} K^{-1} at 373 K

TABLE A3.11   PROPERTIES OF GASES AND VAPOURS

Atmospheric pressure (standard) $= 1.013 \times 10^5$ Pa

Variation of atmospheric pressure with altitude

h/m	−250	0	+250	+500	+750	+1000	+1500	+2000	+3000	+4000	+5000
$P_A/10^3$ Pa	104.4	101.3	98.4	95.5	92.6	89.9	84.6	79.5	70.1	61.7	54.0

Variation of the saturated vapour pressure of water with temperature

T/K	273	283	293	303	313	323	333	343	353	363	373	383
$P/10^3$ Pa	0.6	1.2	2.3	4.2	7.4	12.3	19.9	31.2	47.4	70.1	101.3	143.3

TABLE A3.12   ELECTRICAL PROPERTIES OF METALS, ALLOYS AND SEMICONDUCTORS (at 293 K)

Resistivity and the temperature coefficient of resistivity/resistance

	Resistivity/ 10^{-8} Ω m	Temperature coefficient of resistivity/K^{-1}
Copper	1.73	0.0039 (0.0043 averaged 0–100 °C)
Iron	10	0.0065
Constantan (55Cu/45Ni) (eureka)	49	Approximately zero ($\pm$0.00004)
Monel (70Ni/30Cu)	45	0.0020
Nichrome (80Ni/20Cr)	108	Approximately zero (0.00001)
Manganin (84Cu/12Mn)	41	Zero
Steel (piano wire)	20	0.0050

Energy gap between valence and conduction bands for selected semiconductors (at 300 K)

Pure germanium 1.07×10^{-19} J or 0.67 eV
Pure silicon 1.83×10^{-19} J or 1.14 eV

Some intermetallic compounds and all doped semiconductors have energy gaps significantly smaller than these values.

SWG refers to standard wire gauge (now obsolete).

SWG	Diameter/mm	Copper	Iron	Constantan	Manganin	Nichrome	Steel (piano wire)
20	0.914	0.0263	0.15	0.746	0.632	1.64	0.30
22	0.711	0.0434	0.25	1.23	1.04	2.72	0.50
24	0.559	0.0703	0.41	2.00	1.69	4.40	0.82
26	0.457	0.105	0.61	2.98	2.53	6.58	1.22
28	0.376	0.155	0.90	4.41	3.74	9.73	1.80
30	0.315	0.221	1.28	6.29	5.33	13.9	2.57
32	0.274	0.292	1.69	8.29	7.02	18.3	3.38
34	0.234	0.402	2.33	11.4	9.68	25.2	4.66
36	0.193	0.589	3.42	16.7	14.2	36.9	6.83
38	0.152	0.946	5.48	26.9	22.8	59.2	11.0
40	0.122	1.48	8.56	42.0	35.5	92.5	17.1
Metric	0.500	0.0879	0.51	2.50	2.11	5.50	1.02
	0.400	0.137	0.80	3.90	3.30	8.59	1.59
	0.315	0.221	1.28	6.29	5.33	13.9	2.57
	0.250	0.351	2.04	10.0	8.45	22.0	4.07
	0.200	0.549	3.18	15.6	13.2	34.4	6.37
	0.160	0.858	4.97	24.4	20.8	53.7	9.95
	0.125	1.41	8.15	39.9	33.8	88.7	16.3
	0.100	2.20	12.7	62.4	52.8	138	25.5

TABLE A3.14   STANDARD CELLS

Weston (cadmium) cell at 20 °C
e.m.f. = 1.0186 V

Clark cell at 15 °C
e.m.f. = 1.4333 V

The temperature variation of the e.m.f. is calculated using the equation:

e.m.f. at θ °C = $1.0186 - a(\theta - 20) - b(\theta - 20)^2$ V.

$a = 4.06 \times 10^{-5}$ K^{-1}, $b = 9.5 \times 10^{-7}$ K^{-2}

The temperature variation of the e.m.f. is calculated using the equation:

e.m.f. at θ °C = $1.4333 - a(\theta - 15) - b(\theta - 15)^2$ V.

$a = 1.19 \times 10^{-3}$ K^{-1}, $b = 7 \times 10^{-6}$ K^{-2}

TABLE A3.15   THERMOELECTRIC e.m.f. FOR SELECTED THERMO-COUPLE JUNCTIONS

e.m.f. in millivolts for a junction temperature difference of 100 °C:

Chromel–alumel 4.10   Copper–constantan 4.28   Iron–constantan 5.40   Platinum–platinum/rhodium (90/10) 0.64

TABLE A3.16   RELATIVE PERMITTIVITY OF SELECTED MATERIALS AT 293 K (STATIC VALUES)

Glass 5–10   Mica 5.7–6.7   Perspex 3.5   Polythene 2.2–2.4   Polystyrene 2.55
Polyvinyl chloride (PVC) (polychloroethane) 4.5   Water 80.37 (78.54 at 298 K)

TABLE A3.17   WORK FUNCTIONS FOR SELECTED MATERIALS

Caesium 2.14 V	Potassium 2.22 V

TABLE A3.18   ENERGY LEVELS FOR ATOMIC HYDROGEN

Principal quantum number (n)	$E/10^{-18}$ J	$E/$eV
1	−2.180	−13.6
2	−0.545	−3.40
3	−0.242	−1.51
4	−0.136	−0.849
5	−0.0872	−0.544
6	−0.0606	−0.378
7	−0.0445	−0.277
8	−0.0341	−0.212
9	−0.0269	−0.168
10	−0.0218	−0.136

The visible emission spectrum of hydrogen (the Balmer series) corresponds to transitions of the electron to the $n = 2$ state.

TABLE A3.19   RADIOACTIVE SOURCES IN COMMON USE IN SCHOOLS

Element	Z	A	Decay	Energy (particle)/MeV	Energy of γ/MeV	Half-life
Co	27	60	β^-, γ	0.31	1.17, 1.33	5.26 years (a)
{ Sr ↓	38	90	β^-	0.54	no gamma	28 years
Y	39	90	β^-	2.27	no gamma	64 hours
Rn(Tn)	86	220	α, γ	6.28	0.54	55 seconds
{ Ra ↓	88	226	α mainly	<u>4.78</u>; 4.60	<u>0.00</u>; 0.19	1620 years
Rn(Em) ↓	86	222	α, γ	5.49	0.51	3.83 days
Po(RaA) ↓	84	218	$\alpha, (\beta^-)$	α:6.00	no gamma	3.05 minutes
Pb(RaB) ↓	82	214	β^-	1.03	0.29–0.35	26.8 minutes
Bi(RaC)	83	214	$\beta^-, (\alpha)$	β^-:3.26	0.60–2.43	19.7 minutes
Pu	94	239	α, γ	<u>5.16</u>, 5.11	<u>0.00</u>, 0.04	24360 years
Am	95	241	α, γ	<u>5.49</u>, 5.44	<u>0.00</u>, 0.06	458 years

Notes: ( ) indicates an alternative decay route; underlined energy indicates the principal decay route; { indicates that these species are in radioactive equilibrium.

TABLE A3.20 ABSORPTION OF α-, β- and γ-RADIATIONS IN SELECTED MATERIALS

E is the particle energy in MeV.

μ_m is the mass absorption coefficient for γ-radiation in lead.

$x_{\frac{1}{2}}$ is the thickness of material required to reduce the initial beam intensity by 50% for γ-radiation in lead and β-particles in aluminium.

$(\rho x)_{\frac{1}{2}}$ is the mass thickness of aluminium required to reduce the β-particle intensity by 50%.

R is the thickness of material required to stop β-particles in aluminium and α-particles in air (at 288 K and 1 atmosphere pressure).

E/MeV	γ-radiation (in Pb)		β-radiation (in Al)			α-radiation (in air)
	$\mu_m/10^{-3}$ m^2 kg^{-1}	$x_{\frac{1}{2}}$/mm	$(\rho x)_{\frac{1}{2}}$/kg m^{-2}	$x_{\frac{1}{2}}$/mm	R/mm	R/mm
0.1	550	0.1	0.013	0.005	0.05	
0.2	99	0.6	0.039	0.01	0.16	
0.3	40	1.4	0.076	0.03	0.29	
0.4	23	2.6	0.11	0.04	0.44	
0.5	16	3.8	0.17	0.06	0.61	
0.6	12	5.0	0.22	0.08	0.78	
0.7	10	6.0	0.27	0.10	0.96	
0.8	8.7	6.9	0.34	0.13	1.1	
0.9	7.8	7.7	0.41	0.15	1.3	
1.0	7.0	8.6	0.48	0.18	1.6	
1.5	5.2	11.5	0.90	0.33	2.5	
2.0	4.5	13.3	1.30	0.48	3.5	
3.0	4.2	14.3	2.0	0.74	5.6	
4.0	4.2	14.3	3.0	1.1	7.4	26
5.0	4.2	14.3	4.5	1.7	9.3	35
6.0						46
7.0						59
8.0						74

μ_m for γ-radiation includes the contribution from Compton scattering.

Production of ion pairs by α-particles

Number of ion pairs produced	Distance from end point/mm
2600–3500	10
4600–5300	20
6330–6670	40
6010–6040	60
5290–5400	80
4800–4900	100

TABLE A3.21 RESISTOR CODES

Colour code

There are four bands: the first band indicates the first digit, the second band the second digit, the third band the number of zeros and the fourth band the tolerance (Fig. A3.1). (Some resistors are marked with five bands with the first three bands giving the digits.)

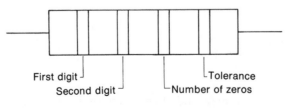

Fig. A3.1 Colour code for resistors.

The colour coding is:

Black 0	Brown 1	Red 2	Orange 3	Yellow 4
Green 5	Blue 6	Violet 7	Grey 8	White 9

Third band multipliers: Silver 0.01   Gold 0.1
Tolerance bands: No band 20%   Silver 10%   Gold 5%   Red 2%   Brown 1%

In composition resistors all bands are of equal width. In wire wound resistors band one is of double width.

Preferred values (from 0.22 Ω to 22 MΩ):

10	15	22	33	47	68	100

Example
Brown, black, orange, silver represents 10 kΩ $\pm$10%.

International code
The first letter shows the position of the decimal point: R ohms, K kilohms, M megohms.
The second letter shows the tolerance: F $\pm$1%, G $\pm$2%, J $\pm$5%, K $\pm$10%, M $\pm$20%.

Examples
1R0M = 1.0 Ω $\pm$20%, 100K0K = 100 kΩ $\pm$10%, 6K8G = 6.8 kΩ $\pm$2%, 4R7J = 4.7 Ω $\pm$5%,
4M7F = 4.7 MΩ $\pm$1%.

TABLE A3.22   CAPACITOR CODES

Colour code for polyester (acrylic) capacitors in picofarads (pF)
The colours used are identical to those used for resistors and represent the same numbers. There are five horizontal bands: the top or first band indicates the first digit, the second band the second digit and the third band the number of zeros. The fourth band indicates the tolerance: green $\pm$5%, white $\pm$10%, black $\pm$20%. The fifth band (nearest to the connecting wires) indicates the maximum working voltage: red 250 V, yellow 400 V (see Fig. A3.2).

Example
Yellow, violet, red, white, yellow represents 4700 pF $\pm$10%, V_{max} = 400 V. Where bands are identical you will see only a single wide band above the bottom two bands: a single red band followed by a white and a yellow band would indicate 2200 pF $\pm$10%, V_{max} = 400 V.

International code
In place of the decimal point a letter is used to indicate the size of the capacitor.

Example
2μ2 = 2.2 μF, 4n7 = 4.7 nF. The μ is often printed as a u.

Capacitors are also marked with two figures: the first figure is the capacitance in microfarads and the second figure is the maximum operating voltage.

Example
0.22/250 is 0.22 μF, V_{max} = 250 V.

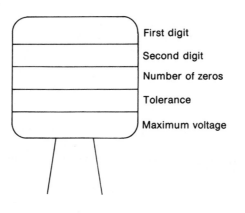

Fig. A3.2   Colour code for capacitors.

HINTS AND FURTHER GUIDANCE

2 MEASUREMENT, INSTRUMENTATION AND EXPERIMENTAL ERROR

Questions on errors (page 13)

a) $N = 15$ in equation [2.1] so $\bar{d} = 1.27$ mm.
From equation [2.2] $\sigma = 0.028$ mm $= 0.03$ mm.
The lowest (1.21 mm) and highest (1.32 mm) values of d are just within two standard deviations of the mean value of d.

b) Using equation [2.4a] $\Delta m = 1.2$ g (maximum error); from equation [2.4b]
$\Delta m_s = \sqrt{0.4^2 + 0.3^2 + 0.5^2} = 0.7$ g (standard error).

c) The error in both the sum and difference is 0.7 g (maximum error) or 0.5 g (standard error). The percentage error in the sum is 0.4% or 0.3%. The percentage error in the difference is 11.7% or 8.3%.

d) $\rho = M/V$, where $V = a \times b \times c$; $\Delta a/a = 1/100$ (1%), $\Delta b/b = 1/50$ (2%), $\Delta c/c = 1/20$ (5%),
$\Delta M/M = 1/270$ (0.4%). The last error may be neglected. Using equation [2.6a]
$\Delta\rho/\rho = 0.01 + 0.02 + 0.05 = 0.08$ (8%). The value of ρ is 2.7 g cm^{-3}. The maximum error in ρ is 0.2(2) g cm^{-3}.
From equation [2.6b], the percentage standard error in
$\rho = \sqrt{1^2 + 2^2 + 5^2} = 5.5\%$. The standard error in ρ is 0.1(5) g cm^{-3}.

e) $p = F/A$, $A = a \times b$; $\Delta F/F = 5/200$ (2.5%), $\Delta a/a = 2/50$ (4%), $\Delta b/b = 5/100$ (5%).
The maximum fractional error in
$p = 0.025 + 0.04 + 0.05 = 0.115$ (11.5%).
The standard fractional error in
$p = \sqrt{(0.025)^2 + (0.04)^2 + (0.05)^2} = 0.069$ (6.9%).

f) $s = v \times t = 60 \times 4 = 240$ km. $\Delta v/v = 3/60$ (5%), $\Delta t/t = 0.25/4$ (6.25%). The maximum percentage error in $s = 5 + 6.25 = 11\%$. $\Delta s = 27$ km and $s = (240 \pm 30)$ km.

The standard percentage error in $s = \sqrt{5^2 + 6.25^2} = 8\%$. $\Delta s = 19$ km and $s = (240 \pm 20)$ km.

g) $A = \pi r^2$. $A = 0.670$ m^2. From equation [2.7]
$\Delta A/A = 2\Delta r/r = 2 \times 5/146 = 0.068$ (6.8%).
The error in $A = 0.046$ m^2. $A = (0.67 \pm 0.05)$ m^2.

h) $g = 4\pi^2 l/T^2$. The value of $g = 9.86$ m s^{-2}.
$\Delta l/l = 2/600$ (0.3%).
$\Delta T/T = 1/155$ (0.65%). The maximum fractional error in $g = (\Delta l/l) + (2\Delta T/T) = 0.003 + 0.013 = 0.016$ (1.6%).
$\Delta g = 0.16$ m s^{-2}, $g = (9.9 \pm 0.2)$ m s^{-2}.

The standard percentage error in
$g = \sqrt{0.3^2 + 1.3^2} = 1.3\%$. $\Delta g = 0.13$ m s^{-2}, $g = (9.9 \pm 0.1)$ m s^{-2}.

i) $\mu = \sin i/\sin r$. $\mu = 1.51$. To calculate the error in μ calculate the maximum and minimum values of μ:
$\mu_{max} = \sin 48°/\sin 28° = 1.58$, $\mu_{min} = \sin 46°/\sin 30° = 1.44$. $\Delta\mu = (0.07 + 0.07)/2 = 0.07$ and $\mu = (1.51 \pm 0.07)$.

Vernier calliper readings (page 17)

a Between 12.2 and 12.3 cm; reading 12.27 cm.
b Between 3.6 and 3.7 cm; reading 3.63 cm.

Micrometer screw gauge readings (page 17)

a Main scale 3.00 mm, micrometer 0.47 mm (47 divisions); reading 3.47 mm.
b Main scale 17.50 mm, micrometer 0.24 mm (24 divisions); reading 17.74 mm.

3 INVESTIGATING RELATIONSHIPS : GRAPHICAL ANALYSIS

Advice on plotting a graph (page 20)

The defects on Fig. 3.9 are as follows:
a) Volume axis: no units (m^3).

b) Volume axis: awkward scale divisions.

c) Pressure should be the independent variable (x-axis) and volume the dependent variable (y-axis).

d) Pressure axis: poorly chosen scale, it should be from 0 to 2 N m^{-2} (or Pa) instead of 0 to 10 N m^{-2} (or Pa) and the units should probably have been $P/10^6$ N m^{-2} (or Pa) anyway.

e) If the purpose of the experiment was to investigate the relationship between pressure and volume, it would have been better to plot $1/V$ against P ($PV = $ constant), or PV against P to obtain a straight line and see whether Boyle's law is valid for the gas (see section 3.3).

4 DATA ANALYSIS

4A (page 30)

c   A graph of N against $1/x^2$ should be a straight line of slope c passing through the origin. The graph deviates from linearity for small x values (those of less than about 0.08 m).

f   Plot x against $1/N^{\frac{1}{2}}$. The slope of the line $= c^{\frac{1}{2}}$ and the intercept on the *negative* x-axis $= -e$.

g $c^{\frac{1}{2}} = (1.30 \pm 0.01)$, $c = (1.69 \pm 0.02)$, $e = (0.07 \pm 0.01)$ m. There is quite a large spread of experimental points. The introduction of the second variable e does improve the linearity of the data.

4B (page 31)

e   A graph of $\log_{10} (T/\text{s})$ against $\log_{10} (l/\text{m})$ should be a straight line. Note that logarithms of numbers less than unity are negative.

f   Slope $= n = (1.3 \pm 0.1)$; intercept on the $\log_{10} (T/\text{s})$ axis $= \log_{10} k = (-0.20 \pm 0.01)$; $k = (0.63 \pm 0.02)$.

g   The main reason for deviations from the theoretical relationship $(n = 1.5)$ is a result of the effective mass of the metre rule. This effect will decrease as the projecting length l decreases.

4C (page 31)

c $t_{\frac{1}{2}} = (75 \pm 5)$ s.

d   Slope $= -\lambda$; $\lambda = (0.0044 \pm 0.0001)$ s^{-1}.

e $t_{\frac{1}{2}} = (68 \pm 2)$ s. This result is considered to be more reliable since it is obtained as a result of drawing the best straight line, the equivalent of averaging over all the experimental results. The value obtained in (c) depends on how accurately a single point can be located on a curve.

4D (page 32)

c   A graph of $1/v$ against $1/u$ should be a straight line of slope -1; the intercepts on both axes are $1/f$. The values of the intercepts are both (0.067 ± 0.001) cm^{-1}.

d   Slope $= (-1.02 \pm 0.03)$; $f = (14.9 \pm 0.2)$ cm.

4E (page 32)

c   Values of $d\theta/dt$ in K min^{-1}: -2.4, -1.8, -1.5, -1.1, -0.9 (all ± 0.2).

d   Slope $= -k$; $k = (0.72 \pm 0.02) \times 10^{-3}$ s^{-1} (0.043 min^{-1}).

f   A graph of $\log_e [(\theta - \theta_R)/\text{K}]$ against t in s should be a straight line of slope $-k$. $k = (0.72 \pm 0.01) \times 10^{-3}$ s^{-1}.

4F (page 33)

c T should range from 300 K to 2300 K.

e   The best straight line at high temperatures, greater than about 1200 K, has a slope of (3.4 ± 0.4).

f   The correction varies from 2 W (at 1000 K) to 5 W (at 2500 K).

g   The range over which a single straight line can be drawn is larger than in (e). The slope is much closer to the theoretical value of 4. However, the main reason for deviations from the theoretical model is now the error in calculating θ (and T) assuming a linear increase in resistance with temperature and an average value for the temperature coefficient of resistance. More correctly, θ should be calculated using $R_\theta = R_0(1 + \alpha\theta + \beta\theta^2)$ with $\alpha = 4.8 \times 10^{-3}$ K^{-1} and $\beta = 1.0 \times 10^{-6}$ K^{-2} and solving the quadratic equation for θ. The error in θ is about 300 °C at 1700 °C.

5 INTRODUCTORY EXPERIMENTS

5A (page 36)

h   A graph of V against I should be a straight line of slope $-r$; the intercept on the V-axis (corresponding to V for $I = 0$) is $\mathcal{E}$. $r = (10.4 \pm 0.8)$ Ω; $\mathcal{E} = (1.60 \pm 0.04)$ V for a new dry cell.

The graph may curve slightly downwards at large values of I as a result of polarisation of the electrodes.

i   In principle the reading V_0 should be equal to the e.m.f. of the cell provided that a high resistance voltmeter (greater than 10 kΩ) is used. The value of $\mathcal{E}$ determined from the graph is not likely to be more reliable than the first value for V_0; an intercept is quite susceptible to experimental error. The second value for V_0 is probably too low as a result of drawing too high a current from a dry cell.

j   The switch is opened between readings to avoid draining too much electrical energy from the cell at these large currents. It is a bad method for the measurement of the e.m.f. of a dry cell since it is most likely that the e.m.f. has fallen or the internal resistance has risen by the end of the experiment. Ideally, a measurement of e.m.f. should draw no current from the source.

5B (page 36)

c   Using $l = T^2 g / 4\pi^2$, l should be about 1 metre.

i   Formally T is the dependent variable so a graph of T^2/s^2 (ordinate) against y/m (abscissa) should be plotted. Then the slope $s = 4\pi^2/g$ and the intercept on the T^2-axis $= 4\pi^2 a/g$. $a = $ intercept $\div$ slope. However, here it may be preferable to plot a graph of y/m (ordinate) against T^2/s^2 (abscissa), with a slope $s = g/4\pi^2$ and the intercept on the *negative y*-axis giving a directly.

$g = (9.8 \pm 0.4)$ N kg^{-1}; $a = (0.02 \pm 0.01)$ m.

l   You should find a way of fitting a protractor in line with the pendulum suspension with Plasticine. One problem in performing this experiment is the damping of the pendulum, so that the angle decreases over 10 oscillations. θ should be taken as the mean of its initial and final values.

Specimen results $(l = 1$ m$)$ requiring a stopwatch reading to 0.1 s for 10 oscillations are given in the table below.

T/s	$\theta_{mean}/°$	percentage error in T	percentage error in approximation $\sin \theta = \theta$
2.01	10	Reference	0.5
2.02	20	<0.15	2.0
2.03	30	1.0	4.5
2.06	40	2.4	7.9
2.09	50	4.0	12.2

Since $\sin \theta$ is less than θ in radians $(\sin \theta = \theta - \theta^3/6 + \ldots)$ it is expected that the measured value of T will be larger than that calculated using the simple pendulum equation.

m   The period T of a conical pendulum $= 2\pi\sqrt{l \cos \theta / g}$, where θ is the semi-angle of the cone.

For small angles, less than about 8°, the periods of the two pendulums are identical $(\cos 8° = 0.99)$ within experimental error.

5C (page 39)

i   For aluminium with $V = 10$ V and $I = 3.3$ A $(P = 33$ W$)$ the block takes about 20 minutes to reach a temperature 40 °C above room temperature.

j   The time taken to cool 10 °C below the maximum temperature is about 20 minutes.

l   Without a cooling correction $c_{Al} \simeq 960$ J kg^{-1} K^{-1}. Do not forget to convert t_1 into seconds.

m   The area A_2 is about twice the area A_1 (the values will depend on the scales you used for your axes). $\delta\theta_1 \simeq 5$ °C. $c_{Al} = (890 \pm 10)$ J kg^{-1} K^{-1}.

p   For the heating process $(d\theta/dt) = K\theta$, where $K = k/mc$ is a constant. Integrating this equation between the appropriate limits:

$$\int_0^{\delta\theta_1} d\theta = \int_0^{t_1} K\theta \, dt$$

The first integral is just $\delta\theta_1$ and the second integral is K times the area under the heating part of the $(\theta - t)$ curve, A_1. Thus $\delta\theta_1 = KA_1$.

For the cooling process the same equation is valid but the integration limits are different:

$$\int_0^{\delta\theta_2} d\theta = \int_{t_1}^{(t_1 + t_2)} K\theta \, dt$$

The first integral is $\delta\theta_2$ and the second integral is K times the area under the cooling curve between t_1 and $(t_1 + t_2)$, A_2. Thus $\delta\theta_2 = KA_2$.

The ratio $\delta\theta_1/\delta\theta_2$ is thererfore equal to A_1/A_2.

6 MECHANICS AND MECHANICAL PROPERTIES OF MATTER

6A (page 44)

l   A graph of $\tan \theta$ (ordinate) against m (abscissa) should be a straight line of slope $2/M$. $M = (0.125 \pm 0.005)$ kg.

m The agreement should be within ± 0.005 kg or 5 g.

o $m = 50$ g (0.05 kg): $mg = 0.49$ N, $Mg = 1.23$ N gives $R = 1.31$ N and $\alpha = 22°$. $m = 250$ g (0.25 kg): $mg = 2.45$ N, $Mg = 1.23$ N gives $R = 2.74$ N and $\alpha = 63°$.

q $m = 50$ g: $\theta = 40$–$45°$, so $\alpha = 23$–$27°$; $m = 250$ g: $\theta = 75$–$77°$, so $\alpha = 62$–$65°$. Agreement should be within $5°$.

r The assumption that the horizontal force is equal to mg depends on the friction between the pulley and thread being significantly less than mg. If there is any systematic deviation from linearity, it is expected to occur for low values of m. You may therefore expect a small intercept on the m axis. The intercept $\times g$ is a measure of this frictional force.

6B (page 46)

i A graph of s (ordinate) against t^2 (abscissa) should be a straight line of slope $g/2$. $g = (9.4 \pm 0.4)$ m s^{-2}. Alternatively a graph of $s^{\frac{1}{2}}$ against t can be plotted to give a straight line of slope $\sqrt{g/2}$. In both plots the intercepts on the time axes are within experimental error (0.02 s).

j All the factors listed will lead to high values for t and hence a low value for g. Only (iii) can be neglected as an insignificant effect.

l Take the square root of both sides of the equation: $(t_m - t_0) = \sqrt{2s/g}$ or $t_m = (\sqrt{2/g})s^{\frac{1}{2}} + t_0$. A graph of t_m (ordinate) against $s^{\frac{1}{2}}$ (abscissa) should be a straight line of slope $\sqrt{2/g}$. The intercept on the t_m axis is t_0. The value for g obtained is little different from the value determined in (i). The intercept on the t_m-axis is (0.02 ± 0.02) s and is therefore not statistically significant.

m If the smallest ball-bearing opens the shutter, you should find a significant effect as a result of air resistance. However, as this effect is likely to be less than 0.04 s, the effect for the largest ball-bearing is less than 0.01 s.

n The ball-bearing or other high density object (such as a steel bar) could be dropped between two photocells or phototransistors linked to a timer. Since the first photocell or phototransistor would be below the point of release of the ball-bearing, its initial velocity u would not be zero. In order to avoid the problem of determining u rearrange the equation as $(s/t) = u + \frac{1}{2}gt$. A graph of s/t against t should be a straight line of slope $\frac{1}{2}g$. The intercept on the s/t axis will be u.

6C (page 49)

h The error in u and v is about 0.05 m s^{-1} corresponding to a variation of 1 mm in the spacing on the dots on the ticker-tape.

j If $m_1 = m_2$, the initial kinetic energy is $\frac{1}{2}m_1u^2$ and the final kinetic energy is m_1v^2. From the principle of conservation of momentum $m_1u = 2m_1v$; hence $u = 2v$. The ratio final/initial kinetic energy is 0.5 or 50% loss in kinetic energy.

k This is not a very accurate calculation: although the velocity u just before collision can be measured accurately, the velocity on impact has to be calculated from very closely spaced dots. A reasonable value for m_1a is 10–20 N.

p The trolley m_1 should reverse its direction of motion after the collision. This result is expected and is derived in (q).

q Within experimental error the final velocity of m_1 is zero and the trolley of the same mass continues with the same initial velocity as m_1.

From the conservation of momentum $u_1 + 0 = v_1 + v_2$ for $m_1 = m_2$.
From the conservation of kinetic energy $\frac{1}{2}u_1^2 = \frac{1}{2}v_1^2 + \frac{1}{2}v_2^2$.

From the first equation substitute for u_1 in the kinetic energy equation: $(v_1 + v_2)^2 = v_1^2 + v_2^2$; hence $v_1v_2 = 0$ so $v_1 = 0$ or $v_2 = 0$. The latter result is of no interest since it indicates that the first trolley misses the second trolley. If $v_1 = 0$, $u_1 = v_2$. The result observed in (p) can be derived in a similar way using $m_2 = 2m_1$. The two equations are: $u_1 = v_1 + 2v_2$ and $u_1^2 = v_1^2 + 2v_2^2$. Substitute for $v_1 = 2v_2 - u_1$ in the second equation and show that $6v_2^2 = 4u_1v_2$. So $v_2 = 2u_1/3$ or 0 (of no interest). Hence $v_1 = -u_1/3$, that is, the first trolley travels backwards with a third of its initial velocity u_1.

r The agreement is usually quite poor. Friction compensation is not perfect. But the main factor is the impossibility of obtaining a perfectly elastic collision between the trolleys.

w The agreement is very good for trolleys of equal mass. Frictional forces affect the larger of the two masses more adversely. For equal masses, the frictional forces have exactly the same effect so v_2 is almost invariably equal to $-v_1$.

y The kinetic energy of the system is usually not constant. The release of the spring, and particularly the effect on the trolley it strikes, are quite variable.

6D (page 52)

h A graph of $P = Mg$ (ordinate) against T^{-2} (abscissa) should be a straight line through the origin. Frictional forces between the nylon line and tube will be most significant for the lever values of M. There may therefore be a small intercept on the P axis.

i The slope of the graph in (h) is $4\pi^2 mr$. $m = (0.02 \pm 0.01)$ kg.

j The agreement is unlikely to be better than ± 0.01 kg.

n A graph of T^2 (ordinate) against r (abscissa) should be a straight line of slope $4\pi^2 m/P$ passing through the origin. The value of m is usually the same as determined in (i) within experimental error.

o Friction between the nylon line and tube means that P is less than Mg. The intercept on the P-axis is not significant within experimental error.

p The monofilament has to support the weight of the rubber bung, mg. Thus a component of the tension P must be vertically upwards to support this weight and the filament must then be inclined to the horizontal.

The equation is quite correct but the value of the tension in the horizontal section of the line cannot be taken to be the same as the tension in the vertical section of the line. Friction acts between the inclined line and the edge of the tube and this factor must be included in any resolution of the forces acting.

6E (page 54)

h Dividing equation [6.11] by equation [6.10] for the same value of Mgh gives the required result.

i The slope is usually significantly greater than 0.75 as a result of the assumption that the mass of the hollow cylinder is all distributed at R. A value between 0.8 and 0.85 is quite reasonable.

j The second straight line corresponding to sliding of the cylinders is very difficult to draw. Its slope should theoretically be 1, since the rotational kinetic energy is zero. A value between 1.0 and 1.5 is usually obtained.

m The approximation is in error by 10–15% depending on the value of the internal radius in comparison with the external radius of the cylinder. The value of the ratio then increases to about 0.8. The agreement with experiment is improved.

6F (page 56)

k A typical value of I would be (0.020 ± 0.001) kg m^{-2}.

l The kinetic energy of the falling mass is usually less than 0.5% of the total kinetic energy $(= mgh)$.

n The frictional torque depends on the precise design of the flywheel bearing surfaces. It should be constant throughout the table with a typical value of 0.002 N m. The fractional loss in kinetic energy varies from 0.3 for the smallest mass down to 0.05 for the largest mass used.

o Values for the frictional torque agree with those in (n) within experimental error, $\pm 10\%$.

6G (page 57)

f The value of $F = Mg$ to cause fracture is about 3.6 N or a value of M of about 360 g.

j Since $F = (EA/l)e$, the slope of the straight line $\Delta F/\Delta e$ is EA/l. The value of E is (120 ± 20) GPa. The tensile strength is (200 ± 20) MPa. The fractional elongation at fracture is between 5% and 10%.

k The main difficulty in obtaining the complete curve is that the force is changed by using masses. It is not easy to remove or add these masses. The simplest way to obtain this curve is to use a horizontal version with the force applied using a spring balance attached to the end of the wire. The applied force is changed by using a screw mechanism attached to the other end of the spring balance with the mechanism firmly fixed to the bench. As the wire reaches its plastic region, a decrease in the spring balance reading should be observed.

l The breaking force should be about 2.9 N. But often nylon in the form of a monofilament only breaks at significantly larger forces.

n The slope of the force–extension graph is EA/l. For nylon $E = (2 \pm 1)$ GPa depending on the precise type of nylon.

r For cross-linked rubber $E = 1$–2 MPa.

u The linear polymer chains in natural rubber are coiled randomly. An applied force will first straighten these polymer chains and correspondingly the Young modulus is quite low. When the polymer chains are fully uncoiled, a much larger force is required to stretch the chains further. Natural rubber then behaves much more like a cross-linked polymer, where the chain movement is restricted by covalently bonded cross-links.

v The two values for E are about 0.5 MPa and 2 MPa.

y From a very short linear region only an approximate value of E can be obtained. For low density polythene (as used for most plastic bags) $E = 0.15$–0.20 GPa.

6H (page 61)

f For 26 SWG wire of diameter 0.457 mm, the maximum force should be less than 98 N. Subtracting 10 N as a safety margin, the wire can be loaded up to 88 N, corresponding to the addition of eight or nine 1 kg masses.

m Since $F = Mg = (EA/l)e$, a graph of M (ordinate) against e (abscissa) should be a straight line of slope (EA/lg) passing through the origin. The slope $s = (1300 \pm 10)$ kg m^{-1}, although this does depend on the diameter of wire used. $E = 202$ GPa.

n The fractional error in l is 0.005 (0.5%); the fractional error in d is 0.02 (2%) and for A it is therefore 0.04 (4%); the fractional error in the slope is usually very small, less than 0.01 (1%). The fractional error in E is therefore 0.05 (5%), so $\Delta E = 10$ GPa. $E = (200 \pm 10)$ GPa.

o The effect of the yielding of the support is minimised. With only one wire a yielding of 1 mm only would be significant. A second reason is the reduction of the effect of thermal expansion. A change in temperature of 1 K would produce a change in length of about 0.03 mm. This is small (although greater than the experimental error in measuring e) but it can be eliminated by using two identical wires.

p Consider what would happen if you were to suddenly add a load of 100 N to the wire. A suggestion is that the force would cause the wire to execute simple harmonic motion (as would occur if a mass were added to a spring). The amplitude of the oscillations would be small, but sufficient energy would be dissipated to explain the difference in the two energies.

6I (page 63)

g The density of steel is (7810 ± 40) kg m^{-3}.

n The graph gives a value of η of approximately 1.5 N s m^{-2} at 20 °C. Note that η is very dependent on temperature and the amount of water in the glycerol. A complete table of η is given in appendix 3 (Table A3.5, page 308).

p Theoretically it can be shown that the largest ball-bearing used reaches within 0.99 of its terminal velocity within a distance of 20 mm for $\eta = 1.5$ N s m^{-2}. Any differences found for the speed of the largest ball-bearing are more likely to be a result of temperature variations down the column of liquid. A change of temperature of 1 K causes a 0.1 N s m^{-2} change in η.

r The Ladenburg factor varies from 1.07 for the smallest ball-bearing to 1.38 for the largest ball-bearing and $R = 25$ mm.

s The slope of the graph is approximately 7% larger and so the value of η is likely to be lower than the value determined in (n). The point on the graph for the largest sphere still deviates significantly from the expected theoretical value.

t For the largest sphere the Reynolds number is about 0.4. This is not significantly less than one.

u The method is unsuitable for water because the terminal velocity for even the smallest sphere will approach 10 m s^{-1} (which cannot be measured accurately by hand timing) and it is unlikely that the terminal velocity will be achieved in a fall of less than 20 m. One solution would be to use spheres of a low density material but the lower limit for ρ_s is, of course, 1000 kg m^{-3}; this is an improvement of only a factor of 8 at most. η for low viscosity liquids is usually determined from the flow of the liquid through a capillary tube.

7 OSCILLATIONS AND WAVES

7A (page 67)

f The slope of the graph of M (ordinate) against e (abscissa) will depend on the spring used, but it should be about 1.5 kg m^{-1}. $k \simeq 15$ N m^{-1}.

j The occurrence of this phenomenon depends on the spring used, but it is likely to occur for a value of M between 100 and 200 g.

k A graph of T^2 (ordinate) against M (abscissa) should be a straight line of slope $4\pi^2/k$. This should be about 3 s^2 kg^{-1} (or m N^{-1}). k should again be about 15 N m^{-1}.

I Both graphs are normally linear, but you may notice that the T^2 against M graph does not go exactly through the origin (if you happen to have included this on your graph). This is a result of compression of the spring even for small oscillations and the effective mass of the spring m_0. Even for $M = 0$ the spring would oscillate with a finite period determined by m_0 equals approximately a third of the actual spring mass. Usually the intercept is less than 0.01 kg on the M-axis.

p $2T_v \approx T_h$.

q The correspondence is quite good, with $T_h \approx 1.6$–2.0 s $(T_v \approx 0.8$–1.0 s).

For T_h to be equal to T_v, l would have to be equal to e. This is only possible if the natural length of the spring l_0 is zero!

The other possibility is that the frequency of the vertical oscillation f_v is twice that of the horizontal oscillation f_h, that is $2T_v = T_h$. This will occur when $l = 4e$; you can confirm that the extension e is approximately 0.25 of the total length of the oscillating system l. The next possibility is $f_v = 3f_h$ or $3T_v = T_h$. This leads to $l = 9e$, a point that is not usually detected for normal loading of the spring.

7B (page 71)

p Taking logarithms to the base 10 of both sides of the equation gives $\log_{10} a_N = \log_{10} a_0 - N \log_{10} \delta$. A graph of $\log_{10} a_N$ (ordinate) against N (abscissa) should be a straight line of slope $-\log_{10} \delta$. The intercept on the $\log_{10} a_N$ axis is $\log_{10} a_0$. The values for $\log_{10} \delta$ depend on the galvanometer used and the precise values for the resistances used. The first values with R_d effectively infinite should be between 0.04 and 0.08 for $\log_{10} \delta$ and between 1.1 and 1.2 for δ. With $R_d = 3000$ Ω, $\log_{10} \delta = 0.10$–0.25 and $\delta = 1.3$–1.8.

7C (page 72)

d $f_0 = (0.50 \pm 0.01)$ Hz.

g This cannot usually be observed because the amplitude of the second resonance is significantly smaller than that of the first resonance. Its effect will then only be seen as a slight flattening of the resonance curve around $f = 2f_0$.

h There is no significant difference in the resonant frequency.

7D (page 75)

e The separation of the minima should be about 0.15 m.

f You should be able to detect 4 or 5 minima.

g $\lambda \approx 0.3$ m. The error in detecting the minima is about 10 mm.

h You should be able to detect about 10 minima.

i It is usually possible to just detect two minima, but the one nearest to the loudspeaker is poorly defined. Therefore it is preferable to use a sufficiently high frequency to give several measurable minima well away from the loudspeaker.

j A graph of λ (ordinate) against $1/f$ (abscissa) should be a straight line of slope c. $c = (340 \pm 20)$ m s^{-1} provided λ was plotted in metres.

k $c_{273} = c_T (273/T)^{\frac{1}{2}}$. $c = (330 \pm 20)$ m s^{-1}.

7E (page 76)

g $l_1 \approx \lambda/4$. Since $\lambda = c/f \approx 0.59$ m, $l_1 \approx 0.15$ m.

h $\Delta l_1 \approx 0.005$ m.

k Rearranging equation [7.5] $l_1 = c/4f - e$. A graph of l_1 (ordinate) against $1/f$ (abscissa) should be a straight line with a slope of $c/4$. The intercept on the l_1 axis is $-e$. $c = (340 \pm 5)$ m s^{-1} provided you plotted l_1 in metres. $e = (10 \pm 5)$ mm.

l $c_{273} = c_T (273/T)^{\frac{1}{2}}$. $c = (330 \pm 5)$ m s^{-1}.
Theoretically $c = \sqrt{\gamma RT/M_m}$ for a gas of relative molar mass M_m. Water vapour should decrease γ and decrease the average value of M_m. A simple analysis predicts that the decrease in γ is significantly smaller than that in M_m. Thus c for damp air is expected to be larger than for dry air. In practice, since water vapour behaves only approximately like a perfect gas, the variation of c is much more complicated. c decreases to 0.999 of the value for dry air at 14% humidity and increases to 1.003 of the value for dry air at 100% humidity.

o $l_2 - l_1 = \lambda/2$, $l_3 - l_2 = \lambda/2$, $l_3 - l_1 = \lambda$.
$\lambda = (0.65 \pm 0.01)$ m.

p $c = (330 \pm 5)$ m s^{-1}.

r The graphical method is preferred, since experimental uncertainties in l_1 are averaged by drawing the best straight line. Also it is difficult to detect the position of the third resonance, because of the low intensity of the sound produced at the open end of the tube.

7F (page 79)

l Since l_0 is proportional to $\sqrt{1/\mu}$, l_0 is proportional to $1/d$. Thus if the diameter of the wire is only 0.4 mm, the resonance will occur for $l_0 \approx 0.5 \times (0.5/0.4) = 0.63$ m.

m l_0 is proportional to $1/f$, so l_0 should decrease as f increases.

n A graph of l_0 (ordinate) against $1/f$ (abscissa) should be a straight line through the origin. The slope of the graph is $\frac{1}{2}k\sqrt{P/\mu}$.

o The slope should be about 140 m s^{-1} for $d = 0.46$ mm. Hence $k = 2 \times$ slope $\sqrt{\mu/P} = (1.00 \pm 0.05)$. The intercept on the l_0 axis is usually less than 0.01 m.

r A graph of l_0 (ordinate) against $\sqrt{P}$ (abscissa) should be a straight line through the origin. The slope is $k/(2f\sqrt{\mu})$. Alternatively l_0^2 can be plotted against P. The slope is then $k^2/(4f^2\mu)$.

s The slope of the graph of l_0 against $\sqrt{P}$ should be about 0.05 m N$^{-\frac{1}{2}}$. $k = $ slope $\times 2f\sqrt{\mu} = (1.0 \pm 0.1)$. The intercept on the l_0 axis is usually less than 0.01 m.

u The points on the l_0 against $\sqrt{P}$ graph are usually very close together for large values of P and become significantly spaced only for small values of P. Thus the slope of the line is determined by relatively few points near to the origin. The l_0 against $1/f$ graph is determined by a large number of points some distance from the origin of coordinates, but these points are much more uniformly distributed along the straight line. This value of k is probably more reliable.

7G (page 81)

l The third harmonic would be between 600 and 700 Hz for a steel wire of diameter $d = 0.46$ mm.

o A graph of f (ordinate) against $1/l$ (abscissa) should be a straight line. The origin of coordinates need not be included. The slope of the graph is $\frac{1}{2}\sqrt{P/\mu}$. For $d = 0.46$ mm the slope is about 140 m s^{-1}.
$\mu = P/(4 \times (\text{slope})^2) = (1.30 \pm 0.05) \times 10^{-3}$ kg m^{-1} for $d = 0.46$ mm. The theoretical value of $\mu = \pi d^2 \rho/4 = 1.28 \times 10^{-3}$ kg m^{-1} for $d = 0.46$ mm.

q $f_n = nf_1$ exactly.

r A graph of f_n (ordinate) against n (abscissa) should be a straight line through the origin. The slope

$$\left(= \frac{1}{2l}\sqrt{\frac{P}{\mu}}\right)$$

is about 230 Hz (s^{-1}) for $d = 0.46$ mm. $\mu = (1.30 \pm 0.05) \times 10^{-3}$ kg m^{-1}.

v This experiment has a number of advantages:

   i) It is easier to fix l and vary the forcing frequency f to obtain resonance. This is only possible with a signal generator, since f can be varied only in fixed steps using tuning forks.

   ii) Resonance is easier to detect because the magnitude of the applied force F is generally much larger than can be obtained using a tuning fork.

   iii) Harmonics are relatively easier to detect because of the large amplitude of vibration at resonance. Also a continuous range of frequencies is available. At best a standard set of tuning forks could be used to produce only the first and second harmonics ($f = 256$ and 512 Hz).

The principal disadvantage is that the frequency calibration of a signal generator is less reliable than that of a tuning fork.

8 GEOMETRICAL AND PHYSICAL OPTICS

8A (page 87)

h A graph of $\sin i$ (ordinate) against $\sin r$ (abscissa) should be a straight line of slope $_an_s$. The values of $_an_s$ should be between 1.48 and 1.61 for crown glass; for Perspex $_an_s = 1.49$.

i The error is about ± 0.02.

m The value obtained for $_an_s$ should agree to within 0.05 of the value determined in (h).

n The error in d can be as large as 0.1 mm depending on the thickness of the lycopodium powder. The error in the refractive index can be as large as 0.05.

r The values of θ_c are $(62 \pm 2)°$ for water, $(78 \pm 2)°$ for glycerol, and $(81 \pm 2)°$ for liquid paraffin, using a Perspex sample. The values will be lower than this for the more (optically) dense crown glasses.

s Water (1.33 ± 0.02), glycerol (1.47 ± 0.01), liquid paraffin (1.48 ± 0.01) neglecting the error in measuring $_a n_s$.

t If $_a n_l$ is less than $_a n_s$ then $\sin \theta_c$ will be less than one. If the two refractive indices are equal, $\sin \theta_c = 1$ and $\theta_c = 90°$. This is the maximum angle that can be measured. Thus no critical ray can be observed for $_a n_l \geqslant {}_a n_s$.

w The error in $2\theta_c$ is about 2°, so the error in θ_c is about 1°. The errors in the refractive indices are about half the values given in (s).

x For the critical ray shown in Fig. 8.12:
$_l n_g = \sin i / \sin r$ with $i = \theta_c$ measured,
$_g n_a = \sin r / \sin 90°$ or $_a n_g = 1 / \sin r$.

Since $_a n_l = {}_a n_g / {}_l n_g$, $_a n_l = 1 / \sin i$, independent of the refractive index of the material used to make the air cell.

8B (page 90)

f The error is approximately 0.01 m.

g If the source is placed at the focal point of the lens, a parallel beam will be produced by the lens. Since this beam is incident normally on the plane mirror, it will be reflected back along its original path. The image will therefore be coincident with the source.

h The error is approximately 0.01 m.

i When $u = v$ in the lens equation, $2f = u = v$.

m A graph of $1/v$ (ordinate) against $1/u$ (abscissa) should be a straight line with a slope of -1. The intercept on both axes is $1/f$. The two values of f should differ by less than 0.01 m. The error in the slope is usually about 0.01.

n The values from (m) are considered to be more reliable, because they are obtained from a straight line plot, which averages experimental uncertainties in u and v. Method (l) depends on determining a single point on a curve. Only if a significant number of points is obtained near to $u = v$ can the method be considered reliable.

t A graph of $1/v$ (ordinate) against $1/u$ (abscissa) should have a slope of 1, because $1/u$ is now negative. The intercepts on both negative axes should be $1/f$. For this reason you will need a negative $1/v$ axis of the same length as the positive axis in order to obtain two values for f.

y Since $4lf = l^2 - d^2$, a graph of $(l^2 - d^2)$ (ordinate) against l (abscissa) should be a straight line of slope $4f$.

z For a single real image $d = 0$, so the minimum value for l is given by $l^2 - 4lf = 0$, or $l = 4f$.

More rigorously, equation [8.5] is a quadratic in l:

$$l = \frac{+4f \pm \sqrt{16f^2 + 4d^2}}{2}$$

For a real image l must be positive. Thus the minimum value for l is $(4f + 4f)/2 = 4f$.

8C (page 93)

d and **e** The error in f is about 0.005 m.

j When $u = v$ in the mirror equation, $2f = u = v$.

k A graph of $1/v$ (ordinate) against $1/u$ (abscissa) should be a straight line of slope -1. The intercept on both axes is $1/f$. The two values of f should differ by less than 0.01 m. The error in the slope is usually about 0.01.

l The values from (k) are considered to be more reliable, because they have been obtained from a straight line graph, which averages experimental uncertainties in u and v. Method (j) depends on measuring a single point on a curve; only if a significant number of readings have been taken near to $u = v$ will this method give reliable results.

p The error in f is about 0.005 m.

8D (page 96)

o The value of A is normally 60°. The error should be less than 0.5°.

t D_{min} is approximately 40° depending on the material of the prism. The error is about 0.5°.

u   The refractive index should be between 1.48 and 1.61 for crown glass. The maximum error in $(A + D)/2$ is 0.5° and the error in $A/2$ is 0.25°. The maximum error in the refractive index can be calculated by taking (say) the maximum value of $(A + D)/2$ and the minimum value of $A/2$. The error is about 0.02.

8E (page 100)

l $\Delta x \approx 0.2\text{--}1.0$ mm.

o $\alpha \approx (0.3\text{--}1.5) \times 10^{-3}$ rad, giving t values in the range 20–80 μm. The value determined using the micrometer screw gauge is likely to be about 20 μm.

q n_{max} is about 30.

s   The slope of the graph λR is approximately $(0.60 \pm 0.01) \times 10^{-6}$ m^2 for $R = 1$ m. The value for R has an uncertainty of about 0.02 m. The intercept on the negative n axis is usually between -1 and -3, provided that both the lens and glass plate surfaces are clean and free from dust. The value of p is usually between 0 and 2 to the nearest integer.

8F (page 103)

n d should be between 1.5 and 3.0 μm (1500–3000 nm) for the gratings specified in the apparatus list. The error in d is about 0.01 μm (10 nm). $N = 300$ (large d)–600 (small d) lines mm^{-1}, with an error of ± 2.

r   Violet ≈ 405 nm (very difficult to see), blue ≈ 436 nm, green ≈ 546 nm and yellow $\approx 577\text{--}579$ nm.

9 THERMAL PROPERTIES OF MATTER

9A (page 107)

j   For aluminium the temperature increases by 40 K in about 20 minutes.

k   For aluminium the temperature falls by 20 K in about 30 minutes.

m $c \approx 1000$ J kg^{-1} K^{-1} for aluminium.

n   The temperature correction is usually between 6 and 8 K. This is expected to be an overestimate in still air, where Newton's law of cooling is not strictly valid. $c = (880 \pm 20)$ J kg^{-1} K^{-1}.

o   The slope should be between 0.6 and 1.0 K min^{-1}. The rate of energy loss at θ_{max} is between 10 and 15 J s^{-1}; so the average rate of energy loss during the heating process is between 5 and 8 J s^{-1}.

r $\log_{10} s = n \log_{10} \theta + \log_{10} k$. A graph of $\log_{10} s$ (ordinate) against $\log_{10} \theta$ (abscissa) should be a straight line of slope n. For forced convection n is between 0.8 and 1.0; slightly higher values for n (1.2–1.4) are obtained in still air.

The intercept on the $\log_{10} s$-axis is $\log_{10} k$. $k \approx 0.05$ min^{-1} or 0.001 s^{-1}.

s $\log_e \theta = -kt + \log_e \theta_0$. A graph of $\log_e \theta$ (ordinate) against t should be a straight line of slope $-k$. $k \approx 0.05$ min^{-1} or 0.001 s^{-1}.

9B (page 109)

j   For a 50 W immersion heater, a temperature gradient of about 100 K m^{-1} can be established for a water flow rate of about 2 g s^{-1}. The temperature difference for the water is about 5 K.

n $\lambda = (400 \pm 20)$ W m^{-1} K^{-1} for copper.

o $\lambda = (360 \pm 20)$ W m^{-1} K^{-1} for copper.

p   The value in (n) is an overestimate, because energy will be lost before reaching θ_2. The value in (o) is an underestimate because energy will be lost between θ_1 and the cooling water. It is reasonable to take an average of the two values: $\lambda = (380 \pm 20)$ W m^{-1} K^{-1}.

q   The energy loss along the bar is about 4–5 W, or about 10% of the total energy input.

9C (page 111)

h θ_1 depends on the thickness of the specimen, but it is expected to be between 40 and 60 °C.

l   Slope ≈ 0.02 K s^{-1} (do not forget the conversion to seconds for the time axis in minutes). Rate of energy loss ≈ 5 J s^{-1}.

m $\lambda \approx 0.2$ W m^{-1} K^{-1} for Perspex and cardboard; $\lambda \approx 1$ W m^{-1} K^{-1} for glass.

o The fraction of the energy lost from the sides $= 2\pi r x / \pi r^2 = 2x/r$; this is usually less than 0.05 (5%).

The thermal conductivity of brass is between 100–500 times greater than the thermal conductivity of the sample. So a 5 mm thickness of brass would be equivalent to between 0.05–0.01 mm of the sample. The error in the temperature measurement is therefore likely to be less than 5% even for the thinnest sample of 1 mm thickness.

q The simplest way to estimate the effect of a layer of air is to calculate its equivalent thickness of the sample. For glass ($\lambda \approx 1$ W m^{-1} K^{-1}), this equivalent thickness is about 0.3 mm. The percentage error will depend on the value of x, but it is likely to be between 10 and 30%. Alternatively, the error in the temperature at one face of the disc can be calculated by considering a composite specimen consisting of 0.01 mm air and x mm of sample. This gives a temperature error of between 5 and 15 K, consistent with the above estimate of the error.

9D (page 113)

j SVP values for water: 70 kPa at 90 °C, 85 kPa at 95 °C.

l The major limitation is that the SVP can only be determined for temperatures more than 5 °C below the boiling point of the liquid. Two possible reasons are the pressure exerted by the water index (10–20 mm in length, equivalent to 100–200 Pa) and the surface tension effects between the water and the capillary. The excess pressure over a curved surface $\approx 2 \times$ surface tension/ radius of curvature of the surface. At room temperature the surface tension of water is about 0.08 N m^{-1}, the radius of curvature $\approx$ radius of the capillary ≈ 0.5 mm; the excess pressure is then about 200 Pa. Since the surface tension of a liquid decreases rapidly with increasing temperature, the effect decreases to negligible proportions above 40 °C.

9E (page 115)

g For a rate of heating of 60 W, it will take about 30 minutes to collect 50 ml of water and 15 minutes to collect 50 ml of ethanol.

h V should be reduced to $V_1/\sqrt{2}$ and *not* $V_1/2$, since I_1 decreases by a factor of $\sqrt{2}$ as well (the resistance of the coil is constant).

j For water $L_v = 2.26$ MJ kg^{-1}; for ethanol $L_v = 0.84$ MJ kg^{-1}; for methanol $L_v = 1.12$ MJ kg^{-1}.

k For the vapour jacket apparatus h is less than 1 J s^{-1} and there is no significant improvement in the value of L_v. As a result of the combination of errors in the differences $(I_1 V_1 - I_2 V_2)$ and $(m_1 - m_2)$, the fractional error in L_v can be larger than 0.05 (5%); this is normally larger than the fractional error in L_v resulting from energy losses (0.02 or 2%).

10 CURRENT ELECTRICITY

10A (page 126)

g When $I = 500$ μA, $R \approx 500$ Ω and $r \approx 100$ Ω.

h Take natural logarithms of both sides of equation [10.4]: $\log_e I = (eV/kT) + \log_e I_0$. Plot $\log_e I$ (ordinate) against V (abscissa); slope $= e/kT \approx 40$ V^{-1} (this is the theoretical value, but your value may be a little less, especially if your graph tends to curve as suggested); intercept on $(\log_e I)$-axis $= \log_e I_0$; intercept on V-axis $= -kT(\log_e I_0)/e \approx 0.3$ V. $I_0 \approx 0.1$ nA. Non-linearity of the graph is caused by increasing temperature of the diode as the power dissipated in it increases with I. Thus T in equation [10.4] is no longer a constant.

i When $I = 500$ μA, $R \approx 200$ Ω and $r \approx 100$ Ω. $I_0 \approx 0.1$ μA.

10B (page 127)

g (i) Circuit X is more suitable for measuring small resistances.
(ii) Circuit Y is more suitable for measuring larger resistances.

h e_X increases with R, reaching about -1200 Ω for $R = 4000$ Ω (fractional error then -30%). e_Y should be constant at around 100 Ω (fractional error decreases from 30% for $R = 300$ Ω to 2.5% for $R = 4000$ Ω).

k $R \approx 1000$ Ω; percentage error $\approx \pm 10\%$.

l See answer to (h).

10C (page 129)

g Plot $1/I$ (ordinate) against R (abscissa); slope $= 1/\mathcal{E} \approx 0.2$ V^{-1}; intercept on $(1/I)$-axis $= r/\mathcal{E} \approx 10$ A^{-1}.

k
(i) $R \approx 50 \ \Omega$.
(ii) $V \approx 2.3$ V; $\eta = 50\%$.
(iii) As $\eta \to 100\%$, $P \to 0$: highly efficient circuits delivered no power!

10D (page 131)

d $\mathcal{E} = (\mathcal{E}_s/l_s)l_0$.

h Plot $1/R$ (ordinate) against $1/l$ (abscissa); intercept on $(1/R)$-axis $= -1/r \approx -0.1 \ \Omega^{-1}$. Or, slope $= l_0/r \approx 0.075$ m Ω^{-1} and intercept on $(1/l)$-axis $= 1/l_0 \approx 1.3$ m^{-1} (both for $l_{AB} = 1$ m).

i Requirements: (1) constant current during course of experiment – check by repeating (b) at the end; (2) uniform resistance wire – check by turning wire around (i.e. by swapping connections to A and B) and repeating (b).

10E (page 133)

h If $R < 3.3 \ \Omega$, choose $S = 1 \ \Omega$.
If $3.3 \ \Omega < R < 33 \ \Omega$, choose $S = 10 \ \Omega$.
If $33 \ \Omega < R$, $S = 100 \ \Omega$.

i The wire is made from nichrome. $\rho = 1.08 \times 10^{-6} \ \Omega$ m.

10F (page 135)

g The tolerance of S might be 1%.

10G (page 137)

i A suitable value for $(R_1 + R_2)$ should lie in the range from 800 Ω (for $R_{AB} = 2 \ \Omega$) to 2500 Ω (for $R_{AB} = 7 \ \Omega$).

k I should lie in the range from 2.5 mA (for $(R_1 + R_2) = 800 \ \Omega$) down to 0.8 mA (for $(R_1 + R_2) = 2500 \ \Omega$).

l $V_{AB} \approx 6$ mV.

10H (page 139)

f Example: If $L = 0.75$ m and $d = 0.3$ mm, $L/d^2 = (0.75 \text{ m})/(0.3 \times 10^{-3} \text{ m})^2 \approx 8 \times 10^6$ m^{-1}.

g Slope $= 4\rho/\pi \approx 1.4 \times 10^{-6} \ \Omega$ m.

h Different slopes; wires are made from different alloys or there is an error in one or other diameter measurement. Separate though parallel lines; there is a consistent error in measurement of L for one or other wire.

10I (page 141)

f Rearrange equation [10.15]: $R = R_0\alpha\theta + R_0$. Plot R (ordinate) against θ (abscissa); slope $= R_0\alpha \approx 0.015 \ \Omega$ K^{-1}; intercept on R-axis $= R_0 \approx 4 \ \Omega$.

g Copper is such a good conductor of electricity that if a resistance of only a few ohms is to be made from copper wire, several metres of very thin wire (diameter here ≈ 0.2 mm) must be chosen. Glycerol is a relatively good conductor of heat (water is better), but it has a much higher boiling point than most common liquids.

10J (page 142)

g R decreases from about 100 Ω at 0 °C to 4 Ω at 100 °C.

i Take natural logarithms of both sides of equation [10.16]: $\log_e R = \log_e R_0 + (E_g/kT)$. Plot $\log_e R$ (ordinate) against $1/T$ (abscissa); slope $= E_g/k \approx 3000$ K.

j $E_g \approx 0.3$ eV.

k Used to protect circuits when switched on: a high resistance when cold limits initial current, but internal Joule heating causes temperature to rise; so the resistance falls; and the current rises to the normal value.

11 ELECTRIC AND MAGNETIC FIELDS

11A (page 147)

h For $B = 0.2$ T, V_H should be between 50 and 100 mV.

k　For an n-type semiconductor $n = (2-5) \times 10^{20}$ m^{-3}. For a p-type semiconductor $n = (5-10) \times 10^{20}$ m^{-3}.

p　$B = (1-2)$ mT gives an output of about 100 mV after amplification, that is, $V_H \approx 1$ mV. This value is constant to within 10% right up to the centres of the two coils. Outside the coils B falls to about 0.35 of its constant value at a distance corresponding to the radius a of the coils. B is about 0.09 of its constant value at a distance $2a$.

11B (page 149)

(I) COMPARISON OF CAPACITORS

f　$x_1 \approx 50$ mm; damping correction ≈ 5 mm.

h　The ratio is expected to be about one.

(II) USE OF THE SEARCH COIL TO MEASURE MAGNETIC FIELDS

l　The charge sensitivity is usually about 80 mm μC^{-1}.

m　If $B = 0.2$ T and the search coil parameters are $N = 5000$, $A = 10^{-4}$ m^2, $R_s = 2$ kΩ, then $(R_s + R) = 100$ kΩ　and　$R = 98$ kΩ. The nearest value for R is 100 kΩ.

p　For $B = 1$ mT, the deflection is about 20 mm with no added resistor.

q　B is constant until 10–20 mm from each end of the solenoid.

11C (page 152)

f　$\mathcal{E}_0 \approx 0.3$ V.

g　$\mathcal{E}_0$ should increase to about 3 V.

h　A graph of $\mathcal{E}_0$ (ordinate) against f (abscissa) should be a straight line passing through the origin. The slope $(2\pi NAB_0)$ should be about 4×10^{-4} V s, giving a value for B_0 of 0.2 mT.

i　The measured and calculated values of B_0 should agree to within $\pm 10\%$.

l　The field is within 0.95 of the field at the centre until about 40 mm from the end of the solenoid.

n　The action of a transformer depends on mutual induction in the two coils. A changing magnetic flux in the primary coil produces an induced e.m.f. in the secondary coil. However, there is also a varying magnetic flux in the secondary coil, which induces an e.m.f. in the primary coil opposing the applied voltage. This mutual induction ensures that the ratio of the primary to secondary voltage is equal to the turns ratio irrespective of the frequency of the primary voltage (assuming 100% flux linkage between the coils).

The magnetic flux in the solenoid passes through the small search coil and produces the induced e.m.f. measured. However, the magnetic flux produced in the search coil links with only a few turns of the solenoid in the vicinity of the search coil. Thus the changing magnetic flux through the whole solenoid due to the search coil is very small. Mutual induction effects are therefore negligible and no transformer action is evident.

11D (page 153)

f　V_s/V_p is usually about 0.8.

h　The voltage ratio decreases from about 0.8 to 0.3.

i　The abscissa is marked as a logarithmic scale, $\log_{10} f$, with 2, 3, 4 and 5 corresponding to 100 Hz, 1 kHz, 10 kHz and 100 kHz respectively. Intermediate values of f can be marked by taking the logarithm of f.

j　An explanation for this behaviour can be made on the basis of the domain structure of ferromagnetic materials. At low frequencies, the alignment of the domains can alter in response to an alternating applied field. At high frequencies the domain structure is unable to alter fully in response to the applied field and so the magnetic flux linking the two coils is reduced as f increases.

The band width is about 10 kHz.

l　Allowing for the flux linkage of 80% only, the results are consistent with the turns ratios.

p　A graph of $\log_{10} (V_s/V_p)$ (ordinate) against $\log_{10} x$ (abscissa) is expected to be a straight line graph of slope $-n$. No reasonable straight line can be drawn, except for the larger values of $\log_{10} x$. From this part of the graph $n \approx 0.5$.

q A graph of $\log_e (V_s/V_p)$ (ordinate) against x (abscissa) should be a straight line with a slope $-k$. The intercept on the $\log_e (V_s/V_p)$ axis corresponds to $\log_e A$.

The graph is a straight line giving $k = 5\text{–}8$ m^{-1} and $\log_e A \approx -0.2$ or $A \approx 0.8$.

11E (page 157)

k Rearrange equation [11.12] $r^2 = (2m_e/B^2 e)V_A$. Thus a graph of r^2 (ordinate) against V_A (abscissa) should be a straight line of slope $(2m_e/B^2 e)$ passing through the origin. Note that the units of r^2 should be converted to m^2. Alternatively a graph of V_A (ordinate) against r^2 (abscissa) may be drawn; the slope is then $(B^2 e/2m_e)$.

l There are significant deviations from linearity for d values greater than 0.1 m for the Teltron fine beam tube.

m $B \approx 1$ mT, giving a value for $e/m_e = (1.8 \pm 0.1) \times 10^{11}$ C kg^{-1}.

11F (p. 158)

j A current of about 0.2 A will give a vertical deflection of 25 mm at $x = 80$ mm.

m With $V_d = 2500$ V and $d = 50$ mm, $E = 5 \times 10^4$ V m^{-1}.

n With x and y both in metres the slope is about 5 m^{-1}.

q $r \approx 0.4$ m; you may assume that $2r$ is much greater than y, so $r = x^2/2y$. $B \approx 0.4$ mT.

r For $I = 0.5$ A, $r \approx 0.1$ m and $B \approx 2$ mT.

s $1/r$ should be in m^{-1} and B in tesla. The slope of the line is about 6000 T^{-1} m^{-1}.

u I should be about 0.4 A with a variation of about 0.05 A.

v $v \approx 3 \times 10^7$ m s^{-1}.

w–y The two values for e/m_e should be consistent. $e/m_e = (1.8 \pm 0.2) \times 10^{11}$ C kg^{-1}.

12 CAPACITANCE

12A (page 165)

f and **g** For $f = 100$ Hz the deflection x should be about 20 mm. $I \approx 1\mu$A, $Q \approx 10$ nC.

i The graph of $I(\mu$A) against f(Hz) should have a slope of about 10^{-8} C. $C = (40 \pm 5)$ nF (depending, of course, on the actual values of d and A in your capacitor).

j $C = (40 \pm 5)$ nF.

l $\varepsilon_0 = (8.9 \pm 0.4) \times 10^{-12}$ F m^{-1}.

o and **p** polythene $\varepsilon_r = (2.2 \pm 0.2)$,
Perspex $\varepsilon_r = (3.3 \pm 0.3)$,
glass $\varepsilon_r = (7.0 \pm 0.5)$.

w ε_r for water $= (80 \pm 10)$.

12B (page 167)

e V_R should decrease to about 1/10 of $\mathcal{E}$ in about $2RC \approx 250$ s. If it is significantly slower than this, the electrolytic capacitor may have been damaged and it should be replaced.

f and **g** For a Unilab grey meter (f.s.d. $= 100$ μA, $R_G = 1000$ Ω), the multiplier resistance for a 5 V f.s.d. is 49.9 kΩ. Thus R should be 50 kΩ. Allowing for a $\pm10\%$ error in C, $RC = (110 \pm 10)$ s and $R = (50 \pm 5)$ kΩ.

h From equation [12.8] $\log_e V_R = \log_e V_0 - t/RC$. Thus a graph of $\log_e V_R$ (ordinate) against t (abscissa) should be a straight line with a slope of $-1/RC$. $RC = (110 \pm 10)$ s. This value of RC is considered to be more reliable than that obtained from the actual curves for V_R and V_C. It is obtained from a straight line thus averaging out any experimental uncertainties in measurements of V_R and 02t. Measuring RC from the curves depends on determining a single point accurately on a curve. If you are fortunate, there may be several points near to $V_R = 0.37\mathcal{E}$, but widely spaced points will make this determination of RC unreliable.

m From equation [12.11] obtain a straight line by plotting $\log_e V_C$ (ordinate) against t (abscissa). The gradient of the graph will be $-1/RC$. $RC = (50 \pm 5)$ s giving $C = (1000 \pm 100)$ μF.

12C (page 168)

e   With $f = 100$ Hz, you should obtain a suitable CRO trace with $RC = 0.1$ ms. A CRO time base setting of 1 ms div^{-1} is usually suitable. You can increase f if you obtain a trace such as Fig. 12.12a and decrease f if you obtain a trace such as Fig. 12.12b. You may need to alter the time base setting to obtain a stationary trace suitable for measurement.

k $V_C = \dfrac{Q}{C} = \dfrac{1}{C}\displaystyle\int_0^t I\, dt', \qquad V_R = IR = R\dfrac{dQ}{dt}$

Thus:

$$V_R = RC\, dV_C/dt$$

that is, V_R is the differential of V_C with respect to time; or:

$$V_C = \frac{1}{RC}\int_0^t V_R\, dt'$$

that is, V_C is the integral of V_R with respect to time.

Differentiating circuit
(small RC)

$$V_C \approx V_{in}$$
$$V_R = RC\frac{dV_{in}}{dt}$$

Integrating circuit
(large RC)

$$V_R \approx V_{in}$$
$$V_C = \frac{1}{RC}\int_0^t V_{in}\, dt'$$

13 ALTERNATING CURRENTS

13A (page 174)

d and **e**   As f is varied from 100 Hz to 1000 Hz, I should increase from about 2 mA to 20 mA with $V = 3$ V.

g X_C varies from about 1600 Ω at 100 Hz to 160 Ω at 1000 Hz.

h   Since $X_C = 1/2\pi f C$, a graph of X_C (ordinate) against $1/f$ (abscissa) should be a straight line through the origin. The slope $= 1/2\pi C = (1.6 \pm 0.2)\times 10^5$ F^{-1} giving $C = (1.0 \pm 0.1)$ µF.

j   At 100 Hz: $V = 3$ V, $V_R = (1.6 \pm 0.1)$ V, $V_C = (2.5 \pm 0.1)$ V, $I = (1.6 \pm 0.1)$ mA, so $Z = (1900 \pm 100)$ Ω; the theoretical value of Z should be within 100 Ω of this value.

k   At 1000 Hz: $V = 3$ V, $V_R = (2.9 \pm 0.1)$ V, $V_C = (0.5 \pm 0.1)$ V, $I = (3.0 \pm 0.1)$ mA, so $Z = (1000 \pm 100)$ Ω.

13B (page 176)

e and **f**   For $V = 3$ V, I should decrease from about 60 mA to 5 mA as f increases from 10 Hz to 1000 Hz.

h Z should vary from about 50 Ω at 10 Hz to 600 Ω at 1000 Hz. The slope of the linear section of the graph for $f > 300$ Hz $= 2\pi L = (0.60 \pm 0.05)$ H so $L = (100 \pm 10)$ mH. The extrapolated value of Z at $f = 0$ is $R = (50 \pm 10)$ Ω.

j   The most reliable value for L is obtained from the analysis used in (i), since it is dominated by high frequency data. The most reliable value for R is probably obtained from the Z–f graph, provided enough low frequency points are used. At 10 Hz, the contribution to Z from X_L is negligible. If $R = 50$ Ω, $X_L = 6$ Ω, so $Z = 50.4$ Ω at $f = 10$ Hz (see equation [13.15]). At $f = 100$ Hz, X_L increases to 63 Ω, and so there is a significant contribution to Z from the inductive component ($Z = 80$ Ω).

13C (page 177)

f f_0 should be about 500 Hz for $L = 100$ mH and $C = 1$ µF.

g   The maximum value for I will be about 40 mA giving a value for R_L of 50–70 Ω.

j   Theoretically $f_0 = 503$ Hz for $L = 100$ mH and $C = 1$ µF.

q   The resonance maximum should be absent for $R \geqslant 450$ Ω, for $L = 100$ mH and $C = 1$ µF. It is more difficult to confirm the variation of f_0 with R unless very careful measurements are made on the frequency values for which V_C (and hence Q) is a maximum.

f and g   The value of I should be about 70 mA at 100 Hz for $R_L = 50$–$70\ \Omega$. The minimum value of I should be about 4 mA at $f = 500$ Hz, for $L = 100$ mH and $C = 1\ \mu F$.

h–j   For $L = 100$ mH, and $C = 1\ \mu F$, the following values of f_0 are calculated from equation [13.21]:

R/Ω	$\left[\left(\dfrac{2R^2C}{L}+1\right)^{\frac{1}{2}}-\dfrac{R^2C}{L}\right]^{\frac{1}{2}}$	f_0/Hz
50	1.00	503
100	1.00	502
200	0.97	488
300	0.88	442
400	0.67	337
450	0.47	237
500	no resonance minimum	

$1/(2\pi\sqrt{LC}) = 503$ Hz.

13E (page 180)

b   Consider two oscillations $x = a\sin(2\pi ft + \phi)$ and $y = a\sin(2\pi ft)$, of the same frequency f and amplitude a with a phase difference of ϕ:

$\phi = 0$ $x = y$ is a straight line of slope 1

$\phi = \pi/2$ $x = a\cos(2\pi ft)$, $y = a\sin(2\pi ft)$
       $\therefore\ x^2 + y^2 = a^2$ which is a circle of radius a

$\phi = \pi$ $x = -a\sin(2\pi ft)$, $y = a\sin(2\pi ft)$
       $\therefore\ x = -y$, which is a straight line of slope -1

c   For two oscillations of different amplitudes a_x and a_y of the same frequency:

$$x = a_x\sin(2\pi ft + \phi)$$

$$y = a_y\sin(2\pi ft)$$

Thus: $x/a_x = \sin(2\pi ft)\cos\phi + \cos(2\pi ft)\sin\phi$

and: $y/a_y = \sin(2\pi ft)$

Since: $\cos 2\pi ft = \sqrt{1 - \sin^2(2\pi ft)} = \sqrt{1 - y^2/a_y^2}$

   $x/a_x = (y/a_y)\cos\phi + \sqrt{1 - y^2/a_y^2}\sin\phi$

This is the general equation of an ellipse. Fortunately this equation does not need to be rearranged for our purposes. For the intercept of the ellipse on the x-axis, x_0, put $y = 0$:

$$x_0/a_x = \sin\phi$$

Similarly for the intercept on the y-axis, y_0, put $x = 0$:

$$(y_0/a_y)\cos\phi + \sqrt{1 - y_0^2/a_y^2}\sin\phi = 0$$

giving: $y_0/a_y = \sin\phi$

h   At $f = 50$ Hz, the ellipse will be quite broad with large intercepts on the x- and y-axes, ϕ is nearly 90°.

k   As f increases, the ellipse becomes narrower and the intercepts on the x- and y-axes decreases. Thus $\phi \to 0$ as f increases. As $f \to 0$ the circuit is purely capacitive so $\phi \to 90°$; as $f \to \infty$ the circuit is purely resistive and so $\phi \to 0$.

l   For $C = 1\ \mu F$ and $R = 1000\ \Omega$:

f/Hz	ϕ (experimental)	ϕ (theoretical)
50	$(73 \pm 5)°$	73°
100	$(58 \pm 5)°$	58°
250	$(32 \pm 3)°$	32°
500	$(18 \pm 3)°$	18°
1000	$(\ 9 \pm 3)°$	9°

There is no systematic difference. The main error at high frequencies is a result of the difficulty of measuring small intercepts. At low frequencies ϕ increases rapidly with decreasing f.

p   There is occasionally an inconsistency between the frequency readings on the 10–100 Hz and the 100–1000 Hz scales for the 100 Hz setting.

q and s   If the frequency dial has been incorrectly fixed, Δf may be a constant difference. Otherwise, if the signal generator includes a component of an incorrect value, Δf will systematically increase with f. Normally the error is random, mainly as a result of misreading the dial position.

14 ELECTRONS, ATOMS AND NUCLEI

14A (page 192)

m V_s should vary from about 0.9 V down to almost zero for the longest wavelength filter.

p   A graph of V_s (ordinate) against $1/\lambda$ (abscissa) should be a straight line. The slope $= hc/e$. $h = (6 \pm 1) \times 10^{-34}$ J s.

q The intercept on the negative V_s-axis is $-\phi$. If the intercept on the $1/\lambda$-axis is $1/\lambda_0$ (corresponding to $V_s = 0$), then $hc/e\lambda_0 = \phi$. Thus $\phi = $ slope $\times$ intercept.
$\phi = (2.0 \pm 0.3)$ V.

s As in (p) above.

t $h = (4 \pm 1) \times 10^{-34}$ J s; values of h obtained by using wavelength band filters are normally low.

u $\phi = (2 \pm 1)$ V; the intercept value is very sensitive to the line chosen in (t) above.

14B (page 196)

l A graph of $1/\lambda$ (ordinate) against $1/n^2$ (abscissa) should be a straight line. The slope $= R_H$ and the intercept on the $1/\lambda$-axis $= R_H/2^2 = R_H/4$.
$R_H = (1.10 \pm 0.04) \times 10^7$ m^{-1}.

m Approximate values of hf and E_n (experimental) and E_n (calculated):

n	hf/eV	E_n (exp)/eV	E_n (calc)/eV
3	1.9	-1.5	-1.51
4	2.6	-0.8	-0.85
5	2.9	-0.5	-0.54
6	3.1	-0.3	-0.38

14C (page 198)

m $\log_e N = \log_e N_0 - \mu_m \rho x$. A graph of $\log_e N$ (ordinate) against ρx (abscissa) should be a straight line of slope $-\mu_m$. The intercept on the $\log_e N$-axis should be $\log_e N_0$, where N_0 is the theoretical value of the γ-activity for $\rho x = 0$. The straight line is not well defined and so there is a large error in measuring its slope and hence μ_m.

n Slope $= -\mu_m = -(8 \pm 2) \times 10^{-3}$ m^2 kg^{-1} for the $^{226}_{88}$Ra series. $(\rho x)_{\frac{1}{2}} = \log_e 2/\mu_m = (87 \pm 18)$ kg m^{-2} or $x_{\frac{1}{2}} = (\rho x)_{\frac{1}{2}}/\rho = (8 \pm 2)$ mm. This gives an estimate for the energy of the γ-radiation of 0.7–1.3 MeV. The main reason for the error is that in the Ra series there are several γ-emitters producing different γ-ray energies. Therefore there is no single exponential curve. You will measure an average value for μ_m and hence the average energy of the γ-radiation.

p The graph of $\log_e N_\beta$ against ρx is definitely a curve.

q Read off $\log_e N_\beta$ for $\rho x = 0$. Calculate N_β for $\rho x = 0$ and hence $N_\beta/2$. Calculate $\log_e N_\beta/2$ and find the value of $(\rho x)_{\frac{1}{2}}$ corresponding to this value. $(\rho x)_{\frac{1}{2}} = (0.8 \pm 0.2)$ kg m^{-2} or $x_{\frac{1}{2}} = (0.3 \pm 0.1)$ mm of aluminium. The precise value is difficult to determine because of the steepness of the curve.

r The maximum β-particle energy is 1.0–1.7 MeV.

14D (page 200)

c Differentiating $N = N_0 \exp(-\lambda t)$:

$$A = -\frac{dN}{dt} = \lambda N_0 \exp(-\lambda t)$$

At $t = 0$, the activity $A = $ initial activity A_0:

$$A_0 = \lambda N_0$$
$$\therefore A = A_0 \exp(-\lambda t)$$

j The background current is usually about 0.02 mA $= 20$ μA.

k $T_{\frac{1}{2}} \approx 60$ s. To obtain a well defined decay curve the time intervals should not be longer than 10 s.

o $T_{\frac{1}{2}} = (60 \pm 5)$ s.

p $\log_e I = -\lambda t + \log_e I_0$. The graph of $\log_e I$ (ordinate) against t (abscissa) should be a straight line with slope $-\lambda$. The intercept on the $\log_e I$-axis should be equal to $\log_e I_0$. $\lambda = (12.0 \pm 0.5) \times 10^{-3}$ s^{-1}; $T_{\frac{1}{2}} = (58 \pm 3)$ s.

q The accepted value of $T_{\frac{1}{2}}$ for $^{220}_{86}$Rn is 55 s. The value produced in (p) is considered more reliable since random fluctuations (errors) in I are effectively averaged by the process of drawing the best straight line. The results from (o) depend on an accurately drawn curve. The method given in (p) is more general since in principle the straight line can be produced for times t of much less than $T_{\frac{1}{2}}$. To use the curve to determine $T_{\frac{1}{2}}$ requires a curve falling at least to $I_0/2$. This is clearly difficult or impossible to achieve for radioactive sources whose half-life exceeds a few hours.

r The polonium isotope decays in such a short time compared with the time of measurement of random decay that it has no significant effect on the shape of the thoron activity curve. The ionisation current measured is, however, doubled as a result of the emission of α-particles by the polonium. The lead isotope decays so slowly (compared with the thoron) that the number of β-particles emitted is negligible.

15 ANALOGUE ELECTRONICS

15A (page 208)

d   Whichever of the two inputs is grounded, $V_{out} = +V'_s$ when $V_+ > V_-$, and $V_{out} = -V'_s$ when $V_+ < V_-$.

i   Interchange the connections to the op-amp inputs, or interchange the power supply connections to the potential divider networks.

m   For the 741 op-amp, slew rate $\approx 5 \times 10^5$ V s^{-1}.

15B (page 211)

j   (i) $A_0 \approx 10^5$.
      (ii) $f \approx 1$ MHz.

o   See answer to (j).

15C (page 215)

j   When $f = 10$ kHz, A rises to about 30, and V_{out} lags behind V_{in} by only $\frac{1}{3}$ cycle.

k   When $f = 10$ kHz, A falls to about 3, and V_{out} lags behind V_{in} by $\frac{2}{3}$ cycle.

l   When $f = 100$ Hz, A is only about 4, and V_{out} lags behind V_{in} by only $\frac{1}{3}$ cycle.

m   When $f = 100$ Hz, A is about 30, and V_{out} lags behind V_{in} by $\frac{2}{3}$ cycle.

15E (page 221)

j   Pulse duration varies from about 3.5 s down to 0.7 s.

k V_{out} remains high while S is closed, but drops immediately S is opened, and the pulse then ends.

m   In (j) the pulse duration varies because the potential divider is used to set the value of V_- ($= +kV_s$) down to which V_+ must decay to end the pulse. In (k) V_- is held at $-V_s$ while S remains closed, but since V_+ decays from $+2V'_s$ down to only zero, it will never reach V_- to end the pulse.

p $T = 2.2$ ms (equation [15.12]).

q

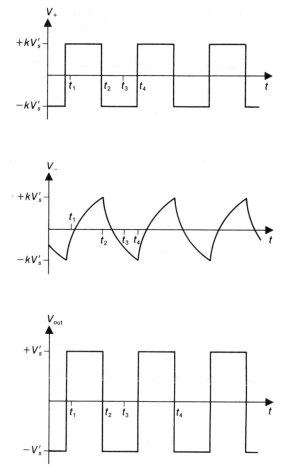

s $T_1 = 1.1$ ms and $T_2 = 0.4$ ms. (equation [15.11]).

15F (page 225)

g   Time $= 13$ s (equation [15.14]).

i   Time $= 19$ s (equation [15.14]).

l $dV_{out}/dt = 10$ V s^{-1} (equation [15.15]).

n   Amplitude of $V_{out} = 3.2$ V (equation [15.16]).

q   Amplitude of $V_{out} = 6.2$ V (equation [15.18]).

15G (page 229)

f   Time $= 10$ s (equation [15.21]).

g   Time $= 7$ s; time $= 13$ s (equation [15.21]).

j   Time = 6.3 s (equation [15.23]).

k   (i) Maximum height = 12 m (equation of motion).
(ii) Time = 13 s (equation [15.23]).

n   Half-life = $\dfrac{\log_e 2}{\lambda}$ = 6.9 s (equation [15.25]).

q   Time = 6.9 s (equation [15.27]).

t T = 6.3 s; T = 8.9 s (equation [15.29]).
The amplitude decreases; caused by residual resistive damping.

16 DIGITAL ELECTRONICS

16A (page 241)

c   OR gate

Inputs		Output
A	B	Q
0	0	0
0	1	1
1	0	1
1	1	1

d   NOT gate

Input	Output
A	Q
0	1
1	0

e   NAND gate

Inputs		Output
A	B	Q
0	0	1
0	1	1
1	0	1
1	1	0

f   NOR gate

Inputs		Output
A	B	Q
0	0	1
0	1	0
1	0	0
1	1	0

g   For the AND gate, Q is 1 only when both A and B are 1.

16B (page 243)

e   For the NAND gate, Q = NOT A if B = 1.

h

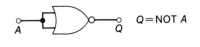

Q = NOT A

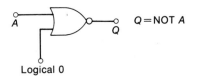

Logical 0

Q = NOT A

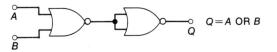

Q = A OR B

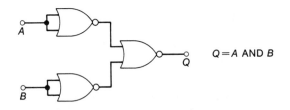

Q = A AND B

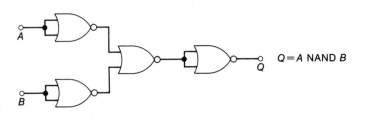

Q = A NAND B

334

16C (page 244)

k Completion of Table 16.9:

A	B	C	$B+C$	$A \cdot B$	$A \cdot C$	$A \cdot (B+C)$	$(A \cdot B) + (A \cdot C)$
0	0	0	0	0	0	0	0
0	0	1	1	0	0	0	0
0	1	0	1	0	0	0	0
0	1	1	1	0	0	0	0
1	0	0	0	0	0	0	0
1	0	1	1	0	1	1	1
1	1	0	1	1	0	1	1
1	1	1	1	1	1	1	1

l Completion of Table 16.10:

A	B	$A+B$	$A \cdot (A+B)$
0	0	0	0
0	1	1	0
1	0	1	1
1	1	1	1

m Completion of Table 16.11:

A	B	$\overline{A}$	$\overline{B}$	$A \cdot B$	$\overline{A \cdot B}$	$\overline{A+B}$
0	0	1	1	0	1	1
0	1	1	0	0	1	1
1	0	0	1	0	1	1
1	1	0	0	1	0	0

16E (page 251)

k The effect of setting C_{in1} at logical 1 is to add an extra 001 to the sum, which is therefore $001 + 101 + 010 = 1000$. The effect of setting either A_4 or B_4 at logical 1 is to add an extra 1000 to the sum, which is therefore $1000 + 101 + 010 = 1111$.

m $D = A + B$; $R = A \cdot D$ (also $R = A \cdot \overline{B}$ and $R = \overline{B} \cdot D$).

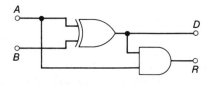

Circuit for half subtractor; the EOR gate could be constructed as in Figs. 16.22, 16.23, 16.24 or 16.29.

16F (page 254)

c Change the state also by connecting whichever input is at logical 0 to logical 1.

e Completion of Table 16.17:

	A	B	Q_A	Q_B
Start	0	0	1	1
	1	0	0	1
	1	1	0	1
Restart	0	0	1	1
	0	1	1	0
	1	1	1	0

h Completion of Table 16.18:

	A	B	Q_A	Q_B
Start	0	0	1	1
1	1	0	0	1
2	1	1	0	1
3	0	1	1	0
4	1	1	1	0
5	0	1	1	0
6	1	1	1	0
7	1	0	0	1
8	1	1	0	1
9	1	0	0	1
10	1	1	0	1
11	0	1	1	0
12	1	1	1	0

Completion of Fig. 16.36:

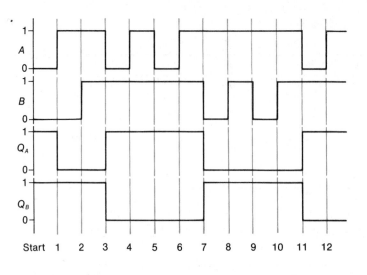

n Completion of Table 16.19 for the NAND gate *SR*
bistable:

	A	B	Q_A	Q_B
Start	1	1	1	1
	1	0	1	0
	0	0	1	0
Restart	1	1	1	1
	0	1	0	1
	0	0	0	1

p Completion of Table 16.19 for the NOR gate *SR*
bistable:

	A	B	Q_A	Q_B
Start	1	1	0	0
	1	0	0	1
	0	0	0	1
Restart	1	1	0	0
	0	1	1	0
	0	0	1	0

16G (page 258)

g Truth table for the *D* bistable:

D	Q_n	Q_{n+1}
	0	0
0	1	0 0
	0	1
1	1	1 1

l Q (and $\overline{Q}$) alternate with a period of less than 100 ns
(frequency $>$ 10 MHz). Light would travel about 30 m in
this time.

16H (page 262)

i Timing diagram for a 2-bit binary up-counter:

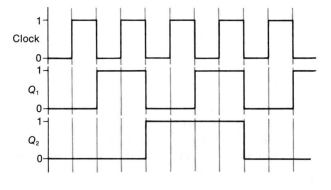

If a switch with contact bounce is used to supply clock
pulses, the count will appear to be random: any one of the
four output combinations can arise at the end of every
clock pulse.

j To construct a binary down-counter adopt $\overline{Q}_2$ and $\overline{Q}_1$
as the outputs (instead of Q_2 and Q_1); *or* feed the clock
input of the second bistable from $\overline{Q}_1$ and not from Q_1 (*vice
versa* if the CMOS 4027 IC is used). If you apply *both* of
these modifications your circuit will still count up!

o   Allocation of colours in the traffic light sequence to the outputs of the 3-bit binary up-counter. Green is on when neither red nor amber are on:

Clock pulse	Q_3	Q_2	Q_1	Colours
Start	0	0	0	⎫
1	0	0	1	⎬ Red
2	0	1	0	⎭
3	0	1	1	Red and amber
4	1	0	0	⎫
5	1	0	1	⎬ Green
6	1	1	0	⎭
7	1	1	1	Amber
8	0	0	0	⎫
9	0	0	1	⎬ Red

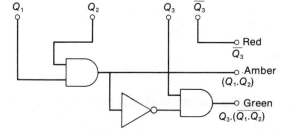

p   There are 16 stages in the 4-bit binary up-counter sequence. The fourth output Q_4 is at logical 0 for the first eight stages and at logical 1 for the second eight. The first eight lines of the sequence in table in (o) above are repeated twice.

r   If the clear signal is not applied to the third bistable, the count restarts at 0010 (= the decimal number 2).

s   The duodecimal counter is suitable with the TTL 7476 IC; use an AND gate with CMOS 4027 IC.

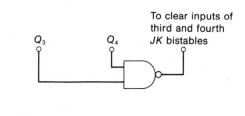

16J (page 267)

b   After a few seconds Q returns to logical 0 to complete a single pulse.

d   (i) If C is increased the decay of V_{iY} takes longer so the pulse duration is increased; (ii) if R is decreased the decay of V_{iY} is more rapid so the pulse duration is reduced; (iii) the pulse lasts as long as the trigger pulse or until V_{iY} decays to the threshold switching level of gate Y, whichever is the longer; (iv) the output pulse is shorter because V_{iY} decays from a lower initial value during the dead time.

g   Variations with time of V_{iX}, Q_X, V_{iY} and Q_Y below:

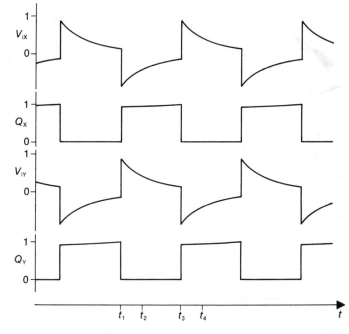

INDEX